INSTRUCTOR'S SOLUTIONS MANUAL

BO LOU
Ferris State University

COLLEGE PHYSICS

FIFTH EDITION

WILSON

BUFFA

Upper Saddle River, NJ 07458

Assistant Editor: Christian Botting
Senior Editor: Erik Fahlgren
Editor in Chief: John Challice
Executive Managing Editor: Kathleen Schiaparelli
Assistant Managing Editor: Dinah Thong
Production Editor: Elizabeth Klug
Supplement Cover Manager: Paul Gourhan
Supplement Cover Designer: Joanne Alexandris
Manufacturing Buyer: Ilene Kahn

© 2003 by Pearson Education, Inc.
Pearson Education, Inc.
Upper Saddle River, NJ 07458

Printed in the United States of America

10 9 8 7 6 5 4 3 2 1

ISBN 0-13-047194-1

Pearson Education Ltd., *London*
Pearson Education Australia Pty. Ltd., *Sydney*
Pearson Education Singapore, Pte. Ltd.
Pearson Education North Asia Ltd., *Hong Kong*
Pearson Education Canada, Inc., *Toronto*
Pearson Educación de Mexico, S.A. de C.V.
Pearson Education—Japan, *Tokyo*
Pearson Education Malaysia, Pte. Ltd.
Pearson Education, *Upper Saddle River, New Jersey*

PREFACE

This instructor's solutions manual is written to accompany "**COLLEGE PHYSICS**" by Jerry D. Wilson and Anthony J. Buffa, fifth edition. It contains detailed solutions to all end-of-chapter exercises. At the end of the solution, you can find comparison grids that tell you whether the exercises are new for the fifth edition, unchanged from the fourth edition, or modified from the fourth edition.

Correctness and accuracy of the solutions and answers are of paramount importance to both instructors and students. Every possible effort has been taken to ensure an error free and accurate solutions manual. Every exercise has been worked out, checked, rechecked, and rechecked by the authors of the text and myself during the four stages (manuscripts, revised manuscripts, page proofs and second page proofs) of the book. Every exercise was also checked for accuracy by at least two other physics professors at other institutions.

Since this manual is written mainly for instructors, verbal explanations in the solutions have been kept to a minimum and some algebraic procedures are only outlined.

The answers given here were reached by working the exercises step-by-step and rounding the result at each step following the general rules of thumb of significant figures (an extra digit or two are carried in intermediate results). If you work the exercises fully and then round only your final result, your *correct* answer may differ slightly from the answer you find here. Variations may be due to rounding or to calculator differences.

This manual was typeset with Microsoft Word for Windows Version 97. The diagrams are drafted either with Word 97 or Coreldraw 6.0. Since I typed all the solutions and drafted all the diagrams, I bear the final and ultimate responsibilities for any error. Should you find any error, I would be grateful if you could notify me.

Please contact the publisher (Prentice Hall) to get a copy.

I certainly hope you find this manual helpful in your teaching.

ACKNOWLEDGMENT

I would like to thank the following people and organizations for their enormous help and support.

First to the authors, Jerry D. Wilson and Anthony J. Buffa, for their meticulous checking of my work and numerous constructive and helpful comments and discussions.

To John Kinard and Jerry Wilson for their solutions manual of the second edition Wilson book. Although this is the fifth edition, some of the solutions are from their work.

To David Curott (University of North Alabama) and Willam McCorkle (West Luberty State College) for checking the solutions and answers.

To Prentice Hall for the financial support and the editors, Erik Fahlgren and Christian Botting, for their guidance and assistance.

To Jane Loftus for proof-reading this manual.

Last but not the least, to my family, Lingfei and Alina, for their essential and generous support and love. I dedicate this manual to them.

Bo Lou, Ph.D., Professor of Physics
Department of Physical Sciences
Ferris State University
Big Rapids, MI 49307

TABLE OF CONTENTS

CHAPTER 1

MEASUREMENT AND PROBLEM SOLVING

Remind students that their answers to odd-numbered exercises may be slightly different from those given here because of rounding. Refer to Problem-Solving Hint: The "Correct" Answer in Chapter 1.

1.   (b).

2.   (c).

3.   (c).

4.   (a) Since 1 gal = 3.785 L, $300 \text{ L} = (300 \text{ L}) \times \dfrac{1 \text{ gal}}{3.785 \text{ L}} = 79.3$ gal. $\boxed{\text{Not reasonable}}$.

(b) Since 1 in. = 2.54 cm, $225 \text{ cm} = (225 \text{ cm}) \times \dfrac{1 \text{ in.}}{2.54 \text{ cm}} = 88.6$ in. = 7 ft 5 in.. $\boxed{\text{Yes}}$.

(c) Since 1 m = 3.28 ft, $120 \text{ m}^2 = (120 \text{ m}^2) \times \left(\dfrac{3.28 \text{ ft}}{1 \text{ m}}\right)^2 = 1.29 \times 10^3 \text{ ft}^2$. $\boxed{\text{Not reasonable}}$.

5.   (b)

6.   Since 1 in. = 2.54 cm, $3 \text{ cm} = (3 \text{ cm}) \times \dfrac{1 \text{ in.}}{2.54 \text{ cm}} = 1.2$ in. That would have been a huge lady bug. $\boxed{\text{No}}$.

Since 1 kg is equivalent to 2.2 lb., $10 \text{ kg} = (10 \text{ kg}) \times \dfrac{2.2 \text{ lb.}}{1 \text{ kg}} = 22$ lb. Salmon are quite large. $\boxed{\text{Yes}}$

7.   The decimal system (base 10) has a dime worth 10¢ and a dollar worth 10 dimes, or 100¢. By analogy, a duodecimal system would have a dime worth 12¢ and a dollar worth 12 "dimes," or $1.44 in decimal dollars. Then a penny would be $\dfrac{1}{144}$ of a dollar.

8.   (a) Different ounces are used for volume and weight measurements. 16 oz = 1 pt is a volume measure and 16 oz = 1 lb. is a weight measure.

(b) Two different pound units are used. Avoirdupois lb. = 16 oz, troy lb. = 12 oz.

9.   That is because 1 nautical mile = 6076 ft = 1.15 mi. A nautical mile is larger than a (statute) mile.

10.   (d).

11.   (d).

12.   No , it only tells if the equation is dimensionally correct.

13.   (c).

14.   Dividing something is equivalent to multiplying by the reciprocal. $m/s \div s = \dfrac{m}{s} \times \dfrac{1}{s} = \boxed{m/s^2}$.

15.   Dimensional analysis uses the fundamental dimensions of physical quantities such as, length ([L]), mass ([M]), and time ([T]). Unit analysis uses a specific system of units. For example, if the mks system is used, then meter (m), kilogram (kg), and second (s) are used in unit analysis.

16. $[L] = [L] + \dfrac{[L]}{[T]} \times [T] = [L] + [L]$.

17.   (d).

18. $[T] = \sqrt{\dfrac{[L]}{[L]/[T]^2}} = \sqrt{[T]^2} = [T]$. The equation is dimensionally correct.

19. $m^2 = (m)^2 = m^2$.

20.   Yes , since $[m^3] = [m]^3 = [m^3]$.

21.   No . $V = 4\pi r^3/3 = 4\pi \, (8r^3)/24 = 4\pi(2r)^3/24 = \pi d^3/6$. So it should be $\boxed{V = \pi d^3/6}$.

22. $x = \dfrac{gt^2}{2}$ ☞ $g = \dfrac{2x}{t^2}$.   So the units of g are $\boxed{m/s^2}$.

23.   No , because $m/s \neq m/s - (m/s^2)(s)^2 = m/s - m$.

24.   Since $\rho = \dfrac{m}{V}$, the unit of mass is kg, and the unit of volume is m^3, the unit of ρ is equal to $\dfrac{kg}{m^3} = \boxed{kg/m^3}$.

25.   Yes , because $[L^2] = \frac{1}{2}[L]([L] + [L]) = [L^2] + [L^2]$.

26.   The first student , because $m/s = \sqrt{(m/s^2)(m)} = \sqrt{m^2/s^2} = m/s$.

27.   Since $f = \dfrac{1}{2\pi}\sqrt{\dfrac{g}{L}}$, hertz $= \sqrt{\dfrac{m/s^2}{m}} = \boxed{1/s \text{ or } s^{-1}}$.

28.   (a) Since $F = ma$, newton $= (kg)(m/s^2) = \boxed{kg \cdot m/s^2}$.

        (b) $\boxed{Yes}$, because $(kg) \times \dfrac{m^2/s^2}{m} = kg \cdot m/s^2$ $(F = mv^2/r)$.

29.   (a) Since $E = mc^2$, the units of energy $= (kg)(m/s)^2 = \boxed{kg \cdot m^2/s^2}$.

        (b) $\boxed{Yes}$, because $(kg)(m/s^2)(m) = kg \cdot m^2/s^2$ $(E = mgh)$.

30.   (c).

31.   (a). kg is a unit of mass and lb. is a unit of force. On the surface of the Earth, 1 kg is *equivalent* to 2.2 lb.

32. $130 \text{ ft} = (130 \text{ ft}) \times \dfrac{1 \text{ m}}{3.281 \text{ ft}} = \boxed{39.6 \text{ m}}$.

33.   (a) $\boxed{Centimeter}$, as it is the smallest unit among those listed.

        (b) Since 1 ft = 30.5 cm, $6.00 \text{ ft} = (6.00 \text{ ft}) \times \dfrac{30.5 \text{ cm}}{1 \text{ ft}} = \boxed{183 \text{ cm}}$.

34.   (a) Since 1 m = 3.28 ft, $100 \text{ m} = (100 \text{ m}) \times \dfrac{3.28 \text{ ft}}{1 \text{ m}} = \boxed{3.28 \times 10^2 \text{ ft}}$.

        (b) $2.4 \text{ m} = (2.4 \text{ m}) \times \dfrac{3.28 \text{ ft}}{1 \text{ m}} = \boxed{7.9 \text{ ft}}$.

35. $40\,000 \text{ mi} = (40\,000 \text{ mi}) \times \dfrac{1609 \text{ m}}{1 \text{ mi}} = 64\,400\,000 \text{ m}$.

        So $\dfrac{64\,400\,000 \text{ m}}{1.75 \text{ m}} = \boxed{37\,000\,000 \text{ times}}$.

36.   Since 1 m = 3.28 ft, $452 \text{ m} = (452 \text{ m}) \times \dfrac{3.28 \text{ ft}}{1 \text{ m}} = \boxed{1.48 \times 10^3 \text{ ft}}$.

37. $239 \text{ ft, 6 in.} = 2874 \text{ in.} = (2874 \text{ in.}) \times \dfrac{0.0254 \text{ m}}{1 \text{ in.}} = \boxed{73.0 \text{ m}}$.

        $261 \text{ ft, 10 in.} = 3142 \text{ in.} = (3142 \text{ in.}) \times \dfrac{0.0254 \text{ m}}{1 \text{ in.}} = \boxed{79.8 \text{ m}}$.

        $79 \text{ ft, 1 in.} = 949 \text{ in.} = (949 \text{ in.}) \times \dfrac{0.0254 \text{ m}}{1 \text{ in.}} = \boxed{24.1 \text{ m}}$.

38.   (a) Since 1 gal = 3.785 L < 4 L, or ½ gal < 2 L, ½ gal holds $\boxed{\text{less}}$.

         (b) 0.5 gal = (0.5 gal) $\times \dfrac{3.785 \text{ L}}{1 \text{ gal}}$ = 1.89 L.   2 L − 1.89 L = 0.11 L.   So $\boxed{\text{2 L by 0.11 L more}}$.

39.   18 gal = (18 gal) $\times \dfrac{3.785 \text{ L}}{1 \text{ gal}}$ = $\boxed{68 \text{ L}}$.

40.   (a) 300 ft = (300 ft) $\times \dfrac{1 \text{ m}}{3.28 \text{ ft}}$ = 91.5 m.   160 ft = (160 ft) $\times \dfrac{1 \text{ m}}{3.28 \text{ ft}}$ = 48.8 m.

         So the dimensions are $\boxed{\text{91.5 m by 48.8 m}}$.

         (b) 11 in. = (11 in.) $\times \dfrac{2.54 \text{ cm}}{1 \text{ in.}}$ = 27.9 cm.   11.25 in. = (11.25 in.) $\times \dfrac{2.54 \text{ cm}}{1 \text{ in.}}$ = 28.6 cm.

         So the length is $\boxed{\text{27.9 cm to 28.6 cm}}$.

41.   From Exercise 1.40, the $\boxed{\text{metric field}}$ is larger.

         A_{current} = (91.4 m)(48.8 m) = 4.46×10^3 m². A_{metric} = (100 m)(54 m) = 5.4×10^3 m².

         So the difference is 5.4×10^3 m² − 4.46×10^3 m² = $\boxed{9.4 \times 10^2 \text{ m}^2}$.

42.   0.35 m/s = (0.35 m/s) $\times \dfrac{1 \text{ mi}}{1609 \text{ m}} \times \dfrac{3600 \text{ s}}{1 \text{ h}}$ = 0.78 mi/h. So $\boxed{0.78 \text{ mi}}$.

43.   763 mi/h = (763 mi/h) $\times \dfrac{1609 \text{ m}}{1 \text{ mi}} \times \dfrac{1 \text{ h}}{3600 \text{ s}}$ = $\boxed{341 \text{ m/s}}$.

         (b) 300 ft = (300 ft) $\times \dfrac{1 \text{ m}}{3.28 \text{ ft}}$ = 91.46 m.   So the time is $\dfrac{91.46 \text{ m}}{341 \text{ m/s}}$ = $\boxed{0.268 \text{ s}}$.

44.   (a) 1 km/h = (1 km/h) $\times \dfrac{1000 \text{ m}}{1 \text{ km}} \times \dfrac{1 \text{ h}}{3600 \text{ s}}$ = 0.8 m/s < 1 m/s.

         1 ft/s = (1 ft/s) $\times \dfrac{1 \text{ m}}{3.28 \text{ ft}}$ = 0.30 m/s < 1 m/s.

         1 mi/h = (1 mi/h) $\times \dfrac{1609 \text{ m}}{1 \text{ mi}} \times \dfrac{1 \text{ h}}{3600 \text{ s}}$ = 0.45 m/s < 1 m/s.

         So $\boxed{1 \text{ m/s}}$ represents the greatest speed.

         (b) 15.0 m/s = (15.0 m/s) $\times \dfrac{1 \text{ mi}}{1609 \text{ m}} \times \dfrac{3600 \text{ s}}{1 \text{ h}}$ = $\boxed{33.6 \text{ mi/h}}$.

45. (a) $10 \text{ mi/h} = (10 \text{ mi/h}) \times \dfrac{1.609 \text{ km}}{1 \text{ mi}} = \boxed{16 \text{ km/h for each } 10 \text{ mi/h}}$.

(b) $70 \text{ mi/h} = (70 \text{ mi/h}) \times \dfrac{1.609 \text{ km}}{1 \text{ mi}} = \boxed{113 \text{ km/h}}$.

46. (a) $25.0 \text{ mi/gal} = (25.0 \text{ mi/gal}) \times \dfrac{1.609 \text{ km}}{1 \text{ mi}} \times \dfrac{1 \text{ gal}}{3.785 \text{ L}} = \boxed{10.6 \text{ km/L}}$.

(b) $6000 \text{ km requires } (6000 \text{ km}) \times \dfrac{1 \text{ L}}{10.6 \text{ km}} = 565 \text{ L}$,

which costs $(565 \text{ L}) \times \dfrac{1 \text{ gal}}{3.785 \text{ L}} \times \dfrac{\$5.00}{1 \text{ gal}} = \boxed{\$746}$.

47. (a) $2 \text{ fl. oz} = (2 \text{ fl. oz}) \times \dfrac{473 \text{ mL}}{16 \text{ fl. oz}} = \boxed{59.1 \text{ mL}}$.

(b) $100 \text{ g} = (100 \text{ g}) \times \dfrac{14.5 \text{ oz}}{411 \text{ g}} = \boxed{3.53 \text{ oz}}$.

48. $(250 \text{ mL/min})(4.5 \times 10^{6} \text{ /mm}^{3}) \times \dfrac{1 \text{ min}}{60 \text{ s}} \times \dfrac{1 \text{ L}}{10^{-3} \text{ mL}} \times \dfrac{10^{6} \text{ mm}^{3}}{1 \text{ L}} = \boxed{1.9 \times 10^{10} \text{ /s}}$.

49. $18 \text{ in.} = (18 \text{ in.}) \times \dfrac{2.54 \text{ cm}}{1 \text{ in.}} = 45.7 \text{ cm.} \quad 5 \text{ ft, } 6 \text{ in.} = 66 \text{ in.} = (66 \text{ in.}) \times \dfrac{2.54 \text{ cm}}{1 \text{ in.}} = 167.6 \text{ cm.}$

So the growth per year is $\dfrac{167.6 \text{ cm} - 45.7 \text{ cm}}{20} = \boxed{6.1 \text{ cm}}$.

50. (a) $x = (19 \text{ in.}) \cos 37° = 15.2 \text{ in.} \quad \text{and} \quad y = (19 \text{ in.}) \sin 37° = 11.4 \text{ in.}$

So the area $= xy = (15.2 \text{ in.})(11.4 \text{ in.}) = \boxed{1.7 \times 10^{2} \text{ in}^{2}}$.

(b) $1.7 \times 10^{2} \text{ in.}^{2} = (1.7 \times 10^{2} \text{ in.}^{2}) \times \left(\dfrac{2.54 \text{ cm}}{1 \text{ in.}}\right)^{2} = \boxed{1.1 \times 10^{3} \text{ cm}^{2}}$.

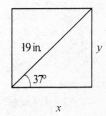

51. (a) $W = 3.2 \text{ yd} = (3.2 \text{ yd}) \times \dfrac{3 \text{ ft}}{1 \text{ yd}} \times \dfrac{1 \text{ m}}{3.28 \text{ ft}} = 2.93 \text{ m.} \quad L = 4.0 \text{ yd} = 3.66 \text{ m.}$

$H = 8.0 \text{ ft} = (8.0 \text{ ft}) \times \dfrac{1 \text{ m}}{3.28 \text{ ft}} = 2.44 \text{ m.}$

The volume $V = LWH = (3.66 \text{ m})(2.93 \text{ m})(2.44 \text{ m}) = \boxed{26 \text{ m}^{3}}$.

(b) $V = 26.2 \text{ m}^{3} = (26.2 \text{ m}^{3}) \times \left(\dfrac{3.28 \text{ ft}}{1 \text{ m.}}\right)^{3} = \boxed{9.2 \times 10^{2} \text{ ft}^{3}}$.

52.   (a) $13.6 \text{ g/cm}^3 = (13.6 \text{ g/cm}^3) \times \dfrac{1 \text{ kg}}{1000 \text{ g}} \times \left(\dfrac{100 \text{ cm}}{1 \text{ m}}\right)^3 = \boxed{1.36 \times 10^4 \text{ kg/m}^3}$.

       (b) $\rho = \dfrac{m}{V}$, ☞ $m = \rho V = (13.6 \text{ g/cm}^3)(0.250 \text{ L}) \times \dfrac{1000 \text{ cm}^3}{1 \text{ L}} = 3.40 \times 10^3 \text{ g} = \boxed{3.40 \text{ kg}}$.

53.   (a) The density of water is $\rho = 1000 \text{ kg/m}^3$. Since 1 m = 3.27 ft, $(1 \text{ m})^3 = (3.28 \text{ ft})^2$ or $1 \text{ m}^3 = 35.29 \text{ ft}^3$.

       Also 1 kg = 2.2 lb. So the weight density of water is $(1000 \text{ kg/m}^3) \times \dfrac{1 \text{ m}^3}{35.29 \text{ ft}^3} \times \dfrac{2.2 \text{ lb.}}{1 \text{ kg}} = \boxed{62.3 \text{ lb/ft}^3}$.

       (b) $(1 \text{ gal}) \times \dfrac{0.134 \text{ ft}^3}{1 \text{ gal}} \times (62.3 \text{ lb/ft}^3) = \boxed{8.34 \text{ lb}}$.

54. $L = 300 \text{ cubits} = (300 \text{ cubits}) \times \dfrac{0.5 \text{ yd}}{1 \text{ cubit}} \times \dfrac{3 \text{ ft}}{1 \text{ yd}} \times \dfrac{1 \text{ m}}{3.28 \text{ ft}} = 137 \text{ m}$.

       $W = 50.0 \text{ cubits} = 22.9 \text{ m}$, $H = 30.0 \text{ cubits} = 13.7 \text{ m}$.

       So the dimensions are $\boxed{137 \text{ m by } 22.9 \text{ m by } 13.7 \text{ m}}$.

       (b) $V = LWH = (137 \text{ m})(22.9 \text{ m})(13.7 \text{ m}) = \boxed{4.30 \times 10^4 \text{ m}^3}$.

55.   (a).

56.   (b).

57. $50\,500 \ \mu\text{m} = (50\,500 \ \mu\text{m}) \times \dfrac{1 \text{ cm}}{10\,000 \ \mu\text{m}} = \boxed{5.05 \text{ cm}} = \boxed{5.05 \times 10^{-1} \text{ dm}} = \boxed{5.05 \times 10^{-2} \text{ m}}$.

58. $\boxed{0.001 \text{ m or 1 mm}}$.

59. $\boxed{\text{No}}$, only one doubtful digit (1/10 mm or 1/100 cm) can be measured. The best measurement is 25.48 cm.

60.   (a) $\boxed{4}$.   (b) $\boxed{3}$.   (c) $\boxed{5}$.   (d) $\boxed{2}$.

61.   (a) $\boxed{1.0 \text{ m}}$.   (b) $\boxed{8.0 \text{ cm}}$.   (c) $\boxed{16 \text{ kg}}$.   (d) $\boxed{1.5 \times 10^{-2} \ \mu\text{s}}$.

62. $\boxed{\text{(b) and (d)}}$. (a) has 4 and (c) has 6.

63.   (a) $\boxed{10.1 \text{ m}}$.   (b) $\boxed{775 \text{ km}}$.   (c) $\boxed{2.55 \times 10^{-3} \text{ kg}}$.   (d) $\boxed{9.30 \times 10^7 \text{ mi}}$.

64. $A = LW = (0.274 \text{ m})(0.222 \text{ m}) = \boxed{6.08 \times 10^{-2} \text{ m}^2}$.

65. $r = d/2 = (12 \text{ cm})/2 = 6.0 \text{ cm} = 0.060 \text{ m}. \quad A = \pi r^2 = \pi(0.060 \text{ m})^2 = \boxed{1.1 \times 10^{-2} \text{ m}^2}$.

66. $V = a^3, \quad \mathscr{F} \quad a = \sqrt[3]{V} = \sqrt[3]{2.5 \times 10^2 \text{ cm}^3} = \boxed{6.3 \text{ cm}}$.

67. (a) $\boxed{\text{Three}}$, since the height has only three significant figures.

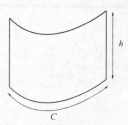

(b) The area is the sum of that of the top, the bottom, and the side. The side of the can is a rectangle with a length equal to the circumference and width equal to the height of the can.

$$A = \frac{\pi d^2}{4} + \frac{\pi d^2}{4} + Ch = \frac{\pi d^2}{4} + \frac{\pi d^2}{4} + (\pi d)h$$

$$= \frac{\pi(12.559 \text{ cm})^2}{4} + \frac{\pi(12.559 \text{ cm})^2}{4} + \pi(12.559 \text{ cm})(5.62 \text{ cm}) = \boxed{470 \text{ cm}^2}.$$

68. (a) $\boxed{\text{Zero}}$, since 38 m has zero decimal place.

(b) $46.9 \text{ m} + 5.72 \text{ m} - 38 \text{ m} = \boxed{15 \text{ m}}$.

69. (a) $v = \dfrac{x}{t} = \dfrac{8.5 \text{ m}}{2.7 \text{ s}} = 3.1 \text{ m/s}, \quad p = mv = (0.66 \text{ kg})(3.1 \text{ m/s}) = \boxed{2.0 \text{ kg·m/s}}$.

(b) $p = \dfrac{mx}{t} = \dfrac{(0.66 \text{ kg})(8.5 \text{ m})}{2.7 \text{ s}} = \boxed{2.1 \text{ kg·m/s}}$.

(c) $\boxed{\text{No}}$, the results are not the same. The difference comes from $\boxed{\text{rounding}}$.

70. (a).

71. (c).

72. $\boxed{\text{No}}$. Order of magnitude calculation is only an estimate of the approximate value.

73. According to Pythagorean theorem, $c = \sqrt{a^2 + b^2} = \sqrt{(37 \text{ m})^2 + (42.3 \text{ m})^2} = \boxed{56 \text{ m}}$.

74. $\rho = \dfrac{m}{V} = \dfrac{6.0 \times 10^{25}\ \text{kg}}{1.1 \times 10^{21}\ \text{m}^3} = \boxed{5.5 \times 10^3\ \text{kg/m}^3}$.

75. Since 1 m = 100 cm, $(1\ \text{m})^3 - (100\ \text{cm})^3$ or $1\ \text{m}^3 = 10^6\ \text{cm}^3$.

$\rho = \dfrac{m}{V}$, ☞ $m = \rho V = (0.10\ \text{g/cm}^3)(1\ \text{m}^3) \times \dfrac{10^6\ \text{cm}^3}{1\ \text{m}^3} = \boxed{1.0 \times 10^5\ \text{g} = 100\ \text{kg}}$.

76. $A = \pi r^2$. Since $3.1 \times 10^{-4}\ \text{m} \approx 10^{-4}\ \text{m}$, $A \approx (10^{-4}\ \text{m})^2 = 10^{-8}\ \text{m}^2$. So it is $\boxed{\text{about } 10^{-8}\ \text{m}^2}$.

Some people might note that the squaring of 3.1×10^{-4} would give an order of magnitude of 10^7 instead of the 10^{-8}, as obtained from first taking the order of magnitude as suggested in the text and squaring 10^{-4}. Both methods and answers are acceptable because this is simply an estimate.

77. (a) The percentage is $\dfrac{(18\ \text{g})(9\ \text{cal/g})}{310\ \text{cal}} = 0.52 = \boxed{52\%}$.

(b) Total fat $= \dfrac{18\ \text{g}}{0.28} = \boxed{64\ \text{g}}$; saturated fat $= \dfrac{7\ \text{g}}{0.35} = \boxed{20\ \text{g}}$.

78. (a) One sheet has two pages. 860 pages has 430 sheets.

The average thickness per sheet is $\dfrac{3.75\ \text{cm}}{430\ \text{sheets}} = \boxed{8.72 \times 10^{-3}\ \text{cm}}$.

(b) About $\dfrac{1\ \text{cm}}{100\ \text{sheets}} = \boxed{10^{-2}\ \text{cm}}$.

79. 1 light-year $= 1\ \text{ly} = (365.25\ \text{d})(86400\ \text{s/d})(3.00 \times 10^8\ \text{m/s}) = \boxed{9.47 \times 10^{15}\ \text{m}}$.

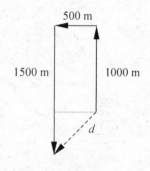

80. (a) From the sketch, it is clear that the stadium is $\boxed{\text{south of west}}$, relative to your house.

(b) Consider the right triangle on the bottom of the sketch. The two sides perpendicular to each other are 500 m each.
Using Pythagorean theorem,

$d = \sqrt{(500\ \text{m})^2 + (500\ \text{m})^2} = \boxed{707\ \text{m}}$.

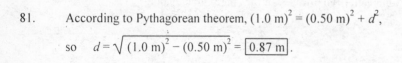
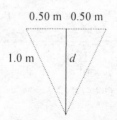

81. According to Pythagorean theorem, $(1.0\ \text{m})^2 = (0.50\ \text{m})^2 + d^2$,

so $d = \sqrt{(1.0\ \text{m})^2 - (0.50\ \text{m})^2} = \boxed{0.87\ \text{m}}$.

82. The $\boxed{12\text{-in.}}$ pizza is a better buy. A better buy gives you more *area* (more pepperoni) per dollar and the area of a pizza depends on the square of the diameter.

For the 12 in.: $\dfrac{\pi(6.0\text{ in.})^2}{\$13.50} = \boxed{8.4\text{ in.}^2/\text{dollar}}$

For the 9.0 in.: $\dfrac{\pi(4.5\text{ in.})^2}{\$7.95} = \boxed{8.0\text{ in.}^2/\text{dollar}}$.

83. For the center circle: $A = \pi r^2 = \pi(0.64\text{ cm})^2 = 1.3\text{ cm}^2$.

For the outer ring: $A = \pi(r_2^2 - r_1^2) = \pi[(1.78\text{ cm})^2 - 1.66\text{ cm})^2] = 1.3\text{ cm}^2$.

So $\boxed{\text{same area for both}}$ if calculated to two significant figures.

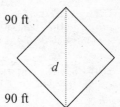

84. $d = \sqrt{(90\text{ ft})^2 + (90\text{ ft})^2} = 127\text{ ft} = (127\text{ ft}) \times \dfrac{1\text{ m}}{3.28\text{ ft}} = \boxed{39\text{ m}}$.

85. $t = \dfrac{x}{v} = \dfrac{31\text{ mi}}{75\text{ mi/h}} = 0.41\text{ h} = \boxed{25\text{ min}}$.

86. $118\text{ mi} = (118\text{ mi}) \times \dfrac{1609\text{ m}}{1\text{ mi}} = 10^5\text{ m},\qquad 307\text{ mi} = (307\text{ mi}) \times \dfrac{1609\text{ m}}{1\text{ mi}} = 10^5\text{ m},$

$279\text{ ft} = (279\text{ ft}) \times \dfrac{1\text{ m}}{3.28\text{ ft}} = 10^2\text{ m}.$

So $V = LWD \approx (10^5\text{ m})(10^5\text{ m})(10^2\text{ m}) = \boxed{10^{12}\text{ m}^3}$.

87. $d = x\tan 30° = (50\text{ m} - x)\tan 40° = (50\text{ m})\tan 40° - x\tan 40°$.

So $x = \dfrac{(50\text{ m})\tan 40°}{\tan 30° + \tan 40°} = 29.6\text{ m}$.

Therefore $d = (29.6\text{ m})\tan 30° = \boxed{17\text{ m}}$.

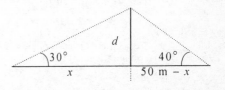

88. (a) $12.634 + 2.1 = \boxed{14.7}$. (b) $13.5 - 2.134 = \boxed{11.4}$.

(c) $\pi(0.25\text{ m})^2 = \boxed{0.20\text{ m}^2}$. (d) $\sqrt{2.37/3.5} = \boxed{0.82}$.

89. These two are very close, so let's calculate to compare.

$\$0.32/\text{L} = (\$0.32/\text{L}) \times \dfrac{3.785\text{ L}}{1\text{ gal}} = \$1.21/\text{gal}.$ So $\boxed{\$0.32/\text{L} = \$1.21/\text{gal}} > \$1.20/\text{gal}.$

Therefore $\$0.32/\text{L}$ is $\boxed{\text{more}}$.

90.   The number of beats = (70 times/min)(70 year)(365 d/year)(24 h/d)(60 min/h) = $\boxed{2.6 \times 10^9 \text{ times}}$.

91. $A = \frac{1}{2}LH = \frac{1}{2}(11.2 \text{ cm})(7.5 \text{ cm}) = \boxed{42 \text{ cm}^2}$.

92.   Since ax^2 is in meters, $a = \dfrac{m}{m^2} = \boxed{1/m}$.

        Since bx is in meters, $b = \dfrac{m}{m} = \boxed{\text{dimensionless}}$. c is in $\boxed{m}$.

93. $V = LWH \approx (1 \text{ cm})(10 \text{ cm})(10 \text{ cm}) = \boxed{10^2 \text{ cm}^3}$.

94.   (a) $A = 4\pi r^2 = 4\pi(12 \text{ cm})^2 = \boxed{1.8 \times 10^3 \text{ cm}^2}$.

        (b) $1.8 \times 10^3 \text{ cm}^2 = (1.8 \times 10^3 \text{ cm}^2) \times \left(\dfrac{1 \text{ m}}{100 \text{ cm}}\right)^2 = \boxed{0.18 \text{ m}^2}$.

        (c) $V = \dfrac{4\pi r^3}{3} = \dfrac{4\pi(0.12 \text{ m})^3}{3} = 7.24 \times 10^{-3} \text{ m}^3$.

        So $\rho = \dfrac{m}{V} = \dfrac{9.0 \text{ kg}}{7.24 \times 10^{-3} \text{ m}} = \boxed{1.2 \times 10^3 \text{ kg/m}^3}$.

95.   The volume of a cylinder is $V = AH$, where $A = \pi r^2$ is the area of the bottom of the cylinder and H is the height of the cylinder.

        $V = (\pi r^2)H = \pi(4.0 \text{ cm})^2(12 \text{ cm}) = 6.03 \times 10^2 \text{ cm}^3 = (6.03 \times 10^2 \text{ cm}^3) \times \dfrac{1 \text{ L}}{1000 \text{ cm}^3} = \boxed{0.60 \text{ L}}$.

96.   (a) The smallest division is $\boxed{\text{cm}}$, as the last digit is estimated.

        (b) $A = LW = (1.245 \text{ m})(0.760 \text{ m}) = \boxed{0.946 \text{ m}^2}$.

97. $\boxed{\text{Not reasonable}}$, because 25 m/s = (25 m/s) $\times \dfrac{1 \text{ mi}}{1609 \text{ m}} \times \dfrac{3600 \text{ s}}{1 \text{ h}}$ = 56 mi/h.

98. $3.36 \text{ g/cm}^3 = (3.36 \text{ g/cm}^3) \times \dfrac{1 \text{ kg}}{1000 \text{ g}} \times \left(\dfrac{100 \text{ cm}}{1 \text{ m}}\right)^3 = 3.36 \times 10^3 \text{ kg/m}^3$.

        $\rho = \dfrac{m}{V}$,   ☞ $m = \rho V = (3.36 \times 10^3 \text{ kg/m}^3) \times \dfrac{4\pi}{3} \times [(1080 \text{ mi})(1609 \text{ m/mi})]^3 = \boxed{7.39 \times 10^{22} \text{ kg}}$,

        which is very close to 7.4×10^{22} kg listed in the inside back cover.

99. (a) Since $d = (13 \text{ mi}) \tan 25°$ and $\tan 25° < 1$ ($\tan 45° = 1$),

d is $\boxed{\text{less than}}$ 13 mi.

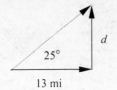

(b) $d = (13 \text{ mi}) \tan 25° = \boxed{6.1 \text{ mi}}$.

100. $d = \sqrt{(200 \text{ mi})^2 + (300 \text{ mi} - 100 \text{ mi})^2} = \boxed{283 \text{ mi}}$.

$\theta = \tan^{-1}\left(\dfrac{300 \text{ mi} - 100 \text{ mi}}{200 \text{ mi}}\right) = \boxed{45° \text{ north of east}}$.

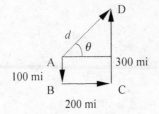

101. The volume of a sphere is $V = \dfrac{4\pi r^3}{3}$.

$\rho = \dfrac{m}{V}$, ☞ $m = \rho V = (1000 \text{ kg/m}^3) \times \dfrac{4\pi(0.12 \text{ m})^3}{3} = \boxed{7.2 \text{ kg}}$.

102. Refer to Fig. 1.13 in the textbook.

The radius of rotation at 28° north is

$r = (6.38 \times 10^6 \text{ m}) \cos 28° = 5.63 \times 10^6 \text{ m}$.

The distance traveled in one day is equal to the circumference of that rotational circle.

So $c = 2\pi r = 2\pi(5.63 \times 10^6 \text{ m}) = \boxed{3.54 \times 10^7 \text{ m}}$.

CHAPTER 2

KINEMATICS: DESCRIPTION OF MOTION

1.   (a) scalar   (b) vector   (c) scalar   (d) vector

2. $\boxed{\text{Yes}}$, the coordinates of the object depend on the reference point. $\boxed{\text{No}}$, displacement is independent of reference point. It remains the same (same direction and magnitude).

3.   (a).

4.   (c).

5. $\boxed{\text{Yes}}$, for a round-trip. $\boxed{\text{No}}$; distance is always greater than or equal to the magnitude of displacement.

6.   No final position can be given. The position could be anywhere from 0 to 500 m.

7.   At constant velocity, speed is the magnitude of velocity.

8. $\boxed{\text{No}}$, this is generally not the case. The average velocity could be zero (for a round trip), while the average speed is never zero.

9. $\boxed{\text{The distance traveled is greater than or equal to 300 m}}$. The object could travel a variety of ways as long as it ends up at 300 m north. If the object travels straight north, then the minimum distance is 300 m.

10.   Displacement is the change in position.

    So the magnitude of the displacement for half a lap is $\boxed{300 \text{ m}}$.

    For a full lap (the car returns to its starting position), the displacement is $\boxed{\text{zero}}$.

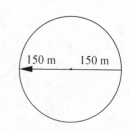

11.   Displacement is the change in position. So it is $\boxed{1.65 \text{ m down}}$.

12. $d = 1 \text{ mi} = 1609 \text{ m}$, $\Delta t = 3 \text{ min, } 43.13 \text{ s} = 223.13 \text{ s}$.

    So $\bar{s} = \dfrac{d}{\Delta t} = \dfrac{1609 \text{ m}}{223.13 \text{ s}} = \boxed{7.2 \text{ m/s}}$.

13. $\bar{s} = \dfrac{d}{\Delta t}$,   ☞ $d = \bar{s} \, \Delta t = (90 \text{ km/h})(\tfrac{1}{3} \text{ h}) = \boxed{30 \text{ km}}$.

    $\boxed{\text{No}}$, this is generally not the magnitude of the actual displacement unless the bus is traveling on a straight road in only one direction.

14. (a) First trip: $\bar{s} = \dfrac{d}{\Delta t} = \dfrac{150 \text{ km}}{2.5 \text{ h}} = \boxed{60 \text{ km/h}}$.   Return trip: $\bar{s} = \dfrac{150 \text{ km}}{2.0 \text{ h}} = \boxed{75 \text{ km/h}}$.

    (b) Total trip: $\bar{s} = \dfrac{150 \text{ km} + 150 \text{ km}}{2.5 \text{ h} + 2.0 \text{ h}} = \boxed{67 \text{ km/h}}$.

15. (a) $\bar{s} = \dfrac{d}{\Delta t} = \dfrac{(0.30 \text{ km})(1000 \text{ m/km})}{(10 \text{ min})(60 \text{ s/min})} = \boxed{0.50 \text{ m/s}}$.

    (b) $\bar{s}_1 = 1.20 \, \bar{s} = 1.20(0.50 \text{ m/s}) = 0.60 \text{ m/s}$.   So $\Delta t = \dfrac{d}{\bar{s}_1} = \dfrac{300 \text{ m}}{0.60 \text{ m/s}} = 500 \text{ s} = \boxed{8.3 \text{ min}}$.

16. (a) The average velocity is $\boxed{\text{zero}}$ because the displacement is zero for a complete lap.

    (b) $\bar{s} = \dfrac{d}{\Delta t} = \dfrac{2\pi r}{\Delta t} = \dfrac{2\pi(500 \text{ m})}{50 \text{ s}} = \boxed{63 \text{ m/s}}$.

17. (a) The magnitude of the displacement is $\boxed{\text{between 40 m and 60 m}}$ because any
side of a triangle cannot be greater than the sum of the other two sides. In this
case, looking at the triangle shown, the two sides perpendicular to each other are
20 m and 40 m, respectively. The magnitude of the displacement is the
hypotenuse of the right triangle, so it cannot be smaller than the longer of the
sides perpendicular to each other.

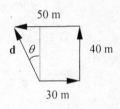

    (b) $d = \sqrt{(40 \text{ m})^2 + (50 \text{ m} - 30 \text{ m})^2} = \boxed{45 \text{ m}}$. $\theta = \tan^{-1}\left(\dfrac{50 \text{ m} - 30 \text{ m}}{40 \text{ m}}\right) = \boxed{27° \text{ west of north}}$.

18. (a) $\bar{s} = \dfrac{d}{\Delta t} = \dfrac{2(7.1 \text{ m})}{2.4 \text{ s}} = \boxed{5.9 \text{ m/s}}$.

    (b) Since the ball is caught at the initial height, the displacement is zero. So the average velocity is $\boxed{\text{zero}}$.

19. (a) $\bar{s} = \dfrac{d}{\Delta t} = \dfrac{27 \text{ m} + 21 \text{ m}}{(30 \text{ min})(60 \text{ s/min})} = \boxed{2.7 \text{ cm/s}}$.

    (b) The displacement is $\Delta x = \sqrt{(27 \text{ m})^2 + (21 \text{ m})^2} = 34.2 \text{ m}$.

    $\bar{v} = \dfrac{\Delta x}{\Delta t} = \dfrac{34.2 \text{ m}}{(30 \text{ min})(60 \text{ s/min})} = \boxed{1.9 \text{ cm/s}}$.

20. (a) $s = \bar{s} = \dfrac{d}{\Delta t} = \dfrac{(1.50 \text{ km})(1000 \text{ m/km})}{(1.10 \text{ min})(60 \text{ s/min})} = \boxed{22.7 \text{ m/s}}$.

    $\boxed{\text{Velocity is not constant}}$ because its direction changes.

21. (a) $\bar{s} = \dfrac{d}{\Delta t}$, ☞ $\Delta t_L = \dfrac{2500 \text{ m}}{3.00 \times 10^8 \text{ m/s}} = 8.33 \times 10^{-6} \text{ s}$, $\Delta t_S = \dfrac{2500 \text{ m}}{340 \text{ m/s}} = 7.35 \text{ s}$.

So the time elapsed is $\Delta t_S - \Delta t_L = \boxed{7.35 \text{ s}}$.

(b) $\boxed{\text{No}}$, the speed of light is already so much greater than that of sound.

22. (a) $\bar{v} = \dfrac{\Delta x}{\Delta t}$, So

$\bar{v}_{AB} = \dfrac{1.0 \text{ m} - 1.0 \text{ m}}{1.0 \text{ s} - 0} = \boxed{0}$; $\bar{v}_{BC} = \dfrac{7.0 \text{ m} - 1.0 \text{ m}}{3.0 \text{ s} - 1.0 \text{ s}} = \boxed{3.0 \text{ m/s}}$;

$\bar{v}_{CD} = \dfrac{9.0 \text{ m} - 7.0 \text{ m}}{4.5 \text{ s} - 3.0 \text{ s}} = \boxed{1.3 \text{ m/s}}$; $\bar{v}_{DE} = \dfrac{7.0 \text{ m} - 9.0 \text{ m}}{6.0 \text{ s} - 4.5 \text{ s}} = \boxed{-1.3 \text{ m/s}}$;

$\bar{v}_{EF} = \dfrac{2.0 \text{ m} - 7.0 \text{ m}}{9.0 \text{ s} - 6.0 \text{ s}} = \boxed{-1.7 \text{ m/s}}$; $\bar{v}_{FG} = \dfrac{2.0 \text{ m} - 2.0 \text{ m}}{11.0 \text{ s} - 9.0 \text{ s}} = \boxed{0}$;

$\bar{v}_{BG} = \dfrac{2.0 \text{ m} - 1.0 \text{ m}}{11.0 \text{ s} - 1.0 \text{ s}} = \boxed{0.10 \text{ m/s}}$.

(b) $\boxed{\text{The motion of BC, CD, and DE are not uniform}}$ since they are not straight lines.

(c) The object changes its direction of motion at point D. So it has to stop momentarily and $v = \boxed{0}$.

23. Use $\bar{s} = \dfrac{d}{\Delta t}$ and $\bar{v} = \dfrac{\Delta x}{\Delta t}$.

(a) $\bar{s}_{0\text{-}2.0 \text{ s}} = \dfrac{2.0 \text{ m} - 0}{2.0 \text{ s} - 0} = \boxed{1.0 \text{ m/s}}$; $\bar{s}_{2.0 \text{ s-}3.0 \text{ s}} = \dfrac{2.0 \text{ m} - 2.0 \text{ m}}{3.0 \text{ s} - 2.0} = \boxed{0}$;

$\bar{s}_{3.0 \text{ s-}4.5 \text{ s}} = \dfrac{4.0 \text{ m} - 2.0}{4.5 \text{ s} - 3.0 \text{ s}} = \boxed{1.3 \text{ m/s}}$; $\bar{s}_{4.5 \text{ s-}6.5 \text{ s}} = \dfrac{4.0 \text{ m} - (-1.5 \text{ m})}{6.5 \text{ s} - 4.5 \text{ s}} = \boxed{2.8 \text{ m/s}}$;

$\bar{s}_{6.5 \text{ s-}7.5 \text{ s}} = \dfrac{-1.5 \text{ m} - (-1.5 \text{ m})}{7.5 \text{ s} - 6.5 \text{ s}} = \boxed{0}$; $\bar{s}_{7.5 \text{ s-}9.0 \text{ s}} = \dfrac{0 - (-1.5 \text{ m})}{9.0 \text{ s} - 7.5 \text{ s}} = \boxed{1.0 \text{ m/s}}$;

(b) $\bar{v}_{0\text{-}2.0 \text{ s}} = \dfrac{2.0 \text{ m} - 0}{2.0 \text{ s} - 0} = \boxed{1.0 \text{ m/s}}$; $\bar{v}_{2.0 \text{ s-}3.0 \text{ s}} = \dfrac{2.0 \text{ m} - 2.0 \text{ m}}{3.0 \text{ s} - 2.0} = \boxed{0}$;

$\bar{v}_{3.0 \text{ s-}4.5 \text{ s}} = \dfrac{4.0 \text{ m} - 2.0}{4.5 \text{ s} - 3.0 \text{ s}} = \boxed{1.3 \text{ m/s}}$; $\bar{v}_{4.5 \text{ s-}6.5 \text{ s}} = \dfrac{-1.5 \text{ m} - 4.0 \text{ m}}{6.5 \text{ s} - 4.5 \text{ s}} = \boxed{-2.8 \text{ m/s}}$;

$\bar{v}_{6.5 \text{ s-}7.5 \text{ s}} = \dfrac{-1.5 \text{ m} - (-1.5 \text{ m})}{7.5 \text{ s} - 6.5 \text{ s}} = \boxed{0}$; $\bar{v}_{7.5 \text{ s-}9.0 \text{ s}} = \dfrac{0 - (-1.5 \text{ m})}{9.0 \text{ s} - 7.5 \text{ s}} = \boxed{1.0 \text{ m/s}}$.

(c) $v_{1.0 \text{ s}} = \bar{s}_{0\text{-}2.0 \text{ s}} = \boxed{1.0 \text{ m/s}}$; $v_{2.5 \text{ s}} = \bar{s}_{2.0 \text{ s-}3.0 \text{ s}} = \boxed{0}$;

$v_{4.5 \text{ s}} = \boxed{0}$ since the object reverses its direction of motion; $v_{6.0 \text{ s}} = \bar{s}_{4.5 \text{ s-}6.5 \text{ s}} = \boxed{-2.8 \text{ m/s}}$.

(d) $v_{4.5 \text{ s-}9.0 \text{ s}} = \dfrac{0 - 4.0 \text{ m}}{9.0 \text{ s} - 4.5 \text{ s}} = \boxed{-0.89 \text{ m/s}}$.

24.   (a) $\bar{s} = \dfrac{d}{\Delta t}$,   ☞ $\Delta t = \dfrac{1\ \text{mi}}{65\ \text{mi/h}} = 0.0154\ \text{h} = \boxed{55\ \text{s}}$.

(b) $\bar{s} = \dfrac{1\ \text{mi}}{(65\ \text{s})(1\ \text{h}/3600\ \text{s})} = \boxed{55\ \text{mi/h}}$.

25.   From $\bar{s} = \dfrac{d}{\Delta t}$, we have $\Delta t_{\text{transverse}} = \dfrac{d}{8.9\ \text{km/s}}$; $\Delta t_{\text{longitudinal}} = \dfrac{d}{5.1\ \text{km/s}}$.

The time difference is $\Delta t_{\text{longitudinal}} - \Delta t_{\text{transverse}} = \dfrac{d}{5.1\ \text{km/s}} - \dfrac{d}{8.9\ \text{km/s}} = 73\ \text{s}$.

Solving, $d = \boxed{8.7 \times 10^2\ \text{km}}$.

26.   The distance is the same for both aircraft.

$\bar{s} = \dfrac{d}{\Delta t}$,   ☞ $d = \bar{s}\,\Delta t$.

So $(565\ \text{mi/h})(4.50\ \text{h}) = (505\ \text{mi/h})\Delta t_{\text{slow}}$. $\Delta t_{\text{slow}} = 5.03\ \text{h}$.

The extra time for the slow one to complete the same trip is $5.03\ \text{h} - 4.50\ \text{h} = 0.53\ \text{h} = \boxed{32\ \text{min}}$.

27.   The minimum speed is $\bar{s} = \dfrac{d}{\Delta t} = \dfrac{675\ \text{km}}{7.00\ \text{h}} = 96.4\ \text{km/h} = \boxed{59.9\ \text{mi/h}}$.

$\boxed{\text{No}}$, she does not have to exceed the 65 mi/h speed limit.

28.   To the runner on the right, the runner on the left is running at a velocity of

$+4.50\ \text{m/s} - (-3.50\ \text{m/s}) = +8.00\ \text{m/s}$.   So it takes $\Delta t = \dfrac{\Delta x}{\bar{v}} = \dfrac{100\ \text{m}}{8.00\ \text{m/s}} = \boxed{12.5\ \text{s}}$.

They meet at $(4.50\ \text{m/s})(12.5\ \text{s}) = \boxed{56.3\ \text{m from the initial position of the runner on left}}$.

29.   Let the distance to school be d, Δt_1 be the time to school, Δt_2 be the time to home,

and $\bar{s}_2$ be the average speed to home. Apply $\bar{s} = \dfrac{d}{\Delta t}$,   ☞ $\Delta t = \dfrac{d}{\bar{s}}$.

To school: $\Delta t_1 = \dfrac{d}{30\ \text{km/h}}$;   to home: $\Delta t_2 = \dfrac{d}{\bar{s}_2}$;   total trip: $\Delta t_1 + \Delta t_2 = \dfrac{2d}{60\ \text{km/h}}$.

So $\dfrac{d}{30\ \text{km/h}} + \dfrac{d}{\bar{s}_2} = \dfrac{2d}{60\ \text{km/h}}$,   or $\dfrac{1}{30\ \text{km/h}} + \dfrac{1}{\bar{s}_2} = \dfrac{2}{60\ \text{km/h}}$,

$\dfrac{1}{\bar{s}_2} = \dfrac{2}{60\ \text{km/h}} - \dfrac{1}{30\ \text{km/h}} = 0$.

Thus $\bar{s}_2$ would have to be infinity. Hence it is $\boxed{\text{impossible}}$.

30.   (d). Any change in either magnitude or direction results in a change in velocity. The brakes and gearshift change the magnitude and the steering wheel changes the direction.

31.   Yes . Although the speed of the car is constant, its velocity is not, because of the change in direction. A change in velocity results in acceleration.

32.   (b), it is a straight line that is neither horizontal (zero acceleration) nor vertical (infinite acceleration).

33. v_o . Since an equal amount of time is spent on acceleration and deceleration of the same magnitude.

34.   Not necessarily . The change in velocity is the key. If a fast-moving object does not change its velocity, its acceleration is zero. However, if a slow-moving object changes its velocity, it will have some acceleration.

35.   Yes , this is entirely possible. For example, an object moving in the $+x$-axis (positive velocity) slows down (negative acceleration, or acceleration in the $-x$-axis).

36.   In Fig. 2.21(a), the object accelerates uniformly first, maintains constant velocity for a while, and then accelerates uniformly at the same rate again as in the first segment.
In Fig. 2.21(b), the object accelerates uniformly.

37. $25.0 \text{ km/h} = (25.0 \text{ km/h}) \times \dfrac{1000 \text{ m}}{1 \text{ km}} \times \; = 6.944 \text{ m/s}, \quad 65.0 \text{ km/h} = 18.06 \text{ m/s}.$

So $\bar{a} = \dfrac{\Delta v}{\Delta t} = \dfrac{18.06 \text{ m/s} - 6.944 \text{ m/s}}{6.00 \text{ s}} = \boxed{1.85 \text{ m/s}^2}$.

38. $60 \text{ mi/h} = (60 \text{ mi/h}) \times \dfrac{1609 \text{ m}}{1 \text{ mi}} \times \dfrac{1 \text{ h}}{3600 \text{ s}} = 26.8 \text{ m/s}. \qquad \bar{a} = \dfrac{\Delta v}{\Delta t} = \dfrac{26.8 \text{ m/s} - 0}{3.9 \text{ s}} = \boxed{6.9 \text{ m/s}^2}$.

39. $\Delta t = \dfrac{26.8 \text{ m/s} - 0}{7.2 \text{ m/s}^2} = \boxed{3.7 \text{ s}}$.

40.   (a) The direction of the acceleration vector is opposite to velocity as the object slows down.

(b) $40.0 \text{ km/h} = (40 \text{ km/h}) \times \dfrac{1000 \text{ m}}{1 \text{ km}} \times \dfrac{1 \text{ h}}{3600 \text{ s}} = 11.1 \text{ m/s}.$

So $\bar{a} = \dfrac{\Delta v}{\Delta t} = \dfrac{0 - 11.1 \text{ m/s}}{5.0 \text{ s}} = -2.2 \text{ m/s}^2$ or $\boxed{-2.2 \text{ m/s in each s}}$.

The negative sign indicates that the acceleration vector is in opposite direction of motion.

41. $\bar{a} = \dfrac{\Delta v}{\Delta t}$,   ☞ $\Delta v = v - v_0 = \bar{a}\Delta t = (2.0 \text{ m/s}^2)(6.0 \text{ s}) = 12 \text{ m/s}.$

So $v = v_0 + \Delta v = 0 \text{ m/s} + 12 \text{ m/s} = 12 \text{ m/s}.$

The average velocity is then $\bar{v} = (0 \text{ m/s} + 12 \text{ m/s}/2 = 6.0 \text{ m/s}.$

$\Delta x = \bar{v}\Delta t = (6.0 \text{ m/s})(6.0 \text{ s}) = \boxed{36 \text{ m}}.$

42.   The initial velocity is $v_0 = +3.5 \text{ m/s}$. The acceleration in this case is -0.50 m/s^2 as it is opposite to v.

$\bar{a} = \dfrac{\Delta v}{\Delta t}$,   ☞ $\Delta t = \dfrac{\Delta v}{\bar{a}} = \dfrac{0 - 3.5 \text{ m/s}}{-0.50 \text{ m/s}^2} = \boxed{7.0 \text{ s}}.$

43. $\bar{a}_{0\text{-}4.0s} = \dfrac{\Delta v}{\Delta t} = \dfrac{8.0 \text{ m/s} - 0}{4.0 \text{ s} - 0} = \boxed{2.0 \text{ m/s}^2};$ $\bar{a}_{4.0 \text{ s-}10.0s} = \dfrac{8.0 \text{ m/s} - 8.0 \text{ m/s}}{10.0 \text{ s} - 4.0 \text{ s}} = \boxed{0};$

$\bar{a}_{10.0 \text{ s-}18.0 \text{ s}} = \dfrac{0 - 8.0 \text{ m/s}}{18.0 \text{ s} - 10.0 \text{ s}} = \boxed{-1.0 \text{ m/s}^2}.$

The object accelerates at 2.0 m/s^2 first, moves with constant velocity, then decelerates at 1.0 m/s^2.

44.   (a) $\bar{a}_{0\text{-}1.0 \text{ s}} = \dfrac{\Delta v}{\Delta t} = \dfrac{0 - 0}{1.0 \text{ s} - 0} = \boxed{0};$ $\bar{a}_{1.0 \text{ s-}3.0 \text{ s}} = \dfrac{8.0 \text{ m/s} - 0}{3.0 \text{ s} - 1.0 \text{ s}} = \boxed{4.0 \text{ m/s}^2};$

$\bar{a}_{3.0 \text{ s-}8.0 \text{ s}} = \dfrac{-12 \text{ m/s} - 8.0 \text{ m/s}}{8.0 \text{ s} - 3.0 \text{ s}} = \boxed{-4.0 \text{ m/s}^2};$ $\bar{a}_{8.0 \text{ s-}9.0 \text{ s}} = \dfrac{-4 \text{ m/s} - (-12.0 \text{ m/s})}{9.0 \text{ s} - 8.0 \text{ s}} = \boxed{8.0 \text{ m/s}^2};$

$\bar{a}_{9.0 \text{ s-}13.0 \text{ s}} = \dfrac{-4.0 \text{ m/s} - 4.0 \text{ m/s}}{13.0 \text{ s} - 9.0 \text{ s}} = \boxed{0}.$

(b) $\boxed{\text{Constant velocity of } -4.0 \text{ m/s}}.$

45. $72 \text{ km/h} = (72 \text{ km/h}) \times \dfrac{1000 \text{ m}}{1 \text{ km}} \times \dfrac{1 \text{ h}}{3600 \text{ s}} = 20 \text{ m/s}.$

During deceleration, $\Delta t_1 = \dfrac{\Delta v}{\bar{a}} = \dfrac{0 - 20 \text{ m/s}}{-1.0 \text{ m/s}^2} = 20 \text{ s};$ $\Delta x_1 = \bar{v}_1 \Delta t_1 = \dfrac{20 \text{ m/s} + 0}{2}(20 \text{ s}) = 200 \text{ m}.$

It would have taken the train $\dfrac{200 \text{ m}}{20 \text{ m/s}} = 10 \text{ s}$ to travel 200 m.

So it lost only $20 \text{ s} - 10 \text{ s} = 10 \text{ s}$ during deceleration.

During acceleration, $\Delta t_2 = \dfrac{20 \text{ m/s} - 0}{0.50 \text{ m/s}^2} = 40 \text{ s};$ $\Delta x_2 = \dfrac{0 + 20 \text{ m/s}}{2}(40 \text{ s}) = 400 \text{ m}.$

It would have taken the train $\dfrac{400 \text{ m}}{20 \text{ m/s}} = 20 \text{ s}$ to travel 400 m. So it lost only $40 \text{ s} - 20 \text{ s} = 20 \text{ s}$ during

acceleration. Therefore, the train lost $2 \text{ min} + 10 \text{ s} + 20 \text{ s} = \boxed{150 \text{ s}}$ in stopping at the station.

46.   (c).

47.   (d), because it is a parabola (depending on time squared).

48.   The acceleration is $\boxed{\text{zero}}$ because the velocity is a constant.

49.   (a). Since $v = v_o + at = 0 + at$, $\bar{v} = \dfrac{v_o + v}{2} = \frac{1}{2}at$.

50. $\boxed{\text{No}}$. If the object has a negative initial velocity or $v_o = 0$, it will accelerate in the negative direction.

51.   The average velocity is $\bar{v} = \dfrac{\Delta x}{\Delta t} = \dfrac{100 \text{ m}}{4.5 \text{ s}} = 22.2$ m/s. $\bar{v} = \dfrac{v_o + v}{2} = \dfrac{v}{2}$.

     So the final velocity must be $v = 2(22.2 \text{ m/s}) = 44.4$ m/s.

     $\bar{a} = \dfrac{\Delta v}{\Delta t}$,   ☞ $\Delta t = \dfrac{\Delta v}{\bar{a}} = \dfrac{44.4 \text{ m/s} - 0}{9.0 \text{ m/s}^2} = 4.9 \text{ s} > 4.5$ s.

     So $\boxed{\text{no}}$, the driver did not do it.   The acceleration must be $\dfrac{44.4 \text{ m/s} - 0}{4.5 \text{ s}} = \boxed{9.9 \text{ m/s}^2}$.

52.   Given: $v_o = 0$, $a = 2.0$ m/s^2, $t = 5.00$ s.   Find: v and x (take $x_o = 0$).

     (a) $v = v_o + at = 0 + (2.0 \text{ m/s}^2)(5.0 \text{ s}) = \boxed{10 \text{ m/s}}$.

     (b) $x = x_o + v_o t + \frac{1}{2}at^2 = 0 + 0(5.00 \text{ s}) + \frac{1}{2}(2.0 \text{ m/s}^2)(5.0 \text{ s})^2 = \boxed{25 \text{ m}}$.

53.   Given: $v_o = 35$ mi/h $= 15.6$ m/s, $v = 0$, $x = 35$ m (take $x_o = 0$).   Find: a and t.

     (a) $v^2 = v_o^2 + 2a(x - x_o)$,   ☞ $a = \dfrac{v^2 - v_o^2}{2x} = \dfrac{(0)^2 - (15.6 \text{ m/s})^2}{2(35 \text{ m})} = -\boxed{3.5 \text{ m/s}^2}$.

     The negative sign indicates that the acceleration vector is in opposite direction of velocity.

     (b) $v = v_o + at$,   ☞ $t = \dfrac{v - v_o}{a} = \dfrac{0 - 15.6 \text{ m/s}}{-3.5 \text{ m/s}^2} = \boxed{4.5 \text{ s}}$.

54.   Given: $v_o = 75$ km/h $= 20.8$ m/s, $v = 40$ km/h $= 11.1$ m/s, $x = 50$ m (take $x_o = 0$).   Find: a.

     $v^2 = v_o^2 + 2a(x - x_o)$,   ☞ $a = \dfrac{v^2 - v_o^2}{2x} = \dfrac{(11.1 \text{ m/s})^2 - (20.8 \text{ m/s})^2}{2(50 \text{ m})} = \boxed{-3.1 \text{ m/s}^2}$.

55.   (a) Given: $v_o = 100$ km/h $= 27.78$ m/s, $a = -6.50$ m/s^2, $x = 20.0$ m (take $x_o = 0$).   Find: v.

     $v^2 = v_o^2 + 2a(x - x_o) = (27.78 \text{ m/s})^2 + 2(-6.50 \text{ m/s}^2)(20.0 \text{ m}) = 511.6$ m^2/s^2,

     So $v = 22.62$ m/s $= \boxed{81.4 \text{ km/h}}$.

     (b) $v = v_o + at$,   ☞ $t = \dfrac{v - v_o}{a} = \dfrac{22.62 \text{ m/s} - 27.78 \text{ m/s}}{-6.50 \text{ m/s}^2} = \boxed{0.794 \text{ s}}$.

56.   Given: $v_0 = 0$, $v = 560$ km/h $= 155.6$ m/s, $x = 400$ m (take $x_0 = 0$).   Find: t and a.

(a) $x = x_0 + \bar{v}t = \dfrac{v_0 + v}{2}\,t$,   ☞ $t = \dfrac{2x}{v_0 + v} = \dfrac{2(400 \text{ m})}{0 + 155.6 \text{ m/s}} = \boxed{5.14 \text{ s}}$.

(b) $v = v_0 + at$,   ☞ $a = \dfrac{v - v_0}{t} = \dfrac{155.6 \text{ m/s} - 0}{5.14 \text{ s}} = \boxed{30.3 \text{ s}}$.

57.   Given: $v_0 = 250$ km/h $= 69.44$ m/s, $a = -8.25$ m/s^2, $x = 175$ m (Take $x_0 = 0$).   Find: t.

$x = x_0 + v_0 t + \tfrac{1}{2}at^2$,   ☞ 175 m $= 0 + (69.44 \text{ m/s})t + \tfrac{1}{2}(-8.25 \text{ m/s}^2)t^2$.

Reduce to quadratic equation $4.125\,t^2 - 69.44\,t + 175 = 0$.

Solving, $t = \boxed{3.09 \text{ s}}$ or 13.7 s.

The 13.7 s answer is physically possible but not likely in reality. After 3.09 s, it is 175 m from where the reverse thrust was applied, but the rocket keeps traveling forward while slowing down. Finally it stops. However, if the reverse thrust is continuously applied (which is possible, but not likely), it will reverse its direction and be back to 175 m

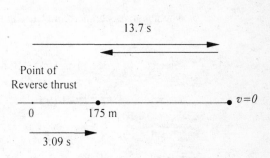

from the point where the initial reverse thrust was applied; a process that would take 13.7 s.

58.   (a) Given: Car A: $a_A = 3.00$ m/s^2, $v_0 = 2.50$ m/s, $t = 10$ s.

                        Car B: $a_B = 3.00$ m/s^2, $v_0 = 5.00$ m/s, $t = 10$ s.

Find: Δx (taking $x_0 = 0$).

From $x = x_0 + v_0 t + \tfrac{1}{2}at^2$, $x_A = 0 + (2.50 \text{ m/s})(10 \text{ s}) + \tfrac{1}{2}(3.00 \text{ m/s})^2(10 \text{ s})^2 = 175$ m,

                        $x_B = 0 + (5.00 \text{ m/s})(10 \text{ s}) + \tfrac{1}{2}(3.00 \text{ m/s})^2(10 \text{ s})^2 = 200$ m.

So $\Delta x = x_B - x_A = 200$ m $- 175$ m $= \boxed{25 \text{ m}}$.

(b) From $v = v_0 + at$, $v_A = 2.50$ m/s $+ (3.00 \text{ m/s})(10 \text{ s}) = 32.5$ m/s,

                        $v_B = 5.00$ m/s $+ (3.00 \text{ m/s})(10 \text{ s}) = 35.0$ m/s.

So $\boxed{\text{car B}}$ is faster.

59.   (a) $\boxed{\text{The object will travel in the } +x\text{-direction and then reverse its direction}}$. This is because the object has initial velocity in the $+x$-direction, and it takes time for the object to decelerate, stop, and then reverses direction. We take $x_0 = 0$.

Given: $v_0 = 40$ m/s, $a = -3.5$ m/s^2, $x = 0$ ("returns to the origin").   Find: t and v.

(b) $x = x_0 + v_0 t + \frac{1}{2}at^2$, ☞ $0 = 0 + (40\ \text{m/s})t + \frac{1}{2}(-3.5\ \text{m/s}^2)t^2$.

Reduce to quadratic equation: $1.75t^2 - 40t = 0$. Solving for $t = 0$ or 22.9 s.

The $t = 0$ answer corresponds to the initial time. So the answer is $t = \boxed{23\ \text{s}}$.

(c) $v = v_0 + at = 40\ \text{m/s} + (-3.5\ \text{m/s}^2)(22.9\ \text{s}) = \boxed{-40\ \text{m/s}}$.

The negative sign means the object is traveling in the $-x$-direction.

60.   Given: $v_0 = 330$ m/s, $v = 0$, $x = 30$ cm $= 0.30$ m (Take $x_0 = 0$). Find: a.

$v^2 = v_0^2 + 2a(x - x_0)$, ☞ $a = \dfrac{v^2 - v_0^2}{2x}) = \dfrac{(0)^2 - (330\ \text{m/s})^2}{2(0.30\ \text{m})} = -\boxed{1.8 \times 10^5\ \text{m/s}^2}$.

The negative sign here indicates that the acceleration vector is in the opposite direction of velocity.

61.   Given: $v_0 = 350$ m/s, $v = 210$ m/s, $x = 4.00$ cm $= 0.0400$ m (take $x_0 = 0$). Find: t.

$x = x_0 + \bar{v}\,t = \dfrac{v_0 + v}{2}t$, ☞ $t = \dfrac{2x}{v_0 + v} = \dfrac{2(0.0400\ \text{m})}{350\ \text{m/s} + 210\ \text{m/s}} = \boxed{1.43 \times 10^{-4}\ \text{s}}$.

62.   Given: $v_0 = 10$ m/s, $v = 0$, $x = 25$ cm $= 0.25$ m (take $x_0 = 0$). Find: a.

$v^2 = v_0^2 + 2a(x - x_0)$, ☞ $a = \dfrac{v^2 - v_0^2}{2x} = \dfrac{(0\ \text{m/s})^2 - (10\ \text{m/s})^2}{2(0.25\ \text{m})} = -\boxed{2.0 \times 10^2\ \text{m/s}^2}$.

The negative sign here indicates that the acceleration vector is in the opposite direction of velocity.

63.   Given: $v_0 = 0$, $x = 94$ m (take $x_0 = 0$), $t = 2.5$ s. Find: a and v.

(a) $x = x_0 + v_0 t + \frac{1}{2}at^2$, ☞ $a = \dfrac{2(x - v_0 t)}{t^2} = \dfrac{2(94\ \text{m} - 0)}{(2.5\ \text{s})^2} = \boxed{30\ \text{m/s}^2}$.

(b) $v = v_0 + at = 0 + (30\ \text{m/s}^2)(2.5\ \text{s}) = \boxed{75\ \text{m/s}}$.

64. $40\ \text{km/h} = (40\ \text{km/h}) \times \dfrac{1000\ \text{m}}{1\ \text{km}} \times \dfrac{1\ \text{h}}{3600\ \text{s}} = 11.11$ m/s.

During reaction, the car travels a distance of $d = (11.11\ \text{m/s})(0.25\ \text{s}) = 2.78$ m.

So the car really has only $13\ \text{m} - 2.78\ \text{m} = 10.2$ m to come to rest.

Let's calculate the stopping distance of the car. We take $x_0 = 0$.

Given: $v_0 = 11.1$ m/s, $v = 0$, $a = -8.0\ \text{m/s}^2$. Find: x. (Take $x_0 = 0$.)

$v^2 = v_0^2 + 2a(x - x_0)$, ☞ $x = \dfrac{v^2 - v_0^2}{2a} = \dfrac{0 - (11.1\ \text{m/s})^2}{2(-8.0\ \text{m/s}^2)} = 7.70$ m.

So it takes the car only $2.78\ \text{m} + 7.70\ \text{m} = \boxed{10.5\ \text{m} < 13\ \text{m}}$ to stop.

$\boxed{\text{Yes}}$, the car will stop before hitting the child.

65. Repeat the calculation of Exercise 2.64.

$d = (11.1 \text{ m/s})(0.50 \text{ s}) = 5.55 \text{ m}.$

$5.55 \text{ m} + 7.70 \text{ m} = \boxed{13.3 \text{ m}} > 13 \text{ m}.$

$\boxed{\text{No}}$, the car will not stop before hitting the child.

66. (a) For constant acceleration, the v vs. t plot is a straight line. Point p has coordinates of $(0, v_0)$ and point q has coordinates of $(t, v_0 + at)$. The distance from point q to point o is therefore at. The area under the curve is the area of the triangle $\frac{1}{2}(at)t$ plus the area of the rectangle $v_0 t$.

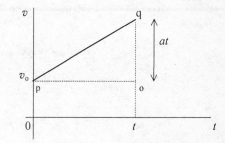

So $A = v_0 t + \frac{1}{2}at^2 = x - x_0$. (Here $x - x_0$ is displacement.)

(b) The total area consists of two triangles from 0 to 4.0 s and from 10.0 s to 18.0 s and a rectangle from 4.0 s to 10.0 s.

$x - x_0 = A = \frac{1}{2}(4.0 \text{ s} - 0)(8.0 \text{ m/s}) + (10.0 \text{ s} - 4.0 \text{ s})(8.0 \text{ m/s}) + \frac{1}{2}(18.0 \text{ s} - 10.0 \text{ s})(8.0 \text{ m/s}) = \boxed{96 \text{ m}}.$

67. (a) $v(8.0 \text{ s}) = \boxed{-12 \text{ m/s}}; \quad v(11.0 \text{ s}) = \boxed{-4.0 \text{ m/s}}.$

(b) Use the result of Exercise 2.66a. The total area consists of a rectangle from 0 to 1.0 s, a triangle from 1.0 s to 5.0 s, a trapezoid from 5.0 s to 11.0 s, and a triangle from 6.0 s to 9.0 s with baseline at –4.0 m/s.

$x - x_0 = A$

$= 0 + \frac{1}{2}(5.0 \text{ s} - 1.0 \text{ s})(8.0 \text{ m/s}) + \dfrac{(11.0 \text{ s} - 6.0 \text{ s}) + (11.0 \text{ s} - 5.0 \text{ s})}{2} \times (-4.0 \text{ m/s})$

$+ \frac{1}{2}(9.0 \text{ s} - 6.0 \text{ s})[(-12.0 \text{ m/s}) - (-4.0 \text{ m/s})] = \boxed{-18 \text{ m}}.$

(c) The total distance (not displacement) is the addition of the absolute values of the areas.

$d = \Sigma A_i = 0 + \frac{1}{2}(5.0 \text{ s} - 1.0 \text{ s})(8.0 \text{ m/s}) + \dfrac{(11.0 \text{ s} - 6.0 \text{ s}) + (11.0 \text{ s} - 5.0 \text{ s})}{2} \times (4.0 \text{ m/s})$

$+ \frac{1}{2}(9.0 \text{ s} - 6.0 \text{ s})[(12.0 \text{ m/s} - 4.0 \text{ m/s}] = \boxed{50 \text{ m}}.$

68. (a) $v^2 = v_0^2 + 2a(x - x_0), \quad \text{☞} \quad x - x_0 = \dfrac{v^2 - v_0^2}{2a} = \dfrac{0^2 - v_0^2}{2a} = -\dfrac{v_0^2}{2a}.$

Taking $x_0 = 0$, so $(x - x_0) = x$ is proportional to v_0^2. If v_0 doubles, then x becomes 4 times as large.

The answer is then $\boxed{4x}$.

(b) $\dfrac{x_2}{x_1} = \dfrac{v_{2o}^2}{v_{1o}^2} = \dfrac{60^2}{40^2} = 2.25.$ So $x_2 = 2.25 \, x_1 = 2.25 \, (3.00 \text{ m}) = \boxed{6.75 \text{ m}}.$

69. $v = v_0 + at$ $\qquad\qquad\qquad\qquad$ $x = x_0 + \frac{1}{2}(v + v_0)t$

$\qquad$ $x = x_0 + v_0 t + \frac{1}{2}at^2$ $\qquad\qquad$ $v^2 = v_0^2 + 2a(x - x_0)$

$\qquad$ (a) $\qquad x_0$ — initial position, $\qquad\qquad$ x — final position

$\qquad\qquad\qquad$ v_0 — initial velocity, $\qquad\qquad$ v — final velocity

$\qquad\qquad\qquad$ a — acceleration, $\qquad\qquad\qquad$ t — time interval

$\qquad$ (b) The condition under which these equations hold is that the motion needs to have constant acceleration.

70. $\qquad$ Given: $\quad x = 65$ m $- 5.0$ m $= 60$ m (take $x_0 = 0$), $\quad v_0 = 10$ m/s, $\quad t = 2.5$ s. $\quad$ Find: $\quad a$.

$\qquad$ $x = x_0 + v_0 t + \frac{1}{2}at^2$, $\quad \textcircled{a} \quad a = \dfrac{x - v_0 t}{\frac{1}{2}t^2} = \dfrac{60 \text{ m} - (10 \text{ m/s})(2.5 \text{ s})}{\frac{1}{2}(2.5 \text{ s})^2} = \boxed{11 \text{ m/s}^2}$.

71. $\qquad$ (d).

72. $\qquad$ (d). Free fall is a motion under the gravitational acceleration. The initial velocity does not matter.

73. $\qquad$ When it reaches the highest point, its velocity is $\boxed{\text{zero}}$ (velocity changes from up to down, so it has to be zero), and its acceleration is still the constant $\boxed{9.80 \text{ m/s}^2 \text{ downward}}$.

74. $\qquad$ (c). It accelerates at 9.80 m/s², so it increases its speed by 9.80 m/s in each second.

75. $\qquad$ $\boxed{\text{The ball moves with a constant velocity}}$ because there is no gravitational acceleration in space. If the gravitational acceleration is zero, $g = 0$, then $v =$ constant.

76. $\qquad$ The answer is (a). Taking $y_0 = 0$,

$\qquad$ $y = y_0 + v_0 t - \frac{1}{2}gt^2 = -\frac{1}{2}gt^2$. $\quad$ So $\quad y_1 = -\frac{1}{2}gt^2$ $\quad$ and $\quad y_2 = -\frac{1}{2}g(t-1)^2$.

$\qquad$ The distance between the two positions is

$\qquad$ $\Delta y = y_1 - y_2 = -\frac{1}{2}g[t^2 - (t-1)^2] = -\frac{1}{2}g[t^2 - t^2 + 2t - 1] = -\frac{1}{2}g[2t - 1]$.

$\qquad$ Therefore, Δy increases as t increases.

77. $\qquad$ First find the gravitational acceleration (the Exercise did not say that it happens on the Earth).

$\qquad$ Given: $\quad v_0 = 0$, $\quad y = -19.6$ m (take $y_0 = 0$), $\quad t = 2.00$ s. $\quad$ Find: $\quad g$.

$\qquad$ $y = y_0 + v_0 t - \frac{1}{2}gt^2 = -\frac{1}{2}gt^2$, $\quad \textcircled{a} \quad g = -\dfrac{2y}{t^2} = -\dfrac{2(-19.6 \text{ m})}{(2.00 \text{ s})^2} = 9.80 \text{ m/s}^2$.

$\qquad$ $y(4.00 \text{ s}) = -\frac{1}{2}(9.80 \text{ m/s}^2)(4.00 \text{ s})^2 = -78.4$ m. It will fall $\boxed{78.4 \text{ m}}$.

78.   (a) Given: $v_0 = 0$, $t = 2.8$ s.   Find: v (take $y_0 = 0$).

$v = v_0 - gt = 0 - (9.80 \text{ m/s}^2)(2.8 \text{ s}) = -\boxed{27 \text{ m/s}}$.

(b) $y = y_0 + v_0 t - \frac{1}{2}gt^2 = 0 + 0 - \frac{1}{2}(9.80 \text{ m/s}^2)(2.8 \text{ s})^2 = -\boxed{38 \text{ m}}$.

79.   (a) We take $y_0 = 0$. $y = y_0 + v_0 t - \frac{1}{2}gt^2 = -\frac{1}{2}gt^2$.   So y is proportional to the time squared.

Therefore twice the time means $\boxed{4 \text{ times}}$ the height.

Given: $v_0 = 0$, $t = 1.80$ s.   Find: y_A and y_B.

(b) $y_A = -\frac{1}{2}(9.80 \text{ m/s}^2)(1.80 \text{ s})^2 = -15.9$ m.

So the height of cliff A above the water is $\boxed{15.9 \text{ m}}$.

$y_B = \dfrac{y_A}{4} = \dfrac{15.9 \text{ m}}{4} = \boxed{4.0 \text{ m}}$.

80.   (a) A straight line, slope $= -g$.   (b) A parabola.

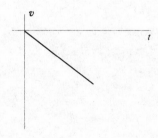   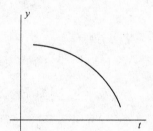

81.   Given: $v_0 = 0$, $y = -0.157$ m (take $y_0 = 0$).   Find: t.

$y - y_0 = v_0 t - \frac{1}{2}gt^2 = -\frac{1}{2}gt^2$,   ☞ $t = \sqrt{\dfrac{2y}{-g}} = \sqrt{\dfrac{2(-0.157 \text{ m})}{-9.80 \text{ m/s}^2}} = 0.18 \text{ s} < 0.20 \text{ s}$.

It takes less than the average human reaction time for the dollar bill to fall.

So the answer is $\boxed{\text{no, not a good deal}}$.

82.   Given: $v_0 = 15$ m/s, $v = 0$ (maximum height).   Find: y. (Take $y_0 = 0$.)

$v^2 = v_0^2 - 2g(y - y_0)$,   ☞ $y = \dfrac{v_0^2 - v^2}{2g} = \dfrac{(15 \text{ m/s})^2 - (0)^2}{2(9.80 \text{ m/s}^2)} = \boxed{11 \text{ m}}$.

83.   From Exercise 2.82, $y = \dfrac{v_0^2 - v^2}{2g} = \dfrac{(15 \text{ m/s})^2 - (0)^2}{2(1.67 \text{ m/s}^2)} = \boxed{67 \text{ m}}$.

84. (a) Given: $v_0 = 21$ m/s, $t = 3.0$ s.   Find: y. (Take $y_0 = 0$.)

$y = y_0 + v_0 t - \frac{1}{2}gt^2 = 0 + (21 \text{ m/s})(3.0 \text{ s}) - \frac{1}{2}(9.80 \text{ m/s}^2)(3.0 \text{ s})^2 = \boxed{19 \text{ m}}$.

(b) $12 \text{ m} = (21 \text{ m/s})t - \frac{1}{2}(9.80 \text{ m/s}^2)t^2$,   or $4.90t^2 - 21t + 12 = 0$.

Solve the quadratic equation for $t = \boxed{0.68 \text{ s (on the way up) or 3.6 s (on the way down)}}$.

85.   The maximum initial velocity is for the apple to reach maximum height just below the ceiling.

Given: $v = 0$ (max height), $(y - y_0) = 3.75 \text{ m} - 0.50 \text{ m} = 3.25 \text{ m}$.   Find: v_0.

$v^2 = v_0^2 - 2g(y - y_0)$,   ☞ $v_0 = \sqrt{v^2 + 2g(y - y_0)} = \sqrt{0 + 2(9.80 \text{ m/s}^2)(3.25 \text{ m})} = 7.98$ m/s.

Therefore it is $\boxed{\text{slightly less than 8.0 m/s}}$.

86.   Taking $y_0 = 0$, $y = y_0 + v_0 t - \frac{1}{2}gt^2 = 0 + 0 - \frac{1}{2}gt^2 = -\frac{1}{2}gt^2$,   so $t = \sqrt{\dfrac{-2y}{g}}$.

For $y = -452$ m, $t = 9.604$ s;   for $y = -443$ m, $t = 9.508$ s.

So $\Delta t = 9.604 \text{ s} - 9.508 \text{ s} = \boxed{0.096 \text{ s}}$.

87.   We take $y_0 = 0$.

(a) Given: $v_0 = -14$ m/s, $t = 2.00$ s.   Find: y.

$y = y_0 + v_0 t - \frac{1}{2}gt^2 = 0 + (-14 \text{ m/s})(2.00 \text{ s}) - \frac{1}{2}(9.80 \text{ m/s}^2)(2.00 \text{ s})^2 = -\boxed{48 \text{ m}}$.

(b) Given: $v_0 = -14$ m/s, $y = -65.0$ m.   Find: v.

$v^2 = v_0^2 - 2g(y - y_0) = (-14 \text{ m/s})^2 - 2(9.80 \text{ m/s}^2)(-65.0 \text{ m}) = 1.47 \times 10^3 \text{ m}^2/\text{s}^2$.

So $v = -\sqrt{1.47 \times 10^3 \text{ m}^2/\text{s}^2} = -38 \text{ m/s} = \boxed{38 \text{ m/s downward}}$.

88.   (a) Given: $y = 35$ m (Take $y_0 = 0$.), $t = 3.0$ s.   Find: v_0.

$y = y_0 + v_0 t - \frac{1}{2}gt^2$,   ☞ $v = \dfrac{y}{t} + \frac{1}{2}gt = \dfrac{35 \text{ m}}{3.0 \text{ s}} + \frac{1}{2}(9.80 \text{ m/s}^2)(3.0 \text{ s}) = \boxed{26 \text{ m/s}}$.

(b) Consider the motion up to the maximum height. The time it takes to reach the maximum height is the same as falling from the maximum height.

Given: $v_0 = 26.4$ m/s, $v = 0$.   Find: $2t$ (the time for up and down).

$v = v_0 - gt$,   ☞ $t = \dfrac{v_0 - v}{g} = \dfrac{26.4 \text{ m/s} - 0}{9.80 \text{ m/s}^2} = 2.7$ s.

So $2t = 2(2.7 \text{ s}) = \boxed{5.4 \text{ s}}$.

89. (a) From Example 2.11(b) in the textbook, $t_{up} = 1.14$ s. Consider the downward motion using the highest spot as the starting point.

Given: $v_0 = 0$, $y = -6.40$ m (take $y_0 = 0$). Find: t.

$$y = y_0 + v_0 t - \tfrac{1}{2}gt^2 = -\tfrac{1}{2}gt^2, \quad \text{☞} \quad t_{down} = \sqrt{\frac{-2y}{g}} = \sqrt{\frac{-2(-6.40 \text{ m})}{9.80 \text{ m/s}^2}} = 1.14 \text{ s}.$$

So the travel times are the [same].

(b) Given: $v_0 = 11.2$ m/s, $y = 0$ (back to starting position). Find: v.

$$v^2 = v_0^2 - 2g(y - y_0) \quad \text{☞} \quad v = -v_0 = -11.2 \text{ m/s}.$$

So the two velocities are [equal, but opposite].

90. (b) Given: $v_0 = 6.0$ m/s, $y = -12$ m (take $y_0 = 0$). Find: t and v.

(a) $y = y_0 + v_0 t - \tfrac{1}{2}gt^2$, ☞ $-12 \text{ m} = 0 + (6.0 \text{ m/s})t - \tfrac{1}{2}(9.80 \text{ m/s}^2)t^2$.

Or $4.9t^2 - 6.0t - 12 = 0$. Solving, $t = $ [2.3 s] or -1.1 s. The negative time is discarded.

(b) $v = v_0 - gt = 6.0$ m/s $- (9.80$ m/s$^2)(2.29$ s$) = -$ [16 m/s].

91. (a) When the ball rebounds, it is a free fall with an initial upward velocity. At the maximum height, the velocity is zero. Taking $y_0 = 0$,

$$v^2 = v_0^2 - 2g(y - y_0), \quad \text{☞} \quad y = \frac{v_0^2 - v^2}{2g}.$$

So $y_{max} = \dfrac{v_0^2}{2g}$.

Therefore, the height depends on the initial velocity squared. $95\% = 0.95$ and $0.95^2 = 0.90 < 0.95$.

The ball would bounce [less than] 95% of the initial height.

(b) First calculate the speed just before impact.

Given: $v_0 = 0$, $y = -4.00$ m. Find: v.

$$v^2 = v_0^2 - 2gy = 0^2 - 2(9.80 \text{ m/s}^2)(-4.00 \text{ m}) = 78.4 \text{ m}^2/\text{s}^2,$$

so $v = -\sqrt{78.4 \text{ m}^2/\text{s}^2} = -8.85$ m/s.

Therefore the speed right after rebound is $0.950(8.85$ m/s$) = 8.41$ m/s.

Now consider the rising motion. Given: $v_0 = 8.41$ m/s, $v = 0$ (max height). Find: y.

$$v^2 = v_0^2 - 2gy, \quad \text{☞} \quad y = \frac{v_0^2 - v^2}{2g} = \frac{(8.41 \text{ m/s})^2 - 0^2}{2(9.80 \text{ m/s}^2)} = \boxed{3.61 \text{ m}}.$$

92.   (a) Ball A: Given: $v_0 = 10.0$ m/s, $y = -60.0$ m (take $y_0 = 0$).   Find: t.

Ball B: Given: $v_0 = -10.0$ m/s, $y = -60.0$ m.   Find: t.

Use $y = y_0 + v_0 t - \frac{1}{2}gt^2$.

For ball A: -60.0 m $= 0 + (10.0$ m/s$)t - \frac{1}{2}(9.80$ m/s$^2)t^2$,   or $4.90t^2 - 10.0t - 60.0 = 0$.

Solving the quadratic equation for $t_A = 4.665$ s.

For ball B: -60.0 m $= 0 + (-10.0$ m/s$)t - \frac{1}{2}(9.80$ m/s$^2)t^2$,   or $4.90t^2 + 10.0t - 60.0 = 0$.

Solving the quadratic equation for $t_B = 2.625$ s.

$\Delta t = t_A - t_B = 4.665$ s $- 2.625$ s $= \boxed{2.04 \text{ s}}$.

(b) $\boxed{\text{No}}$, mass does not matter in free fall if air resistance is ignored.

93.   First find the time it takes for the ball to reach the level of the professor's head.

Given: $(y - y_0) = -(18.0$ m $- 1.70$ m$) = -16.3$ m, $v_0 = 0$.   Find: t.

From $y = y_0 + v_0 t - \frac{1}{2}gt^2 = y_0 + -\frac{1}{2}gt^2$,

$t = \sqrt{-\dfrac{2(y - y_0)}{g}} = \sqrt{-\dfrac{2(-16.3 \text{ m})}{9.80 \text{ m/s}^2}} = 1.824$ s.

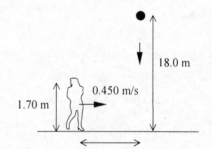

During this time, the professor advances a distance equal to

$(0.450$ m/s$)(1.824$ s$) = 0.821$ m < 1.00 m. $\boxed{\text{No}}$, it does not hit her.

Now calculate the time it takes for the ball to hit the ground.

$t = \sqrt{-\dfrac{2(-18.0 \text{ m})}{9.80 \text{ m/s}^2}} = 1.917$ s.

During this time, the professor advances a distance of $(0.450$ m/s$)(1.917$ s$) = 0.862$ m < 1.00 m.

So the ball hits 1.00 m $- 0.862$ m $= 0.14$ m $= \boxed{14 \text{ cm in front of the professor}}$.

94.   (a) Given: $v_0 = 12.50$ m/s (ascending), $y = -60.0$ m (take $y_0 = 0$).   Find: t.

$y = y_0 + v_0 t - \frac{1}{2}gt^2$,   ☞ -60.0 m $= 0 + (12.50$ m/s$)t - (4.90$ m/s$^2)t^2$.

Reduce to a quadratic equation: $4.90t^2 - 12.50t - 60.0 = 0$.

Solve for $t = \boxed{5.00 \text{ s}}$ or -2.45 s, which is physically meaningless.

(b) $v = v_0 - gt = 12.50$ m/s $- (9.80$ m/s$^2)(5.00$ s$) = -36.5$ m/s $= \boxed{36.5 \text{ m/s}}$ downward.

95.   We take $y_0 = 0$.

(a) $y = y_0 + v_0 t - \frac{1}{2}gt^2 = -\frac{1}{2}gt^2$,   ☞ $t = \sqrt{-\dfrac{2y}{g}}$. $\dfrac{t_M}{t_E} = \dfrac{\sqrt{1/g_M}}{\sqrt{1/g_E}} = \sqrt{\dfrac{g_E}{g_M}} = \boxed{\sqrt{6}}$.

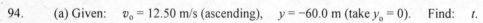

(b) Given: $v_0 = 18.0$ m/s, $v = 0$ ("max height"). Find: y and t.

$$v^2 = v_0^2 - 2g(y - y_0), \quad \text{☞} \quad y = \frac{v_0^2 - v^2}{2g} = \frac{v_0^2}{2g}. \quad \text{So} \quad \frac{y_M}{y_E} = \frac{g_E}{g_M} = 6.$$

For the total trip (up and down), the final position is zero ($y = 0$).

$$\text{So} \quad y = y_0 + v_0 t - \tfrac{1}{2}gt^2 = 0, \quad \text{☞} \quad t = \frac{2v_0}{g}.$$

Therefore $\dfrac{t_M}{t_E} = \dfrac{g_E}{g_M} = 6.$

On the Earth, $\quad y_E = \dfrac{(18.0 \text{ m/s})^2}{2(9.80 \text{ m/s}^2)} = \boxed{16.5 \text{ m}}.$ $\qquad t_E = \dfrac{2(18.0 \text{ m/s})}{9.80 \text{ m/s}^2} = \boxed{3.67 \text{ s}}.$

On the Moon, $\quad y_M = 6\, y_E = \boxed{99.2 \text{ m}}.$ $\qquad t_M = 6\, t_E = \boxed{22.0 \text{ s}}.$

96. The key to this exercise is to find the velocity of the object when it reaches the top of the window (it is not zero). This velocity is the initial velocity for Motion 1 and the final velocity for Motion 2.

Consider Motion 2 first. Taking $y_0 = 0$.

Given: $y = -1.35$ m, $\quad t = 0.210$ s.   Find: v_0.

Apply $\quad y = y_0 + v_0 t - \tfrac{1}{2}gt^2,$

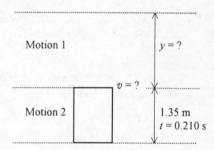

$$v_0 = \frac{y}{t} + \tfrac{1}{2}gt = \frac{-1.35 \text{ m}}{0.210 \text{ s}} + (4.90 \text{ m/s}^2)(0.210 \text{ s}) = -5.40 \text{ m/s}.$$

Now consider Motion 1. Also take its $y_0 = 0$.

Given: $v_0 = 0$, $\quad v = -5.40$ m.   Find: y.

$$v^2 = v_0^2 - 2g(y - y_0), \quad \text{☞} \quad y = \frac{v_0^2 - v^2}{2g} = \frac{0 - (-5.40 \text{ m/s})^2}{2(9.80 \text{ m/s}^2)} = 1.49 \text{ m}.$$

So, it is $\boxed{1.49 \text{ m}}$ above the top of the window.

97. (a) Since 25.0 m is a distance, we need to find the maximum height first.

Given: $v_0 = 7.25$ m/s, $\quad v = 0$.   Find: y (take $y_0 = 0$).

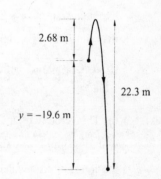

$$v^2 = v_0^2 - 2g(y - y_0), \quad \text{☞} \quad y = \frac{v_0^2 - v^2}{2g} = \frac{(7.25 \text{ m/s})^2 - 0}{2(9.80 \text{ m/s}^2)} = 2.68 \text{ m}.$$

So if it has traveled a distance of 25.0 m, it has traveled a distance of

25.0 m − 2.68 m = 22.3 m downward after reaching maximum height.

So the lowest position is $y = -(22.3 \text{ m} - 2.68 \text{ m}) = -19.6$ m.

$$v^2 = v_0^2 - 2g(y - y_0) = (7.25 \text{ m/s})^2 - 2(9.80 \text{ m/s}^2)(-19.6 \text{ m}) = 4.37 \times 10^2 \text{ m}^2/\text{s}^2.$$

So $\quad v = -\sqrt{v^2} = \boxed{-20.9 \text{ m/s}}.$

(b) $v = v_0 - gt, \quad \text{☞} \quad t = \dfrac{v_0 - v}{g} = \dfrac{7.25 \text{ m/s} - (-20.9 \text{ m/s})}{9.80 \text{ m/s}^2} = \boxed{2.87 \text{ s}}.$

98. $$\bar{v} = \frac{v + v_0}{2} = \frac{v_0 + 0}{2}, \quad \text{☞} \quad v_0 = 2\,\bar{v} = \boxed{-70.0 \text{ km/h}} = \boxed{-19.4 \text{ m/s}}.$$

$$a = \frac{v - v_0}{t} = \frac{0 - (-19.4 \text{ m/s})}{7.00 \text{ s}} = \boxed{+2.78 \text{ m/s}^2}.$$

In this case, the positive 2.78 m/s^2 indicates deceleration because the velocity is negative.

99. (a) Given: $v = 0$ ("max height"), $y = 23$ m (Take $y_0 = 0$). Find: v_0.

$$v^2 = v_0^2 - 2g(y - y_0) = 0, \quad \text{☞} \quad v_0 = \sqrt{2gy} = \sqrt{2(9.80 \text{ m/s}^2)(23 \text{ m})} = \boxed{21 \text{ m/s}}.$$

(b) $y = y_0 + v_0 t - \frac{1}{2}gt^2 = (21 \text{ m/s})(1.3 \text{ s}) - \frac{1}{2}(9.80 \text{ m/s}^2)(1.3 \text{ s})^2 = \boxed{19 \text{ m}}$.

100. (a) Given: $v_0 = 200$ km/h = 55.6 m/s, $v = 20$ km/h = 5.56 m/s, $t = 12$ s. Find: a.

$$a = \frac{v - v_0}{g} = \frac{5.56 \text{ m/s} - 55.6 \text{ m/s}}{12 \text{ s}} = \boxed{-4.2 \text{ m/s}^2}.$$

(b) Take $x_0 = 0$, $x = x_0 + \bar{v}\,t = 0 + \frac{v + v_0}{2}\,t = \frac{55.6 \text{ m/s} + 5.56 \text{ m/s}}{2} \times (12 \text{ s}) = \boxed{3.7 \times 10^2 \text{ m}}$.

101. $$\bar{s} = \frac{d}{\Delta t} = \frac{500 \text{ mi} + 380 \text{ mi} + 600 \text{ mi}}{10 \text{ h} + 8.0 \text{ h} + 15 \text{ h}} = \boxed{45 \text{ mi/h}}.$$

102. Given: $v_0 = 25$ mi/h = 11.2 m/s, $v = 0$, $a = -7.0$ m/s^2. Find: t.

$$v = v_0 + at, \quad \text{☞} \quad t = \frac{0 - 11.2 \text{ m/s}}{-7.0 \text{ m/s}^2} = 1.6 \text{ s} > 1.5 \text{ s}. \text{ So the answer is } \boxed{\text{no}}.$$

103. (a) The answer is $\boxed{\text{greater than } R \text{ but less than } 2R}$. For any right triangle, the hypotenuse is always greater than any one of the other two sides (R) and less than the sum of the sum of the other two sides ($R + R = 2R$).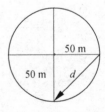

(b) $d = \sqrt{(50 \text{ m})^2 + (50 \text{ m})^2} = \boxed{71 \text{ m}}$.

104. (a) The velocity of the speeder is constant, so its position increases linearly with time and is a straight line on an x vs. t graph (take $x_0 = 0$). The police's motion is motion with constant velocity, so it is a parabola.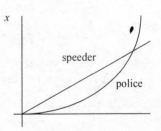

(b) Speeder: $x = x_0 + vt = 0 + (30 \text{ m/s})t$.

Police: $x = x_0 + v_0 t + \frac{1}{2}at^2 = 0 + 0 + \frac{1}{2}(3.5 \text{ m/s}^2)t^2$.

When the police catches the speeder, they are at the same position (same x).

So $(30 \text{ m/s})t = +\frac{1}{2}(3.5 \text{ m/s}^2)t^2$. Solving, $t = 0$ or $\boxed{17 \text{ s}}$.

105.   Given: $v = 0$ (max height), $y = 14.0$ m (take $y_0 = 0$).   Find: v_0.

$$v^2 = v_0^2 - 2g(y - y_0), \quad \text{☞} \quad v_0 = \sqrt{v^2 + 2gy} = \sqrt{0 + 2(9.80 \text{ m/s}^2)(14.0 \text{ m})} = \boxed{16.6 \text{ m/s}}.$$

106.   (a) Given: $v_0 = 45.0$ km/h = 12.5 m/s, $a = 1.50$ m/s^2, $x = 200$ m (take $x_0 = 0$).   Find: v.

$$v^2 = v_0^2 + 2a(x - x_0) = (12.5 \text{ m/s})^2 + 2(1.6 \text{ m/s}^2)(200 \text{ m}) = 756 \text{ m}^2/\text{s}^2, \quad \text{☞} \quad v = \boxed{27.5 \text{ m/s}}.$$

(b) $v = v_0 + at, \quad \text{☞} \quad t = \dfrac{v - v_0}{a} = \dfrac{27.5 \text{ m/s} - 12.5 \text{ m/s}}{1.50 \text{ m/s}^2} = \boxed{10.0 \text{ s}}$.

107.   Given: $v_0 = 85$ km/h = 23.6 m/s, $v = 0$, $t = 10$ s.   Find: x. (Take $x_0 = 0$.)

$$x = x_0 + \bar{v}\,t = 0 + \dfrac{v + v_0}{2}\,t = \dfrac{23.6 \text{ m/s} + 0}{2} \times (10 \text{ s}) = \boxed{1.2 \times 10^2 \text{ m}}.$$

108.   (a) Take $x_0 = 0$ and use $x = x_0 + v_0 t + \frac{1}{2}at^2$.

For car: $d = 0 + \frac{1}{2}(3.70 \text{ m/s}^2)t^2$.   Eq. (1)

For motorcycle: $d + 25.0 \text{ m} = 0 + \frac{1}{2}(4.40 \text{ m/s}^2)t^2$.   Eq. (2)

Eq. (2) − Eq. (1) gives: $25.0 \text{ m} = (0.35 \text{ m/s}^2)t^2$.

Solving, $t = \boxed{8.45 \text{ s}}$.

(b) For car: $x_C = \frac{1}{2}(3.70 \text{ m/s}^2)(8.45 \text{ s})^2 = \boxed{132 \text{ m}}$.

For motorcycle: $x_M = x_C + 25.0 \text{ m} = \boxed{157 \text{ m}}$.

(c) During 8.45 s + 2.00 s = 10.45 s, the motorcycle will be ahead of the car by

$$\Delta x = x_M - x_C = \frac{1}{2}[(4.40 \text{ m/s}^2) - (3.70 \text{ m/s}^2)](10.45 \text{ s})^2 - 25.0 \text{ m} = \boxed{13 \text{ m}}.$$

109.   (a) Given: $v_0 = 15$ m/s, $y = -25$ m (take $y_0 = 0$).   Find: v.

$$v^2 = v_0^2 - 2g(y - y_0) = (15 \text{ m/s})^2 - 2(9.80 \text{ m/s}^2)(-25 \text{ m}) = 715 \text{ m}^2/\text{s}^2.$$

So $v = -\sqrt{715 \text{ m}^2/\text{s}^2} \doteq \boxed{-27 \text{ m/s}}$.

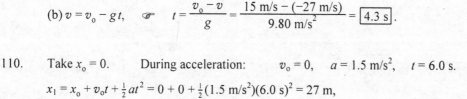

$y = -25$ m

(b) $v = v_0 - g\,t, \quad \text{☞} \quad t = \dfrac{v_0 - v}{g} = \dfrac{15 \text{ m/s} - (-27 \text{ m/s})}{9.80 \text{ m/s}^2} = \boxed{4.3 \text{ s}}$.

110.   Take $x_0 = 0$.   During acceleration: $v_0 = 0$, $a = 1.5$ m/s^2, $t = 6.0$ s.

$x_1 = x_0 + v_0 t + \frac{1}{2}at^2 = 0 + 0 + \frac{1}{2}(1.5 \text{ m/s}^2)(6.0 \text{ s})^2 = 27 \text{ m}$,

$v = v_0 + at = 0 + (1.5 \text{ m/s}^2)(6.0 \text{ s}) = 9.0 \text{ m/s}$.

During constant velocity: $x_2 = (9.0 \text{ m/s})(8.0 \text{ s}) = 72 \text{ m}$.

So $\bar{v} = \dfrac{\Delta x}{\Delta t} = \dfrac{27 \text{ m} + 72 \text{ m}}{14 \text{ s}} = \boxed{7.1 \text{ m/s}}$.

111.　(a) The speed of sound is considered here because it takes time for the sound of the stone hitting water to travel from the bottom of the well to the person.

(b) The time for the stone and sound to travel is 3.65 s – 0.250 s = 3.40 s. Assume the depth of the well is d and it takes t_1 for the stone to reach the bottom and t_2 for sound to travel to the top. Take $y_0 = 0$.

For the stone:　$d = y = y_0 + v_0 t - \frac{1}{2} g t^2 = -\frac{1}{2} g t^2$, ☞ $t_1 = \sqrt{\dfrac{2d}{g}}$.

For sound:　$t_2 = \dfrac{d}{v_s}$.　So　$3.40\ \text{s} = t_1 + t_2 = \sqrt{\dfrac{2d}{9.80\ \text{m/s}^2}} + \dfrac{d}{340\ \text{m/s}}$.

Simplify to a quadratic equation:　$d^2 - (3.950 \times 10^4)d + 1.336 \times 10^6 = 0$.

Solve for　$d = \boxed{51.7\ \text{m}}$.　(Use 4 significant figures.)

112.　(a) When the rocket has fuel, the motion is *not* a free fall but a motion with constant acceleration of $2g$.

Given:　$v_0 = 0$,　$a = 2g$,　$t = t$.　Find:　v,　and　y (take $y_0 = 0$).

$v = v_0 + at = 0 + 2gt = \boxed{2gt}$.　$y = y_0 + v_0 t + \frac{1}{2} a t^2 = 0 + 0 + \frac{1}{2}(2g)t^2 = \boxed{gt^2}$.

(b) When the fuel runs out, the rocket is moving upward with a speed of $2gt$ and at a height of gt^2. From that point on, the acceleration experienced by the rocket is gravitational acceleration.

Given:　$v_0 = 2gt$,　$v = 0$ (maximum height),　$a = -g$,　$y_0 = gt^2$.　Find:　y.

$v^2 = v_0^2 - 2g(y - y_0)$, ☞ $y_{max} = y_0 + \dfrac{v_0^2 - v^2}{2g} = gt^2 + \dfrac{v_0^2}{2g} = gt^2 + \dfrac{(2gt)^2}{2g} = gt^2 + 2gt^2 = \boxed{3gt^2}$.

(c) $y_{max} = 3gt^2 = 3(9.80\ \text{m/s}^2)(30.0\ \text{s})^2 = \boxed{2.65 \times 10^4\ \text{m}}$.

113.　(a) It is a motion with constant acceleration. In each second the velocity increases by 5.0 m/s.

So the acceleration is $\boxed{5.0\ \text{m/s}^2}$.

(b) $\bar{v} = \dfrac{v + v_0}{2} = \dfrac{0 + 25\ \text{m/s}}{2} = \boxed{13\ \text{m/s}}$.

(c)

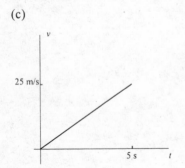

(d)

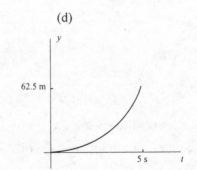

114. (a) $\bar{v}_1 = \dfrac{\Delta x}{\Delta t} = \dfrac{1.80 \text{ km}}{(20.0/60) \text{ h}} = \boxed{5.40 \text{ km/h east}}$ and

$\bar{v}_2 = \dfrac{2.40 \text{ km}}{(35.0/60) \text{ h}} = \boxed{4.11 \text{ km/h north}}$.

$d = \sqrt{(2.40 \text{ km})^2 + (1.80 \text{ km})^2} = 3.00$ km.

$\bar{v} = \dfrac{3.00 \text{ km}}{(20.0/60) \text{ h} + (35.0/60) \text{ h}} = \boxed{3.27 \text{ km/h}}$,

$\theta = \tan^1 \dfrac{2.40 \text{ km}}{1.80 \text{ km}} = \boxed{53° \text{ north of east}}$.

(b) $\bar{s} = \dfrac{d}{\Delta t} = \dfrac{1.80 \text{ km} + 2.40 \text{ km}}{(20.0 + 35.0)/60 \text{ h}} = \boxed{4.58 \text{ km/h}}$.

(c) $\bar{s} = \dfrac{1.80 \text{ km} + 2.40 \text{ km} + 3.00 \text{ km}}{(20.0 + 35.0 + 25.0)/60 \text{ h}} = \boxed{5.40 \text{ km/h}}$. $\bar{v} = \boxed{0}$ since the total displacement is = 0.

115. Assume it takes a time of t hours for the student to arrive at 11:00 AM at 15 km/h. Then it takes $(t + 2)$ hours to arrive at 10 km/h and $(t + 1)$ hours to arrive at noon. Also, the distance is the same for all three.

$d = \bar{s}t = (15 \text{ km/h})(t \text{ h}) = (10 \text{ km/h})[(t + 2) \text{ h}]$,   or $15t = 10t + 20$.

Solving, $t = 4$ h   and $d = (15 \text{ km/h})(4 \text{ h}) = 60$ km.

So it takes 5 hours to arrive at noon, and the average speed is $\dfrac{60 \text{ km}}{5 \text{ h}} = \boxed{12 \text{ km/h}}$.

CHAPTER 3

MOTION IN TWO DIMENSIONS

1.   (a).

2.   The answer is $\boxed{\text{no}}$ to both. The component of a vector can never be greater than the magnitude of a vector.

3. $\boxed{\text{Yes}}$, this is possible. For example, if an object is in circular motion, the velocity (along a tangent) is perpendicular to the acceleration (toward the center of the circle).

4.   (c).

5.   (a) $\boxed{\text{Linear velocity increases or decreases in magnitude only}}$.

       (b) $\boxed{\text{Moves in a parabolic path}}$.

       (c) $\boxed{\text{Moves in a circular path}}$.

6.   (a) For $\theta < 45°$, $\cos\theta > \sin\theta$. Since $v_x = v\cos\theta$ and $v_y = v\sin\theta$, the horizontal velocity component is $\boxed{\text{greater than}}$ the vertical velocity component.

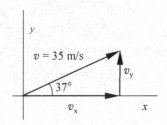

       (b) Horizontal component: $v_x = v\cos\theta = (35 \text{ m/s})\cos 37° = \boxed{28 \text{ m/s}}$.

       Vertical component: $v_y = v\sin\theta = (35 \text{ m/s})\sin 37° = \boxed{21 \text{ m/s}}$.

7.   (a) The magnitude of the acceleration vector is $\boxed{\text{between } 4.0 \text{ m/s}^2 \text{ and } 7.0 \text{ m/s}^2}$ because the hypotenuse of a right triangle can never be smaller than either of the two sides perpendicular to each other (so it must be greater than 4.0 m/s^2) and greater than the sum of the two sides perpendicular to each other (so it must be less than 7.0 m/s^2).

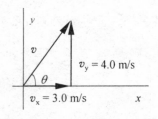

       (b) $v = \sqrt{v_x^2 + v_y^2} = \sqrt{(3.0 \text{ m/s}^2)^2 + (4.0 \text{ m/s}^2)^2} = \boxed{5.0 \text{ m/s}^2}$.

       $\theta = \tan^{-1}\left(\dfrac{4.0 \text{ m m/s}}{3.0 \text{ m/s}}\right) = \boxed{53° \text{ above } +x\text{-axis}}$.

8. $v^2 = v_x^2 + v_y^2$, ☞ $v_y = \pm\sqrt{v^2 - v_x^2} = \pm\sqrt{(7.0 \text{ m/s})^2 - (3.0 \text{ m/s})^2} = \boxed{\pm 6.3 \text{ m/s}}$.

       There are two possible answers because the vector could be either in the first or the fourth quadrant.

9. (a) $\cos 37° = \dfrac{v_x}{v} = \dfrac{4.8 \text{ m/s}}{v}$,

    so $v = \dfrac{4.8 \text{ m/s}}{\cos 37°} = \boxed{6.0 \text{ m/s}}$.

    (b) $v_y = v \sin 37° = (6.0 \text{ m/s}) \sin 37° = \boxed{3.6 \text{ m/s}}$.

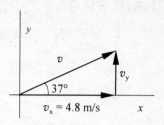

10. (a) From the sketch, it is clear that the displacement that will bring
    the student back to the starting point is pointing from the finishing
    point to the starting point. So it is $\boxed{\text{north of east}}$.

    (b) $d = \sqrt{(50 \text{ m})^2 + (100 \text{ m})^2} = \boxed{1.1 \times 10^2 \text{ m}}$,

    $\theta = \tan^{-1}\left(\dfrac{50 \text{ m}}{100 \text{ m}}\right) = \boxed{27° \text{ north of east}}$.

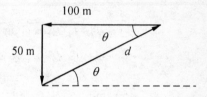

11. (a) $x = (50 \text{ m}) \cos 37° = 40 \text{ m}$, $y = (50 \text{ m}) \sin 37° = 30 \text{ m}$.

    So the distance is $40 \text{ m} + 30 \text{ m} = \boxed{70 \text{ m}}$.

    (b) $\bar{s} = \dfrac{d}{\Delta t} = \dfrac{d}{t} = \dfrac{70 \text{ m}}{60 \text{ s}} = 1.17 \text{ m/s}$.

    The time on each leg is $\dfrac{40 \text{ m}}{1.17 \text{ m/s}} = 34.2 \text{ s} = \boxed{0.57 \text{ min}}$,

    and $\dfrac{30 \text{ m}}{1.17 \text{ m/s}} = 25.6 \text{ s} = \boxed{0.43 \text{ min}}$.

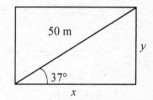

12. $x = -(12.5 \text{ cm}) \cos 30° = \boxed{-10.8 \text{ cm}}$,

    or $x = (12.5 \text{ cm}) \cos 210° = -10.8 \text{ cm}$,

    $y = -(12.5 \text{ cm}) \sin 30° = \boxed{-6.25 \text{ cm}}$,

    or $y = (12.5 \text{ cm}) \sin 210° = -6.25 \text{ cm}$.

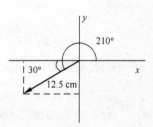

13. $v_x = v_0 \cos\theta = (1.50 \text{ m/s}) \cos 45° = 1.06 \text{ m/s}$,

    $v_y = v_0 \sin\theta = -(1.50 \text{ m/s}) \sin 45° = -1.06 \text{ m/s}$.

    $x = x_0 + v_x t = 0 + (1.06 \text{ m/s})(1.65 \text{ s}) = \boxed{1.75 \text{ m}}$,

    $y = y_0 + v_y t = 0 + (-1.06 \text{ m/s})(1.65 \text{ s}) = \boxed{-1.75 \text{ m}}$.

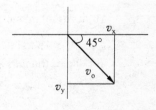

14. Take both x_o and y_o to be 0. $x = v_x t = (0.60 \text{ m/s})(2.5 \text{ s}) = 1.5 \text{ m}$, $y = v_y t = (0.80 \text{ m/s})(2.5 \text{ s}) = 2.0 \text{ m}$.

$$d = \sqrt{x^2 + y^2} = \sqrt{(1.5 \text{ m})^2 + (2.0 \text{ m})^2} = \boxed{2.5 \text{ m}}. \qquad \theta = \tan^{-1}\left(\frac{2.0 \text{ m}}{1.5 \text{ m}}\right) = \boxed{53° \text{ above } +x\text{-axis}}.$$

15. (a) $x = x_o + v_{ox} t + \frac{1}{2} a_x t^2 = 0 + 0 + \frac{1}{2}(2.10 \text{ m/s}^2)(2.50 \text{ s})^2 = \boxed{6.56 \text{ m}}$.

$y = y_o + v_{oy} t + \frac{1}{2} a_y t^2 = 0 + (1.30 \text{ m/s})(2.50 \text{ s}) + 0 = \boxed{3.25 \text{ m}}$.

(b) $v_x = v_{ox} + a_x t = 0 + (2.10 \text{ m/s}^2)(2.50 \text{ s}) = 5.25 \text{ m/s}$, $v_y = v_{oy} + a_y t = 1.30 \text{ m/s} + 0 = 1.30 \text{ m/s}$.

$$v = \sqrt{(5.25 \text{ m/s})^2 + (1.30 \text{ m/s})^2} = \boxed{5.41 \text{ m/s}}. \qquad \theta = \tan^{-1}\left(\frac{1.30 \text{ m/s}}{5.25 \text{ m/s}}\right) = \boxed{13.9° \text{ above } +x\text{-axis}}.$$

16. 150 km/h = (150 km/h)(1000 m/km)(1 h/3600 s) = 41.67 m/s.

$v_x = v_o \cos\theta = (41.67 \text{ m/s}) \cos 37° = 33.28 \text{ m/s}$,

$v_y = v_o \sin\theta = (41.67 \text{ m/s}) \sin 37° = 25.08 \text{ m/s}$.

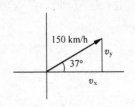

(a) $y = y_o + v_y t = 0 + (25.08 \text{ m/s})(3.00 \text{ s}) = \boxed{75.2 \text{ m}}$.

(b) $x = x_o + v_x t = 0 + (33.28 \text{ m/s})(3.00 \text{ s}) = \boxed{99.8 \text{ m}}$.

17. $\sqrt{(3.0 \text{ m})^2 + (4.0 \text{ m})^2} = 5.0 \text{ m}$.

For ball 1, $t = \dfrac{5.0 \text{ m}}{0.75 \text{ m/s}} = 6.67 \text{ s}$.

For ball 2, $v = \dfrac{3.0 \text{ m} + 4.0 \text{ m}}{6.67 \text{ s}} = \boxed{1.0 \text{ m/s}}$.

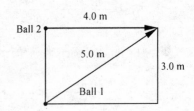

18. $x = x_o + v_x t = 0 + (2.5 \text{ m/s})(4.0 \text{ s}) = 10 \text{ m}$, $y = y_o + v_{yo} t + \frac{1}{2} a_y t^2 = 0 + 0 + \frac{1}{2}(-0.75 \text{ m/s}^2)(4.0 \text{ s})^2 = -6.0 \text{ m}$.

So the position is $\boxed{(10 \text{ m}, -6.0 \text{ m})}$.

19. (a) 60 km/h = 16.7 m/s.

$v_y = v \sin\theta = (16.7 \text{ m/s}) \sin 5.0° = \boxed{1.5 \text{ m/s}}$.

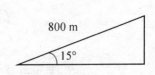

(b) $y = (800 \text{ m}) \sin 5.0° = \boxed{70 \text{ m}}$.

20. (c). For a triangle, a side can never be smaller than the difference of the other two sides and greater than the sum of the other two sides.

21.   The magnitude of the resultant is equal to 1 when the vectors are in ⟨opposite directions⟩, equal to 7 when

they are in the ⟨same direction⟩, and equal to 5 when ⟨at right angle⟩ (90°) to each other.

22.   (d).

23.   ⟨Yes⟩. If the vector is in the y-direction, it has a zero x-component.

24.   ⟨No⟩, a vector quantity cannot be added to a scalar quantity.

25. $v_x = v_0 \cos\theta = (10.0 \text{ m/s}) \cos 30° = $ ⟨8.66 m/s⟩,

$v_y = v_0 \sin\theta = (10.0 \text{ m/s}) \sin 30° = $ ⟨5.00 m/s⟩.

26.   (a)   (b)

 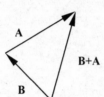   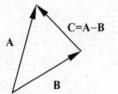

27.   (a) ⟨Yes⟩, vector addition is associative.

(b) See the diagrams below.

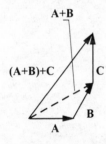 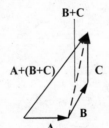

28. $B = \sqrt{(-2.5 \text{ m})^2 + (4.2 \text{ m})^2} = $ ⟨4.9 m⟩.

$\theta = \tan^{-1}\left(\dfrac{4.2 \text{ m}}{-2.5 \text{ m}}\right) = $ ⟨59° above $-x$-axis⟩.

29.   Chose the direction of you as positive.

(a) $v_A = +30$ km/h and $v_B = +45$ km/h. $v_{BA} = v_B - v_A = +45$ km/h $- (+30$ km/h$) = $ ⟨+15 km/h⟩.

(b) $v_A = +30$ km/h and $v_B = -45$ km/h. $v_{BA} = v_B - v_A = -45$ km/h $- (+30$ km/h$) = $ ⟨−75 km/h⟩.

30. (a) $\mathbf{x}_1 + \mathbf{x}_2 = (20 \text{ m}) \hat{\mathbf{x}} + (15 \text{ m}) \hat{\mathbf{x}} = \boxed{(35 \text{ m}) \hat{\mathbf{x}}}$.   (b) $\mathbf{x}_1 - \mathbf{x}_2 = (20 \text{ m } \hat{\mathbf{x}} - 15 \text{ m}) \hat{\mathbf{x}} = \boxed{(5 \text{ m}) \hat{\mathbf{x}}}$.

(c) $\mathbf{x}_2 - \mathbf{x}_1 = (15 \text{ m}) \hat{\mathbf{x}} - (20 \text{ m}) \hat{\mathbf{x}} = \boxed{(-5 \text{ m}) \hat{\mathbf{x}}}$.

31. The ground speed is magnitude of the horizontal component of velocity.

$$v_g = (120 \text{ mi/h}) \cos 25° = \boxed{109 \text{ mi/h}} .$$

32. (a) See the diagram on the right.

(b) For the 15 m vector: $d_{1x} = (15 \text{ m}) \cos 45° = 10.6 \text{ m}$,

$\qquad\qquad\qquad\qquad d_{1y} = (15 \text{ m}) \sin 45° = 10.6 \text{ m}$.

For the 25 m vector: $d_{2x} = 25 \text{ m}$,

$\qquad\qquad\qquad\qquad d_{2y} = 0$.

So $d_x = d_{1x} + d_{2x} = 10.6 \text{ m} + 25 \text{ m} = 35.6 \text{ m}$,

$\qquad d_y = d_{1y} + d_{2y} = 10.6 \text{ m} + 0 = 10.6 \text{ m}$.

Therefore $d = \sqrt{(35.6 \text{ m})^2 + (10.6 \text{ m})^2} = \boxed{37 \text{ m}}$,

$$\theta = \tan^{-1}\left(\frac{10.6 \text{ m}}{35.6 \text{ m}}\right) = \boxed{17° \text{ north of east}} .$$

33. (a) See the diagram on the right.

(b) For the 250 mi vector: $d_{1x} = -(250 \text{ mi}) \cos 45° = -176.8 \text{ mi}$,

$\qquad\qquad\qquad\qquad d_{1y} = (250 \text{ mi}) \sin 45° = 176.8 \text{ mi}$.

For the 150 mi vector: $d_{2x} = -150 \text{ mi}$, $d_{2y} = 0$.

So $d_x = d_{1x} + d_{2x} = -176.8 \text{ mi} + (-150 \text{ mi}) = -326.8 \text{ mi}$,

$\qquad d_y = d_{1y} + d_{2y} = 176.8 \text{ mi} + 0 = 176.8 \text{ mi}$.

Therefore $d = \sqrt{(-326.8 \text{ mi})^2 + (176.8 \text{ mi})^2} = \boxed{372 \text{ mi}}$,

$$\theta = \tan^{-1}\left(\frac{10.6 \text{ m}}{35.6 \text{ m}}\right) = \boxed{28.4° \text{ north of west}} .$$

34.   (a) See the diagram on the right.

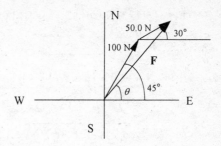

   (b) For the 50.0 N force: $F_{1x} = (50.0 \text{ N}) \cos 30° = 43.3$ N,

   $F_{1y} = (50.0 \text{ N}) \sin 30° = 25.0$ N.

   For the 100 N force: $F_{2x} = (100 \text{ N}) \cos 60° = 50.0$ N,

   $F_{2y} = (100 \text{ N}) \sin 60° = 86.6$ N.

   So $F_x = F_{1x} + F_{2x} = 43.3 \text{ N} + 50.0 \text{ N} = 93.3$ N,

   $F_y = F_{1y} + F_{2y} = 25.0 \text{ N} + 86.6 \text{ N} = 111.6$ N.

   Therefore $F = \sqrt{(93.3 \text{ N})^2 + (111.6 \text{ N})^2} = \boxed{145 \text{ N}}$,

   $\theta = \tan^{-1}\left(\dfrac{111.6 \text{ N}}{93.3 \text{ N}}\right) = \boxed{50.1° \text{ north of east}}$.

35.   (a) We measure the angle from the $+x$-axis.

   $A_x = A \cos\theta = (4.5 \text{ cm}) \cos 40° = 3.45$ cm, $A_y = A \sin\theta = (4.5 \text{ cm}) \sin 40° = 2.89$ cm.

   The vector that will yield a null vector is $-\mathbf{A}$, because $\mathbf{A} + (-\mathbf{A}) = 0$.

   So it is $\boxed{(-3.4 \text{ cm}) \,\hat{x} + (-2.9 \text{ cm}) \,\hat{y}}$.

   (b) $B = \sqrt{(2.0 \text{ cm}) + (-4.0 \text{ cm})^2} = 4.47$ cm, $\theta = \tan^{-1}\left(\dfrac{-4.0}{2.0}\right) = -63.4°$.

   So the vector is $\boxed{4.5 \text{ cm, } 63° \text{ above } -x\text{-axis}}$.

   (c) The angle that $\mathbf{C}$ makes with $+x$-axis is $180° - 60° = 120°$.

   $C_x = C \cos\theta = (8.0 \text{ cm}) \cos 120° = -4.0$ cm, $C_y = C \sin\theta = (8.0 \text{ cm}) \sin 120° = 6.93$ cm.

   So the vector $-\mathbf{C}$ is $\boxed{(4.0 \text{ cm}) \,\hat{x} + (-6.9 \text{ cm}) \,\hat{y}}$.

36.   (a) $A = \sqrt{A_x^2 + A_y^2}$ and $\theta = \tan^{-1}\left(\dfrac{A_y}{A_x}\right)$.   If A_x and A_y doubles,

   $A' = \sqrt{(2A_x)^2 + (2A_y)^2} = \sqrt{4(A_x)^2 + 4(A_y)^2} = 2\sqrt{A_x^2 + A_y^2} = 2A$,

   $\theta' = \tan^{-1}\left(\dfrac{2A_y}{2A_x}\right) = \tan^{-1}\left(\dfrac{A_y}{A_x}\right) = \theta$.

   So $\boxed{\text{the magnitude doubles, but the direction remains unchanged}}$.

   (b) The magnitude triples but the direction remains unchanged. So it is $\boxed{30 \text{ m at } 45°}$.

37. (a) $\mathbf{F}_1 = [(12.0 \text{ N}) \cos 37°]\,\hat{\mathbf{x}} + [(12.0 \text{ N}) \sin 37°]\,\hat{\mathbf{y}} = (9.58 \text{ N})\,\hat{\mathbf{x}} + (7.22 \text{ N})\,\hat{\mathbf{y}}$.

$\mathbf{F}_2 = [-(12.0 \text{ N}) \cos 37°]\,\hat{\mathbf{x}} + [(12.0 \text{ N}) \sin 37°]\,\hat{\mathbf{y}} = (-9.58 \text{ N})\,\hat{\mathbf{x}} + (7.22 \text{ N})\,\hat{\mathbf{y}}$.

So $\mathbf{F}_1 + \mathbf{F}_2 = \boxed{(14.4 \text{ N})\,\hat{\mathbf{y}}}$.

(b) $\mathbf{F}_1 = [(12.0 \text{ N}) \cos 27°]\,\hat{\mathbf{x}} + [(12.0 \text{ N}) \sin 27°]\,\hat{\mathbf{y}} = (10.7 \text{ N})\,\hat{\mathbf{x}} + (5.45 \text{ N})\,\hat{\mathbf{y}}$.

So $\mathbf{F}_1 + \mathbf{F}_2 = (1.1 \text{ N})\,\hat{\mathbf{x}} + (12.7 \text{ N})\,\hat{\mathbf{y}}$.

$F_1 + F_2 = \sqrt{(1.1 \text{ N})^2 + (12.7 \text{ N})^2} = \boxed{12.7 \text{ N}}$.

$\theta = \tan^{-1}\left(\dfrac{12.7 \text{ N}}{1.1 \text{ N}}\right) = \boxed{85.0° \text{ above} +x\text{-axis}}$.

38. (a) See the diagram on the right.

(b) $\mathbf{A} = -[(10.0) \cos 45°]\,\hat{\mathbf{x}} - [(10.0) \sin 45°]\,\hat{\mathbf{y}} = (-7.07)\,\hat{\mathbf{x}} + (-7.07)\,\hat{\mathbf{y}}$.

$\mathbf{B} = (2.0)\,\hat{\mathbf{x}} + (4.0)\,\hat{\mathbf{y}}$.

So $\mathbf{A} + \mathbf{B} = (-7.07 + 2.0)\,\hat{\mathbf{x}} + (-7.07 + 4.0)\,\hat{\mathbf{y}} = \boxed{(-5.1)\,\hat{\mathbf{x}} + (-3.1)\,\hat{\mathbf{y}}}$.

Or $A + B = \sqrt{(-5.07)^2 + (-3.07)^2} = \boxed{5.9}$, $\theta = \tan^{-1}\left(\dfrac{-3.07}{-5.07}\right) = \boxed{31° \text{ below} -x\text{-axis}}$

39. $A_x = 5.0 \text{ m/s}$, $\qquad\qquad\qquad A_y = 0$.

$B_x = (10 \text{ m/s}) \cos 60° = 5.0 \text{ m/s}$, $\qquad B_y = (10.0 \text{ m/s}) \sin 60° = 8.66 \text{ m/s}$.

$C_x = -(15 \text{ m/s}) \cos 30° = -13.0 \text{ m/s}$, $\qquad C_y = (15 \text{ m/s}) \sin 30° = 7.5 \text{ m/s}$.

$(A + B + C)_x = 5.0 \text{ m/s} + 5.0 \text{ m/s} + (-13.0 \text{ m/s}) = -3.0 \text{ m/s}$,

$(A + B + C)_y = 0 + 8.66 \text{ m/s} + 7.5 \text{ m/s} = 16 \text{ m/s}$.

$A + B + C = \sqrt{(-3.0 \text{ m/s})^2 + (16 \text{ m/s})^2} = \boxed{16 \text{ m/s}}$. $\theta = \tan^{-1}\left(\dfrac{16 \text{ m/s}}{3.0 \text{ m/s}}\right) = \boxed{79° \text{ above the} -x\text{-axis}}$.

40. From Exercise 3.39:

$(A - B - C)_x = 5.0 \text{ m/s} - 5.0 \text{ m/s} - (-13.0 \text{ m/s}) = 13 \text{ m/s}$,

$(A - B - C)_y = 0 - 8.66 \text{ m/s} - 7.5 \text{ m/s} = -16 \text{ m/s}$.

So $A - B - C = \sqrt{(13 \text{ m/s})^2 + (-16 \text{ m/s})^2} = \boxed{21 \text{ m/s}}$. $\theta = \tan^{-1}\left(\dfrac{16 \text{ m/s}}{13 \text{ m/s}}\right) = \boxed{51° \text{ below the} +x\text{-axis}}$.

41. The relative orientation of vectors $\mathbf{A}$ and $\mathbf{B}$ is $\boxed{\text{opposite}}$.

$C = A - (-B) = A + B$. This happens only when $\mathbf{A}$ and $\mathbf{B}$ are opposite.

42.   From $\mathbf{F}_1 + \mathbf{F}_2 + \mathbf{F}_3 = 0$,

$\mathbf{F}_3 = -\mathbf{F}_1 - \mathbf{F}_2 = (-3.0\ \text{N})\ \hat{\mathbf{x}} + (-3.0\ \text{N})\ \hat{\mathbf{y}} - [(-6.0\ \text{N})\ \hat{\mathbf{x}} + (4.5\ \text{N})\ \hat{\mathbf{y}}] = (3.0\ \text{N})\ \hat{\mathbf{x}} + (-1.5\ \text{N})\ \hat{\mathbf{y}}.$

So $F_3 = \sqrt{(3.0\ \text{N})^2 + (-1.5\ \text{N})^2} = \boxed{3.4\ \text{N}}$. $\theta = \tan^{-1}\left(\dfrac{-1.5\ \text{N}}{3.0\ \text{N}}\right) = \boxed{27^\circ\ \text{below the } +x\text{-axis}}$.

43. $\mathbf{F}_1 = [(8.0\ \text{N})\cos 60^\circ]\ \hat{\mathbf{x}} + [(8.0\ \text{N})\sin 60^\circ]\ \hat{\mathbf{y}} = (4.0\ \text{N})\ \hat{\mathbf{x}} + (6.93\ \text{N})\ \hat{\mathbf{y}}$,

$\mathbf{F}_2 = (5.5\ \text{N})[(\cos 45^\circ)\ \hat{\mathbf{x}} - (\sin 45^\circ)\ \hat{\mathbf{y}}] = (3.89\ \text{N})\ \hat{\mathbf{x}} + (-3.89\ \text{N})\ \hat{\mathbf{y}}$,

From $\mathbf{F}_1 + \mathbf{F}_2 + \mathbf{F}_3 = 0$,

$\mathbf{F}_3 = -\mathbf{F}_1 - \mathbf{F}_2 = -(4.0\ \text{N}\ \hat{\mathbf{x}} + 6.93\ \text{N}\ \hat{\mathbf{y}}) - (3.89\ \text{N}\ \hat{\mathbf{x}} - 3.89\ \text{N}\ \hat{\mathbf{y}}) = (-7.9\ \text{N})\ \hat{\mathbf{x}} + (-3.0\ \text{N})\ \hat{\mathbf{y}}.$

So $F_3 = \sqrt{(-7.9\ \text{N})^2 + (-3.0\ \text{N})^2} = \boxed{8.5\ \text{N}}$. $\theta = \tan^{-1}\left(\dfrac{-3.0\ \text{N}}{-7.9\ \text{N}}\right) = \boxed{21^\circ\ \text{below } -x\text{-axis}}$.

44.   (a) $\boxed{\text{In the same direction}}$.

    (b) $\boxed{\text{In the opposite direction}}$.

    (c) $\boxed{\text{At right angles}}$.

45.   In the triangle shown, $F_\parallel$ is opposite to and $F_\perp$ is adjacent to the 37° angle.

    So $F_\parallel = (50\ \text{N})\sin 37^\circ = \boxed{30\ \text{N}}$ and $F_\perp = (50\ \text{N})\cos 37^\circ = \boxed{40\ \text{N}}$.

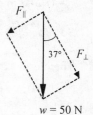

46. $\mathbf{d}_1 = (50.0\ \text{m})\ \hat{\mathbf{x}}$,

$\mathbf{d}_2 = (25.0\ \text{m})[(\cos 30^\circ)\ \hat{\mathbf{x}} + (\sin 30^\circ)\ \hat{\mathbf{y}}]$

$\quad = (21.65\ \text{m})\ \hat{\mathbf{x}} + (12.5\ \text{m})\ \hat{\mathbf{y}}$,

$\mathbf{d}_3 = (15.0\ \text{m})[(\cos 40^\circ)\ \hat{\mathbf{x}} - (\sin 40^\circ)\ \hat{\mathbf{y}}]$

$\quad = (11.49\ \text{m})\ \hat{\mathbf{x}} + (-9.64\ \text{m})\ \hat{\mathbf{y}}$.

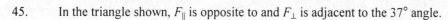

So $\mathbf{d} = \mathbf{d}_1 + \mathbf{d}_2 + \mathbf{d}_3 = (83.1\ \text{m})\ \hat{\mathbf{x}} + (2.9\ \text{m})\ \hat{\mathbf{y}}$.

Therefore $d = \sqrt{(83.1\ \text{m})^2 + (2.9\ \text{m})^2} = \boxed{83.2\ \text{m}}$. $\theta = \tan^{-1}\left(\dfrac{2.9\ \text{m}}{83.1\ \text{m}}\right) = \boxed{2.0^\circ\ \text{above the horizontal}}$.

47. $\mathbf{d}_1 = (20\ \text{m})[(\cos 30^\circ)\ \hat{\mathbf{x}} + (\sin 30^\circ)\ \hat{\mathbf{y}}] = (17.3\ \text{m})\ \hat{\mathbf{x}} + (10.0\ \text{m})\ \hat{\mathbf{y}}$.

$\mathbf{d}_2 = (30\ \text{m})\ \hat{\mathbf{y}}$, $\mathbf{d}_3 = (-40\ \text{m})\ \hat{\mathbf{x}}$,

$\mathbf{d}_4 = [(20\ \text{m})\cos 45^\circ]\ \hat{\mathbf{x}} - [(20\ \text{m})\sin 45^\circ]\ \hat{\mathbf{y}} = (14.1\ \text{m})\ \hat{\mathbf{x}} + (-14.1\ \text{m})\ \hat{\mathbf{y}}$.

So $\mathbf{d} = \mathbf{d}_1 + \mathbf{d}_2 + \mathbf{d}_3 + \mathbf{d}_4 = (-8.6\ \text{m})\ \hat{\mathbf{x}} + (25.9\ \text{m})\ \hat{\mathbf{y}}$.

Therefore $d = \sqrt{(-8.6\ \text{m})^2 + (25.9\ \text{m})^2} = \boxed{27\ \text{m}}$. $\theta = \tan^{-1}\left(\dfrac{25.9\ \text{m}}{-8.6\ \text{m}}\right) = \boxed{72^\circ\ \text{above the } -x\text{-axis}}$.

48. (a) From the sketch on the right, the general direction of the thunderstorm's

velocity is $\boxed{\text{north of west}}$.

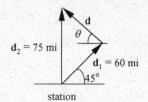

(b) $\mathbf{d}_1 = (60\ \text{mi})[(\cos 45°)\ \hat{\mathbf{x}} + (\sin 45°)\ \hat{\mathbf{y}}] = (42.4\ \text{mi})\ \hat{\mathbf{x}} + (42.4\ \text{mi})\ \hat{\mathbf{y}}$.

$\mathbf{d}_2 = (75\ \text{mi})\ \hat{\mathbf{y}}$.

$\mathbf{d} = \mathbf{d}_2 - \mathbf{d}_1 = (75\ \text{mi})\ \hat{\mathbf{y}} - [(42.4\ \text{mi})\ \hat{\mathbf{x}} + (42.4\ \text{mi})\ \hat{\mathbf{y}}] = (-42.4\ \text{mi})\ \hat{\mathbf{x}} + (32.6\ \text{mi})\ \hat{\mathbf{y}}$.

So $d = \sqrt{(-42.4\ \text{mi})^2 + (32.6\ \text{mi})^2} = 53.48\ \text{mi}$.

Therefore $v = \dfrac{53.48\ \text{mi}}{2.0\ \text{h}} = \boxed{26.7\ \text{mi/h}}$. $\theta = \tan^{-1}\left(\dfrac{32.6\ \text{mi}}{-42.4\ \text{mi}}\right) = \boxed{37.6°\ \text{north of west}}$.

49. (a) From the sketch on the right, the general direction of the airplane's velocity is $\boxed{\text{north of west}}$.

$\mathbf{d}_1 = (-20.0\ \text{mi})\ \hat{\mathbf{y}}$.

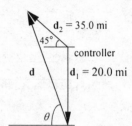

$\mathbf{d}_2 = (35.0\ \text{mi})[(-\cos 45°)\ \hat{\mathbf{x}} + (\sin 45°)\ \hat{\mathbf{y}}] = (-24.7\ \text{mi})\ \hat{\mathbf{x}} + (24.7\ \text{mi})\ \hat{\mathbf{y}}$.

$\mathbf{d} = \mathbf{d}_2 - \mathbf{d}_1 = (-24.7\ \text{mi})\ \hat{\mathbf{x}} + (24.7\ \text{mi})\ \hat{\mathbf{y}} - (-20.0\ \text{mi})\ \hat{\mathbf{y}}$

$= (-24.7\ \text{mi})\ \hat{\mathbf{x}} + (44.7\ \text{mi})\ \hat{\mathbf{y}}$.

So $d = \sqrt{(-24.7\ \text{mi})^2 + (44.7\ \text{mi})^2} = 51.1\ \text{mi}$.

Therefore $v = \dfrac{51.1\ \text{mi}}{0.50\ \text{h}} = \boxed{102\ \text{mi/h}}$. $\theta = \tan^{-1}\left(\dfrac{44.7\ \text{mi}}{-24.7\ \text{mi}}\right) = \boxed{61.1°\ \text{north of west}}$.

50. $\mathbf{d}_1 = (10\ \text{km})\ \hat{\mathbf{x}}$.

$\mathbf{d}_2 = (15\ \text{km})[(-\cos 45°)\ \hat{\mathbf{x}} + (\sin 45°)\ \hat{\mathbf{y}}]$

$= (-10.6\ \text{km})\ \hat{\mathbf{x}} + (10.6\ \text{km})\ \hat{\mathbf{y}}$.

$\mathbf{d} = \mathbf{d}_2 - \mathbf{d}_1 = (-10.6\ \text{km})\ \hat{\mathbf{x}} + (10.6\ \text{km})\ \hat{\mathbf{y}} - (10\ \text{km})\ \hat{\mathbf{y}}$

$= (-20.6\ \text{km})\ \hat{\mathbf{x}} + (10.6\ \text{km})\ \hat{\mathbf{y}}$.

So $d = \sqrt{(-20.6\ \text{km})^2 + (10.6\ \text{km})^2} = \boxed{23\ \text{km}}$. $\theta = \tan^{-1}\left(\dfrac{10.6\ \text{km}}{-20.6\ \text{km}}\right) = \boxed{27°\ \text{north of west}}$.

51. $\mathbf{F}_1 = (100\ \text{N})[(\cos 30°)\ \hat{\mathbf{x}} + (\sin 30°)\ \hat{\mathbf{y}}] = (86.6\ \text{N})\ \hat{\mathbf{x}} + (50.0\ \text{N})\ \hat{\mathbf{y}}$.

$\mathbf{F}_2 = (150\ \text{N})[(\cos 60°)\ \hat{\mathbf{x}} + (\sin 60°)\ \hat{\mathbf{y}}] = (75.0\ \text{N})\ \hat{\mathbf{x}} + (129.9\ \text{N})\ \hat{\mathbf{y}}$.

From $\mathbf{F}_1 + \mathbf{F}_1 + \mathbf{F}_3 = 0$,

$\mathbf{F}_3 = -\mathbf{F}_1 - \mathbf{F}_2 = -[(86.6\ \text{N})\ \hat{\mathbf{x}} + (50.0\ \text{N})\ \hat{\mathbf{y}}] - [(75.0\ \text{N})\ \hat{\mathbf{x}} + (129.9\ \text{N})\ \hat{\mathbf{y}}] = (-161.6\ \text{N})\ \hat{\mathbf{x}} + (-179.9\ \text{N})\ \hat{\mathbf{y}}$.

$F_3 = \sqrt{(-161.6\ \text{N})^2 + (-179.9\ \text{N})^2} = \boxed{242\ \text{N}}$. $\theta = \tan^{-1}\left(\dfrac{-179.9\ \text{N}}{-161.6\ \text{N}}\right) = \boxed{48°\ \text{below the} -x\text{-axis}}$.

52.   (a) $\boxed{\text{Zero}}$.

(b) Use the following subscripts: s = student, t = treadmill, and g = ground.

$\mathbf{v}_{sg} = \mathbf{v}_{st} + \mathbf{v}_{tg}$,   ☞ $\mathbf{v}_{st} = \mathbf{v}_{sg} - \mathbf{v}_{tg} = 0 - (-4.0 \text{ m/s}) = \boxed{4.0 \text{ m/s}}$.

53.   (b) Use the following subscripts: y = you, r = rain, and g = ground.

$\mathbf{v}_{rg} = \mathbf{v}_{ry} + \mathbf{v}_{yg}$.

Since the rain is coming down at an angle relative to you, you should hold the

umbrella so it is tilted forward (perpendicular to $\mathbf{v}_{ry}$).

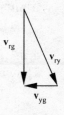

54.   When the player's driving to the basket for a lay-up, she already has an upward motion. Since the ball is

with the player, the ball already has a relative velocity to the ground as the player jumps up.

55.   You throw the ball $\boxed{\text{straight up}}$. This way, both you and the ball have the same horizontal velocity relative

to the ground or you have zero horizontal velocity relative to each other, so the object returns to your hand.

56.   Use the following subscripts: o = other driver, y = you, and g = ground.

So $\mathbf{v}_{og} = 120 \text{ km/h}$, $\mathbf{v}_{yg} = 90 \text{ km/h}$.

(a) $\mathbf{v}_{yg} = \mathbf{v}_{yo} + \mathbf{v}_{og}$,   ☞ $\mathbf{v}_{yo} = \mathbf{v}_{yg} - \mathbf{v}_{og} = 90 \text{ km/h} - 120 \text{ km/h} = \boxed{-30 \text{ km/h}}$.

(b) $\mathbf{v}_{oy} = -\mathbf{v}_{yo} = -(-30 \text{ km/h}) = \boxed{30 \text{ km/h}}$.

57.   Use the following subscripts: s = shopper, e = escalator, and f = floor.

So $\mathbf{v}_{se} = 1.0 \text{ m/s}$, $\mathbf{v}_{ef} = 0.50 \text{ m/s}$. $\mathbf{v}_{sf} = \mathbf{v}_{se} + \mathbf{v}_{ef} = 1.0 \text{ m/s} + 0.50 \text{ m/s} = 1.50 \text{ m/s}$.

Therefore the time is $\dfrac{20 \text{ m}}{1.50 \text{ m/s}} = \boxed{13 \text{ s}}$

58.   Use the following subscripts: t = truck, b = ball, and o = observer.

So $\mathbf{v}_{tg} = 70 \text{ km/h}$, $\mathbf{v}_{bt} = -15 \text{ km/h}$.

(a) $\mathbf{v}_{bo} = \mathbf{v}_{bt} + \mathbf{v}_{to} = -15 \text{ km/h} + 70 \text{ km/h} = \boxed{+55 \text{ km/h}}$.

(b) $\mathbf{v}_{bt} = \mathbf{v}_{bo} - \mathbf{v}_{to} = 55 \text{ km/h} - 90 \text{ km/h} = \boxed{-35 \text{ km/h}}$.

59.   (a) See Exercise 3.58.

$\mathbf{v}_{bo} = \mathbf{v}_{bt} + \mathbf{v}_{to} = 15 \text{ km/h} + 70 \text{ km/h} = \boxed{+85 \text{ km/h}}$.

(b) $\mathbf{v}_{bt} = \mathbf{v}_{bo} - \mathbf{v}_{to} = 85 \text{ km/h} - 90 \text{ km/h} = \boxed{-5 \text{ km/h}}$.

60. Use the following subscripts: b = boat, c = current, and w = water.

Upstream:

So $\mathbf{v}_{bc} = 5.0$ m/s, $\mathbf{v}_{cw} = -3.0$ m/s. $\mathbf{v}_{bw} = \mathbf{v}_{bc} + \mathbf{v}_{cw} = 5.0$ m/s $+ (-3.0$ m/s$) = 2.0$ m/s.

So the distance is $(2.0$ m/s$)(30$ s$) = \boxed{60\text{ m}}$.

Downstream:

So $\mathbf{v}_{bc} = 5.0$ m/s, $\mathbf{v}_{cw} = 3.0$ m/s. $\mathbf{v}_{bw} = \mathbf{v}_{bc} + \mathbf{v}_{cw} = 5.0$ m/s $+ (3.0$ m/s$) = 8.0$ m/s.

So the distance is $(8.0$ m/s$)(30$ s$) = \boxed{240\text{ m}}$.

61. Use the following subscripts: b = boat, c = current, and w = water.

Upstream: $\quad \mathbf{v}_{bc} = 7.5$ m/s, $\quad \mathbf{v}_{cw} = -5.0$ m/s.

$\mathbf{v}_{bw} = \mathbf{v}_{bc} + \mathbf{v}_{cw} = 7.5$ m/s $+ (-5.0$ m/s$) = 2.5$ m/s. $\quad$ So $\quad t_{up} = \dfrac{500\text{ m}}{2.5\text{ m/s}} = 200$ s.

Downstream: $\quad \mathbf{v}_{bc} = 7.5$ m/s, $\quad \mathbf{v}_{cw} = 5.0$ m/s. $\quad \mathbf{v}_{bw} = \mathbf{v}_{bc} + \mathbf{v}_{cw} = 7.5$ m/s $+ 5.0$ m/s $= 12.5$ m/s.

So $\quad t_{down} = \dfrac{500\text{ m}}{12.5\text{ m/s}} = 40$ s. $\quad$ Therefore $t = 200$ s $+ 40$ s $= 240$ s $= \boxed{4.0\text{ min}}$.

62. Use the following subscripts: y = you, m = mast, and w = water.

$\mathbf{v}_{yw} = \mathbf{v}_{ym} + \mathbf{v}_{mw}$.

$v_{yw} = \sqrt{(0.30\text{ m/s})^2 + (0.60\text{ m/s})^2} = \boxed{0.63\text{ m/s}}$,

$\theta = \tan^{-1}\left(\dfrac{0.20\text{ m/s}}{0.60\text{ m/s}}\right) = \boxed{18° \text{ above the water}}$.

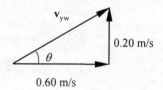

63. The velocity of the passenger relative to the ground is 0.30 m/s for the first 25 m and

$(0.30$ m/s $+ 0.50$ m/s$) = 0.80$ m/s for the rest.

So the total time is $\dfrac{25\text{ m}}{0.30\text{ m/s}} + \dfrac{50\text{ m}}{0.80\text{ m/s}} = 146$ s $= \boxed{2.43\text{ min}}$.

64. (a) From the sketch on the right, the general direction of the swimmer's

velocity, relative to the riverbank, is $\boxed{\text{north of east}}$.

Use the following subscripts: s = swimmer, c = current, and b = bank.

$\mathbf{v}_{sb} = \mathbf{v}_{sc} + \mathbf{v}_{cb}$.

So $\quad v_{sb} = \sqrt{(0.20\text{ m/s})^2 + (0.15\text{ m/s})^2} = \boxed{0.25\text{ m/s}}$.

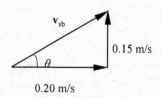

$\theta = \tan^{-1}\left(\dfrac{0.15\text{ m/s}}{0.20\text{ m/s}}\right) = \boxed{37° \text{ north of east}}$.

65. (a) $d = vt = (0.75 \text{ m/s})(1.50 \text{ min})(60 \text{ s/min}) = \boxed{68 \text{ m}}$.

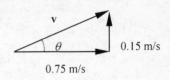

(b) $v = \sqrt{(0.15 \text{ m/s})^2 + (0.75 \text{ m/s})^2} = \boxed{0.76 \text{ m/s}}$,

$\theta = \tan^{-1}\left(\dfrac{0.15 \text{ m/s}}{0.75 \text{ m/s}}\right) = \boxed{11° \text{ relative to shore}}$.

66. Use the following subscripts: b = boat, w = water, and g = ground.

(a) Same both ways, $\theta_1 = \theta_2 = \sin^{-1}\left(\dfrac{0.50}{6.75}\right) = \boxed{4.25° \text{ upstream}}$.

(b) For trip 1 (cross):

$v_{bg} = v_{bw} \ \theta_1 = (6.75 \text{ m/s}) \cos 4.25° = 6.73 \text{ m/s}$,

so the time is $t_1 = \dfrac{150 \text{ m}}{6.73 \text{ m/s}} = 22.3 \text{ s}$.

For trip 2 (back):

$v_{bg} = v_{bw} \cos\theta_2 = (6.75 \text{ m/s}) \cos 4.25° = 6.73 \text{ m/s}$,

so the time is $t_2 = \dfrac{150 \text{ m}}{6.73 \text{ m/s}} = 22.3 \text{ s}$.

Therefore the total time is $22.3 \text{ s} + 22.3 \text{ s} = \boxed{44.6 \text{ s}}$.

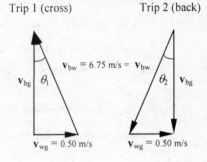

Trip 1 (cross)   Trip 2 (back)

$v_{bw} = 6.75 \text{ m/s} = v_{bw}$

$v_{bg} \ \theta_1$ $\theta_2 \ v_{bg}$

$v_{wg} = 0.50 \text{ m/s}$ $v_{wg} = 0.50 \text{ m/s}$

67. (a) The relative velocity of the rain to that of the car is $\mathbf{v}_{rc} = \mathbf{v}_{rg} - \mathbf{v}_{cg}$, where the subscripts r, c, and g stand for rain, car, and ground, respectively, and the symbol $\mathbf{v}_{cg}$ denotes the relative velocity of the car to the ground, etc. It is clear in the vector diagram that $\mathbf{v}_{rc}$ is not vertical, but at an angle. Since $\tan\theta = v_{cg}/v_{rg}$, the angle θ $\boxed{\text{also increases}}$ as the velocity of the car increases.

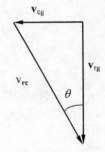

v_{cg}

v_{rg}

v_{rc} θ

(b) $v_{cg} = v_{rg} \tan\theta = (10 \text{ m/s}) \tan 25° = \boxed{4.7 \text{ m/s}}$.

68. (a) $\theta = \tan^{-1}\left(\dfrac{100 \text{ m}}{50 \text{ m}}\right) = 63.4°$

From $\tan\theta = \dfrac{v_{sb}}{v_{cb}}$,

$v_{cb} = \dfrac{v_{sb}}{\tan\theta} = \dfrac{0.15 \text{ m/s}}{\tan 63.4°} = \boxed{0.075 \text{ m/s}}$.

(b) $\theta = \sin^{-1}\left(\dfrac{0.075 \text{ m/s}}{0.15 \text{ m/s}}\right) = \boxed{30°}$ relative to a line directly across the river.

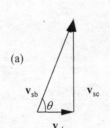

(a)

v_{sb} v_{sc}

θ

v_{cb}

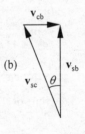

v_{cb}

(b) v_{sb}

v_{sc} θ

69.   (a) Use the following subscripts: p = plane, a = air, and g = ground.

$\mathbf{v}_{pg} = \mathbf{v}_{pa} + \mathbf{v}_{ag}$.

$\theta = \sin^{-1}\left(\dfrac{60.0 \text{ mi/h}}{150 \text{ mi/h}}\right) = \boxed{24° \text{ east of south}}$.

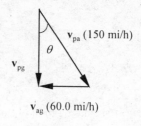

(b) $v_{pg} = \sqrt{(150 \text{ mi/h})^2 - (60.0 \text{ mi/h})^2} = 137.5$ mi/h.

So the time is $\dfrac{200 \text{ mi}}{137.5 \text{ mi/h}} = \boxed{1.5 \text{ h}}$.

70.   (b).

71. $\boxed{45°}$.

72.   The horizontal motion does not affect the vertical motion. The vertical motion of the ball projected horizontally is identical to that of the ball dropped.

73.   The vertical motion does not affect the horizontal motion. The horizontal motion of the ball projected vertically is identical to that of the car.

74.   Given: $v_{xo} = 1.5$ m/s, $v_{yo} = 0$, $y = -2.00$ m.   Find: (a) t,   (b) x.   (Take both x_o and y_o as 0.)

(a) $y = y_o + v_{yo}t - \tfrac{1}{2}gt^2 = 0 + 0 - \tfrac{1}{2}gt^2$, ☞ $t = \sqrt{-\dfrac{2y}{g}} = \sqrt{-\dfrac{2(-2.00 \text{ m})}{9.80 \text{ m/s}^2}} = \boxed{0.64 \text{ s}}$.

(b) $x = x_o + v_{xo}t = 0 + (1.5 \text{ m/s})(0.64 \text{ s}) = \boxed{0.96 \text{ m}}$.

75.   Given: $v_{xo} = 1.5 \times 10^6$ m/s, $v_{yo} = 0$, $x = 0.35$ m.   Find: y.   (Take both x_o and y_o as 0.)
First find the time of flight from the horizontal motion.

$x = x_o + v_{xo}t$, ☞ $t = \dfrac{x}{v_{xo}} = \dfrac{0.35 \text{ m}}{1.5 \times 10^6 \text{ m/s}} = 2.33 \times 10^{-7}$ s.

$y = y_o + v_{yo}t - \tfrac{1}{2}gt^2 = 0 + 0 - (4.9 \text{ m/s}^2)(2.33 \times 10^{-7} \text{ s})^2 = -2.7 \times 10^{-13}$ m. So it falls $\boxed{2.7 \times 10^{-13} \text{ m}}$.

This is a very small distance. So the answer is $\boxed{\text{no}}$, the designer need not worry about gravitational effects.

76.   Given: $v_{xo} = 15$ m/s, $v_{yo} = 0$, $y = -6.0$ m.   Find: x.   (Take both x_o and y_o as 0.)
First find the time of flight from the vertical motion.

$y = y_o + v_{yo}t - \tfrac{1}{2}gt^2 = 0 - \tfrac{1}{2}gt^2$, ☞ $t = \sqrt{-\dfrac{2y}{g}} = \sqrt{-\dfrac{2(-6.0 \text{ m})}{9.80 \text{ m/s}^2}} = 1.11$ s.

$x = x_o + v_{xo}t = 0 + (15 \text{ m/s})(1.11 \text{ s}) = \boxed{17 \text{ m}}$.

77.   From Exercise 3.76, $t = \sqrt{-\dfrac{2y}{g}} = \sqrt{-\dfrac{2(-6.0\ \text{m})}{1.67\ \text{m/s}^2}} = 2.68\ \text{s}.$

$x = x_0 + v_{xo}\,t = (15\ \text{m/s})(2.68\ \text{s}) = \boxed{40\ \text{m}}.$

78.   Given: $v_{yo} = 0$, $x = 8.7\ \text{m}$, $v_{xo} = 7.6\ \text{m/s}.$ Find: $y.$ (Take both x_0 and y_0 as 0.)

First find the time of flight from the horizontal motion.

$x = x_0 + v_{xo}\,t,$ ☞ $t = \dfrac{x}{v_{xo}} = \dfrac{8.7\ \text{m}}{7.6\ \text{m/s}} = 1.14\ \text{s}.$

$y = y_0 + v_{yo}\,t - \tfrac{1}{2}gt^2 = 0 + 0 - \tfrac{1}{2}gt^2 = -\tfrac{1}{2}(9.80\ \text{m/s}^2)(1.14\ \text{s})^2 = -\boxed{6.4\ \text{m}}.$

79. $v_{xo} = v_0 \cos\theta = (30\ \text{m/s})\cos 30° = \boxed{26\ \text{m/s}},$

$v_{yo} = v_0 \sin\theta = (30\ \text{m/s})\sin 30° = \boxed{15\ \text{m/s}}.$

80. $140\ \text{km/h} = 38.89\ \text{m/s}.$ (Take both x_0 and y_0 as 0.)

(a) $x = x_0 + v_{xo}\,t,$ ☞ $t = \dfrac{x}{v_{xo}} = \dfrac{18.4\ \text{m}}{38.89\ \text{m/s}} = 0.473\ \text{s}.$

The time to watch is $0.473\ \text{s} - 0.350\ \text{s} = \boxed{0.123\ \text{s}}.$

(b) $y = y_0 + v_{yo}\,t - \tfrac{1}{2}gt^2 = 0 + 0 - \tfrac{1}{2}(9.80\ \text{m/s}^2)(0.473\ \text{s})^2 = -1.10\ \text{m}.$

So it drops by $\boxed{1.10\ \text{m}}$, or about 3.6 ft.

81.   (a) $\boxed{\text{Ball B collides with ball A}}$ because they have the same horizontal velocity.

(b) (Take both x_0 and y_0 as 0.)

$y = y_0 + v_{yo}\,t - \tfrac{1}{2}gt^2 = 0 - \tfrac{1}{2}gt^2,$ ☞ $t = \sqrt{-\dfrac{2y}{g}} = \sqrt{-\dfrac{2(-1.00\ \text{m})}{9.80\ \text{m/s}^2}} = 0.452\ \text{s}.$

$x = x_0 + v_{xo}\,t = 0 + (0.25\ \text{m/s})(0.452\ \text{s}) = \boxed{0.11\ \text{m}}$ for both.

82.   (a) $140\ \text{km/h} = 38.9\ \text{m/s}.$ (Take both x_0 and y_0 as 0.) First find the range.

$y = y_0 + v_{yo}t - \tfrac{1}{2}gt^2 = 0 + 0 - \tfrac{1}{2}gt^2,$

so $t = \sqrt{-\dfrac{2y}{g}} = \sqrt{-\dfrac{2(-500\ \text{m})}{9.80\ \text{m/s}^2}} = 10.1\ \text{s}.$

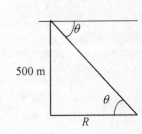

$R = x = x_0 + v_{xo}t = 0 + (38.9\ \text{m/s})(10.1\ \text{s}) = 393\ \text{m}.$ $\theta = \tan^{-1}\left(\dfrac{500}{393}\right) = \boxed{51.8°}.$

(b) $\boxed{\text{Directly over the impact point}}$ since they have the same horizontal velocity.

83.   (a) The horizontal velocities of the cart and the ball are the same. (Take both x_o and y_o as 0.)

First calculate the time of flight of the ball. When the ball returns, $y = 0$.

$$y = y_o + v_{yo} t - \tfrac{1}{2} g t^2, \quad \mathbb{G} \quad t = \frac{v_{yo}}{\tfrac{1}{2} g} = \frac{5.0 \text{ m/s}}{4.90 \text{ m/s}^2} = 1.02 \text{ s}.$$

So $x = x_o + v_{xo} t = 0 + (0.75 \text{ m/s})(1.02 \text{ s}) = \boxed{0.77 \text{ m}}$.

(b) The $\boxed{\text{ball would not fall back in}}$.

84. $v_{xo} = v_o \cos\theta = (20.0 \text{ m/s}) \cos 15.0° = 19.32 \text{ m/s}, \quad v_{yo} = v_o \sin\theta = (20.0 \text{ m/s}) \sin 15.0° = 5.176 \text{ m/s}.$
(Take both x_o and y_o as 0.)

(a) At maximum height, $v_y = 0$. $v_y^2 = v_{yo}^2 - 2g(y - y_o), \quad \mathbb{G} \quad y = \frac{(5.176 \text{ m/s})^2}{2(9.80 \text{ m/s}^2)} = \boxed{1.37 \text{ m}}$.

(b) At impact, $y = 0$. $y = y_o + v_{yo} t - \tfrac{1}{2} g t^2, \quad \mathbb{G} \quad t = \frac{5.176 \text{ m/s}}{\tfrac{1}{2}(9.80 \text{ m/s}^2)} = 1.056 \text{ s}.$

So $R = x = x_o + v_{xo} t = 0 + (19.32 \text{ m/s})(1.056 \text{ s}) = \boxed{20.4 \text{ m}}$.

(c) Kick the ball harder to $\boxed{\text{increase } v_o \text{ and/or increase the angle}}$ so it is as close to 45° as possible.

85. $v_{xo} = v_o \cos\theta = (250 \text{ m/s}) \cos 37° = 199.66 \text{ m/s}, \quad v_{yo} = v_o \sin\theta = (250 \text{ m/s}) \sin 37° = 150.45 \text{ m/s}.$
(Take both x_o and y_o as 0.)

(a) At maximum height, $v_y = 0$. $v_y^2 = v_{yo}^2 - 2g(y - y_o), \quad \mathbb{G} \quad y = \frac{(150.45 \text{ m/s})^2}{2(9.80 \text{ m/s}^2)} = \boxed{1.15 \text{ km}}$.

(b) At impact, $y = 0$. $y = y_o + v_{yo} t - \tfrac{1}{2} g t^2, \quad \mathbb{G} \quad t = \frac{150.45 \text{ m/s}}{\tfrac{1}{2}(9.80 \text{ m/s}^2)} = \boxed{30.7 \text{ s}}$.

(c) $R = x = x_o + v_{xo} t = 0 + (199.66 \text{ m/s})(30.7 \text{ s}) = \boxed{6.13 \text{ km}}$.

86.   (Take both x_o and y_o as 0.)

$$R = x = x_o + v_{xo} t, \quad \mathbb{G} \quad v_{xo} = \frac{x}{t} = \frac{62 \text{ m}}{3.0 \text{ s}} = 20.7 \text{ m/s}.$$

$$y = y_o + v_{yo} t - \tfrac{1}{2} g t^2, \quad \mathbb{G} \quad 0 = 0 + v_{yo} t - \tfrac{1}{2} g t^2.$$

Or $v_{yo} = \tfrac{1}{2} g t = \tfrac{1}{2}(9.80 \text{ m/s}^2)(3.0 \text{ s}) = 14.7 \text{ m/s}.$

$$v_o = \sqrt{(20.7 \text{ m/s})^2 + (14.7 \text{ m/s})^2} = \boxed{25 \text{ m/s}}.$$

$$\theta = \tan^{-1}\left(\frac{14.7 \text{ m/s}}{20.7 \text{ m/s}}\right) = \boxed{35° \text{ to the horizontal}}.$$

87.   (Take both x_o and y_o as 0.)

$$y = y_o + v_{yo}t - \tfrac{1}{2}gt^2, \quad \text{☞} \quad 0 = 0 + v_{yo}t - \tfrac{1}{2}gt^2. \quad \text{So} \quad t = \frac{2v_{yo}}{g} = \frac{2v_o\sin\theta}{g}.$$

$$R = x = x_o + v_{xo}t = 0 + v_o\cos\theta\, t = v_o\cos\theta\frac{2v_o\sin\theta}{g} = \frac{2v_o^2\sin\theta\cos\theta}{g} = \frac{v_o^2\sin2\theta}{g}.$$

Therefore $\quad \sin2\theta = \dfrac{Rg}{v_o^2} = \dfrac{(31\text{ m})(9.80\text{ m/s}^2)}{(18\text{ m/s})^2} = 0.937.$

So $\quad 2\theta = \sin^{-1}(0.938) = 69.7°$ or $110°.$ Therefore $\quad \theta = \boxed{35° \text{ or } 55°}.$

88. $g = (9.80\text{ m/s}^2)/6$ on the surface of the Moon. Use the result from Exercise 3.87.

$$R = \frac{v_o^2\sin2\theta}{g} = \frac{(25\text{ m})^2\sin(2\times45°)}{(9.80\text{ m/s}^2)/6} = \boxed{3.8\times10^2\text{ m}}.$$

89.   (a) $v_{xo} = v_o\cos\theta = (12\text{ m/s})\cos45° = 8.485\text{ m/s}, \quad v_{yo} = v_o\sin\theta = (12\text{ m/s})\sin45° = 8.485\text{ m/s}.$

(Take both x_o and y_o as 0.)

$$y = y_o + v_{yo}t - \tfrac{1}{2}gt^2 = 0 - \tfrac{1}{2}gt^2, \quad \text{☞} \quad -20\text{ m} = 0 + (8.485\text{ m/s})t - \tfrac{1}{2}(9.80\text{ m/s}^2)t^2.$$

Simplifying to quadratic equation: $4.9t^2 - 8.485t - 20 = 0.$

Solving for $t = 3.06$ s (negative time discarded). $R = x = x_o + v_{xo}t = 0 + (8.485\text{ m/s})(3.06\text{ s}) = \boxed{26\text{ m}}.$

(b) $v_y = v_{yo} - gt = 8.485\text{ m/s} - (9.80\text{ m/s}^2)(3.06\text{ s}) = -21.5\text{ m/s}.$

$v = \sqrt{(8.485\text{ m/s})^2 + (-21.5\text{ m/s})^2} = \boxed{23\text{ m/s}}.$ $\theta = \tan^{-1}\left(\dfrac{-21.5\text{ m/s}}{8.485\text{ m/s}}\right) = \boxed{68° \text{ below horizontal}}.$

90.   Use the result from Exercise 3.87.   The range $R = 15$ m.   So $\quad R = \dfrac{v_o^2\sin2\theta}{g} = 15$ m.

or $\quad R = \dfrac{(55\text{ m/s})^2\sin2\theta}{9.80\text{ m/s}^2} = 15\text{ m}, \quad \text{☞} \quad \sin2\theta = 0.0486.$

Therefore $\quad 2\theta = \sin^{-1}(0.0486) = 2.79°, \quad$ hence $\quad \theta = \boxed{1.4°}.$

91.   (Take both x_o and y_o as 0.) $x = x_o + v_{xo}t, \quad \text{☞} \quad v_{xo} = \dfrac{x}{t} = \dfrac{20.0\text{ m}}{0.500\text{ s}} = 40.0\text{ m/s}.$

$$y = y_o + v_{yo}t - \tfrac{1}{2}gt^2, \quad \text{☞} \quad v_{yo} = \frac{y}{t} + \tfrac{1}{2}gt = \frac{(4.00\text{ m} - 1.00\text{ m})}{0.500\text{ s}} + (4.90\text{ m/s}^2)(0.500\text{ s}) = 8.45\text{ m/s}.$$

So $\quad v_o = \sqrt{(40.0\text{ m/s})^2 + (8.45\text{ m/s})^2} = \boxed{40.9\text{ m/s}}, \quad \theta = \tan^{-1}\left(\dfrac{8.45}{40.0}\right) = \boxed{11.9° \text{ above horizontal}}.$

92. Use the result from Exercise 3.87.

$$R = \frac{v_0^{\,2}\sin 2\theta}{g}, \quad \text{☞} \quad v_0 = \sqrt{\frac{Rg}{\sin 2\theta}} = \sqrt{\frac{(2.5\ \text{m} + 1.4\ \text{m})(9.80\ \text{m/s}^2)}{\sin(2\times15°)}} = \boxed{8.7\ \text{m/s}}.$$

93. Let's just calculate the range of the ball, assuming it would have been caught at a height of 5.0 ft above the ground. Use the result from Exercise 3.87.

$$R = \frac{v_0^{\,2}\sin 2\theta}{g} = \frac{(50\ \text{ft})^2\sin(2\times40°)}{32\ \text{ft/s}} = 77\ \text{ft} \approx 26\ \text{yd}. \quad \text{So} \quad \boxed{\text{the pass is short}}.$$

94. (Take both x_0 and y_0 as 0.)

$$x = x_0 + v_{xo}\,t = (v_0\cos\theta)t, \quad \text{☞} \quad t = \frac{x}{v_{xo}} = \frac{x}{v_0\cos\theta},$$

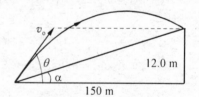
25°
6.02 m
3.05 m − 205 m
=1.0 m

$$y = y_0 + v_{yo}\,t - \tfrac{1}{2}gt^2 = v_0\sin\theta\times\frac{x}{v_0\cos\theta} - \tfrac{1}{2}g\left(\frac{x}{v_0\cos\theta}\right)^2$$

$$= x\tan\theta - \frac{gx^2}{2v_0^2\cos^2\theta}.$$

$$\text{So} \quad v_0 = \frac{x}{\cos\theta}\sqrt{\frac{g}{2(x\tan\theta - y)}} = \frac{6.02\ \text{m}}{\cos 25°}\sqrt{\frac{9.80\ \text{m/s}^2}{2[(6.02\ \text{m})\tan 25° - 1.0\ \text{m}]}} = \boxed{10.9\ \text{m/s}}.$$

95. (a) See the diagram on the right. (Take both x_0 and y_0 as 0.)

(b) $\alpha = \tan^{-1}\left(\dfrac{12.0\ \text{m}}{150\ \text{m}}\right) = 4.57°$, so the launch angle $\theta = 4.57° + 10.0° = 14.6°$.

$$x = x_0 + v_{xo}\,t = (v_0\cos\theta)t, \quad \text{☞} \quad t = \frac{x}{v_{xo}} = \frac{x}{v_0\cos\theta},$$

$$y = y_0 + v_{yo}\,t - \tfrac{1}{2}gt^2 = v_0\sin\theta\times\frac{x}{v_0\cos\theta} - \tfrac{1}{2}g\left(\frac{x}{v_0\cos\theta}\right)^2$$

$$= x\tan\theta - \frac{gx^2}{2v_0^2\cos^2\theta}.$$

v_0

θ

α

150 m

12.0 m

$$v_0 = \frac{x}{\cos\theta}\sqrt{\frac{g}{2(x\tan\theta - y)}} = \frac{150\ \text{m}}{\cos 14.57°}\sqrt{\frac{9.80\ \text{m/s}^2}{2[(150\ \text{m})\tan 14.57° - 12.0\ \text{m}]}} = \boxed{66.0\ \text{m/s}}.$$

(c) $\theta = 4.57° + 10.5° = 15.07°$. First find the time of flight.

$12.0\ \text{m} = (66.0\ \text{m/s})(\sin 15.07°)t - (4.90\ \text{m/s}^2)t^2$, or $4.90\,t^2 - 17.16\,t + 12.0 = 0$.

Solving, $t = 0.97$ s or 2.54 s. The 0.97 s answer is the time it takes to reach 12 m on the way up.

Therefore $x = (66.0\ \text{m/s})(\cos 15.07°)(2.54\ \text{s}) = 162\ \text{m} > 150\ \text{m}$,

$y = (66.0\ \text{m/s})(\sin 15.07°)(2.54\ \text{s}) - (4.90\ \text{m/s}^2)(2.54\ \text{s})^2 = 12.0\ \text{m}$.

So the shot is $\boxed{\text{too long for the hole}}$.

96.   When the bullet travels a horizontal distance x, it takes $t = \dfrac{x}{v_{xo}} = \dfrac{x}{v_o \cos\theta}$. (Take $x_o = 0$)

During this time, the vertical position of the bullet is

$$y_b = y_o + v_{yo}\,t - \tfrac{1}{2}gt^2 = 0 + v_o \sin\theta\,\frac{x}{v_o \cos\theta} - \tfrac{1}{2}g\frac{x^2}{v_o^2 \cos^2\theta} = x\tan\theta - \tfrac{1}{2}g\frac{x^2}{v_o^2\cos^2\theta}.$$

During the same time, the monkey drops by $-\tfrac{1}{2}gt^2 = -\tfrac{1}{2}g\dfrac{x^2}{v_o^2\cos^2\theta}$.

So the vertical position of the monkey is $y_m = y_o - \tfrac{1}{2}g\dfrac{x^2}{v_o^2\cos^2\theta} = x\tan\theta - \tfrac{1}{2}g\dfrac{x^2}{v_o^2\cos^2\theta} = y_b$.

Therefore, when the bullet travels a horizontal distance x, its vertical height is the same as the vertical height of the monkey. Thus, the bullet will hit the monkey.

97. $\mathbf{v} = \mathbf{v}_1 + \mathbf{v}_2 + \mathbf{v}_3 = (3.0\text{ m/s})\,\hat{\mathbf{x}} + (4.0\text{ m/s})\,\hat{\mathbf{y}} + (-4.0\text{ m/s})\,\hat{\mathbf{x}} + (5.0\text{ m/s})\,\hat{\mathbf{y}} + (5.0\text{ m/s})\,\hat{\mathbf{x}} + (-7.0\text{ m/s})\,\hat{\mathbf{y}}$

$= \boxed{(4.0\text{ m/s})\,\hat{\mathbf{x}} + (2.0\text{ m/s})\,\hat{\mathbf{y}}}$.

$v = \sqrt{(4.0\text{ m/s})^2 + (2.0\text{ m/s})^2} = \boxed{4.5\text{ m/s}}$.

$\theta = \tan^{-1}\left(\dfrac{2.0\text{ m/s}}{4.0\text{ m/s}}\right) = \boxed{27° \text{ above the } +x\text{-axis}}$.

98. $v = \sqrt{(40.0\text{ km/h})^2 + (15.0\text{ km/h})^2} = 42.72\text{ km/h} = 11.87\text{ m/s}.$

So $d = vt = (11.87\text{ m/s})(5.00\text{ s}) = \boxed{59.3\text{ m}}$.

$\theta = \tan^{-1}\left(\dfrac{15.0}{40.0}\right) = \boxed{20.6°}$ from its straight line path.

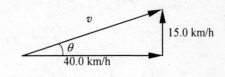

99. $\mathbf{d} = (200\text{ mi})\,\hat{\mathbf{y}}$,

$\mathbf{d}_1 = [-(150\text{ mi})\sin 25°]\,\hat{\mathbf{x}} + [(150\text{ mi})\cos 25°]\,\hat{\mathbf{y}}$

$= (-63.4\text{ mi})\,\hat{\mathbf{x}} + (136\text{ mi})\,\hat{\mathbf{y}}$.

$\mathbf{d} = \mathbf{d}_1 + \mathbf{d}_2$,

so $\mathbf{d}_2 = \mathbf{d} - \mathbf{d}_1 = (-63.4\text{ mi})\,\hat{\mathbf{x}} + (200\text{ mi} - 136\text{ mi})\,\hat{\mathbf{y}}$

$= (-63.4\text{ mi})\,\hat{\mathbf{x}} + (64\text{ mi})\,\hat{\mathbf{y}}$.

Therefore $d_2 = \sqrt{(-63.4\text{ mi})^2 + (64\text{ mi})^2} = \boxed{90\text{ mi}}$.

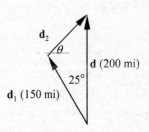

$\theta = \tan^{-1}\left(\dfrac{64\text{ mi}}{-63.4\text{ mi}}\right) = \boxed{45° \text{ north of east}}$.

100. Use the following subscripts: b = boat, w = water, and g = ground.

For the boat to make the trip straight across, v_{bw} must be the hypotenuse of the right-angle triangle. So it must be greater in magnitude than v_{wg}. So if the reverse is true, that is, if $v_{wg} > v_{bw}$, the boat cannot make the trip directly across the river.

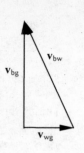

101. (Take both x_o and y_o as 0.) From $y = y_o + v_{yo}t - \frac{1}{2}gt^2 = 0 + 0 - \frac{1}{2}gt^2$,

$$t = \sqrt{-\frac{2y}{g}} = \sqrt{-\frac{2[-(15.0 \text{ m} - 1.50 \text{ m})]}{9.80 \text{ m/s}^2}} = 1.66 \text{ s}.$$

$$x = x_o + v_{xo}t, \quad \text{☞} \quad v_{xo} = \frac{x}{t} = \frac{10.0 \text{ m}}{1.66 \text{ s}} = \boxed{6.02 \text{ m/s}}.$$

102. Use the result from Exercise 3.87.

$$R = \frac{v_o^2 \sin 2\theta}{g}, \quad \text{☞} \quad \frac{R_{35}}{R_{60}} = \frac{\sin[2(35°)]}{\sin[2(60°)]} = 1.1. \quad \text{So } \boxed{R_{35} = 1.1R_{60}}.$$

103. At the maximum height, $y = R/2$ and $v_y = 0$. (Take $y_o = 0$.)

Use the result from Exercise 3.87, $R = \dfrac{v_o^2 \sin 2\theta}{g}$.

$$v_y^2 = v_{yo}^2 - 2gy, \quad \text{☞} \quad 0 = v_o^2 \sin^2 \theta - 2gy_{max} = v_o^2 \sin^2 \theta - 2g\frac{v_o^2 \sin 2\theta}{2g} = v_o^2 \sin^2 \theta - v_o^2 \sin 2\theta.$$

So $\quad v_o^2 \sin^2 \theta = v_o^2 \sin 2\theta \quad$ or $\quad \sin^2 \theta = 2 \sin \theta \cos \theta.$

Therefore $\quad \sin \theta = 2 \cos \theta \quad$ or $\quad \tan \theta = 2.$ Thus $\quad \theta = \boxed{63°}$.

104. First find the time of flight. (Take both x_o and y_o as 0.)

$$y = y_o + v_{yo}t + \frac{1}{2}gt^2, \quad \text{☞} \quad -30 \text{ m} = 0 + -[(25 \text{ m/s}) \sin 45°]t - \frac{1}{2}(9.80 \text{ m/s}^2)t^2.$$

Reduce to quadratic equation: $\quad 4.90t^2 + 17.7t - 30 = 0.$ Solve for $\quad t = 1.26$ s or -4.87 s.

Discard the negative answer. So $\quad x = x_o + v_{xo}t = (25 \text{ m/s})(\cos 45°)(1.26 \text{ s}) = \boxed{22 \text{ m}}$.

105. (a) Use the result from Exercise 3.87.

$$R = \frac{v_o^2 \sin 2\theta}{g}, \quad \text{☞} \quad \sin 2\theta = \frac{Rg}{v_o^2} = \frac{(2.00 \times 10^3 \text{ m})(9.80 \text{ m/s}^2)}{(1.50 \times 10^2 \text{ m/s})^2} = 0.871.$$

$2\theta = 60.6°$ or $119.4°$. So $\quad \theta = \boxed{30.3° \text{ or } 59.7°}$.

(b) $R_{max} = \dfrac{v_o^2 \sin 90°}{g} = \dfrac{(1.50 \times 10^2 \text{ m/s})^2}{9.80 \text{ m/s}^2} = 2.30$ km. So $\boxed{\text{no}}$, the target could not be hit.

106. For the puck to make it into the net, y must be less than 1.2 m when $x = 15$ m. (Take both x_o and y_o as 0.)

$$x = x_o + v_{xo}t = v_o \cos\theta\, t, \quad \Rightarrow \quad t = \frac{x}{v_o \cos\theta} = \frac{15\text{ m}}{(50\text{ m/s})\cos 5.0°} = 0.301\text{ s.}$$

$$y = y_o + v_{yo}t - \tfrac{1}{2}gt^2 = v_o \sin\theta\, t - \tfrac{1}{2}gt^2 = (50\text{ m/s})\sin 5.0°\,(0.301\text{ s}) - \tfrac{1}{2}(9.80\text{ m/s}^2)(0.301\text{ s})^2$$

$$= 0.87\text{ m} < 1.2\text{ m.} \quad \text{So the answer is } \boxed{\text{yes}}, \text{ the puck makes it into the net.}$$

107. (a) First calculate the time of flight. (Take both x_o and y_o as 0.)

$$y = y_o + v_{yo}t - \tfrac{1}{2}gt^2 = 0 + 0 - \tfrac{1}{2}gt^2, \quad \Rightarrow \quad t = \sqrt{-\frac{2y}{g}} = \sqrt{-\frac{2(-32.5\text{ m})}{9.80\text{ m/s}^2}} = 2.575\text{ s.}$$

$$x = x_o + v_{xo}t, \quad \Rightarrow \quad v_{xo} = \frac{x}{t} = \frac{56.0\text{ m}}{2.575\text{ s}} = \boxed{21.7\text{ m/s}}.$$

(b) $v_x = 21.7$ m/s, $\quad v_y = v_{yo} - gt = 0 - (9.80\text{ m/s}^2)(2.575\text{ s}) = -25.2$ m/s.

$$v = \sqrt{(21.7\text{ m/s})^2 + (-25.2\text{ m/s})^2} = \boxed{33.3\text{ m/s}}, \quad \theta = \tan^{-1}\left(\frac{-25.2\text{ m/s}}{21.7\text{ m/s}}\right) = \boxed{49.3°\text{ below horizontal}}.$$

108. First calculate the time it takes for the ball to travel a horizontal distance of 40 yd = 120 ft. (Take both x_o and y_o as 0.)

$$x = x_o + v_{xo}t = 0 + (v_o \cos\theta)t, \quad \Rightarrow \quad t = \frac{x}{v_o \cos\theta} = \frac{120\text{ ft}}{(70.0\text{ ft/s})\cos 45°} = 2.424\text{ s.}$$

During this time $\quad y = y_o + v_{yo}t - \tfrac{1}{2}gt^2 = 0 + (70.0\text{ ft/s})(\sin 45°)(2.424\text{ s}) - \tfrac{1}{2}(32\text{ ft/s}^2)(2.424\text{ s})^2$

$$= 26\text{ ft} > 10\text{ ft.} \quad \text{So } \boxed{\text{the kick is good}}.$$

109. (a) A positive x-component could be $\theta = \pm\cos^{-1}\left(\frac{6.0}{10}\right) = \pm 53°.$

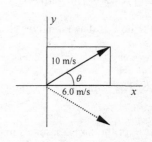

That is $\boxed{53°\text{ above or below the } +x\text{-axis}}$.

(b) $v_y = v\sin\theta = (10\text{ m/s})\sin(\pm 53°) = \boxed{\pm 8.0\text{ m/s}}$.

110. (a) Use the result from Exercise 3.87.

$$R = \frac{v_o^2 \sin 2\theta}{g}, \quad \Rightarrow \quad v_o = \sqrt{\frac{Rg}{\sin 2\theta}} = \sqrt{\frac{(8.20\text{ m})(9.80\text{ m/s}^2)}{\sin(2\times 37°)}} = \boxed{9.14\text{ m/s}}.$$

(b) $R = \dfrac{(4.57\text{ m/s})^2 \sin(2\times 37°)}{(9.80\text{ m/s}^2)/6} = \boxed{12.3\text{ m}}$. There is no air on the Moon!

111. $d_{\text{north}} = (150\text{ km/h})(4.0\text{ h}) = 600\text{ km}, \quad d_{\text{west}} = (30\text{ km/h})(4.0\text{ h}) = 120\text{ km}.$

So the distance $\quad d = \sqrt{(600\text{ km})^2 + (120\text{ km})^2} = \boxed{6.1\times 10^2\text{ km}}$.

1. $\boxed{\text{No}}$. If an object remains at rest, the *net force* is zero. There could still be forces acting on it as long as the net force is zero.

2. (c).

3. According to Newton's first law, your tendency is to remain at rest or move with constant velocity. However, the plane is accelerating to a velocity faster than yours so you are "behind" and feel "pushed" into the seat. The seat actually supplies a forward force to accelerate you to the same velocity as the plane.

4. $\boxed{\text{No}}$, the object could also be moving with constant velocity.

5. (c).

6. (d).

7. $\boxed{\text{No}}$, same mass, same inertia.

8. The bubble moves $\boxed{\text{forward}}$ in the direction of velocity or acceleration, because the inertia of the liquid will resist the forward acceleration. So the bubble of negligible mass or inertia moves forward relative to the liquid. Then it moves $\boxed{\text{backward}}$ opposite the velocity (or in the direction of acceleration) for the same reason.

    (b) The principle is based on the $\boxed{\text{inertia of the liquid}}$.

9. (a) For the same reason as in Exercise 4.6 (now it's the inertia of the air that dominates, since helium has much smaller inertia than air), the balloon moves $\boxed{\text{forward}}$ in the direction of acceleration.

    (b) $\boxed{\text{Backward}}$ in the direction of acceleration again.

10. Even though objects have no weight in deep space, they still have mass. You can distinguish their masses by moving them up and down several times to accelerate them—those that accelerate less have more mass if you use the same force.

11. According to Newton's first law, or the law of inertia, the dishes at rest tend to remain at rest. For the dishes to move, a static force (discussed in Section 4.6) is required. The quick pull of the tablecloth required a force that exceeds the maximum static friction so the cloth can move relative to the dishes.

12. $\boxed{\text{Yes}}$, there is a net force acting on the car because the car is accelerating. The speed of the car is constant, but the direction of the velocity is ever changing. This change in direction makes the car to have a non-constant velocity, so the car has an acceleration.

13. $m = \rho V$, ☞ $\dfrac{m_{Al}}{m_{water}} = \dfrac{(2.7 \text{ g/cm}^3)(10 \text{ cm}^3)}{(1.0 \text{ g/cm}^3)(20 \text{ cm}^3)} = 1.35$ or $\boxed{m_{Al} = 1.35 m_{water}}$.

14. (a) $\boxed{\text{Either (1) or (2) is possible}}$ because "at rest" or "constant velocity" both have zero acceleration.

(b) $\mathbf{F}_1 = (3.6 \text{ N})[(\cos 74°) \, \hat{\mathbf{x}} - (\sin 74°) \, \hat{\mathbf{y}}] = (0.99 \text{ N}) \, \hat{\mathbf{x}} + (-3.46 \text{ N}) \, \hat{\mathbf{y}}$.

$\mathbf{F}_2 = (3.6 \text{ N})[(-\cos 34°) \, \hat{\mathbf{x}} + (\sin 34°) \, \hat{\mathbf{y}}] = (-2.98 \text{ N}) \, \hat{\mathbf{x}} + (2.01 \text{ N}) \, \hat{\mathbf{y}}$.

If $a = 0$, then $\Sigma \mathbf{F} = 0$ from Newton's first law. $\Sigma \mathbf{F} = \mathbf{F}_1 + \mathbf{F}_2 = (-1.99 \text{ N}) \, \hat{\mathbf{x}} + (-1.45 \text{ N}) \, \mathbf{y} \neq 0$.

So the answer is $\boxed{\text{yes}}$, there must be a third force to make $\Sigma \mathbf{F} = 0$.

$\Sigma \mathbf{F} = \mathbf{F}_1 + \mathbf{F}_2 + \mathbf{F}_3 = 0$, ☞ $\mathbf{F}_3 = -(\mathbf{F}_1 + \mathbf{F}_2) = (1.99 \text{ N}) \, \hat{\mathbf{x}} + (1.45 \text{ N}) \, \mathbf{y}$.

$F_3 = \sqrt{(1.99 \text{ N})^2 + (1.45 \text{ N})^2} = \boxed{2.5 \text{ N}}$. $\theta = \tan^{-1}\left(\dfrac{1.45 \text{ N}}{1.99 \text{ N}}\right) = \boxed{36° \text{ above the } +x \text{ axis}}$.

15. $\mathbf{F}_1 = (5.5 \text{ N})[(\cos 30°) \, \hat{\mathbf{x}} - (\sin 30°) \, \mathbf{y}] = (4.76 \text{ N}) \, \hat{\mathbf{x}} + (-2.75 \text{ N}) \, \hat{\mathbf{y}}$,

$\mathbf{F}_2 = (3.5 \text{ N})[(\cos 37°) \, \hat{\mathbf{x}} + (\sin 37°) \, \mathbf{y}] = (2.80 \text{ N}) \, \hat{\mathbf{x}} + (2.11 \text{ N}) \, \hat{\mathbf{y}}$.

$\Sigma \mathbf{F} = \mathbf{F}_1 + \mathbf{F}_2 + \mathbf{F}_3 = 0$, ☞ $\mathbf{F}_3 = -(\mathbf{F}_1 + \mathbf{F}_2) = (-7.6 \text{ N}) \, \hat{\mathbf{x}} + (0.64 \text{ N}) \, \hat{\mathbf{y}}$.

So the x-component of $\mathbf{F}_3$ is $\boxed{(-7.6 \text{ N}) \, \hat{\mathbf{x}}}$.

16. (a) $\mathbf{F}_1 = (5.0 \text{ N})[(\cos 37°) \, \hat{\mathbf{x}} + (\sin 37°) \, \hat{\mathbf{y}}] = (3.99 \text{ N}) \, \hat{\mathbf{x}} + (3.01 \text{ N}) \, \hat{\mathbf{y}}$,

$\mathbf{F}_2 = (2.5 \text{ N}) \, \hat{\mathbf{x}}$,

$\mathbf{F}_3 = -(3.5 \text{ N})[(\cos 45°) \, \hat{\mathbf{x}} + (\sin 45°) \, \hat{\mathbf{y}}] = (-2.47 \text{ N}) \, \hat{\mathbf{x}} + (-2.47 \text{ N}) \, \hat{\mathbf{y}}$,

$\mathbf{F}_4 = (-1.5 \text{ N}) \, \hat{\mathbf{y}}$.

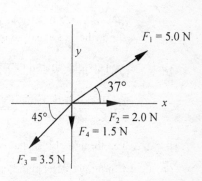

$\Sigma \mathbf{F} = \mathbf{F}_1 + \mathbf{F}_2 + \mathbf{F}_3 + \mathbf{F}_4 = (4.02 \text{ N}) \, \hat{\mathbf{x}} + (-0.96 \text{ N}) \, \hat{\mathbf{y}} \neq 0$. $\boxed{\text{No}}$.

(b) $\Sigma \mathbf{F} = \mathbf{F}_1 + \mathbf{F}_2 + \mathbf{F}_3 + \mathbf{F}_4 + \mathbf{F}_5 = 0$,

so $\mathbf{F}_5 = -(\mathbf{F}_1 + \mathbf{F}_2 + \mathbf{F}_3 + \mathbf{F}_4) = (-4.0 \text{ N}) \, \hat{\mathbf{x}} + (0.96 \text{ N}) \, \hat{\mathbf{y}}$,

or $F_5 = \sqrt{(-4.0 \text{ N})^2 + (0.96 \text{ N})^2} = \boxed{4.1 \text{ N}}$, $\theta = \tan^{-1}\left(\dfrac{0.96 \text{ N}}{-4.0 \text{ N}}\right) = \boxed{13° \text{ above the } -x \text{ axis}}$.

17.   (b).

18.   There will be $\boxed{\text{extra acceleration}}$. A pickup truck in snow (mass increases) and a launched rocket (mass decreases) are examples.

19. $\boxed{\text{No}}$, this is not a violation of Newton's laws. The thrust overcomes the gravitational force and accelerates the rocket. However, when fuel is burned, the mass of the rocket decreases. Also, farther up in space, there is less gravity. So the constant thrust has less gravity to overcome and less rocket to accelerate. This, in turn, increases the velocity and acceleration of the rocket.

20.   The weight is $\boxed{\text{zero}}$ in space because there is no gravity. The mass is still $\boxed{70 \text{ kg}}$ because mass is a measure of inertia and it does not change.

21.   "Soft hands" here result in longer contact time between the ball and the hands. The increase in contact time decreases the magnitude of acceleration. From Newton's second law, this, in turn, decreases the force required to stop the ball and its reaction force, the force on the hands.

22. $\Sigma F = ma$,   ☞ $a = \dfrac{\Sigma F}{m} = \dfrac{3.0 \text{ N}}{1.5 \text{ kg}} = \boxed{2.0 \text{ m/s}^2 \text{ in the direction of the net force}}$.

23. $\Sigma F = ma$,   ☞ $m = \dfrac{\Sigma F}{a} = \dfrac{5.0 \text{ N}}{3.0 \text{ m/s}^2} = \boxed{1.7 \text{ kg}}$.

24. $\Sigma F = ma$,   ☞ $m = \dfrac{\Sigma F}{a} = \dfrac{75 \text{ N}}{0.50 \text{ m/s}^2} = 150 \text{ kg}$.

        So $w = mg = (150 \text{ kg})(9.80 \text{ m/s}^2) = \boxed{1.5 \times 10^3 \text{ N}}$.

25. $\Sigma F = ma = (2.0 \times 10^5 \text{ kg})(3.5 \text{ m/s}^2) = \boxed{7.0 \times 10^5 \text{ N}}$.

26.   (a) The mass is still $\boxed{6.0 \text{ kg}}$ because mass is a measure of inertia, and it does not change.

        (b) $w = mg_{\text{Moon}} = \dfrac{(6.0 \text{ kg})(9.80 \text{ m/s}^2)}{6} = \boxed{9.8 \text{ N}}$.

27. $w = mg$,   ☞ $m = \dfrac{w}{g} = \dfrac{740 \text{ N}}{9.80 \text{ m/s}^2} = \boxed{75.5 \text{ kg}}$.

28. $w = mg = (1.0 \text{ kg})(9.80 \text{ m/s}^2) = \boxed{9.8 \text{ N}}$.

29. $w = mg = (8.0 \text{ kg})(9.80 \text{ m/s}^2) = \boxed{78 \text{ N}} = (78 \text{ N}) \times \dfrac{1 \text{ lb}}{4.45 \text{ N}} = \boxed{18 \text{ lb}}$.

30. $150 \text{ lb} = (150 \text{ lb}) \times \dfrac{4.45 \text{ N}}{1 \text{ lb}} = \boxed{668 \text{ N}}$. $m = \dfrac{w}{g} = \dfrac{668 \text{ N}}{9.80 \text{ m/s}^2} = \boxed{68.2 \text{ kg}}$.

31. (a) This label is correct on the $\boxed{\text{Earth}}$. 1 lb is equivalent to 454 g, or 454 g weighs 1 lb.

    (b) The gravity on the Moon is only 1/6 of that on the Earth. So it takes 6 times the mass to have the same weight on the Moon. Since 1 lb on the Earth is 454 g, 2 lb on the Moon would require

    $2 \times 6 \times (454 \text{ g}) = 5.4 \text{ kg}$. So the label should be $\boxed{5.4 \text{ kg (2 lb)}}$

32. (a) The total force $= 16(400 \text{ N}) = 6.40 \times 10^3 \text{ N} = $ weight of car (why?).

    $m = \dfrac{w}{g} = \dfrac{6.40 \times 10^3 \text{ N}}{9.80 \text{ m/s}^2} = \boxed{653 \text{ kg}}$.

    (b) $w = (6.40 \times 10^3 \text{ N}) \times \dfrac{1 \text{ lb}}{4.45 \text{ N}} = \boxed{1.44 \times 10^3 \text{ lb}}$.

33. (a) $m = \dfrac{w}{g} = \dfrac{98 \text{ N}}{9.80 \text{ m/s}^2} = 10 \text{ kg}$.   So $a = \dfrac{\Sigma F}{m} = \dfrac{12 \text{ N}}{10 \text{ kg}} = \boxed{1.2 \text{ m/s}^2}$.

    (b) For the same object, the mass is still 10 kg. So the acceleration is also the $\boxed{\text{same}}$.

34. The resistive force is opposite the forward force. $a = \dfrac{\Sigma F}{m} = \dfrac{15 \text{ N} - 8.0 \text{ N}}{1.0 \text{ kg}} = \boxed{7.0 \text{ m/s}^2}$.

35. The friction force is opposite the horizontal force. $a = \dfrac{\Sigma F}{m} = \dfrac{300 \text{ N} - 120 \text{ N}}{75 \text{ kg}} = \boxed{2.40 \text{ m/s}^2}$.

36. (a) $\Sigma F = ma$,   ☞ $a = \dfrac{F}{m}$.   So $\dfrac{a_2}{a_1} = \dfrac{F_2}{F_1} \times \dfrac{m_1}{m_2} = \dfrac{1}{2} \times \dfrac{1}{2} = \boxed{1/4 \text{ times as great}}$.

    (b) $\dfrac{a_2}{a_1} = \dfrac{2}{1} \times \dfrac{2}{1} = 4$.   So $a_2 = 4a_1 = 4(1.0 \text{ m/s}^2) = \boxed{4.0 \text{ m/s}^2}$.

37. (a) $a = \dfrac{\Sigma F}{m} = \dfrac{200 \text{ N} + 300 \text{ N} - 300 \text{ N}}{1500 \text{ kg}} = \boxed{0.133 \text{ m/s}^2}$.

    (b) Once the car is moving, ΣF would be zero for constant velocity.

    So $\Sigma F = F - 300 \text{ N} = 0$, we have $F = \boxed{300 \text{ N}}$.

38.   First find acceleration from kinematics.

$v_0 = 90$ km/h $= 25$ m/s, $v = 0$, $t = 5.5$ s.   So $a = \dfrac{v - v_0}{t} = \dfrac{0 - 25 \text{ m/s}}{5.5 \text{ s}} = -4.56$ m/s^2.

$\Sigma F = ma = (60 \text{ kg})(-4.55 \text{ m/s}^2) = -\boxed{2.7 \times 10^2 \text{ N}}$.

The negative sign indicates that the force is opposite the motion or the velocity.

39.   First find acceleration from kinematics.

$v_0 = 0$, $v = 320 \times 0.278$ m/s $= 88.96$ m/s, $t = 2.0$ s. $a = \dfrac{v - v_0}{t} = \dfrac{88.96 \text{ m/s} - 0}{2.0 \text{ s}} = 44.48$ m/s^2.

Therefore $\Sigma F = ma = (2000 \text{ kg})(44.48 \text{ m/s}^2) = \boxed{8.9 \times 10^4 \text{ N}}$.

40.   First find acceleration from kinematics. $v_0 = 0$, $v = 35$ m/s, $x = 0.50$ m. Taking $x_0 = 0$.

$v^2 = v_0^2 + 2a(x - x_0)$,   ☞ $a = \dfrac{v^2 - v_0^2}{2\,x} = \dfrac{(35 \text{ m/s})^2 - 0}{2(0.50 \text{ m})} = 1.23 \times 10^3$ m/s^2.

$\Sigma F = ma = (0.056 \text{ kg})(1.23 \times 10^3 \text{ m/s}^2) = \boxed{69 \text{ N}}$.

41.   (c).

42.   (c).

43.   The forces on different objects cannot cancel. The force by the horse is on the cart so the cart will be pulled. The force by the cart is on the horse.

44.   (d).

45. $\boxed{\text{Yes}}$, there is something wrong with the statement. The two forces mentioned are on two different objects. The force by the bat is on the ball, and the force by the ball is on the bat. Forces on different objects cannot cancel.

46.   (a) There are $\boxed{\text{two}}$ forces acting on the book, the gravitational force (weight, w) and   the

normal force by the surface.

(b) The reaction of w is an upward force on the Earth by the book, and the reaction force of N is a downward force on the horizontal surface by the book.

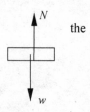

47.   If a brick is hit by a fist with a force of 800 N, the brick hits the fist hard with a force of 800 N. No, this is not something you can try at home.

48. The force on the block by the wall $F_{\text{wall on block}}$ and the force on the
wall by the block $F_{\text{block on wall}}$ are action-reaction pairs.

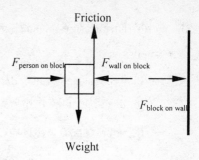

49. The force on the female by the male is

$F = ma = (45 \text{ kg})(2.0 \text{ m/s}^2) = 90 \text{ N}$.

The force on the male by the female is also 90 N according to

Newton's third law.

So $a_{\text{male}} = \dfrac{90 \text{ N}}{60 \text{ kg}} = \boxed{1.5 \text{ m/s}^2}$ opposite to hers.

50. (a) For Jane: $T = ma = (50 \text{ kg})(0.92 \text{ m/s}^2) = 46 \text{ N}$.

The force on John is also 46 N by Newton's third law.

$a_{\text{John}} = \dfrac{46 \text{ N}}{60 \text{ kg}} = \boxed{0.77 \text{ m/s}^2}$ toward Jane.

(b) $x_{\text{John}} = \frac{1}{2} a_{\text{John}} t^2$, $\quad x_{\text{Jane}} = \frac{1}{2} a_{\text{Jane}} t^2$.

So $\dfrac{x_{\text{Jane}}}{x_{\text{John}}} = \dfrac{a_{\text{Jane}}}{a_{\text{John}}} = \dfrac{0.92}{0.767} = 1.2$.

Also $\quad x_{\text{John}} + x_{\text{Jane}} = 10 \text{ m}$, $\quad$ or $\quad x_{\text{John}} + 1.2\, x_{\text{John}} = 10 \text{ m}$.

Therefore $\quad x_{\text{John}} = \boxed{4.5 \text{ m from John's original position}}$.

51. mg – gravitational force.

N – Normal force by the ramp on the car.

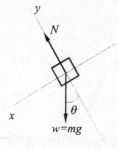

52. (a) The normal force is $\boxed{\text{less than}}$ the weight of the object.

The component of the weight perpendicular to the inclined plane is equal to $w\cos\theta$.

In the y-direction, $\Sigma F_y = N - w\cos\theta = ma_y$.

Since the object does not accelerate in the y-direction, $a_1 = 0$.

So $\quad N = w\cos\theta < w$ (for any $\theta \neq 0$).

(b) $w = mg = (10 \text{ kg})(9.80 \text{ m/s}^2) = \boxed{98 \text{ N}}$.

$N = w\cos\theta = (98 \text{ N}) \cos 30° = \boxed{85 \text{ N}}$.

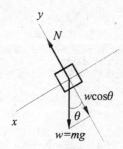

53.   (a) The measured weight is the normal force on the object, N. Chose downward as

positive. $\Sigma F = w - N = ma$,   ☞ $N = w - ma$.

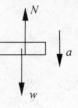

So N can take any value, depending on the value of a.

For example, if $a = 0$, then $N = w$; if $a > 0$, $N < w$; if $a < 0$, then $N > w$.

Therefore, the answer is $\boxed{\text{all of the preceding}}$.

(b) $a = \dfrac{w - N}{m} = \dfrac{(500 \text{ kg})(9.80 \text{ m/s}^2) - 4000 \text{ N}}{500 \text{ kg}} = 1.8 \text{ m/s}^2$.

So the answer is $\boxed{a = 1.8 \text{ m/s}^2 \text{ downward}}$.

54.   (a) The scale reading is equal to the normal force on the person. Chose upward as

positive.

$\Sigma F = N - w = ma = 0$,   ☞ $N = w = mg = (75.0 \text{ kg})(9.80 \text{ m/s}^2) = \boxed{735 \text{ N}}$.

(b) a is still zero. So $N = \boxed{735 \text{ N}}$.

(c) From $\Sigma F = N - w = ma$,

$N = w + ma = mg + ma = m(g + a) = (75.0 \text{ kg})(9.80 \text{ m/s}^2 + 2.00 \text{ m/s}^2) = \boxed{885 \text{ N}}$.

55.   From Exercise 4.54:

(a) $N = \boxed{735 \text{ N}}$.

(b) $N = \boxed{735 \text{ N}}$.

(c) From $\Sigma F = w - N = ma$,

$N = w - ma = mg - ma = m(g - a) = (75.0 \text{ kg})(9.80 \text{ m/s}^2 - 2.00 \text{ m/s}^2) = \boxed{585 \text{ N}}$.

56.   (a) $\mathbf{F}_1 = (600 \text{ N})[(\cos 45°) \, \hat{\mathbf{x}} + (\sin 45°) \, \hat{\mathbf{y}}] = (424 \text{ N}) \, \hat{\mathbf{x}} + (424 \text{ N}) \, \hat{\mathbf{y}}$,

$\mathbf{F}_2 = (600 \text{ N})[(\cos 45°) \, \hat{\mathbf{x}} + (-\sin 45°) \, \hat{\mathbf{y}}] = (424 \text{ N}) \, \hat{\mathbf{x}} + (-424 \text{ N}) \, \hat{\mathbf{y}}$,

$\Sigma \mathbf{F} = \mathbf{F}_1 + \mathbf{F}_2 + \mathbf{F}_3 = 0$,   ☞ $\mathbf{F}_3 = -(\mathbf{F}_1 + \mathbf{F}_2) = (-849 \text{ N}) \, \hat{\mathbf{x}}$.

So it is $\boxed{849 \text{ N}}$.

(b) Now $\mathbf{F}_1 = (495 \text{ N}) \, \hat{\mathbf{x}} + (495 \text{ N}) \, \hat{\mathbf{y}}$,

$\mathbf{F}_2 = (495 \text{ N}) \, \hat{\mathbf{x}} + (-495 \text{ N}) \, \hat{\mathbf{y}}$,

$\mathbf{F}_3 = (-849 \text{ N}) \, \hat{\mathbf{x}}$.

So $\Sigma F = 141 \text{ N}$,   therefore $a = \dfrac{141 \text{ N}}{75.0 \text{ kg}} = \boxed{1.88 \text{ m/s}^2}$.

57. (a) $\mathbf{F}_1 = (400 \text{ N}) \, \hat{\mathbf{x}}$, $\mathbf{F}_2 = (-300 \text{ N}) \, \hat{\mathbf{x}}$, $\mathbf{F}_3 = (50 \text{ N})[(\cos 60°) \, \hat{\mathbf{x}} + (\sin 60°) \, \hat{\mathbf{y}}] = (25.0 \text{ N}) \, \hat{\mathbf{x}} + (43.3 \text{ N}) \, \hat{\mathbf{y}}$.

$\Sigma \mathbf{F} = \mathbf{F}_1 + \mathbf{F}_2 + \mathbf{F}_3 = (125 \text{ N}) \, \hat{\mathbf{x}} + (43.3 \text{ N}) \, \hat{\mathbf{y}}$.

So $\quad \mathbf{a} = \dfrac{\Sigma \mathbf{F}}{m} = \dfrac{(125 \text{ N}) \, \hat{\mathbf{x}} + (43.3 \text{ N}) \, \hat{\mathbf{y}}}{65 \text{ kg}} = (1.92 \text{ m/s}^2) \, \hat{\mathbf{x}} + (0.67 \text{ m/s}^2) \, \hat{\mathbf{y}}$.

Therefore $\quad a = \sqrt{(1.92 \text{ m/s}^2)^2 + (0.67 \text{ m/s}^2)^2} = \boxed{2.0 \text{ m/s}^2}$,

$\theta = \tan^{-1}\left(\dfrac{0.67}{1.92}\right) = \boxed{19° \text{ north of east}}$.

(b) Now the wind and current force is opposite that of Part (a).

$\mathbf{F}_3 = -[(25.0 \text{ N}) \, \hat{\mathbf{x}} + (43.3 \text{ N}) \, \hat{\mathbf{y}}]$. $\quad \Sigma \mathbf{F} = \mathbf{F}_1 + \mathbf{F}_2 + \mathbf{F}_3 = (75 \text{ N}) \, \hat{\mathbf{x}} + (-43.3 \text{ N}) \, \hat{\mathbf{y}}$.

$\mathbf{a} = (1.15 \text{ m/s}^2) \, \hat{\mathbf{x}} + (-0.67 \text{ m/s}^2) \, \hat{\mathbf{y}}$.

$a = \sqrt{(1.15 \text{ m/s}^2)^2 + (-0.67 \text{ m/s}^2)^2} = \boxed{1.3 \text{ m/s}^2}$. $\quad \theta = \tan^{-1}\left(\dfrac{-0.67}{1.15}\right) = \boxed{30° \text{ south of east}}$.

58. (a) $\Sigma F_x = F \cos 30° = (25 \text{ N}) \cos 30° = 21.65 \text{ N} = ma_x$,

so $\quad a_x = \dfrac{21.65 \text{ N}}{30 \text{ kg}} = \boxed{0.72 \text{ m/s}^2}$.

(b) $\Sigma F_y = N + F \sin 30° - w = ma_y = 0$,

so $\quad N = w - F \sin 30° = (30 \text{ kg})(9.80 \text{ m/s}^2) - (25 \text{ N}) \sin 30° = \boxed{2.8 \times 10^2 \text{ N}}$.

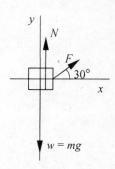

59. (a) $\Sigma F_x = F \cos\theta = (30 \text{ N}) \cos 37° = 23.96 \text{ N} = ma_x$,

so $\quad a_x = \dfrac{23.96 \text{ N}}{25 \text{ kg}} = \boxed{0.96 \text{ m/s}^2}$.

(b) $\Sigma F_y = N - F \sin\theta - w = ma_y = 0$,

so $\quad N = w + F \sin 37° = (25 \text{ kg})(9.80 \text{ m/s}^2) + (30 \text{ N}) \sin 37° = \boxed{2.6 \times 10^2 \text{ N}}$.

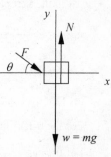

60. (a) There are $\boxed{\text{two}}$ forces acting on the skier, the weight and the normal force.

(b) The x-component of the weight is the side opposite to the angle θ shown,

so sine is used. $\quad \Sigma F_x = mg \sin\theta = ma_x$,

so $\quad a_x = g \sin\theta = (9.80 \text{ m/s}^2) \sin 37° = \boxed{5.9 \text{ m/s}^2}$.

(c) From $v^2 = v_0^2 + 2ax$,

$v = \sqrt{(5.0 \text{ m/s})^2 + 2(5.9 \text{ m/s}^2)(35 \text{ m})} = \boxed{21 \text{ m/s}}$.

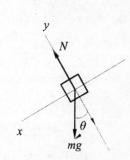

61.   From Exercise 4.60(b), $a_x = g\sin\theta = (9.80 \text{ m/s}^2)\sin 30° = 4.9 \text{ m/s}^2$ down the slope.

If up the slope is chosen as positive, then $a = -4.9 \text{ m/s}^2$. Taking $x_o = 0$.

$$v^2 = v_o^2 + 2a(x - x_o), \quad x = \frac{(0)^2 - (25 \text{ m/s})^2}{2(-4.9 \text{ m/s}^2)} = \boxed{64 \text{ m}}.$$

62.   First find the mass of the first block. $m_1 = \frac{\Sigma F}{a} = \frac{40 \text{ N}}{2.5 \text{ m/s}^2} = 16 \text{ kg}.$

Now $a' = \frac{40 \text{ N}}{16 \text{ kg} + 4.0 \text{ kg}} = \boxed{2.0 \text{ m/s}^2}.$

63.   (a) The angle the rope makes with the horizontal, θ, depends on both the tree separation and sag.

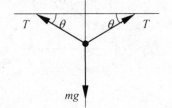

$\Sigma y = 2T\sin\theta - mg = 0, \quad ☞ \quad T = \frac{mg}{2\sin\theta}.$

So the tension depends on $\boxed{\text{both the tree separation and sag}}$.

(b) $\theta = \tan^{-1}\left(\frac{0.20 \text{ m}}{5.0 \text{ m}}\right) = 2.29°. \quad T = \frac{(5.0 \text{ kg})(9.80 \text{ m/s}^2)}{2\sin 2.29°} = \boxed{6.1 \times 10^2 \text{ N}}.$

64.   (a) There are two rings. $\Sigma F_y = T + T - w = 0.$

(b)

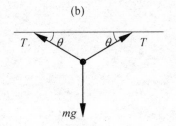

So $T = \frac{w}{2} = \frac{mg}{2} = \frac{(50 \text{ kg})(9.80 \text{ m/s}^2)}{2} = \boxed{2.5 \times 10^2 \text{ N}}.$

(b) In the vertical direction: $\Sigma F_y = T\sin\theta + T\sin\theta - mg = 0.$

So $T = \frac{mg}{2\sin\theta} = \frac{(50 \text{ kg})(9.80 \text{ m/s}^2)}{2\sin 45°} = \boxed{3.5 \times 10^2 \text{ N}}.$

65.   (a) Since the car and the truck accelerate together, they have the same acceleration, a.

For the truck: $\Sigma F_x = 3200 \text{ N} - T = (3000 \text{ kg})a.$ (1)

For the car: $\Sigma F_x = T = (1500 \text{ kg})a.$ (2)

(1) + (2) results $3200 \text{ N} = (3000 \text{ kg} + 1500 \text{ kg})a.$

So $a = \boxed{0.711 \text{ m/s}^2}.$

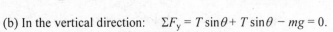

Alternate method: Consider the car and truck as a system of mass.

$3000 \text{ kg} + 1500 \text{ kg} = 4500 \text{ kg}. \quad \Sigma F = 3200 \text{ N} = (4500 \text{ kg})a,$

so $a = 0.711 \text{ m/s}^2.$

(b) From (1) in (a), $T = (1500 \text{ kg})(0.711 \text{ m/s}^2) = \boxed{1067 \text{ N}}.$

66.   (a) Consider the three blocks as a system with mass of

$M = m_1 + m_2 + m_3 = 1.0 \text{ kg} + 2.0 \text{ kg} + 3.0 \text{ kg} = 6.0 \text{ kg}.$

$a = \dfrac{\Sigma F}{M} = \dfrac{18.0 \text{ N}}{6.0 \text{ kg}} = \boxed{3.0 \text{ m/s}^2}.$

(b) For m_1: $F_{\text{net}} = T_1 = m_1 a = (1.0 \text{ kg})(3.0 \text{ m/s}^2) = \boxed{3.0 \text{ N}}.$

For m_2: $F_{\text{net}} = T_2 - T_1 = m_2 a = (2.0 \text{ kg})(3.0 \text{ m/s}^2) = 6.0 \text{ N},$ so $T_2 = 6.0 \text{ N} + T_1 = \boxed{9.0 \text{ N}}.$

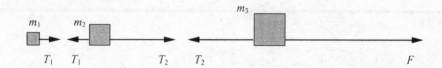

67.   The free-body diagrams of the three objects.

For m_1: $T_1 - m_1 g = m_1 a,$ (1)

For m_3: $T_2 - T_1 = m_3 a,$ (2)

For m_2: $m_2 g - T_2 = m_2 a,$ (3)

$(1) + (2) + (3)$ gives $(m_2 - m_1)g = (m_1 + m_2 + m_3)a,$

so $a = \dfrac{(m_2 - m_1)g}{m_1 + m_2 + m_3}.$

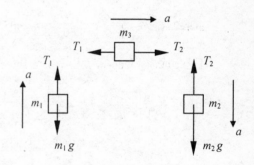

(a) $a = \dfrac{(0.50 \text{ kg} - 0.25 \text{ kg})(9.80 \text{ m/s}^2)}{0.25 \text{ kg} + 0.50 \text{ kg} + 0.25 \text{ kg}} = \boxed{2.5 \text{ m/s}^2 \text{ to right}}.$

(b) $a = \dfrac{(0.15 \text{ kg} - 0.35 \text{ kg})(9.80 \text{ m/s}^2)}{0.35 \text{ kg} + 0.15 \text{ kg} + 0.50 \text{ kg}} = -2.0 \text{ m/s}^2.$ So it is $\boxed{2.0 \text{ m/s}^2 \text{ to left}}.$

68.   (a) Since the two objects accelerate together, they have the same acceleration, a. Also according to Newton's third law, the tension on m_1 (up) is the same as the tension on m_2 (up).

For m_1: $\Sigma F = T - m_1 g = m_1 a.$ (1)

For m_2: $\Sigma F = m_2 g - T = m_2 a.$ (2)

$(1) + (2)$ gives $(m_2 - m_1)g = (m_1 + m_2)a,$

so $a = \dfrac{(m_2 - m_1)g}{m_1 + m_2} = \dfrac{(0.80 \text{ kg} - 0.55 \text{ kg})(9.80 \text{ m/s}^2)}{0.55 \text{ kg} + 0.80 \text{ kg}} = \boxed{1.8 \text{ m/s}^2}.$

(b) From (1), $T = m_1(a + g) = (0.55 \text{ kg})(1.8 \text{ m/s}^2 + 9.80 \text{ m/s}^2) = \boxed{6.4 \text{ N}}.$

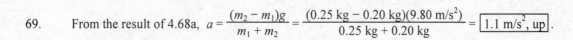

69.   From the result of 4.68a, $a = \dfrac{(m_2 - m_1)g}{m_1 + m_2} = \dfrac{(0.25 \text{ kg} - 0.20 \text{ kg})(9.80 \text{ m/s}^2)}{0.25 \text{ kg} + 0.20 \text{ kg}} = \boxed{1.1 \text{ m/s}^2, \text{ up}}.$

70.   (a) First find the acceleration from dynamics. (Take $x_o = 0$.)

From the result of 4.68a, $a = \dfrac{(m_2 - m_1)g}{m_1 + m_2} = \dfrac{(0.255\text{ kg} - 0.215\text{ kg})(9.80\text{ m/s}^2)}{0.215\text{ kg} + 0.255\text{ kg}} = 0.834\text{ m/s}^2$.

Now $x = x_o + v_o t + \tfrac{1}{2}at^2 = \tfrac{1}{2}at^2$,   ☞ $t = \sqrt{\dfrac{2x}{a}} = \dfrac{2(1.10\text{ m})}{0.834\text{ m/s}^2} = \boxed{1.62\text{ s}}$.

(b) When m_2 hits the floor, m_1 has traveled up a distance of 1.10 m and has a velocity of v, which is

obtained from: $v^2 = v_o^2 + 2a(x - x_o) = 0 + 2(0.834\text{ m/s}^2)(1.10\text{ m}) = 1.835\text{ m}^2/\text{s}^2$,

so $v = 1.35\text{ m/s}$.

Now m_1 will move up as a "free fall" with an initial velocity of 1.35 m/s.

The height from that point is from (taking $y_o = 0$) $v^2 = 0 = v_o^2 - 2g(y - y_o)$,

therefore $y = \dfrac{v_o^2}{2g} = \dfrac{(1.35\text{ m/s})^2}{2(9.80\text{ m/s}^2)} = 0.0936\text{ m}$.

Therefore m_1 will ascend from the floor by 1.10 m + 0.0936 m = $\boxed{1.19\text{ m}}$ before stopping.

71.   First calculate the speed of the ball when it hits the beach.

Given: $v_o = 0$, $y = -10\text{ m}$.   Find: v.   (Take $y_o = 0$.)

$v^2 = v_o^2 - 2gy = (0)^2 - 2(9.80\text{ m/s}^2)(-10\text{ m}) = 196\text{ m}^2/\text{s}^2$.

So $v = -14\text{ m/s}$. The negative sign simply indicates that the velocity is downward.

Now consider the impact. Note that the final velocity of the fall is the initial velocity of the impact.

Given: $v_o = -14\text{ m/s}$, $v = 0$, $x = 5.0\text{ cm} = 0.050\text{ m}$.   Find: a.   (Take $x_o = 0$.)

$v^2 = v_o^2 + 2a(x - x_o)$,   ☞ $a = \dfrac{v^2 - v_o^2}{2a} = \dfrac{(0)^2 - (-14\text{ m/s})^2}{2(0.050\text{ m})} = 1690\text{ m/s}^2$.

Finally, $\Sigma F = ma = (0.20\text{ kg})(1690\text{ m/s}^2) = \boxed{3.9 \times 10^2\text{ N}}$.

The force is positive, so it is upward.

72.   For m_1: $\Sigma F_x = T - m_1 g \sin\theta = m_1 a_x = 0$,   ☞ $T = m_1 g \sin\theta$.

For m_2: $\Sigma F_y = m_2 g - T = m_2 a_y = 0$,   ☞ $m_2 g = T = m_1 g \sin\theta$.

So $m_2 = m_1 \sin\theta = (2.0\text{ kg})\sin 37° = \boxed{1.2\text{ kg}}$.

If both are moving at constant velocity, the answer is the $\boxed{\text{same}}$

1.2 kg because the acceleration is still zero and the forces must still

balance out.

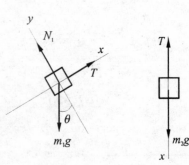

73. (a) For m_1: $\quad \Sigma F_x = T - m_1 g \sin\theta = m_1 a_x.$ (1)

For m_2: $\quad \Sigma F_y = m_2 g - T = m_2 a_y.$ (2)

$a_x = a_y = a$ in magnitude. (1) + (2) results $(m_2 - m_1 \sin\theta)g = (m_1 + m_2)a$.

$$a = \frac{m_2 - m_1 \sin\theta}{m_1 + m_2} g = \frac{2.5 \text{ kg} - (3.0 \text{ kg}) \sin 37^{\circ}}{2.5 \text{ kg} + 3.0 \text{ kg}} \times (9.80 \text{ m/s}^2) = \boxed{1.2 \text{ m/s}^2} \ (m_1 \text{ up and } m_2 \text{ down}).$$

(b) From (2) in (a), $T = m_2(g - a) = (2.5 \text{ kg})(9.80 \text{ m/s}^2 - 1.24 \text{ m/s}^2) = \boxed{21 \text{ N}}$.

74. (c).

75. (a) There is $\boxed{\text{no friction}}$ in this case.

(b) The direction of the friction force is $\boxed{\text{opposite the direction of velocity}}$.

(c) It is $\boxed{\text{sideways}}$ or perpendicular to the direction of velocity.

(d) It is $\boxed{\text{forward}}$ or in the direction of velocity.

76. (c).

77. This is because kinetic friction (sliding) is less than static friction (rolling). A greater friction force can decrease the stopping distance.

78. When it is pushed, the normal force equals the sum of the weight and the vertical component of the pushing force, i.e., $N = w + F \sin\theta$. When it is pulled, $N = w - F \sin\theta$. Since friction force is directly proportional to normal force it is easier to $\boxed{\text{pull}}$ than to push.

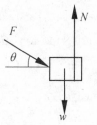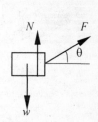

79. The down force will increase the normal force on the car to more than the weight of the car. Since friction force is directly proportional to the normal force, this will increase friction or "grip." If a car is simply made more massive to get more normal force, it will be more difficult to accelerate according to Newton's second law. So the wings can make the car grip better without significantly increasing the weight of the car—net result is more acceleration.

80. (a) $\boxed{\text{No}}$, there is no inconsistency. Here the friction force OPPOSES slipping.

(b) Wind can increase or decrease air friction depending on wind directions. If wind is in the direction of motion, friction decreases, and vice versa.

81. The treads are designed to displace water so cars with regular tires can drive in the rain. However, the wide and smooth drag racing tires increase friction because it uses a softer compound, therefore large coefficient of friction. This does not contradict the fact that friction is independent of the surface area. A common misconception is that the larger area of the racing tires contributes to larger friction. This is not true. Soft compound tires are required to be wider for the sidewall to support the weight of the car. A narrow, soft tire would not be strong enough, nor would it last very long. Wear in a tire is related to surface area.

82. (a) $\Sigma F_y = N - mg = ma_y = 0$, ☞ $N = mg$.

$\Sigma F_x = F - f_s = ma_x = 0$ (on the verge of moving), so $f_{smax} = \mu_s N = F$,

or $\mu_s = \dfrac{F}{mg} = \dfrac{275 \text{ N}}{(35.0 \text{ kg})(9.80 \text{ m/s}^2)} = \boxed{0.802}$.

(b) Similarly, $\mu_k = \dfrac{195 \text{ N}}{(35.0 \text{ kg})(9.80 \text{ m/s}^2)} = \boxed{0.569}$.

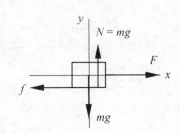

83. Refer to the diagram in Exercise 4.82.

$F = f_{smax} = \mu_s N = \mu_s mg = 0.69(40 \text{ kg})(9.80 \text{ m/s}^2) = \boxed{2.7 \times 10^2 \text{ N}}$.

84. (a) The acceleration will $\boxed{\text{increase, but more than double}}$. There is constant friction involved in this exercise so the net force more than doubles. For a 20-kg object to accelerate at 1.0 m/s^2, the net force is (20 kg)(1.0 m/s^2) = 20 N. That means there is a 100-N friction force (120 N – 20 N = 100 N). When the force doubles from 120 N to 240 N, the net force is then 240 N – 100 N = 140 N. So the acceleration is (160 N)/(20 kg) = 7.0 m/s^2, more than double.

(b) As calculated in (a), it is $\boxed{7.0 \text{ m/s}^2}$.

85. $\Sigma F_y = N - mg = ma_y = 0$, ☞ $N = mg$.

$f_{smax} = \mu_s N = \mu_s mg = 0.60(50 \text{ kg})(9.80 \text{ m/s}^2) = 294 \text{ N}$.

$f_k = \mu_k mg = 0.40(50 \text{ kg})(9.80 \text{ m/s}^2) = 196 \text{ N}$.

(a) Since 250 N $< f_{smax} = 294$ N, the object won't move.

So $a = \boxed{0}$.

(b) Since 350 $> f_{smax} = 294$ N, the object will move and f_k must be used.

$\Sigma F_x = 350 \text{ N} - 196 \text{ N} = 154 \text{ N} = ma = (50 \text{ kg})a$.

So $a = \boxed{3.1 \text{ m/s}^2}$.

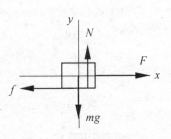

86.   (a) First find acceleration from dynamics and use μ_k from Table 4.1.

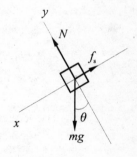

$$\Sigma F_x = -f_k = -\mu_k mg = ma, \quad \text{☞} \quad \mu_k = -\frac{a}{g}.$$

So $a = -\mu_k g = -0.85(9.80 \text{ m/s}^2) = -8.33 \text{ m/s}^2$,

and $v_o = 90 \text{ km/h} = 25 \text{ m/s}, \quad v = 0.$ (Take $x_o = 0$.)

$$v^2 = v_o^2 + 2a(x - x_o), \quad \text{☞} \quad x = \frac{v^2 - v_o^2}{2a} = \frac{0 - (25 \text{ m/s})^2}{2(-8.33 \text{ m/s}^2)} = \boxed{38 \text{ m}}.$$

(b) $a = -0.60(9.80 \text{ m/s}^2) = -5.88 \text{ m/s}^2.$ So $x = \dfrac{0 - (25 \text{ m/s})^2}{2(-5.88 \text{ m/s}^2)} = \boxed{53 \text{ m}}.$

87.   Use the result of 4.86(a), $\mu_k = -\dfrac{a}{g}.$

$$a = \frac{0 - (5.0 \text{ m/s})^2}{2(20 \text{ m})} = -0.625 \text{ m/s}^2, \quad \text{so} \quad \mu_k = -\frac{-0.625 \text{ m/s}^2}{9.80 \text{ m/s}^2} = \boxed{0.064}.$$

88.   (a) First find the minimum angle of inclination required for an object to slide.

$$\Sigma F_y = N - mg\cos\theta = ma_y = 0, \quad \text{☞} \quad N = mg\cos\theta.$$

For on the verge of sliding, $a_x = 0.$ So $\Sigma F_x = mg\sin\theta - f_s = 0.$

So $mg\sin\theta = \mu_s N = \mu_s (mg\cos\theta).$

Therefore $\mu_s = \dfrac{\sin\theta}{\cos\theta} = \tan\theta,$

$\theta = \tan^{-1}\mu_s = \tan^{-1} 0.65 = \boxed{33° > 20°}.$ $\boxed{\text{So it will not move}}.$

89.   See the free-body diagram in 4.58. $\Sigma F_y = N + F\sin 30° - w = ma_y = 0,$

so $N = w - F\sin 30° = (30 \text{ kg})(9.80 \text{ m/s}^2) - (25 \text{ N})\sin 30° = 282 \text{ N}.$

$\Sigma F_x = F\cos 30° - f_k = = F\cos 30° - \mu_k N = (25 \text{ N})\cos 30° - 0.03(282 \text{ N}) = 13.19 \text{ N} = ma_x,$

so $a_x = \dfrac{13.19 \text{ N}}{30 \text{ kg}} = \boxed{0.44 \text{ m/s}^2}.$

90. $\boxed{\text{Yes}}$, the coefficient of kinetic friction can be found.

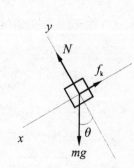

$$\Sigma F_y = N - mg\cos\theta = ma_y = 0, \quad \text{☞} \quad N = mg\cos\theta.$$

For constant velocity, $a_x = 0.$ So $\Sigma F_x = mg\sin\theta - f_k = 0.$

Or $mg\sin\theta = \mu_k N = \mu_k (mg\cos\theta).$

Therefore $\mu_k = \dfrac{\sin\theta}{\cos\theta} = \boxed{\tan\theta}.$

91.   (a) Use the result of Exercise 4.88(a).   When the object starts sliding down the plane,

$\mu_s = \dfrac{\sin\theta}{\cos\theta} = \tan\theta,$ so $\theta = \tan^{-1} 0.58 = \boxed{30°}$ (μ_s from Table 4.1).

(b) Replace μ_s with μ_k (or see Exercise 4.90), $\theta = \tan^{-1} 0.40 = \boxed{22°}$.

92.   Use the result from Exercise 4.88(a). $\mu_s = \tan\theta$, independent of m, size, etc.

So it is still $\boxed{30°}$ and $\mu_s = \tan 30° = \boxed{0.58}$.

93. $\Sigma F_y = N - mg\cos\theta = ma_y = 0,$ ☞ $N = mg\cos\theta.$

$\Sigma F_x = mg\sin\theta - f_k = ma_x.$

Or $mg\sin\theta - \mu_k N = mg\sin\theta - \mu_k (mg\cos\theta) = ma_x.$

So $\mu_k = \dfrac{g\sin\theta - a_x}{g\cos\theta} = \dfrac{(9.80\ \text{m/s}^2)\sin 37° - 0.15\ \text{m/s}^2}{(9.80\ \text{m/s}^2)\cos 37°} = \boxed{0.73}.$

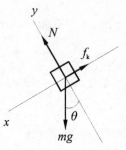

94. $\Sigma F_y = N - mg - F_1\sin 30° + F_2\sin 37° = 0,$

or $N = mg + F_1\sin 30° - F_2\sin 37°.$

$N = (5.0\ \text{kg})(9.80\ \text{m/s}^2) + (5.0\ \text{N})\sin 30° - (4.0\ \text{N})\sin 37° = 49.1\ \text{N}.$

$\Sigma F_x = F_1\cos 30° + F_2\cos 37° - f_{smax} = 0,$

or $F_1\cos 30° + F_2\cos 37° - \mu_s N = 0.$

$\mu_s = \dfrac{F_1\cos 30° + F_2\cos 37°}{N} = \dfrac{(5.0\ \text{N})\cos 30° + (4.0\ \text{N})\cos 37°}{49.1\ \text{N}} = \boxed{0.15}.$

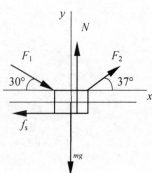

95.   Consider all three objects as a single system and refer to Exercise 4.66.

The total friction force is $f = f_1 + f_2 + f_3 = \mu(N_1 + N_2 + N_3) = \mu(m_1 + m_2 + m_3)g.$

(a) $F = f_{smax} = \mu_s(m_1 + m_2 + m_3)g = 0.45(1.0\ \text{kg} + 2.0\ \text{kg} + 3.0\ \text{kg})(9.80\ \text{m/s}^2) = \boxed{26\ \text{N}}.$

(b) $F = f_k = \mu_k(m_1 + m_2 + m_3)g = 0.35(1.0\ \text{kg} + 2.0\ \text{kg} + 3.0\ \text{kg})(9.80\ \text{m/s}^2) = \boxed{21\ \text{N}}.$

96.   (a) When the system is on the verge of (but not quite) moving, the acceleration is still zero.

For m_1: $\Sigma F_y = N - m_1 g = 0,$ ☞ $N = m_1 g.$

$\Sigma F_x = T - f_{smax} = T - \mu_s N = T - \mu_s m_1 g = 0,$ ☞ $T = \mu_s m_1 g.$

For m_2: $\Sigma F = m_2 g - T = 0,$ ☞ $T = m_2 g = \mu_s m_1 g.$

So $m_2 = \mu_s m_1 = 0.60(10\ \text{kg}) = \boxed{6.0\ \text{kg}}.$

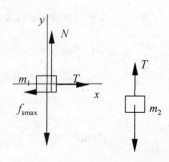

(b) Once the system starts moving, the kinetic friction force is used.

For m_1: $\Sigma F_x = T - f_k = T - \mu_k N = T - \mu_k m_1 g = m_1 a.$ (1)

For m_2: $\Sigma F = m_2 g - T = m_2 a.$ (2)

(1) + (2) gives $m_2 g - \mu_k m_1 g = (m_1 + m_2)a.$

So $a = \dfrac{(m_2 - \mu_k m_1)g}{m_1 + m_2} = \dfrac{[6.0 \text{ kg} - 0.40(10 \text{ kg})](9.80 \text{ m/s}^2)}{10 \text{ kg} + 6.0 \text{ kg}} = \boxed{1.2 \text{ m/s}^2}.$

97. For m_1: $\Sigma F = T_1 - m_1 g = 0,$ (1)

For m_3: $\Sigma F = T_2 - T_1 - f_{smax} = 0,$ (2)

For m_2: $\Sigma F = m_2 g - T_2 = 0,$ (3)

(1) + (2) + (3) gives $(m_2 - m_1)g - f_s = 0,$

or $(m_2 - m_1)g - \mu_s N_3 = (m_2 - m_1)g - \mu_s m_3 g = 0,$

so $\mu_s = \dfrac{m_2 - m_1}{m_3} = \dfrac{0.50 \text{ kg} - 0.25 \text{ kg}}{0.75 \text{ kg}} = \boxed{0.33}.$

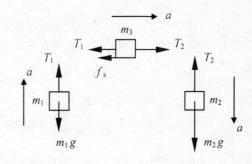

Alternate method (more conceptual).

Since $a = 0,$ $T_1 = m_1 g$ and $T_2 = m_2 g.$

So for m_3, $m_2 g - m_1 g - f_s = 0,$ or $m_2 g - m_1 g - \mu_s m_3 g = 0.$

Therefore $\mu_s = \dfrac{m_2 - m_1}{m_3}.$

98. Use the diagram in Exercise 4.97 but with f_k replacing f_s.

For m_1: $\Sigma F = T_1 - m_1 g = m_1 a,$ Eq. (1)

For m_3: $\Sigma F = T_2 - T_1 - f_k = m_3 a,$ Eq. (2), where $f_k = \mu_k N_3 = \mu_k m_3 g.$

For m_2: $\Sigma F = m_2 g - T_2 = m_2 a,$ Eq. (3)

Eq. (1) + Eq. (2) + Eq. (3) gives $(m_2 - m_1 - \mu_k m_3)g = (m_1 + m_2 + m_3)a,$

so $a = \dfrac{(m_2 - m_1 - \mu_k m_3)g}{m_1 + m_2 + m_3}.$

(a) For constant speed, $a = 0.$

So $m_3 = \dfrac{m_2 - m_1}{\mu_k} = \dfrac{0.250 \text{ kg} - 0.150 \text{ kg}}{0.560} = \boxed{0.179 \text{ kg}}.$

(b) $a = \dfrac{0.250 \text{ kg} - 0.150 \text{ kg} - (0.560)(0.100 \text{ kg})}{0.150 \text{ kg} + 0.250 \text{ kg} + 0.100 \text{ kg}} (9.80 \text{ m/s}^2) = \boxed{0.862 \text{ m/s}^2}.$

99.   (a) First assume that m_1 has the tendency to move up the incline.

For m_1:

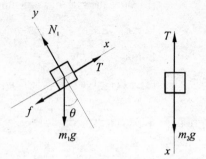

$\Sigma F_y = N_1 - m_1 g \cos\theta = 0$, ☞ $N_1 = m_1 g \cos\theta$.

$\Sigma F_x = T - m_1 g \sin\theta - f_{smax} = T - m_1 g \sin\theta - \mu_s N_1$

$= T - m_1 g \sin\theta - \mu_s m_1 g \cos\theta = 0$.

So $T = m_1 g \sin\theta + \mu_s m_1 g \cos\theta = m_1 g(\sin\theta + \mu_s \cos\theta)$.

For m_2:

$\Sigma F_x = m_2 g - T = 0$, ☞ $m_2 g = T = m_1 g(\sin\theta + \mu_s \cos\theta)$.

Therefore $m_2 = m_1 (\sin\theta + \mu_s \cos\theta) = (2.0 \text{ kg})(\sin 37° + 0.30 \cos 37°) = 1.7$ kg.

Next assume the other extreme, that m_1 has the tendency to move down the incline.

The static friction force will now be pointing up the incline, so the term $\mu_s m_1 g \cos\theta$ becomes negative.

Repeating the calculation: $m_2 = m_1 (\sin\theta - \mu_s \cos\theta) = (2.0 \text{ kg})(\sin 37° - 0.30 \cos 37°) = 0.72$ kg.

Therefore m_2 can be anywhere $\boxed{\text{between 0.72 kg and 1.7 kg}}$.

(b) When both are moving at constant velocity, the acceleration is still zero. However, μ_s is replace by μ_k.

Assume that m_1 has the tendency to move up the incline.

$m_2 = m_1 (\sin\theta + \mu_k \cos\theta) = (2.0 \text{ kg})(\sin 37° + 0.20 \cos 37°) = 1.5$ kg.

Assume that m_1 has the tendency to move down the incline.

$m_2 = m_1 (\sin\theta - \mu_k \cos\theta) = (2.0 \text{ kg})(\sin 37° - 0.20 \cos 37°) = 0.88$ kg.

Therefore m_2 can be anywhere between $\boxed{\text{0.88 kg and 1.5 kg}}$.

100.   First find the acceleration from kinematics.

Given: $v_0 = 25.0$ m/s, $v = 0$, $x = 100$ m.   Find: a.   (Take $x_0 = 0$.)

$v^2 = v_0^2 + 2a(x - x_0)$, ☞ $a = \dfrac{v^2 - v_0^2}{2x} = \dfrac{0^2 - (25.0 \text{ m/s})^2}{2(100 \text{ m})} = -3.125$ m/s^2.

$F = ma = (2.00 \times 10^5 \text{ kg})(-3.125 \text{ m/s}^2) = -\boxed{6.25 \times 10^5 \text{ N}}$.

101.   First find the acceleration from kinematics.

Given: $x = 0.750$ m, $v_0 = 0$, $v = 300$ m/s.   Find: a.   (Take $x_0 = 0$.)

$v^2 = v_0^2 + 2a(x - x_0)$ ☞ $a = \dfrac{v^2 - v_0^2}{2x} = \dfrac{(300 \text{ m/s})^2 - (0)^2}{2(0.750 \text{ m})} = 6.0 \times 10^4$ m/s^2.

Then $F = ma = (0.0250 \text{ kg})(6.0 \times 10^4 \text{ m/s}^2) = \boxed{1.5 \times 10^3 \text{ N}}$.

102.	$\Sigma F = T - mg = ma$,	☞	$a = \dfrac{T}{m} - g = \dfrac{400\ \text{N}}{25\ \text{kg}} - 9.80\ \text{m/s}^2 = \boxed{6.2\ \text{m/s}^2}$.

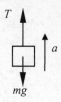

103.	$f_{\text{smax}} = \mu_s N = \mu_s\, mg = 0.45(9.0\ \text{kg})(9.80\ \text{m/s}^2) = 39.7\ \text{N} > 35\ \text{N}$.

So the answer is $\boxed{\text{no}}$.

104.	First calculate the acceleration from dynamics. Choose north as the positive direction.

$a = \dfrac{\Sigma F}{m} = \dfrac{6.5\ \text{N} - 8.5\ \text{N}}{2.0\ \text{kg}} = -1.0\ \text{m/s}^2$.

(a) The object continues to move north with a deceleration.

Given: $v_0 = 4.8\ \text{m/s}$, $v = 0$, $a = -1.0\ \text{m/s}^2$.   Find: x.

(Take $x_0 = 0$.)

$v^2 = 0 = v_0^2 + 2a(x - x_0)$,	☞	$x = -\dfrac{(4.8\ \text{m/s})^2}{2(-1.0\ \text{m/s}^2)} = \boxed{12\ \text{m north}}$.

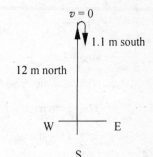

(b) Now the object turns around and moves south with an acceleration.

Given: $v_0 = 0$, $t = 1.5\ \text{s}$, $a = -1.0\ \text{m/s}^2$.   Find: x.

$x = x_0 + v_0 t + \tfrac{1}{2}at^2 = 0 + 0 + \tfrac{1}{2}(-1.0\ \text{m/s}^2)(1.5\ \text{s})^2 = -1.1\ \text{m} = \boxed{1.1\ \text{m south}}$ of where its velocity is zero.

105.	$\Sigma F_y = N - mg - F\sin\theta = 0$, so $N = mg + F\sin\theta$.

$\Sigma F_x = F\cos\theta - f_{\text{smax}} = 0$,

or	$F\cos\theta - \mu_s N = F\cos\theta - \mu_s(mg + F\sin\theta) = 0$.

Therefore $F = \dfrac{\mu_s\, mg}{\cos\theta - \mu_s\sin\theta}$.

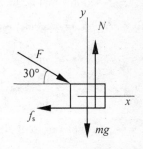

(a) $\mu_s = 0.75$ (Table 4.1),	so $F = \dfrac{0.75(5.0\ \text{kg})(9.80\ \text{m/s}^2)}{\cos 30° - (0.75)\sin 30°} = \boxed{75\ \text{N}}$.

(b) $\mu_s = 0.12$,	so $F = \dfrac{0.12(5.0\ \text{kg})(9.80\ \text{m/s}^2)}{\cos 30° - (0.12)\sin 30°} = 7.3\ \text{N}$. So the factor is $\dfrac{7.3\ \text{N}}{75\ \text{N}} = \boxed{0.097}$.

106.	$\Sigma F_y = N - mg\cos\theta = 0$,	☞	$N = mg\cos\theta$.

$\Sigma F_x = F - mg\sin\theta - f_k = 0$,

or	$F - mg\sin\theta - \mu_k N = F - mg\sin\theta - \mu_k(mg\cos\theta) = 0$.

So	$F = mg(\sin\theta + \mu_k\cos\theta)$

$= (9.80 \times 10^3\ \text{N})[\sin 37° + 0.750\cos 37°] = \boxed{1.18 \times 10^4\ \text{N}}$.

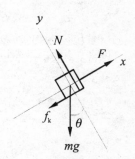

107. Use the result of Exercise 4.68(a), $a = \dfrac{(m_2 - m_1)g}{m_1 + m_2}$, which could be considered as $a = \dfrac{\Sigma F}{M}$.

So after the modification with friction, the result is $a = \dfrac{(m_2 - m_1)g - f}{m_1 + m_2}$,

$f = (m_2 - m_1)g - (m_1 + m_2)a = (0.40 \text{ kg} - 0.30 \text{ kg})(9.80 \text{ m/s}^2) - (0.40 \text{ kg} + 0.30 \text{ kg})(0.95 \text{ m/s}^2) = \boxed{0.32 \text{ N}}$.

108. First find the acceleration with dynamics. $m = \dfrac{w}{g} = \dfrac{2.75 \times 10^6 \text{ N}}{9.80 \text{ m/s}^2} = 2.806 \times 10^5 \text{ kg}$.

$a = \dfrac{F}{m} = \dfrac{6.35 \times 10^6 \text{ N}}{2.806 \times 10^5 \text{ kg}} = 22.63 \text{ m/s}^2$.

Given: $v_o = 0$, $v = 285 \times 0.278 \text{ m/s} = 79.23 \text{ m/s}$, $a = 22.63 \text{ m/s}^2$. Find: x. (Take $x_o = 0$.)

$v^2 = v_o^2 + 2ax = 2a(x - x_o)$, ☞ $x = \dfrac{v^2 - v_o^2}{2a} = \dfrac{(79.23 \text{ m/s})^2 - (0)^2}{2(22.63 \text{ m/s}^2)} = \boxed{139 \text{ m}}$.

109. First find acceleration from dynamics. Use the result of Exercise 4.86(a), $\mu_k = -\dfrac{a}{g}$.

$a = -\mu_k g = -(0.20)(9.80 \text{ m/s}^2) = -1.96 \text{ m/s}^2$.

Now given: $v_o = 4.5 \text{ m/s}$, $v = 0$, $a = -1.96 \text{ m/s}^2$. Find: x. (Take $x_o = 0$.)

$v^2 = 0 = v_o^2 + 2a(x - x_o)$ ☞ $x = -\dfrac{v_o^2}{2a} = -\dfrac{(4.5 \text{ m/s})^2}{2(-1.96 \text{ m/s}^2)} = \boxed{5.2 \text{ m}}$.

110. First find acceleration from kinematics.

Given: $x = 135 \text{ m}$, $v_o = 0$, $v = 24 \text{ m/s}$. Find: a. (Take $x_o = 0$.)

$v^2 = v_o^2 + 2a(x - x_o)$, ☞ $a = \dfrac{v^2 - v_o^2}{2x} = \dfrac{(24 \text{ m/s})^2 - (0)^2}{2(135 \text{ m})} = 2.13 \text{ m/s}^2$.

From Exercise 4.60, $a = g \sin\theta$. So $\sin\theta = \dfrac{a}{g} = \dfrac{2.13 \text{ m/s}^2}{9.80 \text{ m/s}^2} = 0.217$. $\theta = \sin^{-1} 0.217 = \boxed{13°}$.

111. Similar to Exercise 4.86, $a = -0.10(9.80 \text{ m/s}^2) = -0.98 \text{ m/s}^2$, $v_o = 25 \text{ km/h} = 6.94 \text{ m/s}$, $v = 0$.

$x = \dfrac{v^2 - v_o^2}{2a} = \dfrac{0 - (6.94 \text{ m/s})^2}{2(-0.98 \text{ m/s}^2)} = 24.6 \text{ m} < 26 \text{ m}$. So the answer is $\boxed{\text{no}}$.

112. First find the acceleration from kinematics.

$v_o = 15 \text{ m/s}$, $v = 0$, $x = 25 \text{ cm} = 0.25 \text{ m}$. (Take $x_o = 0$.)

$v^2 = 0 = v_o^2 + 2a(x - x_o)$, ☞ $x = -\dfrac{v_o^2}{2a} = -\dfrac{(15 \text{ m/s})^2}{2(0.25 \text{ m})} = -450 \text{ m/s}^2$.

Then $F = ma = 0.14 \text{ kg}(-450 \text{ m/s}^2) = -\boxed{63 \text{ N}}$. The negative sign indicates that the force is opposite the

velocity of the baseball or in the direction of acceleration.

CHAPTER 5

WORK AND ENERGY

1.   (d).

2.   No , you are not doing any work because there is no displacement.

3.   Negative work , because the force to stop the ball and the ball's displacement are opposite (180°).

4.   Yes . For example, when a machine part moves on a conveyor belt, friction does positive work.

5.   (a) No , the weight is not moving, so there is no displacement and therefore, no work.

      (b) Yes , positive work is done by the force exerted by the weightlifter.

      (c) No , as in (a), no work is done.

      (d) Yes , but the positive work is done by gravity, not the weightlifter.

6.   The work done by the carrying force is zero because the angle between the force (upward) and the
      displacement (horizontal) is 90° and $W = F \cos\theta\, d = F \cos 90° \, d = 0$.

7.   Positive on the way down and negative on the way up .

      No, it is not constant .

      Maximum at points B and D ($\theta = 0°$ or 180°)
      and minimum at points A and C ($\theta = 90°$).

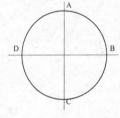

8. $W = F \cos\theta\, d$,   ☞ $F = \dfrac{W}{d \cos\theta} = \dfrac{50 \text{ J}}{(10 \text{ m}) \cos 0°} = \boxed{5.0 \text{ N}}$.

9.   The friction force is $f_k = \mu_k N = \mu_k \, mg$, and the angle between the friction force and displacement is 180°.

      So $W = F \cos\theta\, d = \mu_k \, mg \cos\theta\, d = 0.20(5.0 \text{ kg})(9.80 \text{ m/s}^2) \cos 180° (10 \text{ m}) = \boxed{-98 \text{ J}}$.

10. $W = F \cos\theta\, d = (10 \text{ N}) \cos 25° (200 \text{ m}) = \boxed{1.8 \times 10^3 \text{ J}}$.

11. $W = F \cos\theta\, d$,   ☞ $d = \dfrac{W}{F\cos\theta} = \dfrac{1.44 \times 10^3 \text{ J}}{(250 \text{ N})\cos 30°} = \boxed{6.65 \text{ m}}$.

12. $\boxed{\text{Gravitational force}}$ does work. $W = F_{||}d = mgd\sin\theta = (3.00 \text{ kg})(9.80 \text{ m/s}^2)(1.50 \text{ m})\cos 20° = \boxed{15.1 \text{ J}}$.

13.   The friction force $f_k = \mu_k N = \mu_k (mg\cos 20°) = 0.275(3.00 \text{ kg})(9.80 \text{ m/s}^2)\cos 20° = 7.597 \text{ N}$.

        $W_{\text{net}} = 15.1 \text{ J} + (7.597 \text{ N})(1.5 \text{ m})\cos 180° = \boxed{3.7 \text{ J}}$, where $180°$ is between f_k and displacement.

14. $W = F\cos\theta\, d = (F\cos\theta)\, d = F_{||}d = F(d\cos\theta) = F\, d_{||}$.

15.   (a) The weight does $\boxed{\text{negative}}$ work because its direction is opposite ($180°$) to the displacement (up).

        (b) When the balloon ascends at constant rate, the upward force is equal to its weight.

        $W = F\cos\theta\, d = (mg)\cos\theta\, d = (500 \text{ kg})(9.80 \text{ m/s}^2)(\cos 0°)[(1.50 \text{ m/s})(20.0 \text{ s})] = \boxed{1.47 \times 10^5 \text{ J}}$.

16. $\Sigma F_y = N + F\sin\theta - mg = 0$, $N = mg - F\sin\theta$.

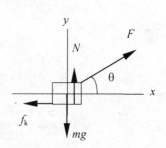

        $\Sigma F_x = F\cos\theta - f_k = 0$,   or $F\cos\theta = \mu_k N = \mu_k (mg - F\sin\theta) = 0$.

        So $F = \dfrac{\mu_k mg}{\cos\theta + \mu_k\sin\theta} = \dfrac{0.20(35 \text{ kg})(9.80 \text{ m/s}^2)}{\cos 30° + 0.20\sin 30°} = 71.0 \text{ N}$.

        Therefore $W = F\cos\theta\, d = (71.0 \text{ N})\cos 30°\,(10 \text{ m}) = \boxed{6.1 \times 10^2 \text{ J}}$.

17. $\Sigma F_y = N - F\sin\theta - mg\cos\theta = 0$,   so $N = mg\cos\theta + F\sin\theta$.

        $\Sigma F_x = F\cos\theta - mg\sin\theta - f_k = 0$,   or $F\cos\theta - mg\sin\theta - \mu_k(mg\cos\theta + F\sin\theta) = 0$.

        So $F = \dfrac{mg(\sin\theta + \mu_k\cos\theta)}{\cos\theta - \mu_k\sin\theta}$

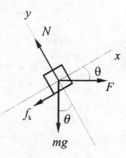

        $= \dfrac{(35 \text{ kg})(9.80 \text{ m/s}^2)(\sin 15° + 0.20\cos 15°)}{\cos 15° - 0.20\sin 15°} = 169.6 \text{ N}$.

        Therefore $W = F\cos\theta\, d = (169.6 \text{ N})\cos 15°\left(\dfrac{3.6 \text{ m}}{\sin 15°}\right) = \boxed{2.3 \times 10^3 \text{ J}}$.

18.   (a) $W = F\cos\theta\, d = (50 \text{ N})\cos 37°\,(25 \text{ m}) = 998 \text{ J} = \boxed{1.0 \times 10^3 \text{ J}}$.

        (b) Refer to the diagram in the solution of 5.14. $\Sigma F_y = N + F\sin\theta - mg = 0$, $N = mg - F\sin\theta$.

        So $f_k = \mu_k N = \mu_k(mg - F\sin\theta) = 0.15[(20 \text{ kg})(9.80 \text{ m/s}^2) - (50 \text{ N})\sin 37°] = 24.89 \text{ N}$.

        Therefore $W = (24.89 \text{ N})\cos 180°\,(25 \text{ m}) = -622 \text{ J} = \boxed{-6.2 \times 10^2 \text{ J}}$.

        (c) $W_{\text{net}} = 998 \text{ J} + (-622 \text{ J}) = 376 \text{ J} = \boxed{3.8 \times 10^2 \text{ J}}$.

19. (a) $\Sigma F = F - mg = ma$,

so $F = m(g + a) = (500 \text{ kg})(9.80 \text{ m/s}^2 + 2.00 \text{ m/s}^2) = 5.90 \times 10^3 \text{ N}$.

In 5.0 s, $d = v_0 t + \frac{1}{2}at^2 = \frac{1}{2}(2.00 \text{ m/s}^2)(5.00 \text{ s}) = 25.0 \text{ m}$.

$W = F \cos\theta\, d = (5.90 \times 10^3 \text{ N}) \cos 0° (25.0 \text{ m}) = 1.475 \times 10^5 \text{ J} = \boxed{1.48 \times 10^5 \text{ J}}$.

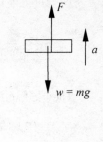

(b) $W = (500 \text{ kg})(9.80 \text{ m/s}^2) \cos 180° (25.0 \text{ m}) = -1.225 \times 10^5 \text{ J} = \boxed{-1.23 \times 10^5 \text{ J}}$.

(c) $W_{\text{net}} = 1.475 \times 10^5 \text{ J} + (-1.225 \times 10^5 \text{ J}) = \boxed{2.50 \times 10^4 \text{ J}}$.

20. (a) Pulling requires the student to do $\boxed{\text{less}}$ work. Compared with pushing, pulling decreases the normal force on the crate. This, in turn, decreases the kinetic friction force.

(b) Minimum work corresponds to motion with constant velocity, so the acceleration is zero.

Pulling

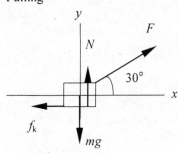

Pushing

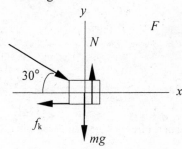

Pulling:

$\Sigma F_y = N + F \sin\theta - mg = 0$, so $N = mg - F \sin\theta$.

$\Sigma F_x = F \cos\theta - f_k = F \cos\theta - \mu_k N = F \cos\theta - \mu_k (mg - F \sin\theta) = 0$.

or $F \cos\theta - \mu_k (mg - F \sin\theta) = 0$. $F = \dfrac{\mu_k mg}{\cos\theta + \mu_k \sin\theta} = \dfrac{0.20(50 \text{ kg})(9.80 \text{ m/s}^2)}{\cos 30° + 0.20 \sin 30°} = 101 \text{ N}$.

$W = F \cos\theta\, d = (101 \text{ N}) \cos 30° (15 \text{ m}) = \boxed{1.3 \times 10^3 \text{ J}}$.

Pushing:

$\Sigma F_y = N - F \sin\theta - mg = 0$, so $N = mg + F \sin\theta$.

$\Sigma F_x = F \cos\theta - f_k = F \cos\theta - \mu_k N = F \cos\theta - \mu_k (mg + F \sin\theta) = 0$.

or $F \cos\theta - \mu_k (mg + F \sin\theta) = 0$. $F = \dfrac{\mu_k mg}{\cos\theta - \mu_k \sin\theta} = \dfrac{0.20(50 \text{ kg})(9.80 \text{ m/s}^2)}{\cos 30° - 0.20 \sin 30°} = 128 \text{ N}$.

$W = (128 \text{ N}) \cos 30° (15 \text{ m}) = \boxed{1.7 \times 10^3 \text{ J}}$.

21. (c).

22. $\boxed{\text{No}}$, it takes more work. This is because the force increases as the spring stretches, according to Hooke's

law: $F_s = -kx$.

23.   (d) $W = \frac{1}{2}k\,(x^2 - x_o^2)$,   ☞ $\dfrac{W_2}{W_1} = \dfrac{x_2^2 - x_1^2}{x_1^2 - x_o^2} = \dfrac{4.0^2 - 2.0^2}{2.0^2 - 0^2} = \boxed{3 \text{ times as much}}$.

24. $F_s = -kx$,   ☞ $k = \left|\dfrac{F_s}{x}\right| = \dfrac{4.0 \text{ N}}{0.050 \text{ m}} = \boxed{80 \text{ N/m}}$.

25. $F_s = -kx$,   ☞ $x = \left|\dfrac{F_s}{k}\right| = \dfrac{10 \text{ N}}{4.0 \times 10^2 \text{ N/m}} = 0.025 \text{ m} = \boxed{2.5 \text{ cm}}$.

26. $W = \frac{1}{2}kx^2 = \frac{1}{2}(40 \text{ N/m})(0.020 \text{ m})^2 = \boxed{8.0 \times 10^{-3} \text{ J}}$.

27. $W = \frac{1}{2}kx^2$,   ☞ $k = \dfrac{2W}{x^2} = \dfrac{2(400 \text{ J})}{(0.0800 \text{ m})^2} = \boxed{1.25 \times 10^5 \text{ N/m}}$.

28.   (a) $W = \frac{1}{2}kx^2$,   ☞ $x = \sqrt{\dfrac{2W}{k}}$. So when W doubles, x becomes $\sqrt{2}$ as much.

Therefore, it will stretch more than by a factor of $\boxed{\sqrt{2}}$.

(b) $\dfrac{W_2}{W_1} = \dfrac{x_2^2}{x_1^2} = \dfrac{(3.0 \text{ cm})^2}{(1.0 \text{ cm})^2} = 9$.   So $W_2 = 9W_1 = 9(100 \text{ J}) = \boxed{900 \text{ J}}$.

29. $F_s = -kx$,   ☞ $k = \left|\dfrac{F_s}{x_1 - x_o}\right| = \dfrac{(0.075 \text{ kg})(9.80 \text{ m/s}^2)}{0.070 \text{ m} - 0.040 \text{ m}} = 24.5 \text{ N/m}$.

The total stretch of the spring is $x = 0.10 \text{ m} + 0.030 \text{ m} = 0.13 \text{ m}$.

$W = \frac{1}{2}kx^2 = \frac{1}{2}(24.5 \text{ N/m})(0.13 \text{ m})^2 = \boxed{0.21 \text{ J}}$.

30.   (a) $W = \frac{1}{2}kx^2 = \frac{1}{2}(2.5 \times 10^3 \text{ N/m})(0.060 \text{ m})^2 = \boxed{4.5 \text{ J}}$.

(b) The difference in work is $\Delta W = \frac{1}{2}k(x_2^2 - x_1^2) = \frac{1}{2}(2.5 \times 10^3 \text{ N/m})[(0.080 \text{ m})^2 - (0.060 \text{ m})^2] = \boxed{3.5 \text{ J}}$.

31.   (a) $m = \dfrac{w}{g} = \dfrac{F}{g} = \dfrac{kx}{g} = \dfrac{(2.5 \times 10^3 \text{ N/m})(0.060 \text{ m})}{9.80 \text{ m/s}^2} = \boxed{15 \text{ kg}}$.

(b) $m = \dfrac{k(x_2 - x_1)}{g} = \dfrac{(2.5 \times 10^3 \text{ N/m})(0.020 \text{ m})}{9.80 \text{ m/s}^2} = \boxed{5.1 \text{ kg more}}$.

32. (a) $F = kx = (60 \text{ N/m})x$, ☞ $k = 60$ N/m. $W = \frac{1}{2}k(x^2 - x_0^2) = \frac{1}{2}(60 \text{ N/m})[(0.15 \text{ m})^2 - 0] = \boxed{0.68 \text{ J}}$.

(b) $W = \frac{1}{2}(60 \text{ N/m})[(0.25 \text{ m})^2 - (0.15 \text{ m})^2] = \boxed{1.2 \text{ J}}$.

33. $W = \text{area} = \frac{1}{2}(6.0 \text{ N})(2.0 \text{ m}) + \frac{1}{2}(-6.0 \text{ N})(5.0 \text{ m} - 2.0 \text{ m}) = \boxed{-3.0 \text{ J}}$.

34. (b), because $\cos\theta < 0$ for $90° < \theta < 270°$ and $W = F\cos\theta \, d = \Delta K$. So K decreases.

35. Because the heel can lift from the blade, the blade will be in contact with the ice longer. This will make the displacement a bit greater (longer strides) so that the work done is greater. Greater work translates to faster speed according to the work-energy theorem.

36. (a) $K = \frac{1}{2}mv^2 = \frac{1}{2}(4m)v^2 = 2mv^2$. (b) $K = \frac{1}{2}(3m)(2v)^2 = 6mv^2$.

(c) $K = \frac{1}{2}(2m)(3v)^2 = 9mv^2$. (d) $K = \frac{1}{2}(m)(4v)^2 = 8mv^2$.

So the answer is (a).

37. $\boxed{\text{Reducing the speed}}$ by half. Since $K = \frac{1}{2}mv^2$, reducing the speed by half will reduce K by ¾, whereas reducing the mass by half will only reduce K by half.

38. $W = \Delta K = \frac{1}{2}mv^2 - \frac{1}{2}mv_0^2 = \frac{1}{2}mv^2 - 0 = \frac{1}{2}mv^2$. So $\dfrac{W'}{W} = \dfrac{v'^2}{v^2} = \dfrac{(2v)^2}{v^2} = 4$.

Therefore $W' = \boxed{4W}$.

39. $W = \Delta K = \frac{1}{2}mv^2 - \frac{1}{2}mv_0^2 = \frac{1}{2}mv^2 - 0 = \frac{1}{2}mv^2$. So $v = \sqrt{\dfrac{2W}{m}}$.

Therefore $\dfrac{v'}{v} = \sqrt{\dfrac{W'}{W}} = \sqrt{\dfrac{2W}{W}} = \sqrt{2}$. Thus $v' = \boxed{\sqrt{2}v}$.

40. $\boxed{\text{The two colliding head on}}$ have more damage. The kinetic energy of each car is the same, and let's assume it is K. For the two cars colliding head on, the total kinetic energy is $2K$, and that amount is shared by the two cars so each gets K and that energy causes certain amount of damage. For the car that crashed into a wall, the total kinetic energy is K, but that is shared by the car and the wall. So the car gets less than K and therefore less damage.

41. (a) $\boxed{75\%}$. Since $K_0 = \frac{1}{2}mv_0^2$, reducing v to $v_0/2$ will reduce K to $0.25K_0$ or 25% of the original. So the kinetic energy lost is $1 - 0.25 = 0.75$ or 75%.

(b) $K_o = \frac{1}{2}(0.20 \text{ kg})(10 \text{ m/s})^2 = 10 \text{ J}.$ $K = \frac{1}{2}(0.20 \text{ kg})(5.0 \text{ m/s})^2 = 2.5 \text{ J}.$

So the kinetic energy lost $= 10 \text{ J} - 2.5 \text{ J} = \boxed{7.5 \text{ J}}$.

42.   90 km/h = 25 m/s.

(a) $K_o = \frac{1}{2}mv_o^2 = \frac{1}{2}(1.2 \times 10^3 \text{ kg})(25 \text{ m/s})^2 = \boxed{3.8 \times 10^5 \text{ J}}$.

(b) $W_{net} = \frac{1}{2}mv^2 - \frac{1}{2}mv_o^2 = 0 - 3.8 \times 10^5 \text{ J} = \boxed{-3.8 \times 10^5 \text{ J}}$.

43.   (a) $W_{net} = \frac{1}{2}mv^2 - \frac{1}{2}mv_o^2 = K - 0,$ ☞ $K = W_{net} = Fd = (75 \text{ N})(0.60 \text{ m}) = \boxed{45 \text{ J}}$.

(b) $K = \frac{1}{2}mv$,   ☞ $v = \sqrt{\dfrac{2K}{m}} = \sqrt{\dfrac{2(45 \text{ J})}{0.20 \text{ kg}}} = \boxed{21 \text{ m/s}}$.

44. $W_{net} = \frac{1}{2}mv^2 - \frac{1}{2}mv_o^2 = 0 - \frac{1}{2}(3.0 \times 10^{-3} \text{ kg})(350 \text{ m/s})^2 = -1.84 \times 10^2 \text{ J}.$

So $F = \dfrac{W_{net}}{d} = \dfrac{-1.84 \times 10^2 \text{ J}}{0.12 \text{ m}} = \boxed{-1.5 \times 10^3 \text{ N}}$, opposite to direction of velocity.

45. $W_{net} = \frac{1}{2}mv^2 - \frac{1}{2}mv_o^2 = 0 - \frac{1}{2}mv_o^2.$ $W_{net} = -fd.$ So $d = \dfrac{v_o^2}{2f} \propto v_o^2.$

$\dfrac{d_2}{d_1} = \dfrac{(90 \text{ km/h})^2}{(45 \text{ km/h})^2} = 4,$ ☞ $d_2 = 4d_1 = 4(50 \text{ m}) = \boxed{200 \text{ m}}$.

46.   (a) The small car will have a $\boxed{\text{longer}}$ stopping distance.

$W_{net} = \frac{1}{2}mv^2 - \frac{1}{2}mv_o^2 = 0 - \frac{1}{2}mv_o^2.$ Also $W_{net} = -fd = -\mu_k Nd = -\mu_k mgd.$

So $d = \dfrac{v_o^2}{2\mu_k g}$ independent of m, but depends on the initial speed squared.

(b) For the large car: $d_1 = \dfrac{v_o^2}{2\mu_k g},$ for the small car: $d_2 = \dfrac{(2v)^2}{2\mu_k g} = 4\dfrac{v_o^2}{2\mu_k g}.$

So $\dfrac{d_2}{d_1} = \boxed{4}$.

47. $W = \frac{1}{2}mv^2 - \frac{1}{2}mv_o^2 = \frac{1}{2}m(v^2 - v_o^2),$ ☞ $\dfrac{W_2}{W_1} = \dfrac{(30 \text{ km/h})^2 - (20 \text{ km/h})^2}{(20 \text{ km/h})^2 - (10 \text{ km/h})^2} = 1.67.$

So $W_2 = 1.67W_1 = 1.67(5.0 \times 10^3 \text{ J}) = \boxed{8.3 \times 10^3 \text{ J}}$.

48.   (d).

49.   (d). $U = \frac{1}{2}kx^2$,   so $\Delta U = \frac{1}{2}k(x^2 - x_o^2) \propto x^2 - x_o^2$.

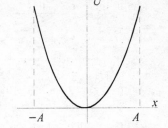

50.   See diagram on the right.

51. $U = mgy = (1.0\ \text{kg})(9.80\ \text{m/s}^2)(50\ \text{m}) = \boxed{4.9 \times 10^2\ \text{J}}$.

52. $U = \frac{1}{2}kx^2$,   ☞ $x = \sqrt{\dfrac{2U}{k}} = \sqrt{\dfrac{2(1.0\ \text{J})}{2.0 \times 10^4\ \text{N/m}}} = \boxed{1.0\ \text{cm}}$.

$x = \sqrt{\dfrac{2(4.0\ \text{J})}{2.0 \times 10^4\ \text{N/m}}} = \boxed{2.0\ \text{cm}}$.

53. $U = mgy$,   ☞ $\Delta U = mg\Delta y = (1.0\ \text{kg})(9.80\ \text{m/s}^2)(1.5\ \text{m} - 0.90\ \text{m}) = \boxed{5.9\ \text{J}}$.

54.   (a) You can determine $\boxed{\text{only the height difference}}$ because the change in potential energy depends only on the height difference, not positions.

(b) $U = mgy$,   ☞ $\Delta U = mg\Delta y$,   so $\Delta y = \dfrac{\Delta U}{mg} = \dfrac{-10\ \text{J}}{(2.0\ \text{kg})(9.80\ \text{m/s}^2)} = -0.51\ \text{m}$.

Therefore it is $\boxed{\text{lowered by 0.51 m}}$.

55.   First, find the maximum height from kinematics.   (Take $y_o = 0$.)

$v^2 = 0^2 = v_o^2 - 2g(y - y_o)$ ☞ $y_{\max} = \dfrac{v_o^2}{2g} = \dfrac{(7.5\ \text{m/s})^2}{2(9.80\ \text{m/s}^2)} = 2.87\ \text{m}$.

(a) $U = mgy = (0.20\ \text{kg})(9.80\ \text{m/s}^2)(1.2\ \text{m} + 2.87\ \text{m}) = \boxed{8.0\ \text{J}}$.

(b) $\Delta U = mg\Delta y = (0.20\ \text{kg})(9.80\ \text{m/s}^2)(2.87\ \text{m}) = \boxed{5.6\ \text{J}}$.

56.   (a) On the board: $U = mgy = (60\ \text{kg})(9.80\ \text{m/s}^2)(5.0\ \text{m}) = \boxed{2.9 \times 10^3\ \text{J}}$.

At the bottom of pool: $U = (60\ \text{kg})(9.80\ \text{m/s}^2)(-3.0\ \text{m}) = \boxed{-1.8 \times 10^3\ \text{J}}$.

(b) To the board: $\Delta U = mg\Delta y = (60\ \text{kg})(9.80\ \text{m/s}^2)(-8.0\ \text{m} - 0) = \boxed{-4.7 \times 10^3\ \text{J}}$.

To the surface: $\Delta U = (60\ \text{kg})(9.80\ \text{m/s}^2)(-3.0\ \text{m} - 5.0\ \text{m}) = \boxed{-4.7 \times 10^3\ \text{J}}$.

To the bottom of pool: $\Delta U = (60\ \text{kg})(9.80\ \text{m/s}^2)(0 - 8.0\ \text{m}) = \boxed{-4.7 \times 10^3\ \text{J}}$.

57.   (a) The change in potential energy is independent of the reference level

so the answer is $\boxed{\text{all the same}}$.

(b) $U_b = mgy = (1.5 \text{ kg})(9.80 \text{ m/s}^2)(-3.0 \text{ m}) = \boxed{-44 \text{ J}}$,

$U_a = (1.5 \text{ kg})(9.80 \text{ m/s}^2)(4.5 \text{ m}) = \boxed{66 \text{ J}}$.

(c) Use the attic as reference:

$\Delta U = mg\Delta y = (1.5 \text{ kg})(9.80 \text{ m/s}^2)(-7.5 \text{ m} - 0) = \boxed{-1.1 \times 10^2 \text{ J}}$.

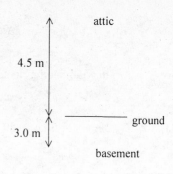

attic

4.5 m

ground

3.0 m

basement

58.   Assume the first book is already on a surface. To put the second book on top of the first, the student has to raise its center of gravity a distance of 0.020 m + 0.040 m = 0.060 m. Similarly the heights for the 3rd, 4th, 5th, and 6th books are 0.10 m, 0.14 m, 0.18m, and 0.22 m.

So the total work is $W = \Delta U = (30 \text{ N})(0.060 \text{ m} + 0.10 \text{ m} + 0.14 \text{ m} + 0.18 \text{ m} + 0.22 \text{ m}) = \boxed{21 \text{ J}}$.

59.   (d).

60.   (c).

61.   Due to the conservation of energy, the initial potential energy is equal to the final potential energy so the final height is equal to the initial height.

62.   Before starting to run, the vaulter has chemical potential energy stored in the molecules in the muscles. When the muscles contract before he runs, some of the chemical energy is converted to kinetic energy of the muscles. When he is running, he has kinetic energy. Part of that kinetic energy and some chemical potential energy in the muscles will bend the pole and store elastic potential energy in the pole. The rest of the kinetic energy and the elastic potential energy will be converted to gravitational potential energy when he is on the way up. At the maximum height, almost all the energy is in gravitational potential energy (he still has some kinetic energy due to some horizontal motion). On the way down, potential energy is converted to kinetic energy, and when the vaulter lands, negative work is done on him to "consume" most of the kinetic energy. Some kinetic energy will be converted to heat and sound and cause permanent deformation on the mattress.

63.   Each time you land on the trampoline, you coil your legs on the way down, then push down on the trampoline as you land, thereby compressing it more; storing more energy, you rebound and go higher. The limit is determined by the "spring constant" of the trampoline and how much you can compress it.

64. $\boxed{\text{Yes}}$. Due to the conservation of energy, the kinetic energy, thus velocity, is the same at the same height or potential energy.

65. $\boxed{\text{No}}$, this is not a violation of the conservation of energy. During the collision, some of the initial mechanical energy of the ball is converted to heat and sound energy and even used to do work on the floor (deform the floor).

66.   (a) $E_o = K_o + U_o = 0 + (0.250 \text{ kg})(9.80 \text{ m/s}^2)(115 \text{ m}) = \boxed{282 \text{ J}}$.

(b) $U_1 = (0.250 \text{ kg})(9.80 \text{ m/s}^2)(115 \text{ m} - 75.0 \text{ m}) = \boxed{98.0 \text{ J}}$.

Since $E = E_o$ is conserved, $K_1 = E_o - U_1 = 282 \text{ J} - 98.0 \text{ J} = \boxed{184 \text{ J}}$.

(c) $E_2 = K_2 + 0 = \boxed{282 \text{ J}}$. $K_2 = \frac{1}{2}mv^2$,   ☞ $v = \sqrt{\dfrac{2K_2}{m}} = \dfrac{2(282 \text{ J})}{0.250 \text{ kg}} = \boxed{47.5 \text{ m/s}}$.

(d) For (a) $E_o = 0 + 0 = \boxed{0}$.

For (b) $U_1 = (0.250 \text{ kg})(9.80 \text{ m/s}^2)(-75.0 \text{ m}) = \boxed{-184 \text{ J}}$. $K_1 = 0 - (-184 \text{ J}) = \boxed{184 \text{ J}}$.

For (c) $E_2 = K_2 + U_2 = \boxed{0}$. $K_2 = 0 - (0.250 \text{ kg})(9.80 \text{ m/s}^2)(-115 \text{ m}) = 282 \text{ J}$.

So $v = \sqrt{\dfrac{2(282 \text{ J})}{0.250 \text{ kg}}} = \boxed{47.5 \text{ m/s}}$.

67.   (a) $K_o = \frac{1}{2}mv_o^2 = \frac{1}{2}(0.300 \text{ kg})(10.0 \text{ m/s})^2 = \boxed{15.0 \text{ J}}$, $U_o = mgy_o = \boxed{0}$, $E_o = K_o + U_o = \boxed{15.0 \text{ J}}$.

(b) From the conservation of energy, $E = E_o = 15.0 \text{ J}$. $U = (0.300 \text{ kg})(9.80 \text{ m/s}^2)(2.50 \text{ m}) = 7.35 \text{ J}$.

So $K = E - U = 15.0 \text{ J} - 7.35 \text{ J} = \boxed{7.65 \text{ J}}$, $U = \boxed{7.35 \text{ J}}$, $E = \boxed{15.0 \text{ J}}$.

(c) At maximum height, $v = 0$.   So $K = \boxed{0}$, $U = \boxed{15.0 \text{ J}}$, $E = \boxed{15.0 \text{ J}}$.

68. $U = mgh$,   ☞ $h = \dfrac{U}{mg} = \dfrac{15.0 \text{ J}}{(0.300 \text{ kg})(9.80 \text{ m/s}^2)} = \boxed{5.10 \text{ m}}$.

69.   (a) The mechanical energy ($E = K + U$) is 80 J. From the conservation of energy, the potential energy at the maximum height is 80 J because the kinetic energy is zero there. At three-fourths of the distance to the maximum height, the potential energy is $U = \frac{3}{4}(80 \text{ J}) = 60 \text{ J}$.

So $K = 80 \text{ J} - 60 \text{ J} = \boxed{20 \text{ J}}$, and $U = \boxed{60 \text{ J}}$.

(b) $K = \frac{1}{2}mv^2$,   ☞ $v = \sqrt{\dfrac{2K}{m}} = \sqrt{\dfrac{2(20 \text{ J})}{0.50 \text{ kg}}} = \boxed{8.9 \text{ m/s}}$.

(c) The kinetic energy is zero at the maximum height, so $U = \boxed{80 \text{ J}}$.

70.   (a) The girl attains the maximum speed $\boxed{\text{at the bottom}}$. Since the mechanical energy is conserved, the

    lower the potential energy (at the bottom is the lowest), the higher the kinetic energy, therefore speed.

    (b) $\frac{1}{2}mv^2 + U = \frac{1}{2}mv_o^2 + U_o$,   ☞ $\frac{1}{2}mv^2 + mg(0.500 \text{ m}) = 0 + mg\,(2.00 \text{ m})$,

    so $v = \sqrt{2(9.80 \text{ m/s}^2)(1.50 \text{ m})} = \boxed{5.42 \text{ m/s at bottom of swing}}$.

71.   (a) $\dfrac{y_1}{y_o} = \dfrac{E_1}{E_o} = 0.820$,   ☞ $y_1 = 0.820\,y_o = (0.82)(1.25 \text{ m}) = \boxed{1.03 \text{ m}}$.

    (b) $y_2 = 0.82 y_1 = (0.820)(1.025 \text{ m}) = \boxed{0.841 \text{ m}}$.

    (c) The kinetic energy of the ball must be equal to the lost mechanical energy.

    $K_o = 0.180\,E_o = 0.180\,(K_o + U_o)$,   ☞ $K_o = \dfrac{0.180\,U_o}{0.820} = 0.2195\,U_o = 0.2195\,mg\,(1.25 \text{ m}) = \frac{1}{2}mv^2$,

    so $v = \sqrt{2(0.2195)(9.80 \text{ m/s}^2)(1.25 \text{ m})} = \boxed{2.32 \text{ m/s}}$.

72.   Choose the bottom of the slope (point B) as the reference for height ($y_o = 0$).

    $\frac{1}{2}mv_B^2 + U_B = \frac{1}{2}mv_A^2 + U_A$,   ☞ $\frac{1}{2}mv_B^2 + mg(0) = \frac{1}{2}m(5.0 \text{ m/s})^2 + mg\,(10 \text{ m})$,

    so $v_B = \sqrt{(5.0 \text{ m/s})^2 + 2(9.80 \text{ m/s}^2)(10 \text{ m})} = \boxed{15 \text{ m/s}}$.

73.   Choose the lowest point on the course (point B) as the reference for height ($y_o = 0$).

    (a) $\frac{1}{2}mv_B^2 + U_B = \frac{1}{2}mv_A^2 + U_A$,   ☞ $\frac{1}{2}mv_B^2 + mg(0) = \frac{1}{2}m(5.0 \text{ m/s})^2 + mg\,(5.0 \text{ m})$,

    so $v_B = \sqrt{(5.0 \text{ m/s})^2 + 2(9.80 \text{ m/s}^2)(5.0 \text{ m})} = \boxed{11 \text{ m/s}}$.

    (b) $E_A = E_B = \frac{1}{2}m\,(11 \text{ m/s})^2 = 60.5m$. $E_C = mg(8.0 \text{ m}) = m(9.80 \text{ m/s}^2)(8.0 \text{ m}) = 78.4m > E_A$.

    So $\boxed{\text{no}}$, it will not reach point C.

    (c) $\frac{1}{2}mv_A^2 + mg(5.0 \text{ m}) = \frac{1}{2}m(0)^2 + mg(8.0 \text{ m})$,   ☞ $v_A = \boxed{7.7 \text{ m/s}}$.

74.   (a) $L - h = L \cos 25°$,   ☞ $y = h = L(1 - \cos 25°)$.

    (b) $K + U = K_o + U_o = 0 + U_o$,

    so $K = U_o - U = mg\,(y_o - y) = mg\,L[(1 - \cos 25°) - (1 - \cos 9.0°)]$

                $= (0.15 \text{ kg})(9.80 \text{ m/s}^2)(0.75 \text{ m})(\cos 9.0° - \cos 25°) = \boxed{9.0 \times 10^{-2} \text{ J}}$.

    (c) $K = (0.15 \text{ kg})(9.80 \text{ m/s}^2)(0.75 \text{ m})(\cos 0° - \cos 25°) = 0.103 \text{ J} = \frac{1}{2}mv^2$,

    so $v = \sqrt{\dfrac{2(0.103 \text{ J})}{0.15 \text{ kg}}} = \boxed{1.2 \text{ m/s}}$.

75. (a) $K = (0.15 \text{ kg})(9.80 \text{ m/s}^2)(0.75 \text{ m})(\cos 0° - \cos 60°) = 0.551 \text{ J} = \frac{1}{2}mv^2$,

so $v = \sqrt{\dfrac{2(0.551 \text{ J})}{0.15 \text{ kg}}} = \boxed{2.7 \text{ m/s}}$.

(b) Final height = initial height. $y = L(1 - \cos 60°) = (0.75 \text{ m})(1 - \cos 60°) = \boxed{0.38 \text{ m}}$.

(c) Half the speed means $\frac{1}{4}$ of the kinetic energy because $K = \frac{1}{2}mv^2$.

$\frac{1}{4}K = \frac{1}{4}(0.15 \text{ kg})(9.80 \text{ m/s}^2)(0.75 \text{ m})(\cos 0° - \cos 60°) = (0.15 \text{ kg})(9.80 \text{ m/s}^2)(0.75 \text{ m})(\cos 0° - \cos\theta)$.

Solving, $\cos\theta = 0.875$, ☞ $\theta = \boxed{29°}$.

76. (a) $\frac{1}{2}mv^2 + U = \frac{1}{2}mv_0^2 + U_0$ ☞ $0 + \frac{1}{2}kx^2 = \frac{1}{2}mv_0^2 + 0$.

So $x = \sqrt{\dfrac{m}{k}}\, v_0 = \sqrt{\dfrac{1.5 \text{ kg}}{2.0 \times 10^3 \text{ N/m}}} \times (12 \text{ m/s}) = \boxed{0.33 \text{ m}}$.

(b) $\frac{1}{2}mv^2 + \frac{1}{2}kx^2 = \frac{1}{2}mv_0^2 + 0$, ☞ $x = \sqrt{\dfrac{1.5 \text{ kg}}{2.0 \times 10^3 \text{ N/m}} \times [(12 \text{ m/s})^2 - (6.0 \text{ m.s})^2]} = \boxed{0.28 \text{ m}}$.

77. $W_{nc} = K + U - K_0 - U_0 = \frac{1}{2}mv^2 + 0 - 0 - mgy_0 = \frac{1}{2}(28 \text{ kg})(2.5 \text{ m/s})^2 - (28 \text{ kg})(9.80 \text{ m/s}^2)(3.0 \text{ m})$

$= \boxed{-7.4 \times 10^2 \text{ J}}$.

78. (a) This system is $\boxed{\text{nonconservative}}$.

$E_{top} = 0 + mg(25 \text{ m}) = (25mg) \text{ J} = (245m) \text{ J}$. $E_{bottom} = \frac{1}{2}m(20 \text{ m/s})^2 + 0 = (200m) \text{ J}$. So $E_{top} > E_{bottom}$.

(b) $W_{nc} = K + U - K_0 - U_0 = \frac{1}{2}mv^2 + 0 - 0 - mgy_0 = \frac{1}{2}(50 \text{ kg})(10 \text{ m/s})^2 - (50 \text{ kg})(9.80 \text{ m/s}^2)(20 \text{ m})$

$= \boxed{-7.3 \times 10^3 \text{ J}}$.

79. $W_{nc} = \Delta E = E - E_0 = [\frac{1}{2}mv_B^2 + mg(0)] - [\frac{1}{2}m(5.0 \text{ m/s})^2 + mg(10 \text{ m})]$.

So $-2500 \text{ J} = [\frac{1}{2}(60 \text{ kg})v_B^2 + mg(0)] - [\frac{1}{2}(60 \text{ kg})(5.0 \text{ m/s})^2 + (60 \text{ kg})(9.80 \text{ m/s}^2)(10 \text{ m})]$.

Solving $v_B = \boxed{12 \text{ m/s}}$.

80. (b).

81. $\boxed{\text{No, paying for energy}}$ because kWh is the unit of Power × Time = Energy.

2.5 kWh = 2500 Wh = (2500 Wh) × $\dfrac{3600 \text{ s}}{1 \text{ h}}$ = $\boxed{9.0 \times 10^6 \text{ J}}$.

82. (a) $\boxed{\text{No}}$, efficiency is only a measure of how much work is done for each unit of energy input (or the ration of work output to energy input).

(b) Again, $\boxed{\text{no}}$. It depends on the amount of energy input into the machines. If the energy input is the same to two machines, then the one with a higher efficiency will do more work.

83. They are doing the same amount of work (same mass, same height). So the $\boxed{\text{one that arrives first}}$ will have expended more power due to shorter time interval.

84. $1/4 \text{ hp} = (1/4 \text{ hp}) \times \dfrac{746 \text{ W}}{1/4 \text{ hp}} = \boxed{187 \text{ W}}$.

85. $\bar{P} = \dfrac{E}{t} = \dfrac{8.4 \times 10^6 \text{ J}}{24 \times 3600 \text{ s}} = \boxed{97 \text{ W}}$.

86. $90 \text{ km/h} = 25 \text{ m/s}$. $W = \Delta K = \frac{1}{2}mv^2 - 0 = \frac{1}{2}mv^2$.

$\bar{P} = \dfrac{W}{t} = \dfrac{mv^2}{2t} = \dfrac{(1500 \text{ kg})(25 \text{ m/s})^2}{2(5.0 \text{ s})} = \boxed{9.4 \times 10^4 \text{ W} = 1.3 \times 10^2 \text{ hp}}$.

87. $P = \dfrac{W}{t} = \dfrac{2mgd}{t} = \dfrac{2(0.50 \text{ kg})(9.80 \text{ m/s}^2)(1.5 \text{ m})}{3 \times 24 \times 2600 \text{ s}} = \boxed{5.7 \times 10^{-5} \text{ W}}$.

88. (a) $P = \dfrac{W}{t} = \dfrac{mgd}{t} = \dfrac{(60 \text{ kg})(9.80 \text{ m/s}^2)(15 \text{ m})}{20 \text{ s}} = \boxed{4.4 \times 10^2 \text{ W}}$.

(b) $(4.4 \times 10^2 \text{ W}) = (4.4 \times 10^2 \text{ W}) \times \dfrac{1 \text{ hp}}{746 \text{ W}} = \boxed{0.59 \text{ hp}}$.

89. $P = (0.45)(2.0 \text{ hp})(746 \text{ W/hp}) = 6.7 \times 10^2 \text{ W} = 6.7 \times 10^2 \text{ J/s}$. In 1 s, the energy is $\boxed{6.7 \times 10^2 \text{ J}}$.

90. 1 L of water has a mass of 1 kg. In one minute, the energy output is

$E = 0.90Pt = 0.90(1.00 \text{ hp})(746 \text{ W/hp})(60 \text{ s}) = 4.028 \times 10^4 \text{ J}$. The work required is $W = Fd = mgd = E$.

So $m = \dfrac{E}{gd} = \dfrac{4.028 \times 10^4 \text{ J}}{(9.80 \text{ m/s}^2)(30.0 \text{ m})} = \boxed{1.37 \times 10^2 \text{ kg}}$.

91. $P = 0.30 \text{ hp} = (0.30 \text{ hp})(746 \text{ W/hp}) = 224 \text{ W}$.

$t = 2 \text{ h } 49 \text{ min} = 2(3600 \text{ s}) + 49(60 \text{ s}) = 1.01 \times 10^4 \text{ s}$.

$E = Pt = (224 \text{ W})(1.01 \times 10^4 \text{ s}) = \boxed{2.3 \times 10^6 \text{ J}}$.

92.   850 km/h = 236.1 m/s.   The work required is

$$W = \Delta E = K + U = \tfrac{1}{2}(3.25 \times 10^3 \text{ kg})(236.1 \text{ m/s})^2 + (3.25 \times 10^3 \text{ kg})(9.80 \text{ m/s}^2)(10.0 \times 10^3 \text{ m})$$

$$= 4.091 \times 10^8 \text{ J}.$$

The energy output is $E = Pt = (1500 \text{ hp})(746 \text{ W/hp})(12.5 \text{ min})(60 \text{ s/min}) = 8.393 \times 10^8$ J.

So the efficiency is $\varepsilon = \dfrac{4.091}{8.393} = \boxed{48.7\%}$.

93.   (a) $\Sigma F_x = F - f - mg \sin\theta = 0$,

so $F = f + mg \sin\theta = 950 \text{ N} + (120 \text{ kg})(9.80 \text{ m/s}^2) \sin 15° = 1254$ N.

Also $v = 5.0$ km/h $= 1.389$ m/s.

So $P = Fv = (1254 \text{ N})(1.389 \text{ m/s}) = 1742 \text{ W} = \boxed{2.3 \text{ hp}}$.

The horse is working hard (it is working as hard as 2.3 horses. In spurts a horse can be more than 1 hp).

(b) 20 km/h = 5.556 m/s.

$$a = \frac{5.556 \text{ m/s} - 1.389 \text{ m/s}}{5.0 \text{ s}} = 0.833 \text{ m/s}^2.$$

Now $\Sigma F_x = F - f - mg \sin\theta = ma$,   ☞ $F = 1254 \text{ N} + (120 \text{ kg})(0.833 \text{ m/s}^2) = 1354$ N.

$P = (1354 \text{ N})(5.556 \text{ m/s}) = 7522 \text{ W} = \boxed{10 \text{ hp}}$.

94. $K = \tfrac{1}{2}mv^2$,   ☞ $v = \sqrt{\dfrac{2K}{m}} = \sqrt{\dfrac{2(3.0 \times 10^3 \text{ J})}{60 \text{ kg}}} = \boxed{10 \text{ m/s}}$.

95.   Power input $= \dfrac{1.5 \text{ hp}}{0.75} = 2.0 \text{ hp} = 2(746 \text{ W}) = 1492 \text{ W} = 1.492$ kW.

$E = Pt = (1.492 \text{ kW})(2.0 \text{ h}) = 2.984$ kWh.   So it costs $(2.984 \text{ kWh})(\$0.12 \text{ /kWh}) = \boxed{\$0.36}$.

96. $W = F \cos\theta\, d = (40 \text{ N}) \cos 25° (0.35 \text{ m}) = \boxed{13 \text{ J}}$.

97.   (a) The work required to stretch if from 10 cm to 20 cm is $\boxed{\text{more}}$ than that required from 0 to 10 cm. This is because the force required is greater (while the displacement is the same) to stretch from 10 cm to 20 cm, according to Hooke's law.

(b) $W_{0\text{-}10} = \tfrac{1}{2}k(x_1^2 - x_0^2) = \tfrac{1}{2}(50 \text{ N/m})[(0.10 \text{ m})^2 - 0] = \boxed{0.25 \text{ J}}$.

$W_{10\text{-}20} = \tfrac{1}{2}k\,(x_2^2 - x_1^2) = \tfrac{1}{2}(50 \text{ N/m})[(0.20 \text{ m})^2 - (0.10 \text{ m})^2] = \boxed{0.75 \text{ J}}$.

98. (a) $F = f_k = \mu_k N = \mu_k\, mg = 0.25(120 \text{ kg})(9.80 \text{ m/s}^2) = 294 \text{ N}.$

$W_F = Fd = (294 \text{ N})(750 \text{ m}) = \boxed{+2.2 \times 10^5 \text{ J}}.$

(b) $W_f = F \cos 180° \, d = -(294 \text{ N})(750 \text{ m}) = \boxed{-2.2 \times 10^5 \text{ J}}.$

99. (a) First calculate the speed at the bottom of the slide from conservation of mechanical energy.

Choose bottom of the slide as $y_o = 0$. $\frac{1}{2}mv^2 + U = \frac{1}{2}mv_o^2 + U_o$,   ☞ $\frac{1}{2}mv^2 + 0 = 0 + mgy$,

so $v = \sqrt{2gy} = \sqrt{2(9.80 \text{ m/s}^2)(4.0 \text{ m})} = 8.85 \text{ m/s}.$

Now the slider is a horizontal projectile with $y' = -1.5 \text{ m}.$

The time of flight is from (taking $y'_o = 0$): $y' = y'_o + v_{yo}t - \frac{1}{2}gt^2 = -\frac{1}{2}gt^2,$

so $t = \sqrt{-\dfrac{2y'}{g}} = \sqrt{-\dfrac{2(-1.5 \text{ m})}{9.80 \text{ m/s}^2}} = 0.553 \text{ s}.$

Therefore $x = (8.85)(0.553 \text{ s}) = \boxed{4.9 \text{ m}}.$

(b) $\boxed{\text{No, it is independent of mass}}.$

100. (a) Refer to Fig. 5.30 and Exercise 5.74. $\theta = \sin^{-1}\left(\dfrac{1.8}{4.0}\right) = 26.7°.$

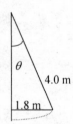

So $y = L(1 - \cos\theta) = (4.0 \text{ m})(1 - \cos 26.7°) = 0.427 \text{ m}.$ $\frac{1}{2}mv^2 + U = \frac{1}{2}mv_o^2 + U_o,$

or $0 + mgy = \frac{1}{2}mv_o^2 + 0.$ So $v_o = \sqrt{2gy} = \sqrt{2(9.80 \text{ m/s}^2)(0.427 \text{ m})} = 2.9 \text{ m/s}.$

Therefore the speed has to be $\boxed{\text{at least } 2.9 \text{ m/s}}.$

(b) $\boxed{\text{Yes, if starting with } v_o < 2.9 \text{ m/s}}$, because of insufficient energy.

101. (a) $20.0 \times 0.278 \text{ m/s} = 5.56 \text{ m/s}.$ $P = Fv = (700 \text{ N})(5.556 \text{ m/s}) = 3892 \text{ W}.$

$W = Pt = (3892 \text{ W})(3.50 \text{ min})(60 \text{ s/min}) = \boxed{8.17 \times 10^5 \text{ J}}.$

(b) As in (a) $P = \boxed{3.90 \times 10^3 \text{ W}}.$

102. (a) $K = \frac{1}{2}mv^2,$ ☞ $\dfrac{v_2}{v_1} = \sqrt{\dfrac{m_1}{m_2}} = \dfrac{1}{\sqrt{3}}.$

So $v_2 = \dfrac{1}{\sqrt{3}}(90 \text{ km/h}) = \boxed{52 \text{ km/h} = 14 \text{ m/s}}.$

(b) $\frac{1}{2}(\frac{1}{2}m_1v_1^2) = \frac{1}{2}m_2v_2^2,$ ☞ $v_2 = \sqrt{\dfrac{m_1}{2m_2}}\, v_1 = \dfrac{1}{\sqrt{6}}(90 \text{ km/h}) = \boxed{37 \text{ km/h} = 10 \text{ m/s}}.$

103. (a) Choose the stopped position as $y = 0$ and assume the ball compresses the spring by x. Then the initial height $y_o = (1.20 \text{ m} + x)$ high. From conservation of mechanical energy:

$mgy_o + 0 = 0 + \frac{1}{2}kx^2$,

so $mg(1.20 \text{ m} + x) = \frac{1}{2}kx^2$, ☞ $175x^2 - 3.53x - 4.23 = 0$.

Solving, $x = \boxed{0.166 \text{ m}}$ or -0.150 m. The $-$ answer has no physical meaning.

(b) $mg(1.20 \text{ m} + 0.0500 \text{ m}) = \frac{1}{2}k(0.0500 \text{ m})^2 + \frac{1}{2}mv^2$,

or $4.41 \text{ J} = 0.438 \text{ J} + \frac{1}{2}(0.360 \text{ kg})v^2$, ☞ $v = \boxed{4.70 \text{ m/s}}$.

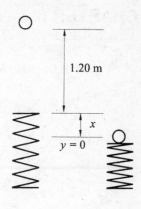

104. (a) $P = Fv$, ☞ $v = \dfrac{P}{F} = \dfrac{50 \text{ W}}{30 \text{ N}} = \boxed{1.7 \text{ m/s}}$.

(b) $W = Pt = (50 \text{ W})(2.5 \text{ s}) = \boxed{1.3 \times 10^2 \text{ W}}$.

105. (a) $P = \dfrac{W}{t} = \dfrac{Fd}{t} = \dfrac{mgd}{t} = \dfrac{(70 \text{ kg})(9.80 \text{ m/s}^2)(8.0 \text{ m})}{10 \text{ s}} = \boxed{5.5 \times 10^2 \text{ W}}$.

(b) $(5.5 \times 10^2 \text{ W}) \times \dfrac{1 \text{ hp}}{746 \text{ W}} = \boxed{0.74 \text{ hp}}$.

106. $\Sigma F_y = N - mg \cos\phi = 0$, ☞ $N = mg \cos\phi$.

$\Sigma F_x = mg \sin\phi - F - f_k = 0$, or $mg \sin\phi - F - \mu_k(mg \cos\phi) = 0$.

$F = mg(\sin\phi - \mu_k \cos\phi) = (50 \text{ kg})(9.80 \text{ m/s}^2)[\sin 25° - (0.33) \cos 25°] = 60.5 \text{ N}$.

$f_k = 0.33(50 \text{ kg})(9.80 \text{ m/s}^2) \cos 25° = 146.5 \text{ N}$.

(a) $W = F \cos\theta \, d = (60.5 \text{ N}) \cos 180° (5.0 \text{ m}) = \boxed{-3.0 \times 10^2 \text{ J}}$.

(b) $W = (146.5 \text{ N}) \cos 180° (5.0 \text{ m}) = \boxed{-7.3 \times 10^2 \text{ J}}$.

(c) $W = (50 \text{ kg})(9.80 \text{ m/s}^2) \cos 65° (5.0 \text{ m}) = \boxed{1.0 \times 10^3 \text{ J}}$.

(d) $W_{net} = (\Sigma F) \cos\theta \, d = \boxed{0}$, where $\Sigma F = 0$ for constant velocity.

CHAPTER 6

1.   (b).

2.   (c).

3. $\boxed{\text{No}}$, mass is also a factor since momentum is mass times velocity.

4. $K = \frac{1}{2}mv^2$ and $p = mv$.

The difference is that kinetic energy depends on the square of the velocity, and linear momentum is linearly proportional to velocity.

5. $\boxed{\text{Not necessarily}}$. Since $K = \frac{1}{2}mv^2$ and $p = mv$, $K = \frac{mmv^2}{2m} = \frac{(mv)^2}{2m} = \frac{p^2}{2m}$.

So even if the momentum is the same, different mass can still have different kinetic energies.

6.   (a) 90 km/h = 25 m/s. $p = mv = (60 \text{ kg})(25 \text{ m/s}) = \boxed{1.5 \times 10^3 \text{ kg·m/s}}$.

(b) The relative velocity is zero, so $p = \boxed{0}$.

7. $p = mv$,   ☞ $m = \dfrac{p}{v} = \dfrac{7.5 \times 10^2 \text{ kg·m/s}}{10 \text{ m/s}} = \boxed{75 \text{ kg}}$.

8.   (a) $p = mv = (7.1 \text{ kg})(12 \text{ m/s}) = \boxed{85 \text{ kg·m/s}}$.

(b) 90 km/h = 25 m/s. $p = (1200 \text{ kg})(25 \text{ m/s}) = \boxed{3.0 \times 10^4 \text{ kg·m/s}}$.

9.   (a) $\boxed{\text{No}}$, because velocity is also a factor in calculating momentum.

(b) Running back: $p = mv = (75 \text{ kg})(8.5 \text{ m/s}) = 638 \text{ kg·m/s}$.

Lineman: $p = (120 \text{ kg})(5.0 \text{ m/s}) = 600 \text{ kg·m/s}$.

So $\boxed{\text{the running back}}$ has more momentum, and the difference is

$\Delta p = 638 \text{ kg·m/s} - 600 \text{ kg·m/s} = \boxed{38 \text{ kg·m/s}}$.

10.   90 km/h = 25 m/s. $p = m_1 v_1 = m_2 v_2$,   ☞ $v_2 = \dfrac{m_1 v_1}{m_2} = \dfrac{(1500 \text{ kg})(25 \text{ m/s})}{1200 \text{ kg}} = \boxed{31 \text{ m/s}}$.

11. $K = \frac{1}{2}mv^2 = \frac{m^2v^2}{2m} = \frac{p^2}{2m} = \frac{(12 \text{ kg·m/s})^2}{2(3.0 \text{ kg})} = \boxed{24 \text{ J}}$.

12.   Since the ball moves in the opposite direction, $v = -34.7$ m/s   and $v_0 = 4.50$ m/s.

$\Delta p = mv - mv_0 = (0.150 \text{ kg})(-34.7 \text{ m/s}) - (0.150 \text{ kg})(4.50 \text{ m/s}) = -5.88$ kg·m/s

$= \boxed{5.88 \text{ kg·m/s in the direction opposite initial velocity}}$.

13.   Since the bullet moves in the opposite direction, $v = -120$ m/s   and $v_0 = 150$ m/s.

$\Delta p = mv - mv_0 = (0.0150 \text{ kg})(-120 \text{ m/s}) - (0.0150 \text{ kg})(150 \text{ m/s}) = -4.05$ kg·m/s

$= \boxed{4.05 \text{ kg·m/s in the direction opposite to initial velocity}}$.

14.   (a) The magnitude of the total momentum of the two-proton system will be $\boxed{\text{equal to the difference}}$

between the magnitudes of momenta of the two protons. Momentum is a vector quantity. When two

momenta are opposite, the magnitude of the addition of the two momenta is equal to the difference of the

magnitudes of the two momenta. If $\mathbf{p} = \mathbf{p}_1 + \mathbf{p}_2$ and $\mathbf{p}_1$ and $\mathbf{p}_2$ are opposite, then $p = p_1 + (-p_2) = p_1 - p_2$.

(b) Since they approach each other, $v_1 = 340$ m/s   and $v_2 = -450$ m/s.

$P = p_1 + p_2 = (1.67 \times 10^{-27} \text{ kg})(340 \text{ m/s} - 450 \text{ m/s}) = -1.84 \times 10^{-25}$ kg·m/s

$= \boxed{1.8 \times 10^{-25} \text{ kg·m/s in the direction of the faster proton}}$.

15.   (a) $p = mv = m(v_0 - gt) = (0.50 \text{ kg})[0 - (9.80 \text{ m/s}^2)(0.75 \text{ s})] = -1.8$ kg·m/s $= \boxed{3.7 \text{ kg·m/s down}}$.

(b) $v^2 = v_0^2 - 2gy = 0 - 2(9.80 \text{ m/s}^2)(-10 \text{ m}) = 196 \text{ m}^2/\text{s}^2$,   ☞ $v = -14$ m/s.

So $p = (0.50 \text{ kg})(-14 \text{ m/s}) = -7.0$ kg·m/s $= \boxed{7.0 \text{ kg·m/s down}}$.

16.   (a) 36 km/h = 10 m/s. $p = mv = (1.29 \text{ kg/m}^3)(1.0 \text{ m}^3)(10 \text{ m/s}) = \boxed{13 \text{ kg·m/s}}$.

(b) 74 mi/h = 33.1 m/s. $p = (1.29 \text{ kg/m}^3)(1.0 \text{ m}^3)(33.1 \text{ m/s}) = \boxed{43 \text{ kg·m/s}}$.

17. $P = p_1 + p_2 = \pm 350$ kg·m/s. It can be either positive or negative because the Exercise does not specify the

direction of the momentum.

± 350 kg·m/s $= (70 \text{ kg})(2.0 \text{ m/s}) + (60 \text{ kg})v_2$,   ☞ $v_2 = +3.5$ m/s or -8.2 m/s.

The velocity of the light runner is $\boxed{3.5 \text{ m/s in the same direction or 8.2 m/s in the opposite direction}}$.

18.	$\Delta p_x = m\Delta v_x = (0.20 \text{ kg})[(15 \text{ m/s}) \sin 60° - (15 \text{ m/s}) \sin 60°] = 0,$

$\Delta p_y = m\Delta v_y = (0.20 \text{ kg})[-(15 \text{ m/s}) \cos 60° - (15 \text{ m/s}) \cos 60°] = -3.0 \text{ kg·m/s}.$

So	$\Delta \mathbf{p} = \boxed{(-3.0 \text{ kg·m/s}) \hat{\mathbf{y}}}.$

19.	$\Delta p_x = m\Delta v_x = (0.20 \text{ kg})[(10 \text{ m/s}) \sin 50° - (15 \text{ m/s}) \sin 60°] = -1.1 \text{ kg·m/s},$

$\Delta p_y = m\Delta v_y = (0.20 \text{ kg})[-(10 \text{ m/s}) \cos 50° - (15 \text{ m/s}) \cos 60°] = -2.8 \text{ kg·m/s}.$

So	$\Delta \mathbf{p} = \boxed{(-1.1 \text{ kg·m/s}) \hat{\mathbf{x}} + (-2.8 \text{ kg·m/s}) \hat{\mathbf{y}}}.$

20.	$\bar{F} = \dfrac{\Delta p}{\Delta t} = \dfrac{mv - mv_0}{\Delta t} = \dfrac{(10 \text{ kg})(4.0 \text{ m/s} - 0)}{2.5 \text{ s}} = \boxed{16 \text{ N}}.$

21.	$v_0 = 3.0 \text{ km/h} = 0.833 \text{ m/s}.$

$\bar{F} = \dfrac{\Delta p}{\Delta t} = \dfrac{mv - mv_0}{\Delta t} = \dfrac{(5.0 \times 10^3 \text{ kg})(0 - 0.833 \text{ m/s})}{0.64 \text{ s}} = -\boxed{6.5 \times 10^3 \text{ N}}.$

22.	First calculate the speed of the ball hitting the ground.

$v^2 = v_0^2 - 2gy = (0)^2 - 2(9.80 \text{ m/s}^2)(-15 \text{ m}) = 294 \text{ m}^2/\text{s}^2, \quad \text{so} \quad v = -17.1 \text{ m/s}.$

For the impact	$\bar{F} = \dfrac{\Delta p}{\Delta t} = \dfrac{mv - mv_0}{\Delta t} = \dfrac{(2.0 \text{ kg})[0 - (-17.1 \text{ m/s})]}{0.50 \text{ s}} = \boxed{68 \text{ N}}.$

23.	The final velocity is equal in magnitude but opposite in direction to the initial velocity.

(a) $\Delta p = m\Delta v = m(v - v_0) = m(-v_0 - v_0) = -2mv_0 = -2(120 \text{ lb}) \times \dfrac{1 \text{ kg}}{2.2 \text{ lb}} \times (4.50 \text{ m/s})$

$= -\boxed{491 \text{ kg·m/s downward}}.$

(b) $\boxed{\text{Yes}}$. $v^2 = v_0^2 - 2gy = (4.50 \text{ m/s})^2 - 2(9.80 \text{ m/s}^2)(-0.25 \text{ m}) = 25.15 \text{ m}^2/\text{s}^2, \quad \text{☞} \quad v = -5.01 \text{ m/s}.$

So	$\Delta p = (120 \text{ lb}) \times \dfrac{1 \text{ kg}}{2.2 \text{ lb}} \times (-5.01 \text{ m/s} - 4.50 \text{ m/s}) = -\boxed{519 \text{ kg·m/s downward}}.$

24.	(c).

25.	Follow through $\boxed{\text{increases the contact time so to increase impulse}}$ because impulse is the product of force and contact time.

26.   By stopping, the contact time is short. From the impulse momentum theorem ($\bar{F}\Delta t = \Delta p = mv - mv_0$), a shorter contact time will result in a greater force if all other factors (m, v_0, v) remain the same.

27.   (a) Drive: large impulse (large $\bar{F}$ and Δt); chip shot: small impulse (small $\bar{F}$ and Δt).
        (b) Jab: small impulse (small $\bar{F}$ and Δt); knock-out punch: large impulse (large $\bar{F}$ and Δt).
        (c) Bunting: small impulse (small F and Δt); home-run swing: large impulse (large $\bar{F}$ and Δt).

28.   In (a), (b), and (c), it is $\boxed{\text{to increase contact time}}$ Δt, to reduce the average force F because
        $\bar{F}\Delta t = \Delta p = mv - mv_0$. It can also decrease the pressure on the body because the force is spread over a larger area.

29. $\boxed{\text{Not necessarily, contact time is also important}}$ because impulse is the product of force and contact time. A smaller force can generate greater impulse if the contact time is sufficiently long.

30.   Consider the horizontal motion.
        $$\bar{F}\Delta t = mv - mv_0 = mv, \quad \text{☞} \quad v = \frac{\bar{F}\Delta t}{m} = \frac{3.0 \text{ N·s}}{0.20 \text{ kg}} = \boxed{15 \text{ m/s}}.$$

31. $$\bar{F}\Delta t = mv - mv_0 = -mv_0, \quad \text{☞} \quad \bar{F} = -\frac{mv_0}{\Delta t} = -\frac{3.0 \times 10^4 \text{ kg·m/s}}{5.0 \text{ s}} = -\boxed{6.0 \times 10^3 \text{ N}}.$$

32. $$\bar{F}\Delta t = mv - mv_0 = mv, \quad \text{☞} \quad v = \frac{\bar{F}\Delta t}{m} = \frac{3.2 \text{ N·s}}{0.25 \text{ kg}} = \boxed{13 \text{ m/s}}.$$

33.   (a) $\bar{F}\Delta t = mv - mv_0 = -mv_0, \quad \text{☞} \quad \bar{F} = -\frac{mv_0}{\Delta t} = -\frac{(0.35 \text{ kg})(10 \text{ m/s})}{3.0 \times 10^{-3} \text{ s}} = -\boxed{1.2 \times 10^3 \text{ N}}.$

        (b) $\bar{F} = -\frac{mv_0}{\Delta t} = -\frac{(0.35 \text{ kg})(10 \text{ m/s})}{0.30 \times 10^{-3} \text{ s}} = -\boxed{1.2 \times 10^4 \text{ N}}.$

34.   (a) The magnitude of the change in momentum of the baseball is $\boxed{\text{equal to the sum}}$ of the magnitudes of momenta of the baseball before and after the bunt. Momentum is a vector quantity. When two momenta are opposite, the magnitude of the difference or subtraction of the two momenta is equal to the sum of the magnitudes of the two momenta. If $\mathbf{p} = \mathbf{p}_1 - \mathbf{p}_2$ and $\mathbf{p}_1$ and $\mathbf{p}_2$ are opposite, then $p = p_1 - (-p_2) = p_1 + p_2$.
        (b) Chose the direction of motion before the bunt as positive. $v = -10$ m/s, $v_0 = 15$ m/s.
        $\Delta p = mv - mv_0 = (0.16 \text{ kg})(-10 \text{ m/s}) - (0.16 \text{ kg})(15 \text{ m/s}) = -\boxed{4.0 \text{ kg·m/s in direction oppsite to } v_0}$.

        (c) $\bar{F} = \frac{\Delta p}{\Delta t} = \frac{-4.0 \text{ kg·m/s}}{0.025 \text{ s}} = -\boxed{160 \text{ N}}$, opposite to v_0.

35.   (a) $\boxed{\text{Hitting it back}}$ requires a greater force. Force is proportional to the change in momentum. When a ball changes its direction, the change in momentum is greater. If $\mathbf{p} = \mathbf{p}_1 - \mathbf{p}_2$ and $\mathbf{p}_1$ and $\mathbf{p}_2$ are opposite (hitting it back), then $p = p_1 - (-p_2) = p_1 + p_2$. Had you caught the ball, then $p_2 = 0$ so $p = p_1$.

(b) The final velocity is opposite to the initial velocity ("hitting it back").

$$\overline{F} = \frac{\Delta p}{\Delta t} = \frac{mv - mv_0}{\Delta t} = \frac{(0.45 \text{ kg})(-7.0 \text{ m/s} - 4.0 \text{ m/s})}{0.040 \text{ s}}$$

$$= -\boxed{1.2 \times 10^2 \text{ N in direction opposite to initial velocity}} .$$

36.   The final velocity is opposite to the initial velocity ("rebounds").

$$\overline{F} = \frac{\Delta p}{\Delta t} = \frac{mv - mv_0}{\Delta t} = \frac{(1.0 \text{ kg})(-13 \text{ m/s} - 15 \text{ m/s})}{0.020 \text{ s}} = -1.4 \times 10^3 \text{ N}.$$

So it is $\boxed{1.4 \times 10^3 \text{ N in direction opposite to initial velocity}}$.

37. $\overline{F}\Delta t = mv - mv_0 = -mv_0,$ ☞ $\overline{F} = -\dfrac{mv_0}{\Delta t}$.   So the magnitude is $\dfrac{mv_0}{\Delta t}$.

$$\overline{F}_1 = \frac{(0.16 \text{ kg})(25 \text{ m/s})}{3.5 \times 10^{-3} \text{ s}} = \boxed{1.1 \times 10^3 \text{ N}}; \quad \overline{F}_2 = \frac{(0.16 \text{ kg})(25 \text{ m/s})}{8.5 \times 10^{-3} \text{ s}} = \boxed{4.7 \times 10^2 \text{ N}} .$$

38.   (a) Impulse = area of the trapezoid $= \frac{1}{2}(0.30 \text{ s} + 0.14 \text{ s})(900 \text{ N}) = \boxed{77 \text{ N·s}}$.

(b) $\overline{F} = \dfrac{\text{impulse}}{\Delta t} = \dfrac{76.5 \text{ N·s}}{0.14 \text{ s}} = \boxed{5.5 \times 10^2 \text{ N}}$.

(c) $\overline{F}\Delta t = mv - mv_0,$ ☞ $v = v_0 + \dfrac{\overline{F}\Delta t}{m} = -6.0 \text{ m/s} + \dfrac{76.5 \text{ N·s}}{3.0 \text{ kg}} = \boxed{20 \text{ m/s}}$.

39.   The velocity of the putty right before impact is (from energy conservation)

$$v = -\sqrt{2gh} = -\sqrt{2(9.80 \text{ m/s}^2)(2.5 \text{ m})} = -7.0 \text{ m/s}.$$

$$\overline{F}\Delta t = mv - mv_0 = -mv_0, \quad ☞ \quad \overline{F} = -\frac{mv_0}{\Delta t} = -\frac{(0.35 \text{ kg})(-7.0 \text{ m/s})}{0.30 \text{ s}} = \boxed{8.2 \text{ N upward}} .$$

40. $\overline{F}\Delta t = \Delta p = -3.0 \text{ kg·m/s},$ ☞ $\overline{F} = \dfrac{-3.0 \text{ N·s}}{0.010 \text{ s}} = -\boxed{3.0 \times 10^2 \text{ N}}$.

41.   40 km/h = 11.1 m/s,   2400 lb = 10 680 N. The force on the infant is opposite to velocity.

$$F\Delta t = mv - mv_0, \quad ☞ \quad \Delta t = \frac{mv - mv_0}{F} = \frac{(55 \text{ kg})(0 - 11.1 \text{ m/s})}{-10\ 680 \text{ N}} = \boxed{0.057 \text{ s}} .$$

42. (d).

43. (a).

44. Air moves backward and the boat moves forward according to momentum conservation. If a sail were installed behind the fan on the boat, the boat would not go forward because the forces between the fan and the sail are internal forces of the system.

45. Throw something or even blow a strong breath of air out of your mouth (there is no friction so you cannot walk).

46. $\boxed{\text{No}}$, it is impossible. Before the hit, the two-object system has some momentum due to the one moving. According to momentum conservation, the system should also have momentum after the hit. Therefore it is not possible for both to be at rest (zero total system momentum).

47. This is because of the fact that the $\boxed{\text{golf ball has a much smaller mass}}$ than the golf club. When the momentum is transferred from the club to the ball, the ball has a greater speed.

48. According to the conservation of momentum, the astronaut moves in the opposite direction.

$m_1 = 0.50$ kg, $m_2 = 60$ kg, $v_{1o} = 0$, $v_{2o} = 0$, $v_1 = 10$ m/s, $v_2 = ?$.

$\mathbf{P_o} = \mathbf{P}$, ☞ $m_1 v_{1o} + m_2 v_{2o} = m_1 v_1 + m_2 v_2$.

$v_2 = \dfrac{m_1 v_{1o} + m_2 v_{2o} - m_1 v_1}{m_2} = \dfrac{0 + 0 - (0.50 \text{ kg})(10 \text{ m/s})}{60 \text{ kg}} = \boxed{0.083 \text{ m/s in opposite direction}}$.

49. $m_1 = 45$ kg, $m_2 = 65$ kg, $v_{1o} = 0, v_{2o} = 0$, $v_1 = 1.5$ m/s, $v_2 = ?$

$\mathbf{P_o} = \mathbf{P}$, ☞ $m_1 v_{1o} + m_2 v_{2o} = m_1 v_1 + m_2 v_2$.

$v_2 = \dfrac{m_1 v_{1o} + m_2 v_{2o} - m_1 v_1}{m_2} = \dfrac{0 + 0 - (45 \text{ kg})(1.5 \text{ m/s})}{65 \text{ kg}} = -1.0 \text{ m/s} = \boxed{1.0 \text{ m/s westward}}$.

50. $m_1 = 0.150$ kg, $m_2 = 70.0$ kg, $v_{1o} = 0$, $v_{2o} = 0$, $v_1 = 2.00$ m/s, $v_2 = ?$

$\mathbf{P_o} = \mathbf{P}$, ☞ $m_1 v_{1o} + m_2 v_{2o} = m_1 v_1 + m_2 v_2$.

$v_2 = \dfrac{m_1 v_{1o} + m_2 v_{2o} - m_1 v_1}{m_2} = \dfrac{0 + 0 - (0.150 \text{ kg})(2.00 \text{ m/s})}{70.0 \text{ kg}} = -4.29 \times 10^{-3}$ m/s.

Therefore it takes $\dfrac{5.00 \text{ m}}{4.29 \times 10^{-3} \text{ m/s}} = \boxed{1.17 \times 10^3 \text{ s} = 19.5 \text{ min}}$.

51. From momentum conservation $\mathbf{P_o} = \mathbf{P}$: $(0.100 \text{ kg})(250 \text{ m/s}) + (14.9 \text{ kg})(0) = (0.100 \text{ kg} + 14.9 \text{ kg})v$,

we have $v = \boxed{1.67 \text{ m/s in the original direction of bullet}}$.

52. (a) According to momentum conservation, the total momentum of the three-fragment system must be zero. Therefore, the third fragment must fly off toward a general direction of $\boxed{\text{north of east}}$.

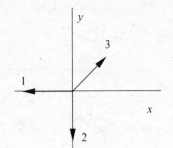

(b) Apply momentum conservation $\mathbf{P}_0 = \mathbf{P}$

in x axis: $(2.0\text{ kg})(0) = (0.50\text{ kg})(-2.8\text{ m/s}) + (1.3\text{ kg})(0) + (1.2\text{ kg})v_x,$

so $v_x = 1.17\text{ m/s};$

in y axis: $(3.0\text{ kg})(0) = (0.50\text{ kg})(0) + (1.3\text{ kg})(-1.5\text{ m/s}) + (1.2\text{ kg})v_y,$

so $v_y = 1.63\text{ m/s}.$

Therefore $v = \sqrt{(1.17\text{ m/s})^2 + (1.63\text{ m/s})^2} = \boxed{2.0\text{ m/s}},$

$\theta = \tan^{-1}\left(\dfrac{1.63}{1.17}\right) = \boxed{54°\text{ north of east}}.$

53. Apply momentum conservation $\mathbf{P}_0 = \mathbf{P}$ in x axis:

$(3.0\text{ kg})(2.5\text{ m/s}) = (0.50\text{ kg})(-2.8\text{ m/s}) + (1.3\text{ kg})(0) + (1.2\text{ kg})v_x, \quad \Rightarrow \quad v_x = 7.42\text{ m/s};$

so $v = \sqrt{(7.42\text{ m/s})^2 + (1.63\text{ m/s})^2} = \boxed{7.6\text{ m/s}}, \quad \theta = \tan^{-1}\left(\dfrac{1.63}{7.42}\right) = \boxed{12°\text{ above }+x\text{ axis}}.$

54. $m_1 = m_2 = m$ (identical), $v_1 = v_2 = v$ (coupling).

$\mathbf{P}_0 = \mathbf{P}, \quad \Rightarrow \quad m_1 v_{1o} + m_2 v_{2o} = (m_1 + m_2)v, \quad \text{so} \quad v = \dfrac{m_1 v_{1o} + m_2 v_{2o}}{m_1 + m_2} = \dfrac{v_{1o} + v_{2o}}{2}.$

(a) $v = \dfrac{90\text{ km/h} + 0}{2} = \boxed{45\text{ km/h}}$ in the direction of moving car.

(b) $v = \dfrac{120\text{ km/h} - 90\text{ km/h}}{2} = \boxed{15\text{ km/h}}$ in the direction of faster car.

(c) $v = \dfrac{90\text{ km/h} + 120\text{ km/h}}{2} = \boxed{105\text{ km/h}}$ in the same direction as initial motion.

55. $m_1 = 1200\text{ kg}, m_2 = 1500\text{ kg}, \quad v_{1o} = 25\text{ m/s}, \quad v_1 = v_2 = v?$ (coupling)

$\mathbf{P}_0 = \mathbf{P}, \quad \Rightarrow \quad m_1 v_{1o} + m_2 v_{2o} = (m_1 + m_2)v, \quad \text{so} \quad v = \dfrac{m_1 v_{1o} + m_2 v_{2o}}{m_1 + m_2}.$

(a) $v = \dfrac{(1200\text{ kg})(25\text{ m/s}) + (0)}{1200\text{ kg} + 1500\text{ kg}} = \boxed{11\text{ m/s to the right}}.$

(b) $v = \dfrac{(1200\text{ kg})(25\text{ m/s}) + (1500\text{ kg})(20\text{ m/s})}{1200\text{ kg} + 1500\text{ kg}} = \boxed{22\text{ m/s to the right}}.$

(c) $v = \dfrac{(1200\text{ kg})(25\text{ m/s}) + (1500\text{ kg})(-20\text{ m/s})}{1200\text{ kg} + 1500\text{ kg}} = 0\text{ or } \boxed{\text{at rest}}.$

56. $m_1 = 0.010$ kg, $\quad m_2 = 3.0$ kg, $\quad v = 3.0$ kg, $\quad v_{1o} = 400$ m/s, $\quad v_{2o} = 0$, $\quad v_1 = 300$ m/s, $\quad v_2 = ?$

$\mathbf{P_o} = \mathbf{P}$, $\quad \text{☞} \quad m_1 v_{1o} + m_2 v_{2o} = m_1 v_1 + m_2 v_2$.

$$v_2 = \frac{m_1 v_{1o} + m_2 v_{2o} - m_1 v_1}{m_2} = \frac{(0.010 \text{ kg})(400 \text{ m/s}) + 0 - (0.010 \text{ kg})(300 \text{ m/s})}{3.0 \text{ kg}} = \boxed{0.33 \text{ m/s}}.$$

57. $p_o = mv_o = p = m' v$, $\quad \text{☞} \quad v = \dfrac{m v_o}{m'} = \dfrac{(1600 \text{ kg})(2.5 \text{ m/s})}{1600 \text{ kg} + 3500 \text{ kg}} = \boxed{0.78 \text{ m/s}}.$

58. 90.0 km/h $= 25.0$ m/s.

First find the horizontal velocity of the "other" segment at top of the trajectory (explosion).

Apply momentum conservation $\mathbf{P_o} = \mathbf{P}$ in the horizontal direction.

$$m(25.0 \text{ m/s}) \cos 60.0° = \frac{m}{2}(0) + \frac{m}{2} v_x, \quad \text{☞} \quad v_x = 25.0 \text{ m/s}.$$

Now the "other" segment will undergo a horizontal projectile motion with $v_{xo} = 25.0$ m/s from a height of

$$y_{max} = \frac{(v_o \sin\theta)^2}{2g} = \frac{(25.0 \text{ m/s})^2 \sin^2 60.0°}{2(9.80 \text{ m/s}^2)} = 23.916 \text{ m} \quad (\text{from } v_y^2 = v_{yo}^2 - 2gy).$$

The time of flight is $t = \sqrt{-\dfrac{2y}{g}} = \sqrt{-\dfrac{2(-23.916 \text{ m})}{9.80 \text{ m/s}^2}} = 2.209$ s $\quad (\text{from } y = v_o t - \frac{1}{2}gt^2).$

So $x = v_{xo} t = (25.0 \text{ m/s})(2.209 \text{ s}) = 55.23$ m, which is the horizontal distance from explosion to landing.

The horizontal distance from the gun to explosion is $x' = (25.0 \text{ m/s}) \cos 60° (2.209 \text{ s}) = 27.62$ m.

Therefore the horizontal distance from the gun to the landing is $x + x' = \boxed{82.8 \text{ m}}.$

59. $m_1 = m_2 = m$ (same mass). Apply momentum conservation $\mathbf{P_o} = \mathbf{P}$

in x axis: $\quad\quad m(0.95 \text{ m/s}) = mv_1 \cos 50° + mv_2 \cos 40°$,

so $\quad\quad 0.95$ m/s $= 0.643 v_1 + 0.766 v_2$ $\quad\quad\quad\quad\quad (1)$

in y axis: $\quad\quad m(0) = mv_1 \sin 50° - mv_2 \sin 40°$,

so $\quad\quad 0 = 0.766 v_1 - 0.643 v_2$ $\quad\quad\quad\quad\quad\quad\quad (2)$

$0.643 \times (1) + 0.766 \times (2)$ yields $\quad 0.611$ m/s $= 0.413 \, v_1 + 0.587 \, v_1.$

Therefore $\quad v_1 = \boxed{0.61 \text{ m/s}}$ $\quad$ and $\quad v_2 = \boxed{0.73 \text{ m/s}}.$

60. First use energy conservation to find the velocity of the bullet and the bob right after collision from the swing motion. The velocity right after the collision is the same as the velocity at the start of the swing.

So $\quad \frac{1}{2}(m + M)v^2 + (m + M)g(0) = \frac{1}{2}(m + M)(0)^2 + (m + M)g(h)$, $\quad \text{☞} \quad v = \sqrt{2gh}.$

Now apply momentum conservation $\quad \mathbf{P_o} = \mathbf{P}$. $\quad mv_o + M(0) = (m + M)v = (m + M)\sqrt{2gh}$,

so $\quad v_o = \dfrac{m + M}{m}\sqrt{2gh}.$

61.   (c).

62.   (a).

63.   This is due to the fact that $\boxed{\text{momentum is a vector and kinetic energy is a scalar}}$. For example, two objects of equal mass traveling with the same speed in opposite directions have positive total kinetic energy but zero total momentum. After they collide inelastically, both stop, resulting in zero total kinetic energy and zero total momentum. Therefore, kinetic energy is lost and momentum is conserved.

64.   In either an elastic or an inelastic collision, the momentum is always conserved. However, in an inelastic collision, the kinetic energy is not conserved whereas the kinetic energy is also conserved in an elastic collision.

65.   It is an $\boxed{\text{elastic}}$ collision because the kinetic energy is conserved (final speed = initial speed so final kinetic energy = initial kinetic energy).

66. $v_1 = \dfrac{m_1 - m_2}{m_1 + m_2}\, v_{1o} = \dfrac{4.0 \text{ kg} - 2.0 \text{ kg}}{4.0 \text{ kg} + 2.0 \text{ kg}}\,(4.0 \text{ m/s}) = \boxed{+1.3 \text{ m/s}}$.

$v_2 = \dfrac{2m_1}{m_1 + m_2}\, v_{1o} = \dfrac{2(4.0 \text{ kg})}{4.0 \text{ kg} + 2.0 \text{ kg}}\,(4.0 \text{ m/s}) = \boxed{+5.3 \text{ m/s}}$.

67. $v_1 = \dfrac{m_1 - m_2}{m_1 + m_2}\, v_{1o} = \dfrac{0.10 \text{ kg} - 5.0 \text{ kg}}{0.10 \text{ kg} + 5.0 \text{ kg}}\,(0.50 \text{ m/s}) = \boxed{-0.48 \text{ m/s}}$.

$v_2 = \dfrac{2m_1}{m_1 + m_2}\, v_{1o} = \dfrac{2(0.10 \text{ kg})}{0.10 \text{ kg} + 5.0 \text{ kg}}\,(0.50 \text{ m/s}) = \boxed{+0.020 \text{ m/s}}$.

68.   (a) It must be the $\boxed{\text{conservation of mechanical energy}}$ because momentum is obviously conserved.

$m(2v_o) = mv_o + mv_o = 2mv_o$.

(b) $E_o = K_o = \frac{1}{2} m \, (2v_o)^2 = 2mv_o^2$ and $E = K = \frac{1}{2} mv_o^2 + \frac{1}{2} mv_o^2 = mv_o^2$.

So mechanical energy is not conserved and it can not happen.

69. $v_p = \dfrac{m_p - m_a}{m_p + m_a}\, v_{po} = \dfrac{m - 4m}{m + 4m}\,(3.0 \times 10^6 \text{ m/s}) = \boxed{-1.8 \times 10^6 \text{ m/s}}$.

$v_a = \dfrac{2m_p}{m_p + m_a}\, v_{ao} = \dfrac{2m}{m + 4m}\,(3.0 \times 10^6 \text{ m/s}) = \boxed{1.2 \times 10^6 \text{ m/s}}$.

70.   First find the velocity of the 6.0-kg ball right after collision from momentum conservation, $P_o = P$.

$m_1 = 2.0$ kg, $m_2 = 6.0$ kg, $v_{1o} = 12$ m/s, $v_{2o} = -4.0$ m/s ("toward each other"),

$v_1 = -8.0$ m/s ("recoil").

$(2.0$ kg$)(12$ m/s$) + (6.0$ kg$)(-4.0$ m/s$) = (2.0$ kg$)(-8.0$ m/s$) + (6.0$ kg$)v_2$,   ☞ $v_2 = 2.67$ m/s.

$K_o = \frac{1}{2}(2.0$ kg$)(12$ m/s$)^2 + \frac{1}{2}(6.0$ kg$)(4.0$ m/s$)^2 = 192$ J;

$K = \frac{1}{2}(2.0$ kg$)(8.0$ m/s$)^2 + \frac{1}{2}(6.0$ kg$)(2.67$ m/s$)^2 = 84.5$ J.

The kinetic energy lost is $K_o - K = \boxed{1.1 \times 10^2 \text{ J}}$.

71.   (a) This kind of collision is $\boxed{\text{completely inelastic}}$ because the fish and the bird are combined after the

"collision" (catch).

(b) The bird and fish have the same velocity after the grab.

$m_1 = 5.0$ kg, $m_2 = 0.80$ kg, $v_{1o} = 6.5$ m/s, $v_{2o} = 0$ m/s, $v_1 = v_2 = v = ?$

$P_o = P$,   ☞ $m_1 v_{1o} + m_2 v_{2o} = m_1 v_1 + m_2 v_2 = (m_1 + m_2)v$.

So $v = \dfrac{m_1 v_{1o} + m_2 v_{2o}}{m_1 + m_2} = \dfrac{(5.0 \text{ kg})(6.5 \text{ m/s}) + (0)}{5.0 \text{ kg} + 0.80 \text{ kg}} = \boxed{5.6 \text{ m/s}}$.

72.   (a) Apply momentum conservation, $P_o = P$

in x: $mv + M(0) = (m + M)v_x'$,   ☞ $v_x' = \dfrac{mv}{m + M} = \dfrac{(2.0 \text{ kg})(3.0 \text{ m/s})}{(2.0 \text{ kg}) + 4.0 \text{ kg}} = \boxed{1.0 \text{ m/s}}$;

in y: $m(0) + M(V) = (m + M)v_y'$,   ☞ $v_y' = \dfrac{MV}{m + M} = \dfrac{(4.0 \text{ kg})(5.0 \text{ m/s})}{(2.0 \text{ kg}) + 4.0 \text{ kg}} = \boxed{3.3 \text{ m/s}}$.

(b) $\theta = \tan^{-1}\left(\dfrac{3.3}{1.0}\right) = \boxed{73°}$.

73.   (a) Right after the collision, the car and minivan will move toward a

general direction $\boxed{\text{south of east}}$, according to momentum

conservation. The initial momentum of the minivan is to the south,

and the initial momentum of the car is to the east, so the two-

vehicle system has a total momentum to the southeast after the

collision.

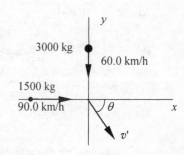

(b) 90.0 km/h = 25.0 m/s,   60.0 km/h = 16.67 m/s.

Using the result of Exercise 6.72,

we have $v_x' = \dfrac{mv}{m + M}$ and $v_y' = \dfrac{MV}{m + M}$.

$$v' = \frac{\sqrt{m^2 v^2 + M^2 V^2}}{m + M} = \frac{\sqrt{(1500\ \text{kg})^2 (25.0\ \text{m/s})^2 + (3000\ \text{kg})^2 (16.67\ \text{m/s})^2}}{1500\ \text{kg} + 3000\ \text{kg}}$$

$$= \boxed{13.9\ \text{m/s}}.$$

$$\theta = \tan^{-1}\left[\frac{(3000\ \text{kg})(16.67\ \text{m/s})}{(1500\ \text{kg})(25.0\ \text{m/s})}\right] = \boxed{53.1°\ \text{south of east}}.$$

74. The balls have the same mass. Apply momentum conservation $\mathbf{P}_o = \mathbf{P}$.

in x: $m(0.750\ \text{m/s}) + m(0) = m(0.250\ \text{m/s}) \cos 37° + m\,v_x'$,

so $v_x' = 0.550\ \text{m/s}$;

in y: $m(0) + m(0) = m(0.250\ \text{m/s}) \sin 37° + m\,v_y'$,

so $v_y' = -0.150\ \text{m/s}$.

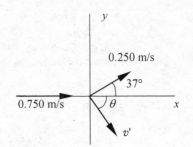

Therefore $\theta = \tan^{-1}\left(\dfrac{0.150}{0.550}\right) = \boxed{15°}.$

$$v' = \sqrt{(0.550\ \text{m/s})^2 + (0.150\ \text{m/s})^2} = \boxed{0.57\ \text{m/s}}.$$

75. Apply momentum conservation $\mathbf{P}_o = \mathbf{P}$.

in x: $P_{xo} = 0$,

$P_x = (0.25\ \text{kg})(4.0\ \text{m/s}) + (0.20\ \text{kg})(6.0\ \text{m/s}) \cos 120° + (0.33\ \text{kg})(2.5\ \text{m/s}) \cos 230° = -0.13\ \text{kg·m/s}$,

in y: $P_{yo} = 0$,

$P_y = (0.25\ \text{kg})(0) + (0.20\ \text{kg})(6.0\ \text{m/s}) \sin 120° + (0.33\ \text{kg})(2.5\ \text{m/s}) \sin 230° = 0.41\ \text{kg·m/s}$.

So $P_o \neq P$.   Therefore, the answer is $\boxed{\text{no}}$.

Now in x: $0 = (0.25\ \text{kg})(4.0\ \text{m/s}) + (0.20\ \text{kg})(6.0\ \text{m/s}) \cos 120° + p_x$,   ☞ $p_x = -0.40\ \text{kg·m/s}$.

in y: $0 = (0.25\ \text{kg})(0) + (0.20\ \text{kg})(6.0\ \text{m/s}) \sin 120° + p_y$,   ☞ $p_y = -1.04\ \text{kg·m/s}$.

So $p = \sqrt{(0.40\ \text{kg·m/s})^2 + (1.04\ \text{kg·m/s})^2} = \boxed{1.1\ \text{kg·m/s}}$,

$$\theta = \tan^{-1}\left(\frac{1.04}{0.40}\right) = 69°\ \text{below}\ x\ \text{axis or}\ \boxed{249°}.$$

76. Since the cars are identical, $m_1 = m_2 = m$.   From momentum conservation $\mathbf{P}_o = \mathbf{P}$:

$$m(v_o) + m(0) = (m + m)v = 2mv, \quad ☞ \quad v = \frac{v_o}{2}. \quad K_o = \tfrac{1}{2}m\,v_o^2 \quad \text{and} \quad K = \tfrac{1}{2}(2m)\left(\frac{v_o}{2}\right)^2 = \tfrac{1}{4}m v_o^2.$$

So the fraction of kinetic energy lost is $\dfrac{|\Delta K|}{K_o} = \dfrac{K_o - K}{K_o} = 1 - \dfrac{K}{K_o} = 1 - \dfrac{1}{2} = \boxed{50\%}$.

77.   (a) Since $v_1 = \dfrac{m_1 - m_2}{m_1 + m_2} v_{1o}$ and $\dfrac{v_1}{v_{1o}} = -\frac{1}{3}$ ("recoils").

we have $-\frac{1}{3} = \dfrac{m_1 - m_2}{m_1 + m_2} = \dfrac{m_1/m_2 - 1}{m_1/m_2 + 1}$,   or $\dfrac{m_1}{m_2} + 1 = -3 \dfrac{m_1}{m_2} + 3$.

So $\dfrac{m_1}{m_2} = \boxed{\frac{1}{2}}$.

(b) $v_2 = \dfrac{2m_1}{m_1 + m_2} v_{1o} = \dfrac{2m_1/m_2}{m_1/m_2 + 1} v_{1o} = \dfrac{2 \times \frac{1}{2}}{\frac{1}{2} + 1} = \boxed{\frac{2}{3} v_{1o}}$.

78.   From momentum conservation $\mathbf{P}_o = \mathbf{P}$: $m v_o + M(0) = (m + M)v$,   ☞ $v = \dfrac{m v_o}{m + M}$.

$K_o = \frac{1}{2} m_1 v_o^2$ and $K = \frac{1}{2}(m + M)v^2 = \frac{1}{2}(m + M)\left(\dfrac{m_1 v_o}{m + M}\right)^2 = \frac{1}{2}\dfrac{(m v_o)^2}{m + M}$.

The fraction of kinetic energy lost is

$\dfrac{|\Delta K|}{K_o} = \dfrac{K_o - K}{K_o} = 1 - \dfrac{K}{K_o} = 1 - \dfrac{\frac{1}{2}\dfrac{(m v_o)^2}{m + M}}{\frac{1}{2} m v_o^2} = 1 - \dfrac{m}{m + M} = \dfrac{M}{m + M}$.

79.   (a) From the result of Exercise 6.78,

$v = \dfrac{m v_o}{m + M} = \dfrac{0.010 \text{ kg}}{0.010 \text{ kg} + 0.890 \text{ kg}} v_o = \boxed{\dfrac{v_o}{90}}$.

(b) From energy conservation: $v = \sqrt{2gh} = \sqrt{2(9.80 \text{ m/s}^2)(0.40 \text{ m})} = 2.8$ m/s.

So $v_o = 90v = \boxed{2.5 \times 10^2 \text{ m/s}}$.

(c) From the result of Exercise 6.78, the fraction of kinetic energy lost is

$\dfrac{M}{m + M} = \dfrac{0.890 \text{ kg}}{0.010 \text{ kg} + 0.890 \text{ kg}} = \boxed{99\%}$.

80. $m_1 = m_2 = m$.   Apply momentum conservation $\mathbf{P}_o = \mathbf{P}$:

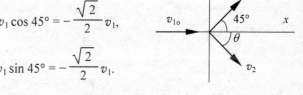

in x: $mv_{1o} + m(0) = mv_1 \cos 45° + mv_{2x}$, so $v_{2x} = -v_1 \cos 45° = -\dfrac{\sqrt{2}}{2} v_1$,

in y: $m(0) + m(0) = mv_1 \sin 45° + mv_{2y}$, so $v_{2y} = -v_1 \sin 45° = -\dfrac{\sqrt{2}}{2} v_1$.

Therefore $v_2 = \sqrt{\left(\dfrac{\sqrt{2}}{2} v_1\right)^2 + \left(\dfrac{\sqrt{2}}{2} v_1\right)^2} = \sqrt{v_1^2(\cos^2 45° + \sin^2 45°)} = \sqrt{v_1^2(1)} = v_1$,

where we used $\sin^2 x + \cos^2 x = 1$.

Since $v_{2x} = v_{2y}$, $\theta = \tan^{-1}(1) = 45°$, the angle between v_1 and v_2 is $45° + 45° = 90°$.

81. (a) From momentum conservation $\mathbf{P_o} = \mathbf{P}$: $m_1 v_{1o} + m_2 v_{2o} = m_1 v_1 + m_2 v_2$,

   or $m_1(v_{1o} - v_1) = m_2(v_2 - v_{2o})$.   Eq. (1)

   From kinetic energy conservation: $\frac{1}{2} m_1 v_{1o}^2 + \frac{1}{2} m_1 v_{2o}^2 = \frac{1}{2} m_1 v_1^2 + \frac{1}{2} m_1 v_2^2$,

   or $m_1(v_{1o}^2 - v_1^2) = m_2(v_2^2 - v_{2o}^2)$, i.e., $m_1(v_{1o} + v_1)(v_{1o} - v_1) = m_2(v_2 - v_{2o})(v_2 + v_{2o})$.   Eq. (2)

   Dividing Eq. (2) by Eq. (1) gives $v_{1o} + v_1 = v_2 + v_{2o}$, so $v_2 - v_1 = -(v_{2o} - v_{1o})$.

   (b) $e = -\dfrac{v_2 - v_1}{v_{2o} - v_{1o}}$.

   For elastic collision, $v_2 - v_1 = -(v_{2o} - v_{1o})$ as in part (a), so $e_{\text{elastic}} = \boxed{1.0}$.

   For completely inelastic collision, $v_1 = v_2$, so $e_{\text{inelastic}} = \boxed{0}$.

82. The steel plate is more massive so its velocities before and after the impact are essentially zero.

   So $e = -\dfrac{v_2 - v_1}{v_{2o} - v_{1o}} = -\dfrac{v_1}{v_{1o}} = 0.95$, or $v_1 = -0.95\, v_{1o}$.

   From energy conservation: $v = \sqrt{2gh}$, or $h = \dfrac{v^2}{2g}$.

   So $\dfrac{h_1}{h_o} = \dfrac{v_1^2}{v_{1o}^2} = (0.95)^2 = 0.90$. Therefore $\boxed{h_1 = 0.90 h_o}$.

83. (d).

84. This pole will $\boxed{\text{lower the center of mass}}$ of the walker-pole system. The pole will also increase the moment of inertia of the system, and with a torque that rotates around the rope, the angular acceleration is smaller, giving the walker more time to recover.

85. The flamingo's center of mass is $\boxed{\text{directly above the foot on the ground}}$ for it to be in equilibrium.

86. In the center of mass reference frame, there is no net force acting on the rocket-spacecraft system, so the momentum of the system is zero. Therefore the $\boxed{\text{CM does not move}}$.

87. (a) $X_{\text{CM}} = \dfrac{\Sigma_i m_i x_i}{M} = \dfrac{(0.10 \text{ kg})(0) + (0.10 \text{ kg}) x_2}{0.10 \text{ kg} + 0.10 \text{ kg}} = 0$, ☞ $x_2 = \boxed{0}$.

   $Y_{\text{CM}} = \dfrac{(0.10 \text{ kg})(0.45 \text{ m}) + (0.10 \text{ kg}) y_2}{0.10 \text{ kg} + 0.10 \text{ kg}} = 0$, ☞ $y_2 = \boxed{-0.45 \text{ m}}$.

   (b) $\boxed{\text{No}}$, only that they are $\boxed{\text{equidistant from CM}}$ due to the equal masses of the particles.

88.   Choose the less massive mass as the origin ($x = 0$).

$$X_{CM} = \frac{\Sigma_i m_i x_i}{M} = \frac{(4.0 \text{ kg})(0) + (7.5 \text{ kg})(1.5 \text{ m})}{4.0 \text{ kg} + 7.5 \text{ kg}} = \boxed{0.98 \text{ m from the less massive sphere}}.$$

89.   (a) $X_{CM} = \dfrac{\Sigma_i m_i x_i}{M} = \dfrac{(6.0 \times 10^{24} \text{ kg})(0) + (6.4 \times 10^{22} \text{ kg})(3.8 \times 10^8 \text{ m})}{6.0 \times 10^{24} \text{ kg} + 7.4 \times 10^{22} \text{ kg}}$

$= \boxed{4.6 \times 10^6 \text{ m from the center of the Earth}}.$

(b) From the surface of the Earth, it is at

$4.6 \times 10^6 \text{ m} - r_e = 4.6 \times 10^6 \text{ m} - 7.37 \times 10^6 \text{ m} = -1.8 \times 10^6 \text{ m}$,

i.e., $\boxed{1.8 \times 10^6 \text{ m below the surface of the Earth}}$.

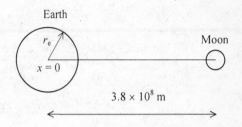

90. $X_{CM} = \dfrac{\Sigma_i m_i x_i}{M} =$

$\dfrac{(3.0 \text{ kg})(-6.0 \text{ m/s}) + (2.0 \text{ kg})(1.0 \text{ m}) + (4.0 \text{ kg})(3.0 \text{ m})}{3.0 \text{ kg} + 2.0 \text{ kg} + 4.0 \text{ kg}} = -0.44 \text{ m},$

$Y_{CM} = 0.$ So the CM is at $\boxed{(-0.44 \text{ m}, 0)}$.

91.   Here are some useful data from Exercise 6.58.

The range of the projectile (center of mass) is $x = 55.23$ m. So the top of the trajectory will have a horizontal distance equal to half the range at $(55.23 \text{ m})/2 = 27.62$ m.

The center of mass should "land" at the $x = 55.23$ m point.

$X_{CM} = \dfrac{\Sigma_i m_i x_i}{M},$ so $55.23 \text{ m} = \dfrac{m(27.62 \text{ m}) + m(x')}{m + m}.$ Therefore $x' = \boxed{82.8 \text{ m}}.$

92.   (a) The center of mass of the system will be $\boxed{\text{near the 6.0-kg mass}}$ because it is the more massive one of the two masses. The center of mass will be "weighted" to the more massive side.

(b) Choose the 4.0-kg mass as the origin ($x = 0$). The center of mass of the rod is then at 2.5 m.

$$X_{CM} = \frac{\Sigma_i m_i x_i}{M} = \frac{(4.0 \text{ kg})(0) + (3.0 \text{ kg})(2.5 \text{ m}) + (6.0 \text{ kg})(5.0 \text{ m})}{4.0 \text{ kg} + 3.0 \text{ kg} + 6.0 \text{ kg}} = \boxed{2.9 \text{ m from the 4.0-kg mass}}.$$

93.   The CM of both the square sheet and the circle are at the center of the square.

So from symmetry, the CM of the remaining portion is still $\boxed{\text{at center of sheet.}}$.

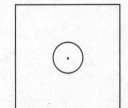

94. (a) The system is symmetrical about the geometrical center of the system, so the CM is at the center of the system, or $\boxed{(2.0 \text{ m}, 2.0 \text{ m})}$.

(b) Again, it is symmetrical about the center. It is still at $\boxed{(2.0 \text{ m}, 2.0 \text{ m})}$.

(c) $X_{CM} = \dfrac{\Sigma_i m_i x_i}{M} = \dfrac{(1.0 \text{ kg})(0) + (2.0 \text{ kg})(0) + (3.0 \text{ kg})(4.0 \text{ m}) + (4.0 \text{ kg})(4.0 \text{ m})}{1.0 \text{ kg} + 2.0 \text{ kg} + 3.0 \text{ kg} + 4.0 \text{ kg}} = 2.8 \text{ m}$,

$Y_{CM} = \dfrac{(1.0 \text{ kg})(0) + (2.0 \text{ kg})(4.0 \text{ m}) + (3.0 \text{ kg})(4.0 \text{ m}) + (4.0 \text{ kg})(0)}{1.0 \text{ kg} + 2.0 \text{ kg} + 3.0 \text{ kg} + 4.0 \text{ kg}} = 2.0 \text{ m}$.

So the CM is at $\boxed{(2.8 \text{ m}, 2.0 \text{ m})}$.

95. $X_{CM1} = \dfrac{\Sigma_i m_i x_i}{M} = \dfrac{m_1 x_1 + m_2 x_2 + m_3 x_3}{m_1 + m_2 + m_3}$ and $X_{CM2} = \dfrac{m_4 x_4 + m_5 x_5}{m_4 + m_5}$.

$X_{CM} = \dfrac{m_1 x_1 + m_2 x_2 + m_3 x_3 + m_4 x_4 + m_5 x_5}{m_1 + m_2 + m_3 + m_4 + m_5}$.

So generally $X_{CM} \neq X_{CM1} + X_{CM2}$.

However if $m_1 = m_2 = m_3 = m_4 = m_5$, then $X_{CM} = X_{CM1} + X_{CM2}$.

96. Due to the lack of external force, the CM is stationary and is located where they meet.

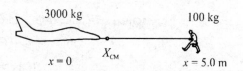

$X_{CM} = \dfrac{\Sigma_i m_i x_i}{M} = \dfrac{(3000 \text{ kg})(0) + (100 \text{ kg})(5.0 \text{ m})}{3000 \text{ kg} + 100 \text{ kg}}$

$= \boxed{0.16 \text{ m from capsule's original position}}$.

97. (a) Due to the lack of external force, the CM is stationary located where they meet.

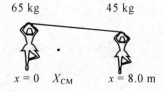

$X_{CM} = \dfrac{\Sigma_i m_i x_i}{M} = \dfrac{(65 \text{ kg})(0) + (45 \text{ kg})(8.0 \text{ m})}{65 \text{ kg} + 45 \text{ kg}} = 3.3 \text{ m}$.

So $\boxed{\text{the 65 kg travels 3.3 m and the 45 kg travels 4.7 m}}$.

(b) Still there is no external force; they travel the $\boxed{\text{same distances}}$ as in part (a).

98. $M = 3(0.25 \text{ kg}) = 0.75 \text{ kg}$. $\mathbf{F}_{net} = -(3.0 \text{ N}) \hat{\mathbf{y}} + (5.0 \text{ N}) \hat{\mathbf{y}} + (4.0 \text{ N}) \hat{\mathbf{x}} = (4.0 \text{ N}) \hat{\mathbf{x}} + (2.0 \text{ N}) \hat{\mathbf{y}}$,

so $\mathbf{A}_{CM} = \dfrac{\mathbf{F}_{net}}{M} = \dfrac{(4.0 \text{ N}) \hat{\mathbf{x}} + (2.0 \text{ N}) \hat{\mathbf{y}}}{0.75 \text{ kg}} = \boxed{(5.3 \text{ m/s}^2) \hat{\mathbf{x}} + (2.7 \text{ m/s}^2) \hat{\mathbf{y}}}$.

Or $A = \sqrt{(5.3 \text{ m/s})^2 + (2.7 \text{ m/s})^2} = \boxed{5.9 \text{ m/s}}$, $\theta = \tan^{-1}\left(\dfrac{2.7}{5.3}\right) = \boxed{27° \text{ above } +x \text{ axis}}$.

99.   (a) $\boxed{\text{No}}$, only if masses are the same.

   (b) $\boxed{\text{In the same direction}}$.

100.   First, calculate the velocity of both objects right after the collision from momentum conservation.

   $(1.0 \text{ kg})(10 \text{ m/s}) + (2.0 \text{ kg})(0) = (1.0 \text{ kg} + 2.0 \text{ kg})v$, ☞ $v = 3.33 \text{ m/s}$.

   From the conservation of energy, $\frac{1}{2} m(3.33 \text{ m/s})^2 = m(9.80 \text{ m/s}^2)h$, ☞ $h = 0.566 \text{ m}$.

   So $x = \dfrac{0.566 \text{ m}}{\sin 37°} = \boxed{0.94 \text{ m}}$.

101.   First find the velocity of the combination (truck and car) right after collision.

   $m_1 = 1500 \text{ kg}$, $m_2 = 1200 \text{ kg}$, $v_{1o} = 25 \text{ m/s}$, $v_{2o} = 0 \text{ m/s}$, $v_1 = v_2 = v = ?$

   $\mathbf{P_o = P}$, ☞ $m_1 v_{1o} + m_2 v_{2o} = m_1 v_1 + m_2 v_2 = (m_1 + m_2)v$.

   So $v = \dfrac{m_1 v_{1o} + m_2 v_{2o}}{m_1 + m_2} = \dfrac{(1500 \text{ kg})(25 \text{ m/s}) + (0)}{1500 \text{ kg} + 1200 \text{ kg}} = 13.9 \text{ m/s}$.

   $K_o = \frac{1}{2}(1500 \text{ kg})(25 \text{ m/s})^2 + \frac{1}{2}(1200 \text{ kg})(0)^2 = 4.69 \times 10^5 \text{ J}$;

   $K = \frac{1}{2}(1500 \text{ kg})(13.9 \text{ m/s})^2 + \frac{1}{2}(1200 \text{ kg})(13.9 \text{ m/s})^2 = 2.61 \times 10^5 \text{ J}$.

   The kinetic energy lost is $K_o - K = \boxed{2.1 \times 10^5 \text{ J}}$.

102.   (a) $p_x = p_y = (0.50 \text{ kg})(3.3 \text{ m/s}) = 1.65 \text{ kg·m/s}$.

   $p = \sqrt{(1.65 \text{ kg·m/s})^2 + (1.65 \text{ kg·m/s})^2} = \boxed{2.3 \text{ kg·m/s}}$,

   $\theta = \tan^{-1}\left(\dfrac{1.65}{1.65}\right) = \boxed{45° \text{ below the } -x \text{ axis}}$.

   (b) $\boxed{\text{No; the same as in (a)}}$. A collision does not have to occur; momentum would be the same.

103.   From momentum conservation $P_o = P$ (note $m_1 = m_2 = m$):

   $m_1 v_{1o} + m_2 v_{2o} = m_1 v_1 + m_2 v_2$, so $v_1 + v_2 = v_{1o} + v_{2o}$;   Eq. (1)

   also from the result of Exercise 6.81(a) $v_2 - v_1 = -(v_{2o} - v_{1o})$.   Eq. (2)

   Eq. (1) + Eq. (2) gives $2v_2 = 2v_{1o}$, so $v_2 = v_{1o} = 2.0 \text{ m/s}$

   and $v_1 = v_{1o} + v_{2o} - v_2 = 2.0 \text{ m/s} + (-2.0 \text{ m/s}) - 2.0 \text{ m/s} = -2.0 \text{ m/s}$,

   where $v_{2o} = -2.0 \text{ m/s}$ is because the balls are "approaching each other."

   Therefore, the speeds are $\boxed{v_1 = v_2 = 2.0 \text{ m/s}}$.

104.   (a) 90 km/h = 25 m/s.

$$p_o = mv = (2400 \text{ kg})(25 \text{ m/s}) = \boxed{6.0 \times 10^4 \text{ kg·m/s}}.$$

(b) $\bar{F}\Delta t = \Delta p = 0 - p_o,$ ☞ $\bar{F} = -\dfrac{p_o}{\Delta t} = -\dfrac{6.0 \times 10^4 \text{ kg·m/s}}{8.0 \text{ s}} = -\boxed{7.5 \times 10^3 \text{ N}}.$

105.   (a) Apply momentum conservation $\mathbf{P}_o = \mathbf{P}$

in x: $\dfrac{7500 \text{ N}}{g}(60 \text{ km/h}) + \dfrac{15\,000 \text{ N}}{g}(0) = \dfrac{7500 \text{ N}}{g}v_x + \dfrac{15\,000 \text{ N}}{g}v_x,$

so $v_x = 20$ km/h.

in y: $\dfrac{7500 \text{ N}}{g}(0) + \dfrac{15\,000 \text{ N}}{g}(45 \text{ km/h}) = \dfrac{7500 \text{ N}}{g}v_y + \dfrac{15\,000 \text{ N}}{g}v_y,$

so $v_y = 30$ km/h.

Therefore $v = \sqrt{(20 \text{ km/h})^2 + (30 \text{ km/h})^2} = \boxed{36 \text{ km/h}},$

$$\theta = \tan^{-1}\left(\frac{30}{20}\right) = \boxed{56° \text{ north of east}}.$$

(b) The percentage of kinetic energy lost is

$$\frac{|\Delta K|}{K_o} = \frac{K_o - K}{K_o} = 1 - \frac{K}{K_o} \propto 1 - \frac{\frac{1}{2}(7500 + 15\,000)(36)^2}{\frac{1}{2}(7500)(60)^2 + \frac{1}{2}(15\,000)(45)^2} = 1 - 0.51 = \boxed{49\%}.$$

Note the proportional sign ∝ in the calculation.

106.   (a) The stunt man has zero horizontal velocity before he jumps onto the sled.

Apply momentum conservation $P_o = P$ in the horizontal direction.

$(75 \text{ kg})(0) + (50 \text{ kg})(10 \text{ m/s}) = (75 \text{ kg} + 50 \text{ kg})v = (125 \text{ kg})v,$ ☞ $v = \boxed{4.0 \text{ m/s}}.$

(b) The stunt man's momentum is still conserved, so he continues to move with a speed of $\boxed{4.0 \text{ m/s}}.$

107.   (a) This is an $\boxed{\text{inelastic}}$ collision because the snowball sticks there.

(b) $\bar{F}\Delta t = mv - mv_o = -mv_o = 0 - (0.15 \text{ kg})(14 \text{ m/s}) = -\boxed{2.1 \text{ N·s}}.$

(c) $\bar{F} = \dfrac{-2.1 \text{ N·s}}{0.10 \text{ s}} = -\boxed{21 \text{ N}}.$

108.   (a) The blocks stick together after collision for a completely inelastic collision.

From momentum conservation $\mathbf{P}_o = \mathbf{P}$: $m_1 v_{1o} + m_2 v_{2o} = m_1 v_1 + m_2 v_2,$

so $(2.5 \text{ kg})(6.0 \text{ m/s}) + (6.5 \text{ kg})(0) = (2.5 \text{ kg} + 6.5 \text{ kg})v,$ ☞ $v = \boxed{1.7 \text{ m/s}}.$

(b) $K_o = \frac{1}{2}mv^2 = \frac{1}{2}(2.5 \text{ kg})(6.0 \text{ m/s})^2 + 0 = 45 \text{ J}$,

$K = \frac{1}{2}(2.5 \text{ kg} + 6.5 \text{ kg})(1.67 \text{ m/s})^2 = 12.6 \text{ J}$.

So the mechanical energy lost is $45 \text{ J} - 12.6 \text{ J} = \boxed{32 \text{ J}}$.

109.   (a) First find the recoil velocity of the astronaut from momentum conservation $\mathbf{P}_o = \mathbf{P}$.

$m_1 v_{1o} + m_2 v_{2o} = m_1 v_1 + m_2 v_2$, ☞ $(0.50 \text{ kg})(0) + (90 \text{ kg})(0) = (0.50 \text{ kg})(4.0 \text{ m/s}) + (90 \text{ kg})v$,

so $v = -0.0222 \text{ m/s}$.   Therefore it takes him $\dfrac{6.0 \text{ m}}{0.0222 \text{ m/s}} = 2.7 \times 10^2 \text{ s} = 4.5 \text{ min}$.

So the answer is $\boxed{\text{no}}$, he does not get back in time.

(b) The recoil velocity of the astronaut must be $v = -\dfrac{6.0 \text{ m}}{4.0(60 \text{ s})} = -0.025 \text{ m/s}$.

So $(0.50 \text{ kg})(0) + (90 \text{ kg})(0) = (0.50 \text{ kg})(v') + (90 \text{ kg})(-0.025 \text{ m/s})$.   Therefore $v' = \boxed{4.5 \text{ m/s}}$.

110.   (a) $v_1 = \dfrac{m_1 - m_2}{m_1 + m_2} v_{1o} = \dfrac{m - 12m}{m + 12m} v_{1o} = \frac{11}{13} v_{1o}$.

So the fraction of kinetic energy lost is

$\dfrac{|\Delta K|}{K_o} = \dfrac{K_o - K}{K_o} = 1 - \dfrac{K}{K_o} = 1 - \dfrac{\frac{1}{2}m\left(\frac{11}{13}\right)^2 v_{1o}^2}{\frac{1}{2}mv_{1o}^2} = 0.28 = \boxed{28\%}$.

(b) $v_1 = \frac{11}{13}(1.5 \times 10^7 \text{ m/s}) = \boxed{1.3 \times 10^7 \text{ m/s}}$.

111.   First, from energy conservation find the velocity of the athlete right after leaving.

$v_o = \sqrt{2gh} = \sqrt{2(9.80 \text{ m/s}^2)(2.25 \text{ m})} = 6.64 \text{ m/s}$.

Now from momentum conservation $\mathbf{P}_o = \mathbf{P}$: $m_1 v_{1o} + m_2 v_{2o} = m_1 v_1 + m_2 v_2$,

$(70 \text{ kg})(0) + (6.0 \times 10^{24} \text{ kg})(0) = (70 \text{ kg})(6.64 \text{ m/s}) + (6.0 \times 10^{24} \text{ kg})v$,

so $v = -\boxed{7.7 \times 10^{-23} \text{ m/s}}$.

112.   If the triangle is suspended at one corner, the CM will be on a line
perpendicular to the base and through the corner. If the triangle is
suspended at a second corner, the CM will be where the two lines cross
(see diagram).

From symmetry $Y_{CM} = 15 \text{ cm}$, and $X_{CM} = (15 \text{ cm})\tan 30° = 8.7 \text{ cm}$.

Thus the CM is at $\boxed{(8.7 \text{ cm}, 15 \text{ cm})}$.

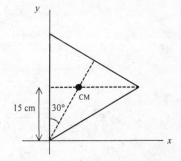

CHAPTER 7

CIRCULAR MOTION AND GRAVITATION

1.   (c).

2.   (c).

3.   No , points at different radius travel different distances.

   Yes , all points travel the same angular distance (angle).

4. $r = \sqrt{(1.5\text{ m})^2 + (2.0\text{ m})^2} = \boxed{2.5\text{ m}}, \quad \theta = \tan^{-1}\left(\dfrac{2.0}{1.5}\right) = \boxed{53°}.$

5. $x = r\cos\theta = (5.3\text{ m})\cos 32° = \boxed{4.5\text{ m}}.$ $y = r\sin\theta = (5.3\text{ m})\sin 32° = \boxed{2.8\text{ m}}.$

6. $r^2 = x^2 + y^2$, so the equation of a circle is $\boxed{r = a}$.

7.   (a) $(15°) \times \dfrac{\pi\text{ rad}}{180°} = \boxed{0.26\text{ rad}}.$ (b) $(45°) \times \dfrac{\pi\text{ rad}}{180°} = \boxed{0.79\text{ rad}}.$

   (c) $(90°) \times \dfrac{\pi\text{ rad}}{180°} = \boxed{1.6\text{ rad}}.$ (d) $(120°) \times \dfrac{\pi\text{ rad}}{180°} = \boxed{2.1\text{ rad}}.$

8.   (a) $(\pi/6\text{ rad}) \times \dfrac{180°}{\pi\text{ rad}} = \boxed{30°}.$ (b) $(5\pi/12\text{ rad}) \times \dfrac{180°}{\pi\text{ rad}} = \boxed{75°}.$

   (c) $(3\pi/4\text{ rad}) \times \dfrac{180°}{\pi\text{ rad}} = \boxed{135°}.$ (d) $(\pi\text{ rad}) \times \dfrac{180°}{\pi\text{ rad}} = \boxed{180°}.$

9. $s = r\theta = (1.5 \times 10^{11}\text{ m})(0.535°) \times \dfrac{\pi\text{ rad}}{180°} = \boxed{1.4 \times 10^9\text{ m}}.$

10. $s = r\theta, \quad \Rightarrow \quad r = \dfrac{s}{\theta} = \dfrac{5.0\text{ m}}{2.0°(\pi\text{ rad}/180°)} = \boxed{1.4 \times 10^2\text{ m}}.$

11.   (a) $\theta = \dfrac{s}{r} = \dfrac{1.00 \times 10^3\text{ m}}{0.250 \times 10^3\text{ m}} = \boxed{4.00\text{ rad}}.$

   (b) $(4.00\text{ rad}) \times \dfrac{180°}{\pi\text{ rad}} = \boxed{229°}.$

12.   In 3 months, the Earth travels $\frac{3}{12} = \frac{1}{4}$ of a circle or $\frac{1}{4} \times (2\pi \text{ rad}) = \frac{\pi}{2}$ rad.

So $s = r\theta = (1.5 \times 10^8 \text{ km}) \times \frac{\pi \text{ rad}}{2} = \boxed{2.4 \times 10^8 \text{ km}}$.

13.   (a) For a full circle $\frac{2\pi r}{2\pi \text{ rad}} = \frac{2\pi r}{360°}$,   so 2π rad = 360°,

or $\frac{2\pi \text{ rad}}{2\pi} = \frac{360°}{2\pi}$,   i.e., $\boxed{1 \text{ rad} = 57.3°}$.

(b) As in part (a), $\boxed{2\pi \text{ rad} = 360°}$.

14.   In 30 minutes, the hour hand travels $\pi/12$ rad, the minute hand π rad, and the second hand $30(2\pi) = 60\pi$ rad.

Hour hand: $s = r\theta = (0.25 \text{ m})(\pi/12 \text{ rad}) = \boxed{0.065 \text{ m}}$.

Minute hand: $s = (0.30 \text{ m})(\pi \text{ rad}) = \boxed{0.94 \text{ m}}$.

Second hand: $s = (0.35 \text{ m})(60\pi \text{ rad}) = \boxed{66 \text{ m}}$.

15. $\theta = \frac{s}{r} = \frac{(3.00 \text{ mi})(1600 \text{ m/mi})}{0.450 \times 10^3 \text{ m}} = \boxed{10.7 \text{ rad}}$.

16.   The circumference is $c = \pi d = \pi(12 \text{ in.})(00254 \text{ m/1 in.}) = 0.958 \text{ m}$.

So the arc length for each piece is $s = \frac{0958 \text{ m}}{5} = \boxed{0.19 \text{ m arc length}}$.

Or the angular width of each piece is $\theta = \frac{360°}{5} = \boxed{72°}$.

17.   (a) $\theta = \frac{s}{r} = \frac{3500 \text{ km}}{3.8 \times 10^5 \text{ km}} = \boxed{9.2 \times 10^{-3} \text{ rad} = 0.53°}$.

(b) $\theta = \frac{2(6.4 \times 10^3 \text{ km})}{3.8 \times 10^5 \text{ km}} = \boxed{3.4 \times 10^{-2} \text{ rad} = 1.9°}$.

18.   (a) $151° - 22° = \boxed{129°}$.

(b) $s = r\theta = (6.4 \times 10^3 \text{ km})(129°) \times \frac{\pi \text{ rad}}{180°} = \boxed{1.4 \times 10^4 \text{ km}}$.

19.   (a) When $s = r$, $\theta = s/r = 1$ rad $= 57.3°$. This cannot be divided into an integer by 360°. The answer is $\boxed{\text{no}}$.

(b) $2\pi = 6.28$ rad. So we can cut $\boxed{6 \text{ such pieces and one 0.28 rad piece}}$.

20.   (a) The number of turns of wire that can be wound on the spool is

$\dfrac{24 \text{ cm}}{0.75 \text{ cm}} = 32$ turns. So $\theta = (2\pi \text{ rad/turn})(32 \text{ turns}) = \boxed{2.0 \times 10^2 \text{ rad}}$.

(b) The radius at the center of the wire is $R = 0.30 \text{ m} + 0.0075 \text{ m}/2 = 0.30375 \text{ m}$.

$s = R\theta = (0.30375 \text{ m})(2.0 \times 10^2 \text{ rad}) = \boxed{61 \text{ m}}$.

21.   (b).

22.   (d).

23. $\boxed{\text{Yes}}$, they all sweep through the same angle. $\boxed{\text{No}}$, they do not have the same tangential speed because the distances to the center of the wheel are different.

24. $\boxed{\text{Viewing from opposite sides would give different circular senses}}$, i.e., make clockwise counterclockwise and vice versa.

25.   The $\boxed{\text{point farthest from the center}}$ has the greatest tangential speed and $\boxed{\text{the point closest to the center}}$ has the smallest tangential speed, because the tangential speed is directly proportional to the radius. The angular speeds are $\boxed{\text{all the same}}$ for all points.

26. $200 \text{ rpm} = (200 \text{ rev/min}) \times \dfrac{2\pi \text{ rad}}{1 \text{ rev}} \times \dfrac{1 \text{ min}}{60 \text{ s}} = \boxed{21 \text{ rad/s}}$.

$500 \text{ rpm} = (500 \text{ rev/min}) \times \dfrac{2\pi \text{ rad}}{1 \text{ rev}} \times \dfrac{1 \text{ min}}{60 \text{ s}} = \boxed{52 \text{ rad/s}}$

27. $f = \dfrac{1}{T} = \dfrac{1}{(10 \text{ h})/(24 \text{ h/d})} = \boxed{2.4 \text{ rev/d}}$.

28. $\omega = \dfrac{\Delta\theta}{\Delta t} = \dfrac{2.5(2\pi \text{ rad})}{(3.0 \text{ min})(60 \text{ s/min})} = \boxed{0.087 \text{ rad/s}}$.

29. $\omega = \dfrac{\Delta\theta}{\Delta t}$, ☞ $\Delta t = \dfrac{\Delta\theta}{\omega} = \dfrac{2\pi \text{ rad}}{3.5 \text{ rad/s}} = \boxed{1.8 \text{ s}}$.

30.   (a) $f = 12\,000 \text{ rev/min}$,   so $T = \dfrac{1}{f} = \dfrac{1}{12\,000 \text{ rev/min}} = 8.33 \times 10^{-5} \text{ min} = 5.0 \times 10^{-3} \text{ s} = \boxed{5.0 \text{ ms}}$.

(b) $T = \dfrac{1}{10\,000 \text{ rev/min}} = 1.0 \times 10^{-4} \text{ min} = \boxed{6.0 \text{ ms}}$.

31. $\omega_A = \dfrac{\Delta\theta}{\Delta t} = \dfrac{(160°)(\pi \text{ rad}/180°)}{2.00 \text{ s}} = 1.40 \text{ rad/s}, \quad \omega_B = \dfrac{4\pi \text{ rad}}{8.00 \text{ s}} = 1.57 \text{ rad/s}.$

So $\boxed{\text{B has greater angular speed}}$.

32. $\omega = \dfrac{v}{r} = \dfrac{3.0 \text{ m/s}}{0.20 \text{ m}} = 15 \text{ rad/s}.$

$\omega = \dfrac{\Delta\theta}{\Delta t}, \quad \text{☞} \quad \Delta t = \dfrac{\Delta\theta}{\omega} = \dfrac{2\pi \text{ rad}}{15 \text{ rad/s}} = \boxed{0.42 \text{ s}}.$

33. (a) $\omega = \dfrac{\Delta\theta}{\Delta t} = \dfrac{(24 \text{ rev})(2\pi \text{ rad/rev})}{(3.0 \text{ min})(60 \text{ s/min})} = \boxed{0.84 \text{ rad/s}}.$

(b) $v = r\omega, \quad v_4 = (4.0 \text{ m})(0.838 \text{ rad/s}) = \boxed{3.4 \text{ m/s}} \quad \text{and} \quad v_5 = (5.0 \text{ m})(0.838 \text{ rad/s}) = \boxed{4.2 \text{ m/s}}.$

34. (a) $\omega = \dfrac{\Delta\theta}{\Delta t} = \dfrac{(0.5 \text{ rev})(2\pi \text{ rad/rev})}{(1.5 \text{ min})(60 \text{ s/min})} = \boxed{3.5 \times 10^{-2} \text{ rad/s}}.$

(b) $v_t = r\omega = (500 \text{ m})(3.49 \times 10^{-2} \text{ rad/s}) = \boxed{17 \text{ m/s}}.$

35. (a) The $\boxed{\text{rotating angular speed}}$ is greater because the time is less and the angular displacement is the same.

(b) The Earth rotates once a day. $\omega = \dfrac{\Delta\theta}{\Delta t} = \dfrac{2\pi \text{ rad}}{(24)(3600 \text{ s})} = \boxed{7.27 \times 10^{-5} \text{ rad/s}}.$

(c) The Earth revolves the Sun once a year. $\omega = \dfrac{2\pi \text{ rad}}{(365)(24)(3600 \text{ s})} = \boxed{1.99 \times 10^{-7} \text{ rad/s}}.$

36. $15\,000 \text{ rpm} = (15\,000 \text{ rpm}) \times \dfrac{2\pi \text{ rad}}{1 \text{ rev}} \times \dfrac{1 \text{ min}}{60 \text{ s}} = 1.57 \times 10^3 \text{ rad/s}. \quad 1 \text{ rev} = 2\pi \text{ rad}.$

$\bar{\omega} = \dfrac{\Delta\theta}{\Delta t}, \quad \text{☞} \quad \Delta t = \dfrac{\Delta\theta}{\bar{\omega}} = \dfrac{2\pi \text{ rad}}{1.57 \times 10^3 \text{ rad/s}} = \boxed{4.0 \times 10^{-3} \text{ s}}.$

37. (a) $v = r\omega, \quad \text{☞} \quad \omega = \dfrac{v}{r} = \dfrac{15 \text{ m/s}}{(120 \text{ m})/2} = 0.25 \text{ rad/s}.$

$\theta = \omega\Delta t = (0.25 \text{ rad/s})(4.00 \text{ min})(60 \text{ s/min}) = \boxed{60 \text{ rad}}.$

(b) $s = r\theta = \dfrac{120 \text{ m}}{2} \times (60 \text{ rad}) = \boxed{3.6 \times 10^3 \text{ m}}.$

38. (b).

39. (d).

40.   Centripetal force is proportional to the square of the speed. When there is insufficient centripetal force (provided by friction and adhesive forces), the mud cannot maintain the circular path, and it flies off along a tangent.

41.   No , it is not possible. When an object is in uniform circular motion, it always has a nonzero centripetal acceleration and a zero tangential acceleration.

42.   There is insufficient centripetal force (provided by friction and adhesive forces) on the water drops, so the water drops fly out along a tangent and the clothes get dry.

43.   The floats of the little mass will move in direction of acceleration, inward . It works the same way as the accelerometer in Fig. 4.24. No , it does not make a difference since the centripetal acceleration is always inward.

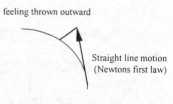

feeling thrown outward

Straight line motion
(Newtons first law)

44.   The inertia of your body has a tendency to keep moving forward along a straight line (Newton's first law), and the car makes a turn by the centripetal force between the tires and the road. So we feel as if we were being "thrown outward."

45.   Centripetal force is required for a car to maintain its circular path. When a car is on a banked turn, the horizontal component of the normal force on the car is pointing toward the center of the circular path. This component will enable the car to negotiate the turn even when there is no friction.

46.   Both are somewhat right but for safety, wearing a safety harness at all times is required. When the roller coaster goes upside-down and maintains certain speed, the weight of the person is used to provide the centripetal acceleration required for the person to maintain the circular motion. So at that moment, not having a safety harness might be OK. But as soon as the coaster is not in that position, the harness is definitely required.

47. $a_c = r\omega^2$,   ☞ $\omega = \sqrt{\dfrac{a_c}{r}} = \sqrt{\dfrac{9.80 \text{ m/s}^2}{(4000 \text{ m})}} = \boxed{0.049 \text{ rad/s or about } 680 \text{ rev/day}}$.

48.   120 km/h = 33.33 m/s. $a_c = \dfrac{v^2}{r} = \dfrac{(33.33 \text{ m/s})^2}{(1.00 \times 10^3 \text{ m})} = \boxed{1.11 \text{ m/s}^2}$.

49. $a_c = \dfrac{v^2}{r}$,　☞　$v = \sqrt{a_c r} = \sqrt{(1.2 \text{ m/s}^2)(1.5 \text{ m})} = \boxed{1.3 \text{ m/s}}$.

50. $a_c = r\omega^2 = (3.80 \times 10^8 \text{ m})\left[\dfrac{2\pi \text{ rad}}{(27.3 \text{ day})(86400 \text{ s/day})}\right]^2 = \boxed{2.69 \times 10^{-3} \text{ m/s}^2}$.

51. $83.0 \text{ km/h} = 23.06 \text{ m/s}$,　$a_c = \dfrac{v^2}{r} = \dfrac{(23.06 \text{ m/s})^2}{0.400 \times 10^3 \text{ m}} = 1.33 \text{ m/s}^2 > 1.25 \text{ m/s}^2$.　$\boxed{\text{No}}$.

52. (a) $\boxed{\text{No}}$, it cannot be exactly horizontal. There must be something upward (a component of the tension) to balance the downward gravitational force.

    (b) $v = \dfrac{d}{t} \dfrac{2\pi r}{t} = \dfrac{2\pi(1.50 \text{ m})}{1.20 \text{ s}} = \boxed{7.85 \text{ m/s}}$.

    (c) $F_c = ma_c = m\dfrac{v^2}{r} = \dfrac{(0.250 \text{ kg})(7.85 \text{ m/s})^2}{1.50 \text{ m}} = \boxed{10.3 \text{ N}}$.

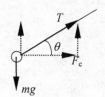

53. $\theta = \sin^{-1}\left(\dfrac{mg}{T}\right) = \sin^{-1}\left[\dfrac{(0.250 \text{ kg})(9.80 \text{ m/s}^2)}{12.5 \text{ N}}\right] = \boxed{11.3°}$.

54. (a) $\boxed{\text{The weight is supplying the centripetal force}}$ to maintain itself in the circular motion. Or it "falls" along a circle now.

    (b) $mg = F_c = m\dfrac{v^2}{r}$,　☞　$v = \sqrt{gr} = \sqrt{(9.80 \text{ m/s}^2)(1.0 \text{ m})} = \boxed{3.1 \text{ m/s}}$.

55. Static friction force provides centripetal force.

    $f_s = \mu_s N = \mu_s mg = F_c = m\dfrac{v^2}{r}$,　☞　$v = \sqrt{\mu_s gr} = \sqrt{0.50(9.80 \text{ m/s}^2)(20 \text{ m})} = \boxed{9.9 \text{ m/s}}$.

56. (a) The normal force is greater $\boxed{\text{when at the bottom}}$ because at that position, the normal force has to provide the upward centripetal force, in addition to supporting the weight of the pilot.

    (b) $700 \text{ km/h} = 194 \text{ m/s}$. At the bottom, the centripetal force is provided by the difference $N - mg$. So $F_c = N - mg = m\dfrac{v^2}{r}$,

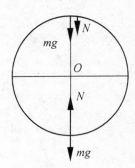

    $N = mg + m\dfrac{v^2}{r} = mg + m\dfrac{(194 \text{ m/s})^2}{2.0 \times 10^3 \text{ m}} = mg + m(18.8 \text{ m/s}^2)$

    $= mg + 1.9mg = \boxed{2.9mg}$.

(b) At the top, the centripetal force is provided by $N + mg$.

$$N = m\frac{v^2}{r} - mg = m\frac{(194 \text{ m/s})^2}{2.0 \times 10^3 \text{ m}} - mg = m(18.8 \text{ m/s}^2) - mg = 1.93mg - mg = \boxed{0.93mg}.$$

57. (a) A normal force by the loop must act on the block to provide extra centripetal force. Minimum speed corresponds to a minimum normal force of zero so the only force on the block is gravity, which is the sole source of centripetal force.   So $F_c = mg = m\dfrac{v^2}{r}$,   ☞ $v = \boxed{\sqrt{rg}}$.

(b) From energy conservation: $mgh + \frac{1}{2}m(0)^2 = + mg(2r) + \frac{1}{2}mv^2$,

so $h = 2r + \frac{1}{2}\dfrac{rg}{g} = \boxed{(5/2)r}$.

58. To clear the gully the truck must travel a minimum horizontal distance of 10.0 m + 4.25 m = 14.25 m. First use kinematics to calculate the velocity of the truck which is a horizontal projectile.

The time of flight is $t = \sqrt{-\dfrac{2y}{g}} = \sqrt{-\dfrac{2(-2.96 \text{ m})}{9.80 \text{ m/s}^2}} = 0.777 \text{ s}$ (from $y = v_o t - \frac{1}{2}gt^2$).

So $v_x = \dfrac{14.25 \text{ m}}{0.777 \text{ s}} = 18.3 \text{ m/s}.$ Therefore $a_c = \dfrac{v^2}{r} = \dfrac{(18.3 \text{ m/s})^2}{333 \text{ m}} = \boxed{1.01 \text{ m/s}^2}.$

59. (a) In the vertical direction: $N\cos\theta - mg = 0$,   ☞ $N = \dfrac{mg}{\cos\theta}.$

In the horizontal direction: $F_c = N\sin\theta = \dfrac{mg}{\cos\theta}\sin\theta = mg\tan\theta = m\dfrac{v^2}{r}$,   so $\tan\theta = \dfrac{v^2}{gr}.$

(b) Since mass is not in the result in part (a), the angle is $\boxed{\text{independent of mass}}$.

(c) If there is friction, it will point along the inclined plane,

so the contribution from friction to centripetal force is $f_s\cos\theta = (\mu_s N)\cos\theta = \mu_s\dfrac{mg}{\cos\theta} = \mu_s mg.$

Therefore $mg\tan\theta + \mu_s mg = m\dfrac{v^2}{r}$,   ☞ $\boxed{\tan\theta = \dfrac{v^2}{gr} - \mu_s}.$

As expected, the angle does not need to be as big as in part (a) when there is friction.

60. (a) The static friction force, which equals the product of the coefficient of static friction and the normal force, between you and the wall provides the upward force to balance your weight. The normal force on you by the wall provides centripetal force and it depends on speed.

(b) $N = F_c = mr\omega^2$.   So $f_s = \mu_s N = \mu_s mr\omega^2 = mg,$

Therefore $\omega = \sqrt{\dfrac{g}{\mu_s r}} = \sqrt{\dfrac{9.80 \text{ m/s}^2}{0.30(2.5 \text{ m})}} = \boxed{3.6 \text{ rad/s}}.$

61.   (d).

62. $\boxed{\text{Yes}}$, a car in circular motion always has centripetal acceleration.

   $\boxed{\text{Yes}}$, it also has angular acceleration as its speed is increasing.

63. $\boxed{\text{No}}$, this is not possible. Any car in traveling on a circular track always has centripetal acceleration. It

   could have angular acceleration if its speed changes.

64.   700 rpm = 73.3 rad/s,   3000 rpm = 314 rad/s.

$$\alpha = \frac{\Delta\omega}{\Delta t} = \frac{314 \text{ rad/s} - 73.3 \text{ rad/s}}{3.0 \text{ s}} = \boxed{80 \text{ rad/s}^2}.$$

65.   Given: $\omega_0 = 0$, $\omega = 2.5$ rpm = 0.262 rad/s, $\theta = 5$ rev = 10π rad.   Find: α.

$$\omega^2 = \omega_0^2 + 2\alpha\theta, \quad \text{☞} \quad \alpha = \frac{\omega^2 - \omega_0^2}{2\theta} = \frac{(0.262 \text{ rad/s})^2 - 0}{2(10\pi \text{ rad})} = \boxed{1.1 \times 10^{-3} \text{ rad/s}^2}.$$

66.   (a) Given: $\omega_0 = 0$, $\omega = 33\text{-}\frac{1}{3}$ rpm = 3.49 rad/s, $t = 2.45$ s.   Find: θ.

$$\theta = \frac{\omega + \omega_0}{2} t = \frac{0 + 3.49 \text{ rad/s}}{2} \times (2.45 \text{ s}) = \boxed{4.28 \text{ rad}}.$$

   (b) $s = r\theta = (6.0 \text{ in})(4.28 \text{ rad}) = 25.7 \text{ in} = \boxed{2.14 \text{ ft}}.$

67.   Given: $\omega_0 = 60$ rpm = 6.28 rad/s, $\omega = 0$, $t = 15$ s.   Find: θ.

$$\theta = \frac{\omega + \omega_0}{2} t = \frac{6.28 \text{ rad/s} + 0}{2} \times (15 \text{ s}) = 47.1 \text{ rad} = \boxed{7.5 \text{ rev}}.$$

68.   (a) Given: $\omega_0 = 0$, $\omega = \dfrac{v}{r} = \dfrac{2.20 \text{ m/s}}{17.5 \text{ m}} = 0.126$ rad/s, $t = 15.0$ s.   Find: α.

$$\alpha = \frac{\omega - \omega_0}{t} = \frac{0.126 \text{ rad/s} - 0}{15.0 \text{ s}} = \boxed{8.40 \times 10^{-3} \text{ rad/s}^2}.$$

   (b) After reaching the constant operating speed, $\alpha = 0$ and so $a_t = r\alpha = \boxed{0}$.

69.   (a) Given: $\omega_0 = 250$ rpm = 26.18 rad/s, $\omega = 350$ rpm = 36.65 rad/s, $t = 5.75$ s.   Find: α.

$$\alpha = \frac{\omega - \omega_0}{t} = \frac{36.65 \text{ rad/s} - 26.18 \text{ rad/s}}{5.75 \text{ s}} = \boxed{1.82 \text{ rad/s}^2}.$$

   (b) $\theta = \dfrac{\omega + \omega_0}{2} t = \dfrac{26.18 \text{ rad/s} + 36.65 \text{ rad/s}}{2} \times (5.75 \text{ s}) = 181 \text{ rad} = \boxed{28.7 \text{ rev}}.$

70. Given: $\omega_0 = 4500$ rpm = 471 rad/s, $\omega = 0$, $t = 5.0$ s. Find: θ.

$\theta = \dfrac{\omega + \omega_0}{2}\, t = \dfrac{471 \text{ rad/s} + 0}{2} \times (5.0 \text{ s}) = 1.18 \times 10^3 \text{ rad} = \boxed{1.9 \times 10^2 \text{ rev}}$.

71. (a) $\boxed{\text{Both}}$ angular and centripetal accelerations. There is always centripetal acceleration for any car in circular motion. When the car increases its speed on a circular track, there is also angular acceleration.

(b) Given: $\omega_0 = 0$, $\alpha = 4.5 \times 10^{-3}$ rad/s^2, $\theta = 1$ rev $= 2\pi$ rad. Find: t.

$\theta = \omega_0 t + \frac{1}{2}\alpha t^2 = 0 + \frac{1}{2}\alpha t^2$, ☞ $t = \sqrt{\dfrac{2\theta}{\alpha}} = \sqrt{\dfrac{2(2\pi \text{ rad})}{4.5 \times 10^{-3} \text{ rad/s}^2}} = \boxed{53 \text{ s}}$.

(c) After half a lap, $\omega^2 = \omega_0^2 + 2\alpha\theta = 0 + 2(4.5 \times 10^{-3} \text{ rad/s}^2)(\pi \text{ rad}) = 0.0283 \text{ rad}^2/\text{s}^2$,

so $\omega = 0.168$ rad/s.

The centripetal acceleration is $a_c = r\omega^2 = (0.30 \times 10^3 \text{ m})(0.168 \text{ rad/s})^2 = 8.5 \text{ m/s}^2$,

the tangential acceleration is $a_t = r\alpha = (0.30 \times 10^3 \text{ m})(4.5 \times 10^{-3} \text{ rad/s}^2) = 1.4 \text{ m/s}^2$.

So the total acceleration is $\mathbf{a} = \boxed{(8.5 \text{ m/s}^2)\,\hat{\mathbf{r}} + (1.4 \text{ m/s}^2)\,\hat{\mathbf{t}}}$.

72. (a) There is $\boxed{\text{not enough centripetal force to hold the dime in circular motion}}$ (provided by friction).

(b) $\omega = \omega_0 + \alpha t = 0 + (1.42 \text{ rad/s}^2)(2.25 \text{ s}) = 3.195$ rad/s.

$F_c = f_s = \mu_s N = \mu_s mg = mr\omega^2$, ☞ $\mu_s = \dfrac{r\omega^2}{g} = \dfrac{(0.10 \text{ m})(3.195 \text{ rad/s})^2}{9.80 \text{ m/s}^2} = \boxed{0.10}$.

73. (c).

74. (d).

75. $\boxed{\text{No}}$, these terms are not correct. Gravity acts on the astronauts and the spacecraft, providing the necessary centripetal force for the orbit, so g is not zero and there is weight by definition ($w = mg$). The "floating" occurs because the spacecraft and astronauts are "falling" ("accelerating" toward Earth at the same rate).

76. When the cup is held, water runs out the holes. However if the cup is released, water will not run out since both the cup and the water are in free fall.

77. $\boxed{\text{Yes}}$, if you also know the radius of the Earth. The acceleration due to gravity near the surface of the Earth can be written as $a_g = \dfrac{GM_E}{R_E^2}$. By simply measuring a_g, you can determine $M_E = \dfrac{a_g R_E^2}{G}$.

78.　(a) $\boxed{\text{No}}$. Although the scale is calibrated in kilograms, it is still measuring gravitational force. Due to the different gravitational accelerations on the Earth and the Moon, it will not read correctly.

(b) Due to its rotation, the Earth bulges at the equator. So it will read $\boxed{\text{less}}$ on the equator because the gravitational force depends on $1/r^2$.

79.　$g_M = \dfrac{GM_M}{R_M^{\,2}} = \dfrac{(6.67 \times 10^{-11}\ \text{N·m}^2/\text{kg}^2)(7.4 \times 10^{22}\ \text{kg})}{(1.75 \times 10^6\ \text{m})^2} = \boxed{1.6\ \text{m/s}^2}.$

80.　$F = \dfrac{GM_E M_M}{r_{\text{E-M}}^{\,2}} = \dfrac{(6.67 \times 10^{-11}\ \text{N·m}^2/\text{kg}^2)(5.98 \times 10^{24}\ \text{kg})(7.4 \times 10^{22}\ \text{kg})}{(3.8 \times 10^8\ \text{m})^2} = \boxed{2.0 \times 10^{20}\ \text{N}}.$

81.　(a) The force is greater during a $\boxed{\text{lunar eclipse}}$ because the forces by the Sun and the Earth on the Moon are in the same direction so they add up.

(b) Solar eclipse:

$F_E = \dfrac{GM_E M_M}{r_{\text{E-M}}^{\,2}} = \dfrac{(6.67 \times 10^{-11}\ \text{N·m}^2/\text{kg}^2)(5.98 \times 10^{24}\ \text{kg})(7.4 \times 10^{22}\ \text{kg})}{(3.8 \times 10^8\ \text{m})^2} = 2.0 \times 10^{20}\ \text{N},$

$F_S = \dfrac{(6.67 \times 10^{-11}\ \text{N·m}^2/\text{kg}^2)(2.0 \times 10^{30}\ \text{kg})(7.4 \times 10^{22}\ \text{kg})}{(1.5 \times 10^{11}\ \text{m} - 3.8 \times 10^8\ \text{m})^2} = 4.4 \times 10^{20}\ \text{N}.$

So　$F_M = F_S - F_E = 4.4 \times 10^{20}\ \text{N} - 2.0 \times 10^{20}\ \text{N} = \boxed{2.4 \times 10^{20}\ \text{N toward the Sun}}.$

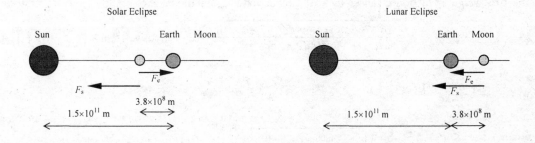

Lunar eclipse:

$F_E = \dfrac{(6.67 \times 10^{-11}\ \text{N·m}^2/\text{kg}^2)(5.98 \times 10^{24}\ \text{kg})(7.4 \times 10^{22}\ \text{kg})}{(3.8 \times 10^8\ \text{m})^2} = 2.0 \times 10^{20}\ \text{N},$

$F_S = \dfrac{(6.67 \times 10^{-11}\ \text{N·m}^2/\text{kg}^2)(2.0 \times 10^{30}\ \text{kg})(7.4 \times 10^{22}\ \text{kg})}{(1.5 \times 10^{11}\ \text{m} + 3.8 \times 10^8\ \text{m})^2} = 4.4 \times 10^{20}\ \text{N}.$

So　$F_M = F_S + F_E = 4.4 \times 10^{20}\ \text{N} + 2.0 \times 10^{20}\ \text{N} = \boxed{6.4 \times 10^{20}\ \text{N toward the Sun}}.$

82. When the Earth's gravitational force equals the lunar gravitational force,

$$F_E = \frac{GM_E m}{x^2} = F_M = \frac{GM_M m}{(3.8 \times 10^8 \text{ m} - x)^2}.$$

Taking the square root on both sides gives

$$\frac{\sqrt{M_E}}{x} = \frac{\sqrt{M_M}}{3.8 \times 10^8 \text{ m} - x}, \quad \text{or}$$

$$\sqrt{7.4 \times 10^{22} \text{ kg}}\ x = \sqrt{5.98 \times 10^{24} \text{ kg}}\ (3.8 \times 10^8 \text{ m} - x). \quad \text{Solving,} \quad x = \boxed{3.4 \times 10^8 \text{ m from Earth}}.$$

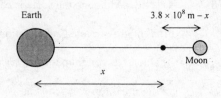
Earth $3.8 \times 10^8 \text{ m} - x$

Moon

x

$\boxed{\text{No}}$, there are still other gravitational forces from the other planets and the Sun.

83. $$F_1 = F_3 = \frac{Gm^2}{d^2} = \frac{(6.67 \times 10^{-11} \text{ N·m}^2/\text{kg}^2)(2.5 \text{ kg})^2}{(1.0 \text{ m})^2} = 4.17 \times 10^{-10} \text{ N},$$

The diagonal distance is $\sqrt{(1.0 \text{ m})^2 + (1.0 \text{ m})^2} = \sqrt{2}$ m,

so $$F_3 = \frac{(6.67 \times 10^{-11} \text{ N·m}^2/\text{kg}^2)(2.5 \text{ kg})^2}{(\sqrt{2}\ \text{m})^2} = 2.08 \times 10^{-10} \text{ N}.$$

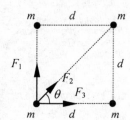
m d m

F_1 d

F_2

θ F_3

m d m

From symmetry the net force is

$$F = \sqrt{(4.17 \times 10^{-10} \text{ N})^2 + (4.17 \times 10^{-10} \text{ m})^2} + 2.08 \times 10^{-10} \text{ N}$$

$$= \boxed{8.0 \times 10^{-10} \text{ N, toward opposite corner}}.$$

84. $$a_g = \frac{GM_E}{(R_E + h)^2} = \frac{(6.67 \times 10^{-11} \text{ N·m}^2/\text{kg}^2)(5.98 \times 10^{24} \text{ kg})}{(6.38 \times 10^6 \text{ m} + 8.80 \times 10^3 \text{ m})^2} = \boxed{9.77 \text{ m/s}^2}.$$

85. The 10% weight reduction is caused by a 10% reduction in gravitational acceleration. $a_g = \frac{GM_E}{(R_E + h)^2}$.

$$h = \sqrt{\frac{GM_E}{a_g}} - R_E = \sqrt{\frac{(6.67 \times 10^{-11} \text{ N·m}^2/\text{kg}^2)(5.98 \times 10^{24} \text{ kg})}{0.90(9.80 \text{ m/s}^2)}} - 6.38 \times 10^6 \text{ m} = \boxed{3.4 \times 10^5 \text{ m}}.$$

86. (a) $F = \frac{Gm_1 m_2}{r^2} \propto \frac{1}{r^2}, \quad \text{☞} \quad \frac{F_2}{F_1} = \frac{r_1^2}{r_2^2}.$

When $r_2 = r_1/2$, $F_2 = 4F_1$. So it $\boxed{\text{increases by a factor of 4}}$.

(b) $\frac{F_2}{F_1} = \frac{r_1^2}{r_2^2} = \frac{1^2}{3^2} = \frac{1}{9}, \quad \text{so} \quad F_2 = \frac{F_1}{9} = \frac{0.90 \text{ N}}{9} = \boxed{0.10 \text{ N}}.$

87. $F = \frac{Gm_1 m_2}{r^2}, \quad \text{☞} \quad \frac{F_{E\text{-}S}}{F_{E\text{-}M}} = \frac{\dfrac{M_S}{r_{E\text{-}S}^2}}{\dfrac{M_M}{r_{E\text{-}M}^2}} = \frac{M_S\ r_{E\text{-}M}^2}{M_m\ r_{E\text{-}S}^2} = \frac{(2.0 \times 10^{30} \text{ kg})(3.8 \times 10^8 \text{ m})^2}{(7.4 \times 10^{22} \text{ kg})(1.5 \times 10^{11} \text{ m})^2} = 1.7 \times 10^2.$

So $\boxed{F_{E\text{-}S} = (1.7 \times 10^2)F_{E\text{-}M}}.$

88.   Assume the thickness of the layer is d. So the mass is $M = \rho V = \rho \dfrac{4\pi}{3}(R_E + d)^3$.

Also $a_g = \dfrac{GM}{(R_E + d)^2} = \dfrac{4\pi}{3} \times G\rho(R_E + d),$ so

$$d = \frac{3a_g}{4\pi G\rho} - R_E = \frac{3(10.0 \text{ m/s}^2)}{4\pi(6.67 \times 10^{-11} \text{ N·m}^2/\text{kg}^2)(5.52 \times 10^3 \text{ kg/m}^3)} - 6.38 \times 10^6 \text{ m}$$

$$= 1.04 \times 10^5 \text{ m} = \boxed{104 \text{ km}}.$$

89.   (a) $U_{\text{tot}} = -\dfrac{Gm_1m_2}{r_{12}} - \dfrac{Gm_1m_3}{r_{13}} - \dfrac{Gm_2m_3}{r_{23}}$

$$= -(6.67 \times 10^{-11} \text{ N·m}^2/\text{kg}^2)\left[\frac{(1.0 \text{ kg})^2}{0.80 \text{ m}} + \frac{(1.0 \text{ kg})^2}{0.80 \text{ m}} + \frac{(1.0 \text{ kg})^2}{0.80 \text{ m}}\right] = \boxed{-2.5 \times 10^{-10} \text{ J}}.$$

(b) From symmetry, the force at the center is zero. So the force per unit mass is also $\boxed{0}$.

90.   (c).

91.   (c), according to Kepler's second law.

92.   (a) $\boxed{0}$, because the direction of the force and the displacement (velocity) are perpendicular and work is equal to $W = Fd \cos \theta (\cos 90° = 0)$.

(b) $\boxed{\text{No}}$. When the person comes down, it is still a free fall.

93.   (a) Rockets are launched $\boxed{\text{eastward}}$ to get more velocity relative to space because the Earth rotates toward the east.

(b) The $\boxed{\text{tangential speed of the Earth is higher in Florida}}$ because Florida is closer to the equator than California hence a greater distance from the axis of rotation. Also, the launch is over the ocean for safety.

94.   (a) $\boxed{\text{No}}$, you cannot speed up in the same orbit with one rocket burst. Speed is dependent on orbital radius. Once you speed up, you will be at a different orbit of different radius.

(b) $\boxed{\text{Decreasing the orbital radius}}$ to increase speed and then increasing the orbital radius to catch the equipment.

95.   (a) From energy conservation: $K + U = $ constant, $\frac{1}{2}mv^2 - \frac{G\,M_E m}{R_E^2} = \frac{1}{2}m(0)^2 - \frac{GM_E m}{(R_E + h)^2}$

$\frac{1}{2}v^2 = \frac{(6.67 \times 10^{-11} \text{ N·m}^2/\text{kg}^2)(6.0 \times 10^{24} \text{ kg})}{6.4 \times 10^6 \text{ m}} - \frac{(6.67 \times 10^{-11} \text{ N·m}^2/\text{kg}^2)(6.0 \times 10^{24} \text{ kg})}{6.4 \times 10^6 \text{ m} + 800 \times 10^3 \text{ m}}$

$= 6.965 \times 10^6 \text{ m}^2/\text{s}^2$,   therefore $v = \boxed{3.7 \times 10^3 \text{ m/s}}$.

(b) The percentage is $\frac{3.7 \times 10^3 \text{ m/s}}{11 \times 10^3 \text{ m/s}} = \boxed{34\%}$.

96.   For the Earth orbiting the Sun, $K = \frac{4\pi^2}{GM_S}$.

Replace the mass of the Sun with the mass of the Earth for satellites orbiting the Earth.

$K = \frac{4\pi^2}{GM_E} = \frac{4\pi^2}{(6.67 \times 10^{-11} \text{ N·m}^2/\text{kg}^2)(5.98 \times 10^{24} \text{ kg})} = 9.90 \times 10^{-14} \text{ s}^2/\text{m}$.

$T = 1 \text{ day} = 24(3600 \text{ s}) = 86\,400 \text{ s}$ (synchronous satellite).

From $T^2 = Kr^3 = K(R_E + h)^3$,

we have $h = \sqrt[3]{\frac{T^2}{K}} - R_E = \sqrt[3]{\frac{(86\,400 \text{ s})^2}{9.90 \times 10^{-14} \text{ s}^2/\text{m}}} - 6.38 \times 10^6 \text{ m} = \boxed{3.6 \times 10^7 \text{ m}}$.

97.   For the Earth orbiting the Sun, $K = \frac{4\pi^2}{GM_S}$.

Replace the mass of the sun with the mass of Venus for satellites orbiting Venus.

$K = \frac{4\pi^2}{GM_V} = \frac{4\pi^2}{(6.67 \times 10^{-11} \text{ N·m}^2/\text{kg}^2)[(0.8150)(5.98 \times 10^{24} \text{ kg})]} = 1.21 \times 10^{-13} \text{ s}^2/\text{m}$.

$T = 1 \text{day} = 243(24)(3600 \text{ s}) = 2.10 \times 10^7 \text{ s}$ (synchronous satellite).

From $T^2 = Kr^3 = K(R_V + h)^3$, we have

$h = \sqrt[3]{\frac{T^2}{K}} - R_V = \sqrt[3]{\frac{(2.10 \times 10^7 \text{ s})^2}{1.21 \times 10^{-13} \text{ s}^2/\text{m}}} - 6.05 \times 10^6 \text{ m} = \boxed{1.53 \times 10^9 \text{ m}}$.

98. $T = 5.0 \text{ y} = (5.0)(365)(24)(3600 \text{ s}) = 1.58 \times 10^8 \text{ s}$.   From $T^2 = Kr^3$,

we have $r = \sqrt[3]{\frac{T^2}{K}} = \sqrt[3]{\frac{(1.58 \times 10^8 \text{ s})^2}{3.0 \times 10^{-19} \text{ s}^2/\text{m}}} = \boxed{4.4 \times 10^{11} \text{ m}}$.

99.   The angular velocity of the Sun's setting is the same as the angular velocity of the Earth's rotation.

$\omega = \frac{\Delta\theta}{\Delta t} = \frac{2\pi \text{ rad}}{24(3600 \text{ s})} = 7.27 \times 10^{-5} \text{ rad/s}$.

$\Delta t = \frac{\Delta\theta}{\omega} = \frac{(0.50°)(\pi \text{ rad}/180°)}{7.27 \times 10^{-5} \text{ rad/s}} = 120 \text{ s} = \boxed{2.0 \text{ min}}$.

100. The Moon's gravitational attraction on the near side is greater on the water than on the Earth and produces one bulge for one tide; the attraction is greater on the Earth than on the water on the far side and so the Earth moves toward the Moon and leaves the water behind for another bulge.

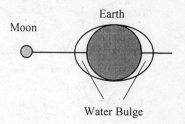

101. The centripetal force is provided by the combination of

$T - mg\cos\theta = m\dfrac{v^2}{r}$, where $\cos\theta = \dfrac{h}{l}$ and v could be found from energy conservation.

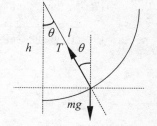

When the girl is h below the original position, $\frac{1}{2}m(0)^2 + mgh = \frac{1}{2}mv^2 + mg(0)$,

so $v^2 = 2gh$.

Therefore $T = mg\cos\theta + m\dfrac{v^2}{r} = \dfrac{mgh}{l} + \dfrac{m(2gh)}{l} = \dfrac{3mgh}{l}$.

(a) $h = 0$,   so $T = \boxed{0}$.

(b) $h = 12\ m - 5.0\ \text{m} = 7.0\ \text{m}$,   so $T = \dfrac{3(60\ \text{kg})(9.80\ \text{m/s}^2)(7.0\ \text{m})}{10\ \text{m}} = \boxed{1.2 \times 10^3\ \text{N}}$.

(c) $h = 12\ \text{m} - 2.0\ \text{m} = 10\ \text{m}$,   so $T = \dfrac{3(60\ \text{kg})(9.80\ \text{m/s}^2)(10\ \text{m})}{10\ \text{m}} = \boxed{1.8 \times 10^3\ \text{N}}$.

102. For a candle to keep burning there needs to be convection of air. The convection of air is caused by gravity (air of different temperature has different weight). $\boxed{\text{There is no gravity so air cannot convect}}$.

103. (a) $\omega = (5.00 \times 10^6\ \text{rpm}) \times \dfrac{2\pi\ \text{rad/rev}}{60\ \text{s/min}} = 5.24 \times 10^5\ \text{rad/s}$.

$a_c = r\omega^2 = (0.0400\ \text{m})(5.24 \times 10^5\ \text{rad/s})^2 = \boxed{1.10 \times 10^{10}\ \text{m/s}^2}$.

(b) $\dfrac{1.1 \times 10^8\ \text{m/s}^2}{g} = \dfrac{1.1 \times 10^{10}\ \text{m/s}^2}{9.80\ \text{m/s}^2} = \boxed{1.12 \times 10^9\ g}$.

104. $s = r\theta = (0.45\ \text{m})(3\ \text{rev})(2\pi\ \text{rad/rev}) = \boxed{8.5\ \text{m}}$.

105. $K + U = 0$,   ☞ $\frac{1}{2}mv_\text{E}^2 - \dfrac{GM_\text{E}\,m}{R_\text{E} + h} = 0$.

So $v_\text{E} = \sqrt{\dfrac{2GM_\text{E}}{R_\text{E} + h}} = \sqrt{\dfrac{2(6.67 \times 10^{-11}\ \text{N·m}^2/\text{kg}^2)(5.98 \times 10^{24}\ \text{kg})}{6.38 \times 10^6\ \text{m} + 750 \times 10^3\ \text{m}}} = \boxed{1.1 \times 10^4\ \text{m/s}}$.

106. $m = \dfrac{w}{g} = \dfrac{735\ \text{N}}{9.80\ \text{m/s}^2} = 75\ \text{kg}.$

$F = \dfrac{GM_E\,m}{(R_E + h)^2} = \dfrac{(6.67 \times 10^{-11}\ \text{N·m}^2/\text{kg}^2)(5.98 \times 10^{24}\ \text{kg})(75\ \text{kg})}{(6.38 \times 10^6\ \text{m} + 450 \times 10^3\ \text{m})^2} = \boxed{641\ \text{N}}.$

107. $T^2 = Kr^3.$ For the Earth, $T = 1$ year   and $r = 1$ AU.

So $(1\ \text{y})^2 = K(1\ \text{AU})^3,$ ☞ $K = \boxed{1\ \text{y}^2/\text{AU}^3}.$

108. (a) $a_t = g\sin\theta = (9.80\ \text{m/s}^2)\sin 15° = \boxed{2.5\ \text{m/s}^2}.$ $a_c = \dfrac{v^2}{r} = \dfrac{(2.7\ \text{m/s})^2}{0.75\ \text{m}} = \boxed{9.7\ \text{m/s}^2}.$

(b) $\boxed{\text{At the lowest point of the swing}}$, since v is maximum there. $a_t = \boxed{0}$ since $\theta = 0.$

CHAPTER 8

ROTATIONAL MOTION AND EQUILIBRIUM

1.   (a).

2.   (b).

3. $\boxed{\text{Yes, rolling motion}}$ is a good example.

4.   If v is less than $R\omega$, the object is $\boxed{\text{slipping}}$. $\boxed{\text{Yes}}$, it is possible for v to be greater than $R\omega$ when the

object is $\boxed{\text{sliding}}$.

5.   (b).

6.   According to $v_t = r\omega$, the reading of the speedometer is $\boxed{v/2}$. The point on the top of the tire has twice the

radius as the center of the tire (the point at which the tire makes contact with the ground is the axis of

rotation), and the speedometer reads the speed of the center of the tire (v_{CM}).

7.   Its speed is $\boxed{\text{zero}}$ as the radius is zero, according to $v_t = r\omega$. The point the tire makes contact with the

ground is the axis of rotation.

8. $s = r\theta = (0.065 \text{ m})(4 \text{ rev})(2\pi \text{ rad/rev}) = \boxed{1.6 \text{ m}}$.

9. $s = r\theta$, ☞ $r = \dfrac{s}{\theta} = \dfrac{3.2 \text{ m}}{5(2\pi \text{ rad})} = \boxed{0.10 \text{ m}}$.

10.   At the nine-o'clock position, the velocity is straight upward. So it is a "free-fall" with an initial upward

velocity. It will rise, reach a maximum height, and then fall back down.

11.   (a) $v_{CM} = r\omega = (0.25 \text{ m})(2.0 \text{ rad/s}) = \boxed{0.50 \text{ m/s}}$.

(b) The disk rotates about a point that makes a contact with the surface. The distance from the top of the

disk to that point is $2r$.   So $v = 2(0.25 \text{ m})(2.0 \text{ rad/s}) = \boxed{1.0 \text{ m/s}}$.

12. $v_{CM} = r\omega$, ☞ $\omega = \dfrac{v_{CM}}{r} = \dfrac{0.25 \text{ m/s}}{0.15 \text{ m}} = \boxed{1.7 \text{ rad/s}}$.

13.   (a) The product of $r\omega$ should be ⬚equal to⬚ v_{CM} when a disk rolls without slipping.

(b) $s = 0.71$ m. $r\theta = (0.15 \text{ m})(270°)(\pi \text{ rad}/180°) = 0.71$ m. So $s = r\theta$, ⬚yes⬚, it rolls without slipping.

14.   Dividing $s = r\theta$ (the condition of "without slipping") by a time interval t gives
$$\frac{s}{t} = r\frac{\theta}{t}, \text{ or } v = r\omega.$$

Dividing $v = r\omega$ by a time interval t again yields
$$\frac{v}{t} = r\frac{\omega}{t}, \text{ or } a = r\alpha.$$

15. $\alpha = \dfrac{a_t}{r} = \dfrac{0.018 \text{ m/s}^2}{0.10 \text{ m}} = 0.18 \text{ rad/s}^2.$ $\omega^2 = \omega_0^2 + 2\alpha\theta,$

so $\theta = \dfrac{\omega^2 - \omega_0^2}{2\alpha} = \dfrac{(1.25 \text{ rad/s})^2 - (0.50 \text{ rad/s})^2}{2(0.18 \text{ rad/s}^2)} = 36.5 \text{ rad} = \boxed{0.58 \text{ rotations}}.$

16.   (b).

17.   (a).

18.   It has a ⬚greater lever arm⬚ at that location so it can exert a greater torque.

19.   When you use the back, the back has to rotate, and the lever arm is greater so the
⬚back muscles have to exert greater torque⬚. If the legs are used, then the back can keep in a straight
position and exert no torque.

20.   In all three cases, ⬚the centers of gravity must be directly below the base of support⬚. The torque is zero
because the force of the CG is through the axis of rotation.

21.   ⬚Yes⬚, the toy clown is in stable equilibrium. Its center of gravity is directly below the tightrope. If the
clown leans to one side, its own weight will restore its equilibrium position. If the weights are removed, the
clown will be in an unstable equilibrium and it will fall.

22.   When the force is applied perpendicular to the length of the wrench, minimum force is required and the
lever arm equals the length of the wrench. At $\theta = 90°$, $r_\perp = 0.15$ m.

$\tau = Fr_\perp,$ ☞ $F = \dfrac{\tau}{r_\perp} = \dfrac{25 \text{ m·N}}{0.15 \text{ m}} = \boxed{1.7 \times 10^2 \text{ N}}.$

23. In this case, $r_\perp = (0.15\ \text{m}) \sin 30°$.

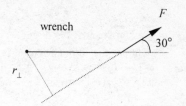
wrench

$$F = \frac{\tau}{r_\perp} = \frac{25\ \text{m·N}}{(0.15\ \text{m}) \sin 30°} = \boxed{3.3 \times 10^2\ \text{N}}.$$

24. Use the numbers from Example 8.1.

$$\tau = F r_\perp, \quad \text{☞} \quad F = \frac{\tau}{r_\perp} = \frac{18\ \text{m·N}}{(0.040\ \text{m}) \cos 37°} = \boxed{5.6 \times 10^2\ \text{N}}.$$

25. $\boxed{6\ \text{stable}}$ (faces) and $\boxed{20\ \text{unstable}}$ (12 edges and 8 corners).

26. $\tau = r_\perp F = r_\perp mg = (0.20\ \text{m})(55\ \text{kg})(9.80\ \text{m/s}^2) = \boxed{1.1 \times 10^2\ \text{m·N}}$.

27. (a) $\boxed{\text{Yes}}$, the seesaw can be balanced if the lever arms are appropriate for the

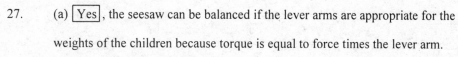

weights of the children because torque is equal to force times the lever arm.

(b) $\Sigma \tau = 0$, ☞ $m_1 g(2.0\ \text{m}) - m_2 g x = 0$,

so $x = \dfrac{m_1}{m_2} (2.0\ \text{m}) = \dfrac{35\ \text{kg}}{30\ \text{kg}} (2.0\ \text{m}) = \boxed{2.3\ \text{m}}$.

28. (a) $\Sigma \tau = 0$, ☞ $(0.100\ \text{kg})g(0.500\ \text{m} - 0.250\ \text{m}) - (0.0750\ \text{kg})g(x - 0.500\ \text{m}) = 0$,

so $x = 0.833\ \text{m} = \boxed{83.3\ \text{cm}}$.

(b) $(0.100\ \text{kg})g(0.500\ \text{m} - 0.250\ \text{m}) - m(0.900\ \text{m} - 0.500\ \text{m}) = 0$,

so $m = 0.0625\ \text{kg} = \boxed{62.5\ \text{g}}$.

29. $N = Mg = (0.025\ \text{kg} + 0.075\ \text{kg} + 0.100\ \text{kg})g = (0.200\ \text{kg})g$.

The net torque about an axis through the 100-cm end is

$\Sigma \tau = (0.025\ \text{kg})g(1.00\ \text{m}) + (0.075\ \text{kg})g(0.80\ \text{m}) - (0.200\ \text{kg})g(0.50\ \text{m}) + (0.100\ \text{kg})g(0.15\ \text{m}) = 0$.

30. (a) $\boxed{\text{No}}$, it is not possible to have the lines perfectly horizontal

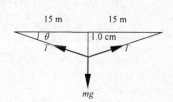

because the weight has to be supported by an upward component of the tensions in the lines. If the lines were horizontal, then they cannot support the weight.

(b) $\theta = \tan^{-1}\left(\dfrac{0.010}{15}\right) = 0.0382°$. $\quad \Sigma F_y = 2T \sin\theta - mg = 0$.

So $T = \dfrac{mg}{2 \sin\theta} = \dfrac{(0.25\ \text{kg})(9.80\ \text{m/s}^2)}{2 \sin 0.0382°} = \boxed{1.8 \times 10^3\ \text{N} > 400\ \text{lb}}$.

31.   Choose the joint (where F_j is) as the axis of rotation.

$\Sigma\tau = F_m (0.18\text{ m}) \sin 15° - (3.0\text{ kg})(9.80\text{ m/s}^2)(0.26\text{ m}) = 0$,   ☞ $F_m = \boxed{1.6 \times 10^2\text{ N}}$.

32.   (a) The tension in the rope attached to m_1 is $T = (4.50\text{ kg})(9.80\text{ m/s}^2) = 44.1\text{ N}$, and there are two such

tensions pulling the leg horizontally. So the reaction force is $R = 2T = \boxed{88.2\text{ N}}$.

(b) $\Sigma F_y = 0$,   ☞ $(m_1 + m_2)g - Mg = 0$,   so $m_2 = M - m_1 = 15.0\text{ kg} - 4.50\text{ kg} = \boxed{10.5\text{ kg}}$.

33. $\Sigma\tau = -(5.0\text{ N})(0.50\text{ m}) - (0.15\text{ kg})(9.80\text{ m/s}^2)(0.75\text{ m}) + F(1.0\text{ m}) = 0$,

so $F = \boxed{3.6\text{ N}}$.

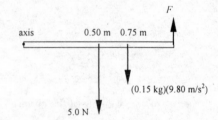

34.   Repeat the calculation of Example 8.6.

$$N = \frac{(15\text{ kg})(9.8\text{ m/s}^2)(1.0\text{ m}) + (65\text{ kg})(9.8\text{ m/s}^2)(1.6\text{ m})}{5.6\text{ m}} = 2.1 \times 10^4 {=} 2\text{ N}.$$

So $f_s = N = \boxed{2.1 \times 10^2\text{ N}}$.

35.   Choose where the string is as the axis and work from the bottom up. Apply $\Sigma\tau = 0$ to the

bees: $m_1 g(40\text{ cm}) - m_2 g(20\text{ cm}) = 0$,   ☞ $m_2 = 2m_1 = \boxed{0.20\text{ kg}}$.

bees–1st bird combination: $(m_1 + m_2)g(25\text{ cm}) - m_3 g(15\text{ cm})$,   ☞ $m_3 = \dfrac{5}{3}(m_1 + m_2) = \boxed{0.50\text{ kg}}$.

bees and 1st bird–2nd bird combination: $m_4 g(30\text{ cm}) - (m_1 + m_2 + m_3)g(15\text{ cm}) = 0$,

so $m_4 = \frac{1}{2}(m_1 + m_2 + m_3) = \boxed{0.40\text{ kg}}$.

36.   (a) The center of gravity (CG) of the first book is at the center. For the last book not to fall, its CG can not

displace more than $(25.0\text{ cm})/2 = 12.5\text{ cm}$ relative to the CG of the first book (within the base). The CG of

each successive book on the top is moved $(3.00\text{ cm})/2 = 1.5\text{ cm}$ relative to that of the one below. The

number of books on top of the first one can be $\dfrac{12.5\text{ cm}}{1.5\text{ cm}} = 8.33$. Thus the total is $1 + 8 = \boxed{9}$ books,

including the first one.

(b) The total height is $9(5.0)\text{ cm} = 45\text{ cm}$. So the center of mass (CM) is at $\dfrac{45\text{ cm}}{2} = \boxed{22.5\text{ cm}}$.

37. $\boxed{\text{Yes}}$. The center of gravity of every stick is at or to the left of the edge of the table.

38.   The height of the center of gravity at stable equilibrium is

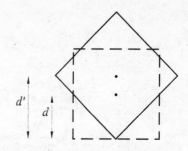

$$d = \frac{0.500 \text{ m}}{2} = 0.250 \text{ m}.$$

The minimum height of the center of gravity at unstable equilibrium is half the diagonal distance

$$d' = \sqrt{2} \, \frac{0.500 \text{ m}}{2} = 0.3536 \text{ m}.$$

So the minimum distance that CG has to be raised is $0.3536 \text{ m} - 0.250 \text{ m} = 0.1036 \text{ m}.$

Therefore the work done against gravity is $W = (10.0 \text{ kg})(9.80 \text{ m/s}^2)(0.1036 \text{ m}) = \boxed{10.2 \text{ J}}.$

39.   When it is about to tip over the left support, the force on the right support is zero.

Choose the left support as the axis of rotation.

Using $\Sigma \tau = 0$, $(70 \text{ kg})g\,x - (15 \text{ kg})g(1.25 \text{ m}) = 0$,   so $x = 0.27 \text{ m}.$

So it is $1.5 \text{ m} - 0.27 \text{ m} = \boxed{1.2 \text{ m from left end of board}}.$

40.   Choose the left end as the axis. $\Sigma \tau = 0$,

$$T_2(0) - (70 \text{ kg})(9.80 \text{ m/s}^2)(1.5 \text{ m}) - (15 \text{ kg})(9.80 \text{ m/s}^2)(2.75 \text{ m}) + T_1(5.5 \text{ m}) = 0,$$

so $T_1 = \boxed{2.6 \times 10^2 \text{ N}}.$

$\Sigma F_y = 0$,   ☞ $T_1 + T_2 = (70 \text{ kg} + 15 \text{ kg})(9.80 \text{ m/s}^2)$,

so $T_2 = 833 \text{ N} - 261 \text{ N} = \boxed{5.7 \times 10^2 \text{ N}}.$

T_2 can also be found by choosing the right end as the axis.

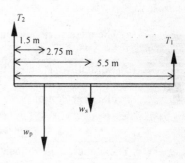

41.   (a) $\tan \theta$ should be $\boxed{\text{equal to}}$ f_s/N.

Assume the distance from the center of gravity (CG) to the point where the wheel touches the ground is d. Choose CG as the axis. $\Sigma \tau = 0$,

$f_s d \cos \theta - Nd \sin \theta = 0$,   ☞ $f_s d \cos \theta = Nd \sin \theta$,   or $\tan \theta = f_s/N$.

(b) $f_s = \mu_s N = N \tan \theta$,   ☞ $\mu_s = \tan \theta = \tan 11° = \boxed{0.19}$.

(c) $\Sigma F_y = N - mg = 0$,   ☞ $N = mg$.

$$f_s = \mu_s N = \mu_s mg = F_c = m \frac{v^2}{r}, \quad ☞ \quad v = \sqrt{\mu_s gr} = \sqrt{0.19(9.80 \text{ m/s}^2)(6.5 \text{ m})} = \boxed{3.5 \text{ m/s}}.$$

42.   (d).

43.   (a).

44.   (a) $\boxed{\text{Yes}}$. Moment of inertia has a minimum value at the center of mass.

       (b) $\boxed{\text{No}}$. Mass would have to be negative.

45.   The moment of inertia $\boxed{\text{depends on how mass is distributed about an axis}}$. Physically, this means that, under a constant torque, the angular acceleration depends on the location of the axis of rotation.

46.   The $\boxed{\text{hard-boiled egg is a rigid body}}$, while the raw egg is not.

47.   This is the rotational analog of "pulling the table cloth" in Exercise 4.11. It takes a certain amount of torque to accelerate the paper tower and the paper can only exert a certain amount of force, and therefore torque. When the paper is pulled quickly (a large force is required to accelerate the roll), the force the paper can provide is not great enough to accelerate the paper roll. However, if the paper is pulled slowly, the paper is strong enough to accelerate the roll because the force required is smaller. The amount of paper on the roll affects the results. The more paper the roll has, the greater the moment of inertia, the greater the force required to accelerate the roll, and therefore the easier to tear.

48.   (a) The meterstick has a higher center of mass; $\boxed{\text{larger moment of inertia and smaller angular acceleration}}$.

       (b) $\boxed{\text{Softball wins, others tie}}$ because the softball (a sphere) has a smaller moment of inertia and so a larger angular acceleration.

49. $\boxed{\text{Yes, it increases}}$. Since $I = I_{CM} + Md^2$ and md^2 can never be negative, I is equal to or greater than I_{CM}.

50.   If the net torque is zero, then the angular acceleration is zero ($\alpha = 0$). That means the rigid body $\boxed{\text{remains at rest or rotates with constant } \omega}$.

51.   (a) $I = \Sigma(mr^2) = (2.00 \text{ kg})(1.50 \text{ m})^2 + (3.00 \text{ kg})(1.50 \text{ m})^2 + (1.00 \text{ kg})(1.50 \text{ m})^2 + (4.00 \text{ kg})(1.50 \text{ m})^2$

           $= \boxed{22.5 \text{ kg·m}^2}$.

       (b) $I = (2.00 \text{ kg})(2.50 \text{ m})^2 + (3.00 \text{ kg})(2.50 \text{ m})^2 + (1.00 \text{ kg})(2.50 \text{ m})^2 + (4.00 \text{ kg})(2.50 \text{ m})^2 = \boxed{62.5 \text{ kg·m}^2}$.

       (c) $r^2 = (1.50 \text{ m})^2 + (2.50 \text{ m})^2 = 8.50 \text{ m}^2$.

           $I = (2.00 \text{ kg})(8.50 \text{ m}^2) + (3.00 \text{ kg})(8.50 \text{ m}^2) + (1.00 \text{ kg})(8.50 \text{ m}^2) + (4.00 \text{ kg})(8.50 \text{ m}^2) = \boxed{85.0 \text{ kg·m}^2}$.

52. $I = \frac{1}{2}mr^2 = \frac{1}{2}(0.15 \text{ kg})(0.075 \text{ m})^2 = 4.219 \times 10^{-4} \text{ kg·m}^2$.

$\tau_{\text{net}} = I\alpha,$ ☞ $\alpha = \dfrac{\tau_{\text{net}}}{I} = \dfrac{6.4 \text{ m·N}}{4.219 \times 10^{-4} \text{ kg·m}^2} = \boxed{1.5 \times 10^4 \text{ rad/s}^2}$.

53.   For a solid ball, $I = \frac{2}{5}MR^2 = \frac{2}{5}(20 \text{ kg})(0.20 \text{ m})^2 = 0.32 \text{ kg·m}^2$.

$\tau_{\text{net}} = I\alpha = (0.32 \text{ kg·m}^2)(2.0 \text{ rad/s}^2) = \boxed{0.64 \text{ m·N}}$.

54.   (a) $I = \Sigma(mr^2) = (2.0 \text{ kg})(0.30 \text{ m})^2 + (4.0 \text{ kg})(0.75 \text{ m})^2 = \boxed{2.4 \text{ kg·m}^2}$.

(b) $X_{\text{CM}} = \dfrac{\Sigma_i(m_i x_i)}{M} = \dfrac{(2.0 \text{ kg})(0.30 \text{ m}) + (4.0 \text{ kg})(0.75 \text{ m})}{2.0 \text{ kg} + 4.0 \text{ kg}} = 0.60 \text{ m}$.

So $I = (2.0 \text{ kg})(0.60 \text{ m} - 0.30 \text{ m})^2 + (4.0 \text{ kg})(0.75 \text{ m} - 0.60 \text{ m})^2 = \boxed{0.27 \text{ kg·m}^2}$.

(c) $I = I_{\text{CM}} + Md^2 = 0.27 \text{ kg·m}^2 + (6.0 \text{ kg})(0.60 \text{ m})^2 = \boxed{2.4 \text{ kg·m}^2 \text{ (same)}}$.

55.   (a) The moment of inertia about the center of mass is the $\boxed{\text{minimum}}$. According to the parallel axis theorem $(I = I_{\text{CM}} + Md^2)$, md^2 can never be negative so $I > I_{\text{CM}}$.

(b) $I = \Sigma(mr^2) = (3.0 \text{ kg})(1.0 \text{ m})^2 + (5.0 \text{ kg})(1.0 \text{ m})^2 = \boxed{8.0 \text{ kg·m}^2}$.

$X_{\text{CM}} = \dfrac{\Sigma_i(m_i x_i)}{M} = \dfrac{(3.0 \text{ kg})(0) + (5.0 \text{ kg})(2.0 \text{ m})}{3.0 \text{ kg} + 5.0 \text{ kg}} = 1.25 \text{ m from the 3.0-kg mass}$.

$I = (3.0 \text{ kg})(1.25 \text{ m})^2 + (5.0 \text{ kg})(0.75 \text{ m})^2 = \boxed{7.5 \text{ kg·m}^2}$.

56.   First calculate the angular acceleration from kinematics.

$\alpha = \dfrac{\Delta\omega}{\Delta t} = \dfrac{2.0 \text{ rad/s} - 0}{12 \text{ s}} = 0.167 \text{ rad/s}^2$.

So $\tau = I\alpha = \frac{1}{2}mr^2\alpha = \frac{1}{2}(2000 \text{ kg})(30 \text{ m})^2(0.167 \text{ rad/s}^2) = \boxed{1.5 \times 10^5 \text{ m·N}}$.

57.   First find the angular acceleration from dynamics.

$I_{\text{CM}} = \frac{2}{5}MR^2$. $I = I_{\text{CM}} + Md^2 = \frac{2}{5}MR^2 + MR^2 = \frac{7}{5}MR^2$.

$\alpha = \dfrac{\tau_{\text{net}}}{I} = \dfrac{\tau_{\text{net}}}{\frac{7}{5}MR^2} = \dfrac{10 \text{ m·N}}{\frac{7}{5}(15 \text{ kg})(0.15 \text{ m})^2} = 21.2 \text{ rad/s}^2$.

So $\omega^2 = \omega_o^2 + 2\alpha\theta,$ ☞ $\theta = \dfrac{\omega^2 - \omega_o^2}{2\alpha} = \dfrac{(7.5 \text{ rad/s})^2 - (3.0 \text{ rad/s})^2}{2(21.2 \text{ rad/s}^2)} = \boxed{1.1 \text{ rad}}$.

58. First find the angular acceleration from kinematics.

$$\omega^2 = \omega_o^2 + 2\alpha\theta, \quad \text{☞} \quad a = \frac{\omega^2 - \omega_o^2}{2\theta} = \frac{(3.0 \text{ rad/s})^2 - (0)^2}{2(2.0)(2\pi \text{ rad})}) = 0.358 \text{ rad/s}^2.$$

$$I = \tfrac{1}{2} MR^2 = \tfrac{1}{2} (10 \text{ kg})(0.50 \text{ m})^2 = 1.25 \text{ kg·m}^2.$$

$$\tau_{net} = I\alpha = (1.25 \text{ kg·m}^2)(0.358 \text{ rad/s}^2) = \boxed{0.45 \text{ m·N}}.$$

59. $I_{CM} = \tfrac{2}{5} MR^2.$ $I = I_{CM} + Md^2 = \tfrac{2}{5} MR^2 + MR^2 = \tfrac{7}{5} MR^2.$

So $\dfrac{I}{I_{CM}} = \dfrac{\frac{7}{5}}{\frac{2}{5}} = 3.5,$ or $\boxed{3.5 \text{ times}}.$

60. (a) $I = I_{CM} + Md^2 = \tfrac{1}{2} MR^2 + M\left(\tfrac{2}{3} R\right)^2 = \tfrac{17}{18} MR^2.$

$$\tau = I\alpha = \tfrac{17}{18}(0.25 \text{ kg})(0.060 \text{ m})^2 (2.0 \text{ rad/s}^2) = \boxed{1.7 \times 10^{-3} \text{ m·N}}.$$

(b) The difference in moment of inertia is $\Delta I = I - I_{CM} = M\left(\tfrac{2}{3} R\right)^2 = \tfrac{4}{9} MR^2.$

So the corresponding difference in torque is

$$\Delta \tau = \tfrac{4}{9}(0.25 \text{ kg})(0.060 \text{ m})^2 (2.0 \text{ rad/s}^2) = \boxed{8.0 \times 10^{-4} \text{ m·N}}.$$

61. Apply Newton's second law and note $a = r\alpha.$

m_2: $\quad m_2 g - T_2 = m_2 a,$ Eq. (1)

pulley: $\quad T_2 R - T_1 R - \tau_f = I\alpha = \tfrac{1}{2} MR^2 \alpha = \tfrac{1}{2} MRa,$

or $\quad T_2 - T_1 - \dfrac{\tau_f}{R} = \tfrac{1}{2} Ma,$ Eq. (2)

m_1: $\quad T_1 - m_1 g = m_1 a.$ Eq. (3)

Eq. (1) + Eq. (2) + Eq. (3) gives $(m_2 - m_1)g - \dfrac{\tau_f}{R} = (m_1 + m_2 + 0.5M)a,$

so $a = \dfrac{(m_2 - m_1)g - \frac{\tau_f}{R}}{m_1 + m_2 + 0.5M} = \dfrac{(0.80 \text{ kg} - 0.40 \text{ kg})(9.80 \text{ m/s}^2) - \frac{0.35 \text{ m·N}}{0.15 \text{ m}}}{0.40 \text{ kg} + 0.80 \text{ kg} + 0.5(0.20 \text{ kg})} = \boxed{1.2 \text{ m/s}^2}.$

62. (a) Apply Newton's second law and note $a = r\alpha.$

m_2: $\quad T_2 - m_2 g = m_2 a,$ Eq. (1)

pulley: $\quad T_1 R - T_2 R = I\alpha = \tfrac{1}{2} MR^2 \alpha = \tfrac{1}{2} MRa,$

or $\quad T_1 - T_2 = 0.5Ma,$ Eq. (2)

m_1: $\quad m_1 g \sin\theta - T_1 = m_1 a,$ Eq. (3)

Eq. (1) + Eq. (2) + Eq. (3) gives $\quad m_1 g \sin\theta - m_2 g = (m_1 + m_2 + 0.5M)a$,

so $\quad a = \dfrac{(m_1 \sin\theta - m_2)g}{m_1 + m_2 + 0.5M} = \dfrac{[(8.0 \text{ kg}) \sin 30° - (3.0 \text{ kg})](9.80 \text{ m/s}^2)}{8.0 \text{ kg} + 3.0 \text{ kg} + 0.5(0.10 \text{ kg})} = \boxed{0.89 \text{ m/s}^2}$.

(b) Pulley: $\quad T_1 R - T_2 R - \tau_f = I\alpha = \frac{1}{2} MR^2\alpha = \frac{1}{2} MRa$,

or $\quad T_1 - T_2 - \dfrac{\tau_f}{R} = 0.5Ma$. $\hfill$ Eq. (2)

So $\quad a = \dfrac{(m_1 \sin\theta - m_2)g - \dfrac{\tau_f}{R}}{m_1 + m_2 + 0.5M} = \dfrac{[(8.0 \text{ kg}) \sin 30° - (3.0 \text{ kg})](9.80 \text{ m/s}^2) - \dfrac{0.050 \text{ m·N}}{0.10 \text{ m}}}{8.0 \text{ kg} + 3.0 \text{ kg} + 0.5(0.10 \text{ kg})}$

$\qquad = \boxed{0.84 \text{ m/s}^2}$.

The tensions are different because of the frictional torque.

63. $\quad \tau = RF = I\alpha = \frac{1}{2} MR^2\alpha$, $\quad \text{☞} \quad F = \frac{1}{2} MR\alpha = \frac{1}{2}(2.0 \text{ kg})(0.50 \text{ m})(4.8 \text{ rad/s}^2) = \boxed{2.4 \text{ N}}$.

64. $\quad$ First find the angular acceleration from dynamics.

The moment of inertia for a disk-shaped wheel $I = \frac{1}{2} MR^2$.

$\tau = RF = I\alpha = \frac{1}{2} MR^2\alpha$, $\quad \text{☞} \quad \alpha = \dfrac{2F}{MR} = \dfrac{2(150 \text{ N})}{(0.30 \text{ kg})(0.090 \text{ m})} = 1.11 \times 10^4 \text{ rad/s}^2$.

So $\quad \omega^2 = \omega_0^2 + 2\alpha\theta = 0 + 2(1.11 \times 10^4 \text{ rad/s}^2)(2\pi \text{ rad}) = 1.39 \times 10^5 \text{ rad}^2/\text{s}^2$, $\quad \text{☞} \quad \omega = \boxed{3.7 \times 10^2 \text{ rad/s}}$.

65. $\quad$ (a) The moment of inertia of a meterstick about its end is $I = \frac{1}{3} ML^2$. The torque is generated by the weight of the stick through its center of mass.

$\tau = RF = \frac{1}{2} LMg = I\alpha = \frac{1}{3} ML^2\alpha$, $\quad \text{☞} \quad \alpha = \dfrac{3g}{2L}$. So $\quad a = r\alpha = L\dfrac{3g}{2L} = \boxed{1.5g}$.

(b) $a = g = r\dfrac{3g}{2L}$, $\quad \text{☞} \quad r = \dfrac{2L}{3} = 0.67 \text{ m} = \boxed{67\text{-cm position}}$.

66. $\quad$ If the finger is pulled away, all the pennies will fall freely under gravity and have acceleration equal to g. From the calculation in Exercise 8.65, the acceleration above the 67-cm position is greater than g. So the last four pennies at 70-, 80-, 90-, and the 100-cm positions will not fall as fast as the meterstick.

67. $\quad$ Apply Newton's second law and note $a = r\alpha$.

For the CM: $\qquad\qquad \Sigma F = Mg - 2T = Ma$, $\hfill$ Eq. (1)

For rotation about CM: $\quad \Sigma\tau = 2TR = I\alpha = \frac{1}{2} MR^2\alpha = \frac{1}{2} MRa$,

or $\qquad\qquad\qquad\qquad 2T = 0.5Ma$, $\hfill$ Eq. (2)

Eq. (1) + Eq. (2) gives $\quad Mg = 1.5Ma$, $\quad$ so $\quad a = \dfrac{g}{1.5} = \dfrac{9.80 \text{ m/s}^2}{1.5} = \boxed{6.5 \text{ m/s}^2}$.

68. The hoop rotates about an instantaneous axis of rotation through the point of contact (point O).

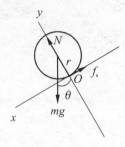

The moment of inertia about this axis is

$I = I_{CM} + Md^2 = MR^2 + MR^2 = 2MR^2.$

The torque by gravity is $\tau = MgR \sin\theta.$

So $a = R\alpha = R\dfrac{\tau}{I} = R\dfrac{MgR \sin\theta}{2MR^2} = \dfrac{g \sin\theta}{2}$

$= \dfrac{(9.80 \text{ m/s}^2) \sin 15°}{2} = \boxed{1.3 \text{ m/s}^2}.$

69. (a) The tangent of the maximum angle of incline (tan θ) should be equal to $\boxed{7\mu_s/2}$.

(b) Refer to the diagram in Exercise 8.68.

$\tau = rf_s = I\alpha = (\tfrac{2}{5} mr^2)(a/r),$ ☞ $f_s = \tfrac{2}{5} ma.$

$\Sigma F_x = mg \sin\theta - f_s = ma,$ or $mg \sin\theta - \tfrac{2}{5} ma = ma.$

Therefore $a = \tfrac{5}{7} g \sin\theta,$ and $f_s = \tfrac{2}{7} Mg \sin\theta.$

Also $\mu_s = \dfrac{f_s}{N} = \dfrac{\tfrac{2}{72} Mg \sin\theta}{Mg \cos\theta} = \dfrac{2}{7} \tan\theta.$ Thus $\theta = \tan^{-1} \dfrac{7\mu_s}{2}.$

(b) $\mu_s = 0.58.$ $\theta = \tan^{-1} (7 \times 0.58)/2 = \tan^{-1} 2.03 = \boxed{63.8°}.$

70. (b).

71. (c).

72. $\boxed{\text{Yes}}$, even the wheel is rotating without slipping. The rotational kinetic energy depends on the moment of inertia, which depends on both the mass and the mass distribution. Translational kinetic energy depends only on the mass.

73. The wheels would have $\boxed{\text{small total mass with more mass near the center}}$. This decreases the moment of inertia, which in turn decreases the rotational kinetic energy for a given angular speed.

74. $W = \tau\theta = \tau\dfrac{s}{r} = (12 \text{ m·N}) \dfrac{15 \text{ m}}{0.40 \text{ m}} = \boxed{4.5 \times 10^2 \text{ J}}.$

75. (a) $W = \tau\theta = rF\theta = (0.90 \text{ m})(15 \text{ N})(120°)(\pi \text{ rad}/180°) = \boxed{28 \text{ J}}.$

(b) $P = \dfrac{W}{\Delta t} = \dfrac{28 \text{ J}}{2.0 \text{ s}} = \boxed{14 \text{ W}}.$

76. From the work-energy theorem:

$$W = \tau\theta = \tfrac{1}{2}I\omega^2 - \tfrac{1}{2}I\omega_0^2 = \tfrac{1}{2}I\omega^2 - \tfrac{1}{2}I(0)^2 = \tfrac{1}{2}I\omega^2 = \tfrac{1}{2}(\tfrac{1}{2}MR^2)\omega^2 = \tfrac{1}{4}MR^2\omega^2.$$

So $\omega = \sqrt{\dfrac{4\tau\theta}{MR^2}} = \sqrt{\dfrac{4(10 \text{ m·N})(2.0)(2\pi \text{ rad})}{(10 \text{ kg})(0.20 \text{ m})^2}} = \boxed{35 \text{ rad/s}}$.

77. From the work-energy theorem:

$$W = \tau\theta = \tfrac{1}{2}I\omega^2 - \tfrac{1}{2}I\omega_0^2 = \tfrac{1}{2}I\omega^2 - \tfrac{1}{2}I(0)^2 = \tfrac{1}{2}I\omega^2 = \tfrac{1}{2}(\tfrac{1}{2}MR^2)\omega^2 = \tfrac{1}{4}MR^2\omega^2.$$

So $\tau = \dfrac{MR^2\omega^2}{4\theta} = \dfrac{(2.5 \text{ kg})(0.15 \text{ m})^2(25 \text{ rad/s})^2}{4(3.0)(2\pi \text{ rad})} = \boxed{0.47 \text{ m·N}}$.

78. (a) The answer is $\boxed{\text{less than}}$. If it were a point mass, then its speed would be $\sqrt{2gh}$.

From conservation of energy, $mgh = \tfrac{1}{2}mv^2$ so $v = \sqrt{2gh}$. However, when the object has rotation, it also has rotational kinetic energy. Therefore, the potential energy is split into two parts and the speed is less.

(b) From energy conservation: $\tfrac{1}{2}m(0)^2 + \tfrac{1}{2}I(0)^2 + mgh = \tfrac{1}{2}mv^2 + \tfrac{1}{2}I\omega^2 + mg(0).$

Since $v = R\omega$ and $I = \tfrac{1}{2}MR^2$,

we have $mgh = \tfrac{1}{2}mv^2 + \tfrac{1}{2}(\tfrac{1}{2}MR^2)\dfrac{v^2}{R^2} = \tfrac{1}{2}mv^2 + \tfrac{1}{4}Mv^2.$

So $v = \sqrt{\dfrac{4mgh}{2m + M}} = \sqrt{\dfrac{4(1.0 \text{ kg})(9.80 \text{ m/s}^2)(2.0 \text{ m})}{2(1.0 \text{ kg}) + 0.30 \text{ kg}}} = \boxed{5.8 \text{ m/s}}$.

79. Apply energy conservation and note $v = r\omega$. $\quad \tfrac{1}{2}Mv^2 + \tfrac{1}{2}I\omega^2 + Mg(0) = \tfrac{1}{2}M(0)^2 + \tfrac{1}{2}I(0)^2 + Mgh,$

or $\quad \tfrac{1}{2}MR^2\omega^2 + \tfrac{1}{2}(\tfrac{2}{5}MR^2)\omega^2 = Mgh,$

so $\quad h = \dfrac{7}{10g}r^2\omega^2 = \dfrac{7}{10(9.80 \text{ m/s}^2)}(0.15 \text{ m})^2(10 \text{ rad/s})^2 = \boxed{0.16 \text{ m}}$.

80. The center of mass (CM) lowers by an amount of $y = 0.50$ m.

From energy conservation: $\quad \tfrac{1}{2}I(0)^2 + mgy = \tfrac{1}{2}I\omega^2 + mg(0),$

so $\omega = \sqrt{\dfrac{2mgy}{I}} = \sqrt{\dfrac{2mgy}{\tfrac{1}{3}mL^2}} = \sqrt{\dfrac{6gy}{L^2}} = \sqrt{\dfrac{6(9.80 \text{ m/s}^2)(0.50 \text{ m})}{(1.0 \text{ m})^2}} = \boxed{5.4 \text{ rad/s}}$.

81. The cylinder has more moment of inertia ($\tfrac{1}{2}MR^2$ versus $\tfrac{2}{5}MR^2$ for the ball).

So the cylinder has more kinetic energy and will go higher.

The total kinetic energy of the cylinder is $K_c = \tfrac{1}{2}Mv^2 + \tfrac{1}{2}I\omega^2 = \tfrac{1}{2}Mv^2 + \tfrac{1}{2}(\tfrac{1}{2}MR^2)\dfrac{v^2}{R^2} = \tfrac{3}{4}Mv^2,$

The total kinetic energy of the sphere is $K_s = \tfrac{1}{2}Mv^2 + \tfrac{1}{2}(\tfrac{2}{5}MR^2)\dfrac{v^2}{R^2} = \tfrac{7}{10}Mv^2.$

So from energy conservation, $K + 0 = 0 + Mgh$, we have

$$\frac{h_c - h_s}{h_s} = \frac{Mgh_c - Mgh_s}{Mgh_s} = \frac{K_c - K_s}{K_s} = \frac{3/4 - 7/10}{7/10} = 7\%$$

Thus $\boxed{\text{cylinder goes higher by 7.1\%}}$.

82.   Apply energy conservation and note $v = r\omega$. $\frac{1}{2}M(0)^2 + \frac{1}{2}I(0)^2 + Mgh = \frac{1}{2}Mv^2 + \frac{1}{2}I\omega^2 + Mg(0)$.

or $\frac{1}{2}Mv^2 + \frac{1}{2}Mv^2 = Mv^2 = Mgh$,   ☞ $v = \sqrt{gh} = \sqrt{(9.80 \text{ m/s}^2)(1.2 \text{ m})} = \boxed{3.4 \text{ m/s}}$.

83.   (a) 7500 rpm = 785.4 rad/s.   From the work-energy theorem:

$$W = \frac{1}{2}I\omega^2 - \frac{1}{2}I\omega_o^2 = \frac{1}{2}I(0)^2 - \frac{1}{2}I\omega_o^2 = -\frac{1}{2}(4.25 \times 10^2 \text{ kg·m}^2)(785.4 \text{ rad/s})^2 = -\boxed{1.31 \times 10^8 \text{ J}}.$$

(b) $P = \dfrac{W}{t} = \dfrac{1.31 \times 10^8 \text{ J}}{1.5(60 \text{ s})} = \boxed{1.46 \times 10^6 \text{ W}}$.

84. $K = \frac{1}{2}mv^2 + \frac{1}{2}I\omega^2 = \frac{1}{2}mv^2 + \frac{1}{2}I\dfrac{v^2}{R^2}$.   So $K_h = \frac{1}{2}mv_h^2 + \frac{1}{2}(mR^2)\dfrac{v_h^2}{R^2} = mv_h^2$,

$K_c = \frac{1}{2}mv_c^2 + \frac{1}{2}(\frac{1}{2}mR^2)\dfrac{v_c^2}{R^2} = \frac{3}{4}mv_c^2$,   and $K_s = \frac{1}{2}mv_s^2 + \frac{1}{2}(\frac{2}{5}mR^2)\dfrac{v_s^2}{R^2} = \frac{7}{10}mv_s^2$.

Since they are all released from the same height, the K's are the same. That means the v is the greatest for the sphere and smallest for the hoop. Therefore the sphere gets to the bottom first and the hoop last.

$$v_s = \sqrt{\frac{10K}{7m}}, \quad v_c = \sqrt{\frac{4K}{3m}}, \quad \text{and} \quad v_h = \sqrt{\frac{K}{m}}.$$

85.   (a) $K_{\text{tot}} = \frac{1}{2}Mv^2 + \frac{1}{2}I\omega^2 = \frac{1}{2}Mv^2 + \frac{1}{2}I\dfrac{v^2}{R^2} = \frac{1}{2}Mv^2 + \frac{1}{2}(\frac{2}{5}MR^2)\dfrac{v^2}{R^2} = \frac{7}{10}Mv^2$, so $\dfrac{K_{\text{rot}}}{K_{\text{tot}}} = \dfrac{1/5}{7/10} = \boxed{29\%}$.

(b) $K_{\text{tot}} = \frac{1}{2}mv^2 + \frac{1}{2}(\frac{2}{3}MR^2)\dfrac{v^2}{R^2} = \frac{5}{6}Mv^2$,   or $\dfrac{K_{\text{rot}}}{K_{\text{tot}}} = \dfrac{1/3}{5/6} = \boxed{40\%}$.

(c) $K_{\text{tot}} = \frac{1}{2}Mv^2 + \frac{1}{2}MR^2\dfrac{v^2}{R^2} = Mv^2$,   so $\dfrac{K_{\text{rot}}}{K_{\text{tot}}} = \frac{1}{2} = \boxed{50\%}$.

86. $\omega = 33\frac{1}{3}$ rpm = 3.49 rad/s. From the work-energy theorem:

$$W = \frac{1}{2}I\omega^2 - \frac{1}{2}I\omega_o^2 = \frac{1}{2}I\omega^2 - \frac{1}{2}I(0)^2 = \frac{1}{2}I\omega^2 = \frac{1}{2}(\frac{1}{2}MR^2)\omega^2 = \frac{1}{4}(0.05 \text{ kg})(0.15 \text{ m})^2(3.49 \text{ rad/s})^2 = \boxed{3.4 \times 10^{-3} \text{ J}}.$$

This work is supplied by $\boxed{\text{the motor}}$.

87.   (a) The centripetal force is provided solely by gravity at the minimum speed. In this case the centripetal force at the top of the track is just equal to the weight of the ball.

$$Mg = F_C = M\frac{v^2}{R}, \quad ☞ \quad v = \boxed{\sqrt{gR}}.$$

(b) From energy conservation:

$$\tfrac{1}{2}M(0)^2 + \tfrac{1}{2}I(0)^2 + Mgh = \tfrac{1}{2}Mv^2 + \tfrac{1}{2}I\omega^2 + Mg(2R) = \tfrac{1}{2}Mv^2 + \tfrac{1}{2}(\tfrac{2}{5}MR^2)\frac{v^2}{R^2} + Mg(2R)$$

$$= \tfrac{7}{10}MgR + 2MgR = \tfrac{27}{10}MgR,$$

so $h = \boxed{2.7R}$.

(c) Since all the gravity is "used up" as centripetal force, the rider feels $\boxed{\text{weightless}}$.

88.   (c).

89.   Walking toward the center decreases the moment of inertia and so increases the rotational speed.

90.   The polar ice caps (with almost zero moment of inertia) will go to the ocean and increase the moment of inertia of the Earth. This results in a slower rotational speed or a $\boxed{\text{longer day}}$.

91.   The arms and legs are put onto these positions to decrease the moment of inertia. This decrease in moment of inertia increases the rotational speed.

92.   In each case, the change in the wheel's angular momentum vector is compensated by the rotation of the person to conserve the total angular momentum, so the vertical angular momentum remains constant.

93.   The cat manipulates its body to change the moment of inertia to rotate or flip over. It is done by twisting one way with part of the body and then the desired part (the feet) may be rotated the other way.

94.   This is possible because of the $\boxed{\text{conservation of angular momentum}}$. The rotating wheels will keep rotating in the absence of any external torque.

95.   The two rotors, rotating in opposite directions, compensate each other so the total angular momentum of the whole system is zero. Had they not been rotating in the same direction or there were only one rotor, any change in the rotational speed of the rotor(s) must be compensated by other mechanisms, according to the conservation of angular momentum.

96. $L = I\omega = MR^2\omega = (2.0 \times 10^{-3}\ \text{kg})(0.15\ \text{m})^2(5\pi\ \text{rad/s}) = \boxed{7.1 \times 10^{-4}\ \text{kg}\cdot\text{m/s toward you}}$.

97. $L = I\omega,$ ☞ $\omega = \dfrac{L}{I} = \dfrac{L}{\tfrac{1}{2}MR^2} = \dfrac{0.45\ \text{kg}\cdot\text{m}^2/\text{s}}{\tfrac{1}{2}(10\ \text{kg})(0.25\ \text{m})^2} = \boxed{1.4\ \text{rad/s}}$.

98. Orbital: The Earth can be considered as a particle (great distance from the Earth to the Sun).

$$\omega_o = \frac{2\pi \text{ rad}}{(365)(24)(3600 \text{ s})} = 1.99 \times 10^{-7} \text{ rad/s}, \quad \text{and} \quad I_o = MR^2.$$

So $L_o = I_o\omega_o = (6.0 \times 10^{24} \text{ kg})(1.5 \times 10^{11} \text{ m})^2(1.99 \times 10^{-7} \text{ rad/s}) = 2.69 \times 10^{40} \text{ kg·m}^2\text{/s}.$

Spin: The Earth has to be considered as a sphere.

$$\omega_s = \frac{2\pi \text{ rad}}{(24)(3600 \text{ s})} = 7.27 \times 10^{-5} \text{ rad/s}, \quad \text{and} \quad I_s = \tfrac{2}{5}Mr^2.$$

So $L_s = \tfrac{2}{5}(6.0 \times 10^{24} \text{ kg})(6.4 \times 10^6 \text{ m})^2 (7.27 \times 10^{-5} \text{ rad/s}) = 7.15 \times 10^{33} \text{ kg·m}^2\text{/s}.$

Therefore $\dfrac{L_o}{L_s} = \dfrac{2.69 \times 10^{40}}{7.15 \times 10^{33}} = \boxed{3.8 \times 10^6}.$

$\boxed{\text{No}}$, these angular momenta are not in the same direction because the Earth's axis is tilted.

99. Similar to Exercise 8.98. $\omega_{rev} = \omega_{rot} = \dfrac{2\pi \text{ rad}}{(27.3)(24)(3600 \text{ s})} = 2.66 \times 10^{-6} \text{ rad/s}.$

$L_{rot} = \tfrac{2}{5}mr^2\omega_{rot} = \tfrac{2}{5}(7.4 \times 10^{22} \text{ kg})(1.75 \times 10^6 \text{ m})^2(2.66 \times 10^{-6} \text{ rad/s}) = \boxed{2.4 \times 10^{29} \text{ kg·m}^2\text{/s}}.$

$L_{rev} = mR^2\omega_{rev} = (7.4 \times 10^{22} \text{ kg})(3.8 \times 10^8 \text{ m})^2(2.66 \times 10^{-6} \text{ rad/s}) = \boxed{2.8 \times 10^{34} \text{ kg·m}^2\text{/s}}.$

100. (a) The angular speed of the coupled disks is $\boxed{\text{less than}}$ the angular speed of the original rotating disk.

This is because one of the disks was stationary and the moment of inertia of two disks is greater than that of one, according to the conservation of angular momentum.

(b) After the coupling, both disks have the same angular speed. From angular momentum conservation:

$I_1\omega_{1o} + I_2\omega_{2o} = I_1\omega_1 + I_2\omega_3, \quad \text{☞} \quad I_1(800 \text{ rpm}) + 0 = I_1\omega + 3I_1\omega = 4I_1\omega.$

So $\omega = \boxed{200 \text{ rpm}}.$

101. Since $V = \dfrac{4\pi}{3}R^3, \quad R \propto \sqrt[3]{V}. \quad \text{So} \quad \dfrac{R}{R_o} = \sqrt[3]{6} = 1.82. \quad I\omega = I\omega_o,$

$\tfrac{2}{5}MR^2\dfrac{2\pi \text{ rad}}{T} = \tfrac{2}{5}MR_o^2\dfrac{2\pi \text{ rad}}{T_o}, \quad \text{☞} \quad \dfrac{T}{T_o} = \dfrac{R^2}{R_o^2} = (1.82)^2 = 3.3.$

Therefore $\boxed{T = 3.3T_o}.$

102. From angular momentum conservation: $I\omega = I_o\omega_o,$

$$\omega = \frac{I_o\omega_o}{I} = \frac{(100 \text{ kg·m}^2)(2.0 \text{ rps})}{75 \text{ kg·m}^2} = \boxed{2.7 \text{ rps}}.$$

103.   (a) From angular momentum conservation: $I\omega = I_{o}\,\omega_{o}$,

so $\omega = \dfrac{I_{o}}{I}\,\omega_{o} = \dfrac{1}{1-0.075}\,(4.0\ \text{rad/s}) = \boxed{4.3\ \text{rad/s}}$.

(b) $\dfrac{K}{K_{o}} = \dfrac{\frac{1}{2}I\omega^{2}}{\frac{1}{2}I_{o}\,\omega_{o}^{2}} = \dfrac{(0.925)(4.32\ \text{rad/s})^{2}}{(1)(4.0\ \text{rad/s})^{2}} = 1.1.$ so $\boxed{K = 1.1K_{o}}$

(c) The extra kinetic energy comes from the $\boxed{\text{work done by the skater}}$ in tucking her arms.

104.   From angular momentum conservation: $I\omega = I_{o}\omega_{o}$,

or $Mb^{2}\,\dfrac{v_{o}}{b} = Md^{2}\,\dfrac{v}{d}.$ So $d = \boxed{b(v_{o}/v)}$.

105.   (a) From angular momentum conservation, the lazy Susan will $\boxed{\text{rotate in the opposite direction}}$.

(b) The initial total angular momentum (before the kitten walks) is zero.

$L = L_{o},$ ☞ $mR^{2}\omega_{k} + \frac{1}{2}M_{l}R^{2}\omega_{l} = m_{k}R^{2}\dfrac{v_{k}}{R} + \frac{1}{2}M_{l}R^{2}\omega_{l} = 0 + 0,$

so $\omega_{l} = -\dfrac{2m_{k}v_{k}}{M_{l}R} = -\dfrac{2(0.50\ \text{kg})(0.25\ \text{m/s})}{(1.5\ \text{kg})(0.30\ \text{m})} = -0.56\ \text{rad/s}.$

Therefore the lazy Susan rotates at $\boxed{0.56\ \text{rad/s}}$.

(c) $\boxed{\text{No}}$, the kitten will not be above the same point due to the rotation of the lazy Susan.

The relative angular velocity of the kitten relative to the ground is

$\dfrac{0.25\ \text{m/s}}{0.30\ \text{m}} + (-0.556\ \text{rad/s}) = 0.277\ \text{rad/s}.$ It takes $\dfrac{2\pi\ \text{rad}}{(0.25\ \text{m/s})/(0.30\ \text{m})} = 7.54\ \text{s}$ for the kitten to go around.

During that time the angular distance from where the kitten was to where the kitten is (relative to the

ground) is $\theta = (0.277\ \text{rad/s})(7.54\ \text{s}) = \boxed{2.1\ \text{rad}}$. (If we all run eastward the Earth would have to rotate

slower in the eastward direction due to angular momentum conservation. This results in a longer day.)

106.   Chose the right support as axis of rotation.

$\Delta\tau = Mg(5.0\ \text{m}) + mg(7.0\ \text{m}) - F_{L}(10\ \text{m}) = 0,$ so

$(10\,000\ \text{kg})(9.80\ \text{m/s}^{2})(5.0\ \text{m}) + (2000\ \text{kg})(9.80\ \text{m/s}^{2})(7.0\ \text{m}) = F_{L}(10\ \text{m})$

$F_{L} = 6.27 \times 10^{4}\ \text{N} = \boxed{6.3 \times 10^{4}\ \text{N}}.$

$\Sigma F_{y} = F_{L} + F_{R} - mg - Mg = 0,$ ☞ $F_{R} = (m + M)g - F_{L}$

$= (10\,000\ \text{kg} + 2000\ \text{kg})(9.80\ \text{m/s}^{2}) - 6.27 \times 10^{4}\ \text{N} = \boxed{5.5 \times 10^{4}\ \text{N}}.$

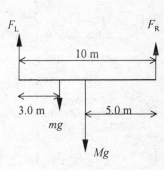

107. $\tau = k\theta,$ ☞ $k = \dfrac{\tau}{\theta}.$ Since $U = \frac{1}{2}k\theta^2$ (analog of $U = \frac{1}{2}kx^2$),

$$U = \frac{1}{2}\frac{\tau}{\theta}\,\theta^2 = \frac{1}{2}\,\tau\theta = \frac{1}{2}(100 \text{ m·N})(60°)\frac{\pi \text{ rad}}{180°} = \boxed{52 \text{ J}}.$$

108. Both rotate about an instantaneous axis though the contact point.

From the parallel-axis theorem: $I_h = I_{CM} + Md^2 = MR^2 + MR^2 = 2MR^2,$

$$I_c = \frac{1}{2}M(R_1^2 + R_2^2) + MR_2^2 = \frac{1}{2}M(R_1^2 + 2R_2^2).$$

From Newton's second law: $Mg(R\sin\theta) = I\alpha = I\dfrac{a}{R},$

so for the hoop: $Mgr\sin\theta = 2MR^2\dfrac{a_h}{R},$ ☞ $a_h = \dfrac{g\sin\theta}{2},$

for the annular cylinder: $MgR_2\sin\theta = \frac{1}{2}M(R_1^2 + 2R_2^2)\dfrac{a_c}{R_2},$

or $a_c = \dfrac{2g\sin\theta}{R_1^2/R_2^2 + 2} = \dfrac{g\sin\theta}{R_1^2/2R_2^2 + 1}.$ Since $R_2 > R_1,$ $R_1^2/2R_2^2 < 1,$ or $R_1^2/2R_2^2 + 1 < 2,$ so $a_c > a_h.$

Therefore the hoop rolls (accelerates) more slowly.

109. (a) For the mass: $\Sigma F = mg - T = ma$ Eq. (1)

For the pulley: $\Sigma\tau = rT = I\alpha = \frac{1}{2}Mr^2\dfrac{a}{r} = \frac{1}{2}Mra,$ or $T = \frac{1}{2}Ma$ Eq. (2)

Solving for $a = \dfrac{mg}{m + \frac{1}{2}M} = \dfrac{(5.0 \text{ kg})(9.80 \text{ m/s}^2)}{5.0 \text{ kg} + \frac{1}{2}(10 \text{ kg})} = \boxed{4.9 \text{ m/s}^2}.$

(b) $\alpha = \dfrac{a}{r} = \dfrac{4.9 \text{ m/s}^2}{0.50 \text{ m}} = \boxed{9.8 \text{ rad/s}^2}.$

110. (a) $\omega = \dfrac{v}{R} = \dfrac{1.5 \text{ m/s}}{0.40 \text{ m}} = \boxed{3.8 \text{ rad/s}}.$

(b) $L = I\omega = MR^2\omega = (2.0 \text{ kg})(0.40 \text{ m})^2(3.75 \text{ rad/s}) = \boxed{1.2 \text{ kg·m}^2/\text{s}}.$

111. Since the angular velocity is constant, the net torque acting on the piece is $\boxed{0}$.

112. (a) The location of the center of gravity is expected to be $\boxed{\text{toward the scale at the person's head}}$ because the mass distribution of the human body is more toward the upper body than the lower body.

(b) Choose the center of gravity as the axis of rotation.

$\Sigma\tau = (25 \text{ kg})gx - (30 \text{ kg})g(1.6 \text{ m} - x) = 0,$ or $25x - 48 + 30x = 0.$

Solving, $x = \boxed{0.87 \text{ m from feet}}.$

113.   (a) The first brick is not displaced.

So for each brick, the maximum displacement is $\dfrac{20\text{ cm}}{8} = \boxed{2.5\text{ cm}}$.

(b) The height of the center of mass is $\dfrac{9(8.0\text{ cm})}{2} = \boxed{36\text{ cm}}$.

114.   (a) $I = Mk = \tfrac{2}{5}MR^2$, ☞ $k = \boxed{\sqrt{\tfrac{2}{5}}R}$.   (b) $I = Mk = \tfrac{1}{2}MR^2$, ☞ $k = \boxed{\sqrt{\tfrac{1}{2}}R}$.

(c) $I = Mk = MR^2$, ☞ $k = \boxed{R}$.

115.   After the child jumps onto the rim the angular speed of the child and the disk are the same. From angular momentum conservation: $\tfrac{1}{2}(100\text{ kg})(2.0\text{ m})^2(2.0\text{ rad/s}) + 0 = \tfrac{1}{2}(100\text{ kg})(2.0\text{ m})^2\omega + (25\text{ kg})(2.0\text{ m})^2\omega$.

Solving for $\omega = \boxed{1.3\text{ rad/s}}$.

116. $\Sigma F_x = -T_1\cos 45° + T_2\cos 30° = 0$,   or $-\sqrt{2}\,T_1 + \sqrt{3}\,T_2 = 0$ Eq. (1)

$\Sigma F_y = T_1\sin 45° - T_2\sin 30° - mg = 0$,   or $\sqrt{2}\,T_1 - T_2 - 2mg = 0$.   Eq. (2)

Eq. (1) + Eq. (2) gives $(\sqrt{3} - 1)T_2 = 2mg$,

so $T_2 = \dfrac{2(1.5\text{ kg})(9.80\text{ m/s}^2)}{\sqrt{3}-1} = \boxed{40\text{ N}}$ and $T_1 = \sqrt{\dfrac{3}{2}}\,T_2 = \boxed{49\text{ N}}$.

117. $\Sigma F_y = T_1\sin 45° - mg = 0$,   ☞ $T_1 = \dfrac{mg}{\sin 45°} = \dfrac{(1.5\text{ kg})(9.80\text{ m/s}^2)}{\sin 45°} = 21\text{ N}$,

$\Sigma F_x = -T_1\cos 45° + T_2 = 0$, $T_2 = T_1\cos 45° = 15\text{ N}$.   So the tensions are $\boxed{21\text{ N and }15\text{ N}}$.

118.   On the verge of the unstable equilibrium, the weight goes through the lower corner

of the trailer.   So $\tan\theta = \dfrac{L/2}{h} = \dfrac{3.66\text{ m}}{2(3.58\text{ m})} = 0.511$.   Therefore $\theta = \boxed{27°}$.

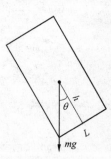

119.   Since $I \propto r^2$, the moment of inertia is more when the axis is on the $\boxed{\text{smaller side}}$.

Let $a = 40$ cm and $b = 30$ cm. From the parallel-axis theorem: $I = I_{CM} + Md^2$,

the moment of inertia for an axis on the smaller side is

$I_s = \tfrac{1}{12}M(a^2 + b^2) + M(a/2)^2 = \tfrac{1}{12}M(4a^2 + b^2)$,

the moment of inertia for an axis on the larger axis is

$I_l = \tfrac{1}{12}M(a^2 + b^2) + M(b/2)^2 = \tfrac{1}{12}M(a^2 + 4b^2)$.

So $\dfrac{I_s}{I_l} = \dfrac{4a^2 + b^2}{a^2 + 4b^2} = \dfrac{4(40)^2 + (30)^2}{(40)^2 + 4(30)^2} = \boxed{1.4\text{ times}}$.

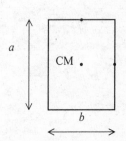

CHAPTER 9

1.   (c).

2.   (a).

3. $\boxed{\text{Steel wire}}$ has a greater Young's modulus. Young's modulus is a measure of the ratio of stress over strain. For a given stress, a greater Young's modulus will have a smaller strain. Steel will have smaller strain here.

4.   Scissors exert large shear forces on materials. So the answer is $\boxed{\text{yes}}$, this name is in physical sense.

5. $\dfrac{F}{A} = Y \dfrac{\Delta L}{L_0}$,   ☞ $F = YA \dfrac{\Delta L}{L_0} = \dfrac{YA}{L_0} \Delta L$.   Compare with $F = k\Delta x$,

     we have $k = \dfrac{YA}{L_0}$.   So the units are $\dfrac{\text{N/m}^2 \cdot \text{m}^2}{\text{m}} = \boxed{\text{N/m}}$.

6. $\text{Stress} = \dfrac{F}{A} = \dfrac{mg}{\pi r^2} = \dfrac{(5.0 \text{ kg})(9.80 \text{ m/s}^2)}{\pi(1.0 \times 10^{-2} \text{ m})^2} = \boxed{1.6 \times 10^5 \text{ N/m}^2}$.

7. $\text{Stain} = \dfrac{\Delta L}{L_0} = \dfrac{0.10 \text{ m}}{5.0 \text{ m}} = \boxed{0.020}$.

8.   (a) The compression stress $= \dfrac{F}{A} = \dfrac{(250 \text{ N}) \sin 37°}{(0.040 \text{ m})(0.040 \text{ m})} = \boxed{9.4 \times 10^4 \text{ N/m}^2}$. $37°$ / 500 N

     (b) The shear stress $= \dfrac{(250 \text{ N}) \cos 37°}{(0.040 \text{ m})(0.040 \text{ m})} = \boxed{1.2 \times 10^5 \text{ N/m}^2}$.

9. $\text{Stress} = \dfrac{F}{A} = \dfrac{mg}{\pi r^2} = \dfrac{(6.0 \text{ kg})(9.80 \text{ m/s}^2)}{\pi(0.50 \times 10^{-3} \text{ m})^2} = 7.49 \times 10^7 \text{ N/m}^2$,

     $\text{strain} = \dfrac{\Delta L}{L_0} = \dfrac{1.4 \times 10^{-3} \text{ m}}{2.0 \text{ m}} = 7.0 \times 10^{-4}$.

     So $Y = \dfrac{\text{stress}}{\text{strain}} = \dfrac{7.49 \times 10^7 \text{ N/m}^2}{7.0 \times 10^{-4}} = \boxed{1.1 \times 10^{11} \text{ N/m}^2}$.

10.   From $Y = \dfrac{F/A}{\Delta L/L_0} = \dfrac{FL_0}{A\Delta L}$,

     $\Delta L = \dfrac{FL_0}{YA} = \dfrac{(5.0 \text{ kg})(9.80 \text{ m/s}^2)(2.0 \text{ m})}{(7.0 \times 10^{10} \text{ N/m}^2)(\pi)(1.0 \times 10^{-3} \text{ m})^2} = 4.5 \times 10^{-4} \text{ m} = \boxed{0.45 \text{ mm}}$.

11. From $Y = \dfrac{F/A}{\Delta L/L_o} = \dfrac{FL_o}{A\Delta L}$,

$F = \dfrac{YA\Delta L}{L_o} = \dfrac{(11 \times 10^{10}\ \text{N/m}^2)(\pi)(1.5 \times 10^{-3}\ \text{m})^2(0.3 \times 10^{-3}\ \text{m})}{5.0\ \text{m}} = \boxed{47\ \text{N}}$.

12. (a) A greater gap should be used $\boxed{\text{on a cold day}}$ because the tracks will expand when the temperature increases.

(b) From $Y = \dfrac{F/A}{\Delta L/L_o} = \dfrac{FL_o}{A\Delta L}$,

$F = \dfrac{YA\Delta L}{L_o} = \dfrac{(20 \times 10^{10}\ \text{N/m}^2)(\pi)(2.5 \times 10^{-3}\ \text{m})^2(3.0 \times 10^{-3}\ \text{m})}{8.0\ \text{m}} = \boxed{1.9 \times 10^5\ \text{N}}$.

This is about 19 tons. So yes, it is a good reason to leave a gap to eliminate this stress.

13. From $Y = \dfrac{F/A}{\Delta L/L_o} = \dfrac{FL_o}{A\Delta L}$,

$\Delta L = \dfrac{FL_o}{YA} = \dfrac{(12.0 \times 10^3\ \text{kg})(9.80\ \text{m/s}^2)(2.00\ \text{m})}{(20 \times 10^{10}\ \text{N/m}^2)(0.200\ \text{m})(0.150\ \text{m})} = \boxed{3.92 \times 10^{-5}\ \text{m}}$.

14. (a) Since the compression strain $= \dfrac{\Delta L}{L_o} = -\dfrac{\text{stress}}{Y}$, the stresses are the same for both, and brass has a smaller Young's modulus. Brass will have a greater strain $\dfrac{\Delta L}{L_o}$, so it will be compressed more. Therefore, the brass will be shorter than the copper, and thus it will bend $\boxed{\text{toward brass}}$.

(b) Brass: $\dfrac{\Delta L}{L_o} = -\dfrac{(5.00 \times 10^4\ \text{N})/[(0.010\ \text{m})(0.020\ \text{m})]}{9.0 \times 10^{10}\ \text{N/m}^2} = \boxed{2.8 \times 10^{-3}}$.

Copper: $\dfrac{\Delta L}{L_o} = -\dfrac{(5.00 \times 10^4\ \text{N})/[(0.010\ \text{m})(0.020\ \text{m})]}{11 \times 10^{10}\ \text{N/m}^2} = \boxed{2.3 \times 10^{-3}}$.

15. Shear strain: $\phi = \dfrac{\text{shear stress}}{S} = \dfrac{F/A}{S} = \dfrac{F}{SA} = \dfrac{500\ \text{N}}{(2.5 \times 10^{10}\ \text{N/m}^2)(0.10\ \text{m})^2} = 2.0 \times 10^{-6} = \dfrac{x}{h}$.

So $x = (2.0 \times 10^{-6})(0.10\ \text{m}) = \boxed{2.0 \times 10^{-7}\ \text{m}}$.

16. (a) $\boxed{\text{The Al post}}$ will show the larger deformation angle because it has a smaller shear modulus.

(b) Shear strain $\phi = \dfrac{\text{shear stress}}{S}$, ☞ $\dfrac{\phi_{Al}}{\phi_{Cu}} = \dfrac{S_{Cu}}{S_{Al}} = \dfrac{3.8 \times 10^{10}\ \text{N/m}^2}{2.5 \times 10^{10}\ \text{N/m}^2} = 1.52$.

So $\boxed{\phi_{Al} = 1.5\,\phi_{Cu}}$.

17. $S = \dfrac{\text{stress}}{\text{strain}} = \dfrac{F/A}{x/h} = \dfrac{Fh}{Ax} = \dfrac{(0.40\ \text{N})(0.040\ \text{m})}{(0.10\ \text{m})(0.080\ \text{m})(0.30 \times 10^{-3}\ \text{m})} = \boxed{6.7 \times 10^3\ \text{N/m}^2}$.

18. To completely shear off the rivets, $x = 0.20$ cm. $S = \dfrac{\text{stress}}{\text{strain}} = \dfrac{F/A}{x/h} = \dfrac{F\,h}{A\,x}$,

    so $F = \dfrac{SAx}{h} = \dfrac{(8.2 \times 10^{10}\ \text{N/m}^2)(\pi)(0.10 \times 10^{-2}\ \text{m})^2(0.20 \times 10^{-2}\ \text{m})}{1.0 \times 10^{-2}\ \text{m}} = 5.15 \times 10^4\ \text{N}$.

    Since there are two rivets, the force required is $2(5.15 \times 10^4\ \text{N}) = \boxed{1.0 \times 10^5\ \text{N}}$.

19. (a) $\boxed{\text{Ethyl alcohol}}$ has the greatest compressibility because it has the smallest bulk modulus.

    $B = -\dfrac{\Delta p}{\Delta V/V_o}$, the smaller the B, the greater the compressibility.

    (b) $\dfrac{\Delta p_w}{\Delta p_e} = \dfrac{B_w}{B_e} = \dfrac{2.2 \times 10^9\ \text{N/m}^2}{1.0 \times 10^9\ \text{N/m}^2} = 2.2$ So $\boxed{\Delta p_w = 2.2 \Delta p_{ea}}$.

20. $\dfrac{\Delta V}{V_o} = -\dfrac{\Delta p}{B} = -\dfrac{1.2 \times 10^7\ \text{N/m}^2}{7.5 \times 10^{10}\ \text{N/m}^2} = 1.6 \times 10^{-4}$.

    So $V = V_o + \Delta V = (1 - 1.6 \times 10^{-4})(0.060\ \text{m})^3 = 2.16 \times 10^{-4}\ \text{m}^3$.

    $\Delta L = L - L_o = \sqrt[3]{V} - L_o = \sqrt[3]{V_o + \Delta V} - L_o = \sqrt[3]{(1 - 1.6 \times 10^{-4})(0.060\ \text{m})^3} - 0.060\ \text{m}$

    $= -\boxed{3.2 \times 10^{-6}\ \text{m}}$.

21. First find the tensions on the cables. The system is symmetrical. So in the vertical direction:

    $2T \sin 15^\circ = mg$,   ☞ $T = \dfrac{(45\ \text{kg})(9.80\ \text{m/s}^2)}{2 \sin 15^\circ} = 852\ \text{N}$.

    $\dfrac{\Delta L}{L_o} = \dfrac{\text{stress}}{Y} = \dfrac{T/A}{Y} = \dfrac{T}{YA} = \dfrac{852\ \text{N}}{(20 \times 10^{10}\ \text{N/m}^2)(\pi)(0.50 \times 10^{-2}\ \text{m})^2} = \boxed{5.4 \times 10^{-5}}$.

22. The pressure is small on any one nail due to the large number of nails (large area).

23. (c).

24. The pressure is determined by depth only so the effect is $\boxed{\text{none—same depth, same pressure}}$.

25. When the bowl is full, the atmospheric pressure on the water does not allow any water out of the bottle. When the water level in the bowl decreases below the neck of the bottle, air bubbles come in and water flows out until the pressures are equalized again. No, the height does not depend on the surface area.

26.   (a) The pressure inside the can is equal to the atmospheric pressure outside. When the liquid is poured from an unvented can, a partial vacuum develops inside, and the pressure difference causes the pouring to be difficult. By opening the vent, you are allowing air to go into the can and the pressures are equalized so the liquid can be easily poured.

(b) When you squeeze a medicine dropper before inserting it into a liquid, you are forcing the air out and reducing the pressure inside the dropper. When you release the top with the dropper in a liquid, the liquid rises in the dropper due to atmospheric pressure.

(c) To inhale, the lungs physically expand, the internal pressure decreases, and air flows into the lungs. To exhale, the lungs contract, the internal pressure increases, and air is forced out.

27.   Bicycle tires have a much smaller contact area with the ground so they need a higher pressure to balance the weight of the bicycle and the rider.

28. $\boxed{\text{Yes}}$. The pressure taken from the calf is higher than that taken from the arm because of a height pressure difference.

29.   Our human bodies are the result of evolution and adaptation. There is internal pressure so $\boxed{\text{pressure inside balances pressure outside}}$.

30.   When you suck on the straw, a partial vacuum (lower pressure) develops inside the straw. So the $\boxed{\text{atmospheric pressure pushes up soda into the straw}}$ due to the pressure difference.

31.   (a) A water barometer should have a $\boxed{\text{higher}}$ height than the mercury barometer due to its low density.

(b) $p_a = \rho g h,$ ☞ $h = \dfrac{1.01 \times 10^5 \text{ Pa}}{(1000 \text{ kg/m}^3)(9.80 \text{ m/s}^2)} = \boxed{10 \text{ m}}$.

32.   (a) $p_w = \rho g h = (1000 \text{ kg/m}^3)(9.80 \text{ m/s}^2)(15 \cdot \text{m}) = \boxed{1.5 \times 10^5 \text{ Pa}}$.

(b) $p = p_o + p_w = 1.01 \times 10^5 \text{ Pa} + 1.5 \times 10^5 \text{ Pa} = \boxed{2.5 \times 10^5 \text{ Pa}}$.

33.   (a) The gasoline column will have a $\boxed{\text{higher}}$ column height because it has a lower density.

(b) The pressure by the water is equal to the pressure by the gasoline.

$\rho_w g h_w = \rho_g g h_g,$ ☞ $h_g = \dfrac{\rho_w h_w}{\rho_g} = \dfrac{(1000 \text{ kg/m}^3)(15 \text{ cm})}{680 \text{ kg/m}^3} = \boxed{22 \text{ cm}}$.

34. $p = \dfrac{F}{A} = \dfrac{mg}{A} = \dfrac{(75\ \text{kg})(9.80\ \text{m/s}^2)}{125 \times 10^{-4}\ \text{m}^2} = \boxed{5.9 \times 10^4\ \text{Pa}}$.

35. $p = \dfrac{F}{2A}$, where A is the contact area of each tire.

   So $A = \dfrac{F}{p} = \dfrac{mg}{2p} = \dfrac{(90\ \text{kg})(9.80\ \text{m/s}^2)}{2(690 \times 10^3\ \text{Pa})} = \boxed{6.39 \times 10^{-4}\ \text{m}^2}$.

36. $p = p_a + \rho_1 g h_1 + \rho_2 g h_2$

   $= 1.013 \times 10^5\ \text{Pa} + (0.75 \times 10^3\ \text{kg/m}^3)(9.80\ \text{m/s}^2)(0.040\ \text{m}) + (1000\ \text{kg/m}^3)(9.80\ \text{m/s}^2)(0.55\ \text{m})$

   $= \boxed{1.07 \times 10^5\ \text{Pa}}$.

37.   (a) This is because of $\boxed{\text{a lower pressure inside the can as steam condenses}}$. Since there is a partial vacuum

   inside the can, the net force exerted by the atmospheric pressure on the outside crushes the can.

   (b) The total surface area of the can is calculated from all six sides.

   $F = PA = (1.01 \times 10^5\ \text{Pa})(2)[(0.24\ \text{m})(0.16\ \text{m}) + (0.24\ \text{m})(0.10\ \text{m}) + (0.16\ \text{m})(0.10\ \text{m})]$

   $= \boxed{1.6 \times 10^4\ \text{N} = 3600\ \text{lb}}$.

38. $\Delta p = \rho g h = (1.29\ \text{kg/m}^3)(9.80\ \text{m/s}^2)(35\ \text{m}) = 442\ \text{Pa}$.

   So the fractional decrease is $\dfrac{\Delta p}{p_a} = \dfrac{442\ \text{Pa}}{1.013 \times 10^5\ \text{Pa}} = 4.37 \times 10^{-3} = \boxed{0.44\%}$.

39. $p = p_a - \rho g h = 1.013 \times 10^5\ \text{Pa} - (1.29\ \text{kg/m}^3)(9.80\ \text{m/s}^2)(29\,028\ \text{ft}) \times \dfrac{1\ \text{m}}{3.28\ \text{ft}} = -1.1 \times 10^4\ \text{Pa}$.

   Obviously, pressure cannot be negative, so this calculation shows that the air density is not a constant, but

   $\boxed{\text{air density decreases rapidly with altitude}}$.

40.   (a) $w = mg = \rho V g = (1000\ \text{kg/m}^3)(5.0 \times 10^{-5}\ \text{m}^2)(12\ \text{m})(9.80\ \text{m/s}^2) = \boxed{5.9\ \text{N}}$.

   (b) $p_w = \rho g h = (1000\ \text{kg/m}^3)(9.80\ \text{m/s}^2)(12\ \text{m}) = \boxed{1.2 \times 10^5\ \text{Pa}}$.

   (c) $F = PA = (1.2 \times 10^5\ \text{Pa})(0.20\ \text{m}^2) = \boxed{2.4 \times 10^4\ \text{N}}$.

41.   The net force due to air pressure is

   $F_{\text{net}} = \Delta p A = (1.01 \times 10^5\ \text{Pa} - 2.7 \times 10^4\ \text{Pa})(3.0\ \text{m}^2) = \boxed{2.2 \times 10^5\ \text{N (about 50\,000 lb)}}$.

42.   Gauge pressure: $p_{\text{gauge}} = \rho g h = (1000\ \text{kg/m}^3)(9.80\ \text{m/s}^2)(0.80\ \text{m}) = \boxed{7.8 \times 10^3\ \text{Pa}}$.

43.   (a) $p = p_a + \rho g h = 1.013 \times 10^5$ Pa $+ (1.03 \times 10^3$ kg/m$^3)(9.80$ m/s$^2)(35\,000$ ft$) \times \dfrac{1\text{ m}}{3.28\text{ ft}} = \boxed{1.1 \times 10^8\text{ Pa}}$.

     (b) $p = \dfrac{F}{A}$,   ☞ $F = p\,A = (1.08 \times 10^8$ Pa$)(\pi)(0.075$ m$)^2 = \boxed{1.9 \times 10^6\text{ N}}$.

44.   (a) From Pascal's principle, $p_i = p_o = \dfrac{F_o}{A_o} = \dfrac{1.5 \times 10^6\text{ N}}{0.20\text{ m}^2} = \boxed{7.5 \times 10^6\text{ Pa}}$.

     (b) $F_i = P_i A_i = (7.5 \times 10^6$ Pa$)(\pi)(0.025$ m$)^2 = \boxed{1.5 \times 10^4\text{ N}}$.

45.   From Pascal's principle, $p_i = p_o$,   ☞ $\dfrac{F_i}{A_i} = \dfrac{F_o}{A_o}$.

     So $F_i = \dfrac{A_i}{A_o} F_o = \dfrac{4.00\text{ cm}^2}{250\text{ cm}^2} \times (3000\text{ kg})(9.80\text{ m/s}^2) = \boxed{470\text{ N}}$.

     $p = \dfrac{F}{A} = \dfrac{470\text{ N}}{4.00 \times 10^{-4}\text{ m}^2} = \boxed{1.2 \times 10^6\text{ Pa}}$.

46.   (a) $p = \dfrac{F}{A} = \dfrac{1.0\text{ N}}{2.5 \times 10^{-4}\text{ m}^2} = \boxed{4.0 \times 10^3\text{ Pa}}$.

     (b) The pressure on the plunger is the same as the pressure on the needle, according to Pascal's law.

     $F = pA = (4.0 \times 10^3$ Pa$)(5.0 \times 10^{-7}$ m$^2) = \boxed{2.0 \times 10^3\text{ N}}$.

     (c) $p = 50$ mmHg $= (50$ mmHg$) \times \dfrac{1.01 \times 10^5\text{ Pa}}{760\text{ mmHg}} = 6.64 \times 10^3$ Pa.

     $F = pA = (6.64 \times 10^3$ Pa$)(2.5 \times 10^{-4}$ m$^2) = \boxed{1.7\text{ N}}$.

47.   The force on the platform must be equal to the weight of the water. So the pressure increase is

     $\Delta p = \dfrac{F}{A} = \dfrac{mg}{A} = \dfrac{(0.25 \times 10^{-3}\text{ kg})(9.80\text{ m/s}^2)}{p(0.55 \times 10^{-2}\text{ m})^2} = 25.78$ Pa.

     So the change in height is $\Delta h = \dfrac{\Delta p}{\rho g} = \dfrac{25.78\text{ Pa}}{(1000\text{ kg/m}^3)(9.80\text{ m/s}^2)} = 2.63 \times 10^{-3}$ m $= \boxed{2.6\text{ mm}}$.

48.   (c).

49.   (a).

50.   (a) A life jacket must have lower density than water, such that the average density of a person and a jacket is less than the density of water.

     (b) Salt water has a higher density so it can exert higher buoyant force.

51.   The level does not change. As the ice melts, the volume of the newly converted water decreases; however, the ice, which was initially above the water surface, is now under the water. This compensated for the decrease in volume. It does not matter whether the ice is hollow or not. Both can be proved mathematically.

52.   Port water (partially fresh) is less dense than seawater . The water in New Orleans is partly fresh or less salty. Seawater has a higher density and therefore more buoyancy than harbor water, so when the ship is in seawater, the Plimsoll mark will be above the water level.

53.   They will receive the same buoyant force because it depends only on the volume of the fluids displaced and is independent of the mass of the object.

54.   They change the temperature of the air inside the balloon, and therefore its density . Hot air is less dense, so the balloon rises, and cold air is more dense, so the balloon descends.

55.   Yes, reading increases due to the reaction force of the buoyant force . The finger receives an upward buoyant force, and its reaction force is a downward force on the water. It is then transmitted to the bucket and finally to the scale.

56.   (a) The object will stay at any height because the weight is exactly balanced by the buoyant force. Wherever the object is placed, it stays at that place.
       (b) $F_b = \rho_f g V_f = (1000 \text{ kg/m}^3)(9.80 \text{ m/s}^2)(0.085 \text{ m})^3 = 6.02 \text{ N}$,
       and $W = mg = (0.65 \text{ kg})(9.80 \text{ m/s}^2) = 6.37 \text{ N}$.   Since $W > F_b$, the object will sink .

57.   (a) He did it by water displacement .
       (b) $\rho = \dfrac{m}{V} = \dfrac{0.750 \text{ kg}}{3.980 \times 10^{-5} \text{ m}^3} = 18.8 \times 10^3 \text{ kg/m}^3 < \rho_g = 19.3 \times 10^3 \text{ kg/m}^3$. No .

58.   When floating, $w = F_b = \rho_f g V_f$.
       $m = \dfrac{w}{g} = \rho_f V = (1000 \text{ kg/m}^3)(4.5 \text{ m})(2.0 \text{ m})(0.29 \text{ m}) = \boxed{2.6 \times 10^3 \text{ kg}}$.

59. $F_b = \rho_f g V_f = (1000 \text{ kg/m}^3)(9.80 \text{ m/s}^2)(0.15 \text{ m})^3 = \boxed{33 \text{ N}}$. If a cube is made of steel, the answer is the same because buoyant force depends only on the weight of fluid displaced.

60. First find the volume of the crown with buoyancy.

$F_b = 8.0 \text{ N} - 4.0 \text{ N} = 4.0 \text{ N} = \rho_f g V_f$,

so $\quad V = \dfrac{F_b}{\rho_f g} = \dfrac{4.0 \text{ N}}{(1000 \text{ kg /m}^3)(9.80 \text{ m/s}^2)} = 4.08 \times 10^{-4} \text{ m}^3$.

$\rho = \dfrac{m}{V} = \dfrac{w/g}{V} = \dfrac{8.0 \text{ N}}{(9.80 \text{ m/s}^2)(4.08 \times 10^{-4} \text{ m}^3)} = \boxed{2.0 \times 10^3 \text{ kg/m}^3}$.

61. First find the volume of the crown with buoyancy. $\quad F_b = (0.80 \text{ kg})(9.80 \text{ m/s}^2) - 7.30 \text{ N} = 0.54 \text{ N}$.

Since $F_b = \rho_f g V_f$, $\quad V = \dfrac{F_b}{\rho_f g} = \dfrac{0.54 \text{ N}}{(1000 \text{ kg/m}^3)(9.80 \text{ m/s}^2)} = 5.51 \times 10^{-5} \text{ m}^3$.

So the density is $\rho = \dfrac{m}{V} = \dfrac{0.80 \text{ kg}}{5.51 \times 10^{-5} \text{ m}^3} = 14.5 \times 10^3 \text{ kg/m}^3 < \rho_g = 19.3 \times 10^3 \text{ kg/m}^3$. $\boxed{\text{No}}$.

62. (a) Measure the weight of the metal twice, once in air and once in water; determine the buoyant force; then find the volume of the metal using Archimedes' principle.

(b) The buoyant force is $F_b = 0.882 \text{ N} - 0.735 \text{ N} = 0.147 \text{ N}$.

$F_b = \rho_f g V_f$, $\quad \Rightarrow \quad V = \dfrac{F_b}{\rho_f g} = \dfrac{0.147 \text{ N}}{(1000 \text{ kg/m}^3)(9.80 \text{ m/s}^2)} = \boxed{1.50 \times 10^{-5} \text{ m}^3}$.

$\rho = \dfrac{m}{V} = \dfrac{w/g}{V} = \dfrac{0.882 \text{ N}}{(1.50 \times 10^{-5} \text{ m}^3)(9.80 \text{ m/s}^2)} = \boxed{6.00 \times 10^3 \text{ kg/m}^3}$.

63. For the boat to float, $\quad w = mg = F_b = \rho_f g V_f = \rho_f g LWH$.

So $\quad H = \dfrac{m}{\rho_f LW} = \dfrac{2000 \text{ kg}}{(1000 \text{ kg/m}^3)(4.0 \text{ m})(1.5 \text{ m})} = \boxed{0.33 \text{ m}}$.

64. For the hollow cube to float, its weight has to be balanced by the buoyant force.

$w = mg = (\rho V) F_b = \rho_f g V_f = \rho_f g L^3$, where ρ is density of the cube (iron), V is the volume of the solid cube, and V_f the volume of the hollow cube.

So $\quad L = \sqrt[3]{\dfrac{m}{\rho_f}} = \sqrt[3]{\dfrac{\rho V}{\rho_f}} = \sqrt[3]{\dfrac{(7.8 \times 10^3 \text{ kg/m}^3)(1.0 \text{ m})^3}{1000 \text{ kg/m}^3}} = \boxed{2.0 \text{ m}}$,

65. For the airship to float, the total weight (weight of the airship plus the weight of helium) must be equal to the buoyant force.

$w = m_{ship} g + m_{helium} g = m_{ship} g + \rho_{helium} g V = m_{ship} g + \rho_{helim} g(\pi r^2 L) = F_b = \rho_f g V = \rho_f g \pi r^2 L$.

So the diameter is

$d = 2r = 2\sqrt{\dfrac{m_{ship}}{\pi L(\rho_f - \rho_{helim})}} = 2\sqrt{\dfrac{30.0 \times 10^3 \text{ kg}}{\pi(110 \text{ m})(1.29 \text{ kg/m}^3 - 0.18 \text{ kg/m}^3)}} = \boxed{17.7 \text{ m}}$.

66. (a) For the girl to float, $w = mg = F_b = \rho_f g V_f = \rho_f g (0.90 V)$.

So $\rho_m = \dfrac{m}{V} = (0.97)\rho_f = (0.97)(1000 \text{ kg/m}^3) = \boxed{9.7 \times 10^2 \text{ kg/m}^3}$.

(b) $\rho_w = \dfrac{w}{V} = \rho_m g = (970 \text{ kg/m}^3)(9.80 \text{ m/s}^2) = \boxed{9.5 \times 10^3 \text{ N/m}^3}$.

67. Assume the volume of the oak is V. Then its mass is $m = \rho_{oak} V$.

$\Sigma F = F_b - w = \rho_{water} g V - mg = \rho_{water} g V - \rho_{oak} g V = (\rho_{water} - \rho_{oak}) g V$.

$a = \dfrac{\Sigma F}{m} = \dfrac{(\rho_{water} - \rho_{oak})g V}{\rho_{oak} V} = \dfrac{\rho_{water} - \rho_{oak}}{\rho_{oak}} g = \dfrac{1000 \text{ kg/m}^3 - 810 \text{ kg/m}^3}{810 \text{ kg/m}^3}(9.80 \text{ m/s}^2) = \boxed{2.3 \text{ m/s}^2}$.

68. (a).

69. $\boxed{\text{There are many more capillaries}}$ than arteries. The total area of the capillaries is greater than that of the arteries. So if A increases, v decreases.

70. According to the equation of continuity, $\boxed{\text{the smaller the area, the greater the speed}}$. A greater speed will have a longer range.

71. (c), because pressure, height, and speed are all in the same equation.

72. The falling water causes a downward airflow inside the curtain. This in turn decreases the pressure inside according to Bernoulli's principle. The pressure difference moves the curtain inward.

73. The concave bottom makes the air travel faster under the car. This increase in speed will reduce the pressure under the car. The pressure difference forces the car on to the ground more to provide a greater normal force and friction for traction.

74. (a) The air flow above the paper decreases the pressure there. This creates a pressure difference, and a lift force results.
(b) The egg is kept aloft by the pressure of the air coming out of the end of the tube. As the eggs move to one side, there is a change in the flow speed around the egg that creates an inward pressure that makes the egg move back to midstream.

75. $\boxed{\text{The side facing the batter should be spinning downward}}$ so as to generate the extra downward force caused by the pressure difference between the top and bottom of the ball.

76. $A_1 v_1 = A_2 v_2,$ ☞ $v_2 = \dfrac{A_1}{A_2} v_1 = \dfrac{\pi(0.20\ \text{m})^2}{\pi(0.35\ \text{m})^2} \times (3.0\ \text{m/s}) = \boxed{0.98\ \text{m/s}}$.

77.   (a) The flow speed will $\boxed{\text{increase by a factor of 4}}$.

$A_1 v_1 = A_2 v_2,$ ☞ $\dfrac{v_2}{v_1} = \dfrac{A_1}{A_2} = \dfrac{\pi(1)^2}{\pi(0.5)^2} = 4$.

(b) $\dfrac{v_2}{v_1} = \dfrac{A_1}{A_2} = \dfrac{\pi(1)^2}{\pi(3)^2} = 1/9$.

So the flow speed $\boxed{\text{decreases by a factor of 9}}$.

78.   From Bernoulli's principle, $p_1 + \tfrac{1}{2}\rho v_1^2 + \rho g y_1 = p_2 + \tfrac{1}{2}\rho v_2^2 + \rho g y_2$.

If $v_1 = v_2 = 0,$ we have $\Delta p = p_1 - p_2 = \rho g(y_2 - y_1)$.

79.   (a) The flow rate is $Q = Av = \pi(0.50\ \text{cm})^2(4.5\ \text{cm/s}) = \boxed{3.5\ \text{cm}^3\text{/s}}$.

(b) The speed in the capillaries is $v = \dfrac{Q}{A} = \dfrac{3.53\ \text{cm}^3\text{/s}}{2500\ \text{cm}^2} = 1.41 \times 10^{-3}\ \text{cm/s}$.

So the percentage is $\dfrac{1.41 \times 10^{-3}\ \text{cm/s}}{4.5\ \text{cm/s}} = 3.1 \times 10^{-4} = \boxed{0.031\%}$.

(c) It is a physiological need. The slow speed is needed to give time for the exchange of substances such as oxygen between the blood and the tissues.

80.   (a) The flow rate is $Q = Av = \dfrac{V}{t} = \dfrac{(3.0\ \text{m})(4.5\ \text{m})(6.0\ \text{m})}{(12\ \text{min})(60\ \text{s/min})} = \boxed{0.11\ \text{m}^3\text{/s}}$.

(b) $v = \dfrac{Q}{A} = \dfrac{0.11\ \text{m}^3\text{/s}}{\pi(0.15\ \text{m})^2} = \boxed{1.6\ \text{m/s}}$.

81.   (a) Use Bernoulli's principle, $p_1 + \tfrac{1}{2}\rho v_1^2 + \rho g y_1 = p_2 + \tfrac{1}{2}\rho v_2^2 + \rho g y_2$.

Here $p_1 = p_2 = p_a,$ and $v_1 \approx 0$ (at the top of the water surface),   so $v_2 = \sqrt{2g\Delta y}$.

For the 40-cm high (upper) hole, $v_u = \sqrt{2(9.80\ \text{m/s}^2)(0.05\ \text{m})} = \boxed{0.99\ \text{m/s}}$;

for the 30-cm high (middle) hole, $v_m = \sqrt{2(9.80\ \text{m/s}^2)(0.15\ \text{m})} = \boxed{1.7\ \text{m/s}}$;

for the 20-cm high (bottom) hole, $v_b = \sqrt{2(9.80\ \text{m/s}^2)(0.25\ \text{m})} = \boxed{2.2\ \text{m/s}}$;

for the 10-cm high (bottom) hole, $v_b = \sqrt{2(9.80\ \text{m/s}^2)(0.35\ \text{m})} = \boxed{2.6\ \text{m/s}}$.

(b) They are all horizontal projectile motions. First find the time of flight from the vertical motion.

$$y = \tfrac{1}{2}gt^2, \quad ☞ \quad t = \sqrt{\frac{2y}{g}}. \quad \text{So the range is} \quad x = v_x\, t = v_x \sqrt{\frac{2y}{g}}.$$

Therefore

$$x_1 = (0.99 \text{ m/s}) \sqrt{\frac{2(0.40 \text{ m})}{9.80 \text{ m/s}^2}} = 0.28 \text{ m};$$

$$x_2 = (1.7 \text{ m/s}) \sqrt{\frac{2(0.30 \text{ m})}{9.80 \text{ m/s}^2}} = 0.42 \text{ m};$$

$$x_3 = (2.2 \text{ m/s}) \sqrt{\frac{2(0.20 \text{ m})}{9.80 \text{ m/s}^2}} = 0.44 \text{ m};$$

$$x_4 = (2.6 \text{ m/s}) \sqrt{\frac{2(0.10 \text{ m})}{9.80 \text{ m/s}^2}} = 0.37 \text{ m}.$$

So the greatest range $\boxed{0.44 \text{ m}}$ is $\boxed{\text{from } y = 20 \text{ cm}}$.

82.   From the flow rate equation, $A_1 v_1 = A_2 v_2$.

$$v_2 = \frac{A_1 v_1}{A_2} = \frac{\pi(0.030 \text{ m})^2 (0.45 \text{ m/s})}{\pi(0.010 \text{ m})^2} = 4.05 \text{ m/s}.$$

From Bernoulli's principle, $\quad p_1 + \tfrac{1}{2}\rho v_1^{\,2} + \rho g y_1 = p_2 + \tfrac{1}{2}\rho v_2^{\,2} + \rho g y_2$.

$$p_2 = p_1 + \tfrac{1}{2}\rho(\,v_1^{\,2} - v_2^{\,2}) + \rho g(y_1 - y_2) = (400 \text{ torr}) \times \frac{1.013 \times 10^5 \text{ Pa}}{760 \text{ torr}}$$

$$+\, \tfrac{1}{2}(1000 \text{ kg/m}^3)[(0.45 \text{ m/s})^2 - (4.05 \text{ m/s})^2] + (1000 \text{ kg/m}^3)(9.80 \text{ m/s}^2)(0 - 4.0 \text{ m}) = \boxed{5.7 \times 10^3 \text{ Pa}}.$$

83. $Q = A_1 v_1, \quad ☞ \quad v_1 = \dfrac{Q}{A_1} = \dfrac{(25 \text{ L/min})(10^{-3} \text{ m}^3/\text{L})(1 \text{ min}/60 \text{ s})}{\pi(0.035 \text{ m})^2} = 0.108 \text{ m/s}.$

From the flow rate equation, $\quad A_1 v_1 = A_2 v_2$.

$$v_2 = \frac{A_1 v_1}{A_2} = \frac{\pi(0.035 \text{ m})^2 (0.108 \text{ m/s})}{(30 \text{ cm}^2)(10^{-4} \text{ m}^2/\text{cm}^2)} = 0.139 \text{ m/s}.$$

From Bernoulli's principle, $\quad p_1 + \tfrac{1}{2}\rho v_1^{\,2} + \rho g y_1 = p_2 + \tfrac{1}{2}\rho v_2^{\,2} + \rho g y_2. \quad$ Here $\quad y_1 = y_2$.

$$p_2 = p_1 + \tfrac{1}{2}\rho(v_1^{\,2} - v_2^{\,2}) = 6.0 \text{ Pa} + \tfrac{1}{2}(1000 \text{ kg/m}^3)[(0.108 \text{ m/s})^2 - (0.139 \text{ m/s})^2] = \boxed{2.2 \text{ Pa}}.$$

84.   From the flow rate equation, $\quad A_1 v_1 = A_2 v_2, \quad ☞ \quad v_2 = \dfrac{A_1 v_1}{A_2}.$

From Bernoulli's principle, $\quad p_1 + \tfrac{1}{2}\rho v_1^{\,2} + \rho g y_1 = p_2 + \tfrac{1}{2}\rho v_2^{\,2} + \rho g y_2.$

Here $\quad \Delta p = p_1 - p_2 = \rho g h \quad$ and $\quad y_1 = y_2. \quad$ So $\quad \rho g h + \tfrac{1}{2}\rho v_1^{\,2} = \tfrac{1}{2}\rho v_2^{\,2} = \tfrac{1}{2}\rho \dfrac{A_1^{\,2} v_1^{\,2}}{A_2^{\,2}},$

or $\quad \tfrac{1}{2}\rho(A_1^{\,2}/A_2^{\,2} - 1)v_1^{\,2} = \rho g h. \quad$ Therefore $\quad v_1 = \sqrt{\dfrac{2gh}{A_1^{\,2}/A_2^{\,2} - 1}}.$

85.   (b).

86.   (c).

87.   (a).

88.   The 10 and 40 measure boxed(viscosity) and the "W" means boxed(winter).

89.   Use the viscosity for whole blood ($\eta = 2.7 \times 10^{-4}$ Pl). $Q = \dfrac{\pi r^4 \Delta p}{8 \eta L}$, so

$$\Delta p = \frac{8 \eta L Q}{\pi r^4} = \frac{8(2.7 \times 10^{-3} \text{ Pl})(0.080 \text{ m})(25 \text{ mL/s})(10^{-6} \text{ m}^3/\text{mL})}{\pi (0.0025 \text{ m})^4} = \boxed{3.5 \times 10^2 \text{ Pa}}.$$

90.   The pressure difference between the bag and the needle is

$\Delta p = \rho g h = (1.05 \times 10^3 \text{ kg/m}^3)(9.80 \text{ m/s}^2)(0.85 \text{ m}) = 8.75 \times 10^3$ Pa.

The flow rate $Q = \dfrac{\pi r^4 \Delta p}{8 \eta L} = \dfrac{\pi (0.5 \times 10^{-3} \text{ m})^4 (8.75 \times 10^3 \text{ Pa})}{8(1.7 \times 10^{-3} \text{ Pl})(0.050 \text{ m})} = 2.53 \times 10^{-6} \text{ m}^3/\text{s}.$

So the time is $t = \dfrac{V}{Q} = \dfrac{(500 \text{ cm}^3)(10^{-6} \text{ m}^3/\text{cm}^3)}{2.53 \times 10^{-6} \text{ m}^3/\text{s}} = \boxed{2.0 \times 10^2 \text{ s}}.$

91. $Y = \dfrac{F/A}{\Delta L/L_o}$,   ☞ $\dfrac{(\Delta L/L_o)_{Al}}{(\Delta L/L_o)_{Cu}} = \dfrac{Y_{Cu}}{Y_{Al}} = \dfrac{11 \times 10^{10} \text{ N/m}^2}{7.0 \times 10^{10} \text{ N/m}^2} = 1.57.$

So $(\Delta L/L_o)_{Al} = \dfrac{L - L_o}{L_o}{}_{Al} = 1.57 \, (\Delta L/L_o)_{Cu} = (1.57) \dfrac{0.02 \text{ cm}}{100.00 \text{ cm}} = 3.14 \times 10^{-4}.$

Therefore, $L_o = \dfrac{L}{1 + 3.14 \times 10^{-4}} = \dfrac{100.02 \text{ cm}}{1 + 3.14 \times 10^{-4}} = \boxed{99.99 \text{ cm}}.$

92.   The tension in the scale (scale reading) is the difference between the weight and buoyant force.

$T = w - F_b = mg - F_b = \rho g V - \rho_f g V = (\rho - \rho_f) g V$

$= (7800 \text{ kg/m}^3 - 1000 \text{ kg/m}^3)(9.80 \text{ m/s}^2)(0.25 \text{ m})^3 = \boxed{1.0 \times 10^3 \text{ N}}.$

93.   (a) $w = mg = F_b = \rho_f g V$,   ☞ $V = \dfrac{m}{\rho_f} = \dfrac{\rho V}{\rho_f} = \dfrac{(700 \text{ kg/m}^3)(0.30 \text{ m})^3}{1000 \text{ kg/m}^3} = 0.0189 \text{ m}^3.$

So the distance from the top of the wood to the water surface is

$0.30 \text{ m} - \dfrac{0.0189 \text{ m}^3}{(0.30 \text{ m})(0.30 \text{ m})} = \boxed{0.09 \text{ m}}.$

(b) The 0.09 m above the water surface can support the mass on top of the wood.

The mass is $\dfrac{(1000 \text{ kg/m}^3)(0.30 \text{ m})^2 (0.09 \text{ m}) g}{g} = \boxed{8.1 \text{ kg}}.$

94. $p = \dfrac{F}{A} = \dfrac{mg}{A} = \dfrac{(60 \text{ kg})(9.80 \text{ m/s}^2)}{(0.015 \text{ m})^2} = 2.6 \times 10^6 \text{ Pa} = \boxed{2.6 \times 10^6 \text{ Pa} = 3.8 \times 10^2 \text{ lb/in.}^2 = 26 \text{ atm}}$.

Here we used 1 atm $= 1.013 \times 10^5 \text{ Pa} = 14.7 \text{ lb/in.}^2$.

95. $F = pA = (1.013 \times 10^5 \text{ Pa})(1.30 \text{ m}^2) = \boxed{1.32 \times 10^5 \text{ N} = 2.96 \times 10^4 \text{ lb}}$.

96. $p = \rho gh = (1000 \text{ kg/m}^3)(9.80 \text{ m/s}^2)(12 \text{ m}) = 1.18 \times 10^5 \text{ Pa}$.

$F = pA = (1.18 \times 10^5 \text{ Pa})(\pi)(0.090 \text{ m})^2 = \boxed{3.0 \times 10^3 \text{ N}}$.

97. $p_\text{o} = \rho_\text{o} g h_\text{o} = \rho_\text{m} g h_\text{m}, \quad ☞ \quad \rho_\text{o} = \dfrac{\rho_\text{m} h_\text{m}}{h_\text{o}} = \dfrac{(13.6 \times 10^3 \text{ kg/m}^3)(5.0 \text{ cm})}{80 \text{ cm}} = \boxed{8.5 \times 10^2 \text{ kg/m}^3}$.

98. $p_\text{a} = \rho gh, \quad ☞ \quad h = \dfrac{p_\text{a}}{\rho g} = \dfrac{1.013 \times 10^5 \text{ Pa}}{(1.29 \text{ kg/m}^3)(9.80 \text{ m/s}^2)} = \boxed{8.0 \times 10^3 \text{ m}}$.

This tells us that the atmosphere extends much higher and is less dense.

99. First calculate the velocity of the water when it comes out of the spout. Use the result of Exercise 9.81.

$v = \sqrt{2g\Delta y} = \sqrt{2gh} = \sqrt{2(9.80 \text{ m/s}^2)(0.45 \text{ m})} = 2.97 \text{ m/s}$, which is the initial velocity for the rise.

From kinematics, the maximum height is $\dfrac{v^2}{2g} = \dfrac{(2.97 \text{ m/s})^2}{2(9.80 \text{ m/s}^2)} = \boxed{0.45 \text{ m}}$.

100. $\dfrac{\Delta L}{L_\text{o}} = \dfrac{F/A}{Y} = \dfrac{10,000 \text{ N}}{(24 \text{ cm}^2)(10^{-4} \text{ m}^2/\text{cm}^2)(20 \times 10^{10} \text{ N/m}^2)} = 2.08 \times 10^{-5} = \boxed{2.1 \times 10^{-3} \%}$.

101. From the result of Exercise 9.81, $v = \sqrt{2g\Delta y} = \sqrt{2(9.80 \text{ m/s}^2)(0.25 \text{ m})} = \boxed{2.2 \text{ m/s}}$.

102. Specific gravity $= \dfrac{w}{w_\text{w}} = \dfrac{mg}{m_\text{w}\, g} = \dfrac{m}{m_\text{w}} = \dfrac{\rho V}{\rho_\text{w} V} = \dfrac{\rho}{\rho_\text{w}}$.

103. (a) $Q = Av, \quad ☞ \quad v_\text{s} = \dfrac{66 \text{ cm}^3/\text{s}}{6.0 \text{ cm}^2} = \boxed{11 \text{ cm/s}}; \quad v_\text{n} = \dfrac{66 \text{ cm}^3/\text{s}}{1.0 \text{ cm}^2} = \boxed{66 \text{ cm/s}}$.

(b) $p_\text{s} + \frac{1}{2}\rho v_\text{s}^2 + \rho gy_\text{s} = p_\text{n} + \frac{1}{2}\rho v_\text{n}^2 + \rho gy_\text{n}.$ So

$\Delta p = p_\text{s} - p_\text{n} = \frac{1}{2}\rho(v_\text{n}^2 - v_\text{s}^2) + \rho g(y_\text{n} - y_\text{s})$

$= \frac{1}{2}(1000 \text{ kg/m}^3)[(0.66 \text{ m/s})^2 - (0.11 \text{ m/s})^2] + (1000 \text{ kg/m}^3)(9.80 \text{ m/s}^2)(0.10 \text{ m}) = \boxed{1.2 \times 10^3 \text{ Pa}}$.

104.   Through capillary action, the wooden peg absorbs water and it swells and splits the rock.

105.   (a) When it is in the water, the force applied is

$$F = mg - F_b = \rho g V - \rho_f g V$$

$$= (\rho - \rho_f) g V = (7.8 \times 10^3 \text{ kg/m}^3 - 1.0 \times 10^3 \text{ kg/m}^3)(9.80 \text{ m/s}^2)(0.25 \text{ m})(0.20 \text{ m})(10 \text{ m})$$

$$= \boxed{3.3 \times 10^4 \text{ N}}.$$

(b) When it is out of water, the force applied is

$$F = mg = \rho g V = (7.8 \times 10^3 \text{ kg/m}^3)(9.80 \text{ m/s}^2)(0.25 \text{ m})(0.20 \text{ m})(10 \text{ m}) = \boxed{3.8 \times 10^4 \text{ N}}.$$

106.   It has to displace an amount of water equal to its weight or mass (if gravity is a constant).
So it is $\boxed{10\,000 \text{ metric tons}}$.

107.   (a) The buoyant force is $F_b = 14.4 \text{ N} - 4.8 \text{ N} = 9.6 \text{ N} = \rho_f g V$.

So $V = \dfrac{9.6 \text{ N}}{(1000 \text{ kg/m}^3)(9.80 \text{ m/s}^2)} = \boxed{9.8 \times 10^{-4} \text{ m}^3}.$

(b) $\rho = \dfrac{m}{V} = \dfrac{w}{gV} = \dfrac{14.4 \text{ N}}{(9.80 \text{ m/s}^2)(9.8 \times 10^{-4} \text{ m}^3)} = \boxed{1.5 \times 10^3 \text{ kg/m}^3}.$

(c) $\boxed{\text{Yes, but less precisely}}$. The sphere would float, and you would have to estimate the portion of its
volume that was submerged.

CHAPTER 10

TEMPERATURE AND KINETIC THEORY

1. (d) is the closest. $T_F = \frac{9}{5}T_C + 32 = \frac{9}{5}(15) + 32 = 59°F$.

2. $\boxed{\text{Fahrenheit}}$. $9\Delta T_F = 5\Delta T_C$.

3. $\boxed{\text{Not necessarily}}$. Internal energy does not depend solely on temperature. It also depends on mass.

4. An $\boxed{\text{incandescent lamp filament}}$ has a temperature of up to 3000 degrees Celsius.

5. $\boxed{\text{Air has water in it and may potentially freeze at high altutudes}}$ because the temperature is low up there.

6. The $\boxed{\text{Celsius}}$ scale will read a smaller change because 1 C° = 9/5 F°, i.e., if the temperature increases by 1 C°, it will increase by 9/5 F°.

7. (a) $T_C = \frac{5}{9}(T_F - 32) = \frac{5}{9}(1000 - 32) = \boxed{538°C}$.　　(b) $T_C = \frac{5}{9}(0 - 32) = \boxed{-18°C}$.

　　(c) $T_C = \frac{5}{9}(-20 - 32) = \boxed{-29°C}$.　　(d) $T_C = \frac{5}{9}(-40 - 32) = \boxed{-40°C}$.

8. (a) $T_F = \frac{9}{5}T_C + 32 = \frac{9}{5}(150) + 32 = \boxed{302°F}$.　　(b) $T_F = \frac{9}{5}(32) + 32 = \boxed{90°F}$.

　　(c) $T_F = \frac{9}{5}(-25) + 32 = \boxed{-13°C}$.　　(d) $T_F = \frac{9}{5}(-273) + 32 = \boxed{-459°F}$.

9. $T_C = \frac{5}{9}(T_F - 32) = \frac{5}{9}(-94 - 32) = \boxed{-70°C}$.

10. $T_F = \frac{9}{5}T_C + 32 = \frac{9}{5}(39.4) + 32 = \boxed{103°F}$.

11. $T_C = \frac{5}{9}(T_F - 32) = \frac{5}{9}(134 - 32) = \boxed{56.7°C}$.　　$T_C = \frac{5}{9}(-80 - 32) = \boxed{-62°C}$.

12. (a) $T_F = \frac{9}{5}T_C + 32 = \frac{9}{5}(245) + 32 = 473°F$.　　So $\boxed{245°F}$ is lower.

　　(b) $T_F = \frac{9}{5}(200) + 32 = 392°F$.　　So $\boxed{375°F}$ is lower.

13. $T_F = \frac{9}{5}T_C + 32 = \frac{9}{5}(58) + 32 = \boxed{136°F}$.　　$T_F = \frac{9}{5}(-89) + 32 = \boxed{-128°F}$.

14.   (a) You would set $\boxed{T_F = T_C}$ because we want to find the one temperature at which the Celsius and

Fahrenheit scales have the same reading.

(b) $T_F = \frac{9}{5}T_C + 32 = T_C,$ ☞ $T_C = \dfrac{32}{1 - 9/5} = \boxed{-40°C = -40°F}$.

15.   (a) Since $T_F = \frac{9}{5}T_C + 32,$ $\Delta T_F = \frac{9}{5}\Delta T_C = \frac{9}{5}(-49 - 7) = \boxed{-101\ F°}$.

(b) $\Delta T_F = \frac{9}{5}\Delta T_C = \frac{9}{5}[127 - (-183)] = \boxed{558\ C°}$.

16.   (a) The y-intercept is found by setting $\boxed{T_C = 0}$ because $T_F = \frac{9}{5}T_C + 32,$ compared to $y = ax + b.$

(b) When $T_C = 0,$ $T_F = \frac{9}{5}T_C + 32 = 0 + 32 = \boxed{32°F}$.

(c) Now $T_C = \frac{5}{9}(T_F - 32),$ the y-intercept is $\frac{5}{9} \times (-32) = \boxed{-18°C}$.

17.   (c).

18.   (d).

19.   (a) If pressure is held constant, the volume will decrease as temperature decreases, according to the ideal

gas law. So the density $\boxed{\text{increases}}$.

(b) If the volume is held constant, the density is $\boxed{\text{constant}}$.

20.   The volume of the gas is held constant. So if the temperature increases, so does the pressure and vice versa, according to the ideal gas law. Therefore, temperature is determined from pressure.

21.   The pressure of the gas is held constant. So if the temperature increases, so does the volume and vice versa, according to the ideal gas law. Therefore, temperature is determined from volume.

22.   (a) Absolute zero implies $\boxed{\text{zero pressure or volume}}$.

(b) Negative absolute temperature implies $\boxed{\text{negative pressure or volume}}$.

23. $\boxed{\text{The balloons collapsed}}$. Due to the decrease in temperature, the volume also decreases.

24.   The $\boxed{\text{same}}$, because mole is defined in terms of the number of molecules.

25.   This is because there is a higher atmospheric pressure at lower altitude, which causes the bag not to inflate because its pressure is lower.

26.   (a) $T_K = T_C + 273.15 = 0 + 273.15 = \boxed{273\ K}$.   (b) $T_K = 100 + 273.15 = \boxed{373\ K}$.

   (c) $T_K = 20 + 273.15 = \boxed{293\ K}$.   (d) $T_K = -35 + 273.15 = \boxed{238\ K}$.

27.   (a) $T_C = T_K - 273.15 = 0 - 273.15 = \boxed{-273°C}$.   (b) $T_C = 250 - 273.15 = \boxed{-23°C}$.

   (c) $T_C = 273.15 - 273.15 = \boxed{0°C}$.   (d) $T_C = 325 - 273 = \boxed{52°C}$.

28.   (a) -40°F = -40°C (from Exercise 10.14). $T_K = T_C + 273 = -40 + 273 = \boxed{233\ K}$.

   (b) $\boxed{233\ K}$.

29. $T_C = \frac{5}{9}(T_F - 32) = \frac{5}{9}(300 - 32) = 149°C = 422\ K$.   So $\boxed{300\ K}$ is lower.

30.   (a) $T_C = T_K - 273 = 30\ 000 - 273 = \boxed{29\ 727°C}$. $T_F = \frac{9}{5}T_C + 32 = \frac{9}{5}(29\ 727) + 32 = \boxed{53\ 541°F}$.

   (b) The percentage error is $\dfrac{30\ 000 - 29\ 727}{30\ 000} = \boxed{0.91\%}$.

31.   (a) H_2O has a molar mass of (2 + 16) h/mole = 18 g/mole. $n = \dfrac{m}{M} = \dfrac{40\ g}{18\ g/mole} = \boxed{2.2\ moles}$.

   (b) H_2SO_4 has a molar mass of (2 + 32 + 64) h/mole = 98 g/mole. $n = \dfrac{245\ g}{98\ g/mole} = \boxed{2.5\ moles}$.

   (c) NO_2 has a molar mass of (14 + 32) g/mole = 46 h/mole. $n = \dfrac{138\ g}{46\ g/mole} = \boxed{3.0\ moles}$.

   (d) At STP, 1 mole occupies 22.4 L.   So $n = \dfrac{56\ L}{22.4\ L} = \boxed{2.5\ moles}$.

32.   (a) $\dfrac{p_1V_1}{T_1} = \dfrac{p_2V_2}{T_2}$.   With $V_1 = V_2$, $\dfrac{T_2}{T_1} = \dfrac{p_2}{p_1}$.   So the temperature of the gas will $\boxed{decrease}$.

   (b) $T_2 = \dfrac{p_2}{p_1}T_1 = \dfrac{1500\ Pa}{1000\ Pa} \times [(273 + 20)K] = 439.5\ K = \boxed{167°C}$.

33. $\dfrac{p_1V_1}{T_1} = \dfrac{p_2V_2}{T_2}$.   Since $T_1 = T_2$, $p_2 = \dfrac{V_1}{V_2} \times p_1 = \dfrac{0.10\ m^3}{0.12\ m^3} \times (1.4 \times 10^5\ Pa) = \boxed{1.2 \times 10^5\ Pa}$.

34. $pV = nRT$,   ☞ $V = \dfrac{nRT}{p} = \dfrac{(1\ mol)[8.31\ /(mol \cdot K)](273\ K)}{1.01 \times 10^5\ Pa} = \boxed{0.0224\ m^3 = 22.4\ L}$.

35. $n = \dfrac{4.00 \text{ g}}{2.00 \text{ g/mol}} = 2.00 \text{ mol.}$

$pV = nRT, \quad \Rightarrow \quad V = \dfrac{nRT}{p} = \dfrac{(2.00 \text{ mol})[8.31 \text{ /(mol·K)}](300 \text{ K})}{2.00(1.01 \times 10^5 \text{ Pa})} = \boxed{0.0247 \text{ m}^3}.$

36. $T = (273 + 37) \text{ K} = 310 \text{ K}$

$pV = Nk_\text{B}T, \quad \Rightarrow \quad N = \dfrac{pV}{k_\text{B}T} = \dfrac{(1.01 \times 10^5 \text{ Pa})(7.5 \times 10^{-3} \text{ m}^3)}{(1.38 \times 10^{-23} \text{ J/K})(310 \text{ K})} = \boxed{1.8 \times 10^{23}}.$

37. (a) $\dfrac{p_1 V_1}{T_1} = \dfrac{p_2 V_2}{T_2}, \quad \Rightarrow \quad \dfrac{p_2}{p_1} = \dfrac{V_1}{V_2}\dfrac{T_2}{T_1}.$ So the temperature will $\boxed{\text{increase}}$.

(b) $\dfrac{p_2}{p_1} = \dfrac{V_1}{V_2}\dfrac{T_2}{T_1} = (2)(2) = 4.$ So $\boxed{p_2 = 4p_1}.$

38. $T_1 = 92°\text{F} = \tfrac{5}{9}(92 - 32) \text{ °C} = 33.3°\text{C} = 306.3 \text{ K}, \quad T_2 = 32°\text{F} = 0°\text{C} = 273 \text{ K.}$

$\dfrac{p_1 V_1}{T_1} = \dfrac{p_2 V_2}{T_2}, \quad \Rightarrow \quad V_2 = \dfrac{p_1 V_1 T_2}{T_1 p_2} = \dfrac{(20.0 \text{ lb/in.}^2)(0.20 \text{ m}^3)(273 \text{ K})}{(306.3 \text{ K})(14.7 \text{ lb/in.}^2)} = \boxed{0.24 \text{ m}^3}.$

Here lb/in.^{2} can be used since it is in a ratio.

39. $T_1 = 61°\text{F} = \tfrac{5}{9}(61 - 32)°\text{C} = 16.1°\text{C} = 289.1 \text{ K}, \quad T_2 = 100°\text{F} = 310.8 \text{ K},$

$p_1 = 30.0 \text{ lb/in.}^2 + 14.7 \text{ lb/in.}^2 = 44.7 \text{ lb/in.}^2. \quad \dfrac{p_1 V_1}{T_1} = \dfrac{p_2 V_2}{T_2}.$

Since $V_1 = V_2, \quad p_2 = \dfrac{p_1 T_2}{T_1} = \dfrac{(44.7 \text{ lb/in.}^2)(310.8 \text{ K})}{289.1 \text{ K}} = 48.1 \text{ lb/in.}^2.$

So the gauge pressure is $48.1 \text{ lb/in.}^2 - 14.7 \text{ lb/in.}^2 = \boxed{33.4 \text{ lb/in.}^2}.$

40. $\dfrac{p_1 V_1}{T_1} = \dfrac{p_2 V_2}{T_2}, \quad \Rightarrow \quad p_2 = \dfrac{p_1 V_1 T_2}{T_1 V_2} = \dfrac{(1 \text{ atm})(2.4 \text{ m}^3)(303 \text{ K})}{(273 \text{ K})(1.6 \text{ m}^3)} = \boxed{1.7 \text{ atm}}.$

41. (a) With $p = p_\text{o}, \quad \dfrac{p_\text{o} V_\text{o}}{T_\text{o}} = \dfrac{pV}{T}$ becomes $\dfrac{V}{V_\text{o}} = \dfrac{Tp_\text{o}}{T_\text{o}p} = \dfrac{T}{T_\text{o}}.$ The volume of the gas $\boxed{\text{increases}}$.

(b) $\dfrac{V}{V_\text{o}} = \dfrac{T}{T_\text{o}} = \dfrac{313 \text{ K}}{283 \text{ K}} = 1.106.$

So the fractional change is $\dfrac{V - V_\text{o}}{V_\text{o}} = \dfrac{V}{V_\text{o}} - 1 = 0.106 = \boxed{10.6\%}.$

42. The pressure 15 m below the surface is

$p_1 = p_\text{a} + \rho gh = 1.01 \times 10^5 \text{ Pa} + (1000 \text{ kg/m}^3)(9.80 \text{ m/s}^2)(15 \text{ m}) = 2.48 \times 10^5 \text{ Pa.}$

$\dfrac{p_1 V_1}{T_1} = \dfrac{p_2 V_2}{T_2}, \quad \Rightarrow \quad V_2 = \dfrac{p_1 T_2}{p_2 T_1} \times V_1 = \dfrac{(2.48 \times 10^5 \text{ Pa})(293 \text{ K})}{(1.01 \times 10^5 \text{ Pa})(280 \text{ K})} \times (2.0 \text{ cm}^3) = \boxed{5.1 \text{ cm}^3}.$

43.   (d).

44.   (c).

45.   (a) Aluminum has a larger α and so it contracts more. Therefore the ice moves upward .

(b) Copper has a larger α so the ice moves downward .

(c) Brass has a larger α and so it will expand more. Therefore, copper should be on the top for the strip to

curve upward.

46.   When the ball alone is heated, it expands and cannot go through the ring.
        When the ring is heated, it expands and the hole gets larger so the ball can go through again.

47.   The volume increases when cooled from 4°C to 2°C because it exhibits abnormal expansion between 0°C

and 4°C.

48.   When the disk is heated, it expands and the mass is farther from the axis of rotation. This increases the

moment of inertia. According to angular momentum conservation, the angular speed decreases .

49.   No , it will not be distorted because both the ring and the bar are made of iron so they will expand at the

same rate as one single piece. Yes , the circular ring will be distorted, if the bar is made of aluminum.

50.   Steel , because it has a smaller coefficient of thermal expansion. Less expansion, more accurate .

51.   Metal has a higher coefficient of thermal expansion than glass. The lid expands more than glass so it is

easier to loosen the lid.

52.   At $-30°C$, $\Delta L = \alpha L_0 \Delta T = (12 \times 10^{-6} \text{ C}^{\circ-1})(10 \text{ m})(-30°C - 20°C) = -6.0 \times 10^{-3}$ m = $\boxed{-6.0 \text{ mm}}$.

At $45°C$, $\Delta L = (12 \times 10^{-6} /\text{C}°)(10 \text{ m})(45°C - 20°C) = 3.0 \times 10^{-3}$ m = $\boxed{3.0 \text{ mm}}$.

53.   (a) It would read high because the tape shrinks. One division on the tape (it is now less than one division

due to shrinkage) still reads one division.

(b) $\Delta L = \alpha L_0 \Delta T$, ☞ $\dfrac{\Delta L}{L_0} = \alpha \Delta T = (24 \times 10^{-6} \text{ C}^{\circ-1})(-5.0°C - 20°C) = -6.0 \times 10^{-4}$, or $\boxed{0.06\%}$.

54. Only the higher temperature needs to be considered because the slabs will not touch under the lower temperature $\Delta L = \alpha L_0 \Delta T = (12 \times 10^{-6} \text{ C}^{\circ-1})(10.0 \text{ m})[45°C - (20°C)] = 3.0 \times 10^{-3} \text{ m} = \boxed{3.0 \text{ mm}}$.

55. $\Delta L = \alpha L_0 \Delta T = (14 \times 10^{-6} \text{ C}^{\circ-1})(2.4 \text{ cm})(100°C - 20°C) = \boxed{0.0027 \text{ cm}}$.

56. $\dfrac{\Delta V}{V} = 0.0010 = \beta \Delta T$, ☞ $\Delta T = \dfrac{0.0010}{2.1 \times 10^{-4} \text{ C}^{\circ-1}} = \boxed{4.8 \text{ C}^\circ}$.

57. (a) $L' = L_0 + \Delta L = L_0(1 + \alpha \Delta T) = (60 \text{ cm})[1 + (17 \times 10^{-6} \text{ C}^{\circ-1})(85°C - 20°C)] = \boxed{60.07 \text{ cm}}$.

(b) $A_0 = \pi r^2 = \pi(0.75 \text{ cm})^2 = 1.77 \text{ cm}^2$.

$\Delta A = 2\alpha A_0 \Delta T = 2(17 \times 10^{-6} \text{ C}^{\circ-1})(1.77 \text{ cm}^2)(85°C - 20°C) = \boxed{3.91 \times 10^{-3} \text{ cm}^2}$.

$\boxed{\text{Yes}}$, the flow speed will be affected according to the equation of continuity.

58. (a) The hole will $\boxed{\text{get larger}}$ due to expansion.

(b) $A_0 = \pi r^2 = \pi(4.00 \text{ cm})^2 = 50.27 \text{ cm}^2$.

$\Delta A = 2\alpha A_0 \Delta T = 2(24 \times 10^{-6} \text{ C}^{\circ-1})(50.27 \text{ cm}^2)(150°C - 20°C) = 0.314 \text{ cm}^2$.

So the final area is $50.27 \text{ cm}^2 + 0.314 \text{ cm}^2 = \boxed{50.6 \text{ cm}^2}$.

59. (a) You should heat $\boxed{\text{the ring}}$, so it expands, then the ball can go through.

(b) $\Delta L = \alpha L_0 \Delta T$, ☞ $\Delta T = \dfrac{\Delta L}{\alpha L_0} = \dfrac{0.10 \text{ mm}}{(12 \times 10^{-6} /\text{C}^\circ)(25 \text{ mm})} = 333°C$.

So the required temperature is $333°C + 20°C = \boxed{353°C}$.

60. $\dfrac{\Delta A}{A_0} = \dfrac{\beta A_0 \Delta T}{A_0} = 2\alpha \Delta T = 2(12 \times 10^{-6} \text{ C}^{\circ-1})(0°C - 350°C) = -7.9 \times 10^{-3} = -\boxed{0.79\%}$.

61. (a) There will be gas $\boxed{\text{spill}}$ because the coefficient of volume expansion is greater for gasoline than steel.

(b) $\Delta V = \beta V_0 \Delta T = (9.5 \times 10^{-4} \text{ C}^{\circ-1})(25 \text{ gal})(30°C - 10°C) = \boxed{0.48 \text{ gal}}$.

62. $\rho = \dfrac{m}{V} = \dfrac{m}{V_0 + \Delta V} = \dfrac{m}{V_0(1 + 3\alpha \Delta T)} = \rho_0 \dfrac{1}{1 + 3\alpha \Delta T}$.

Since $3\alpha \Delta T \ll 1$, $\dfrac{1}{3\alpha \Delta T} \approx 1 - 3\alpha \Delta T$ $\left(\dfrac{1}{1+x} \approx 1 - x \text{ for small } x \right)$.

So $\rho = \rho_0(1 - 3\alpha \Delta T)$.

63. $\rho = \dfrac{m}{V}$, ☞ $\dfrac{\rho}{\rho_0} = \dfrac{V_0}{V} = \dfrac{V_0}{V_0(1 + \beta \Delta T)} = \dfrac{1}{1 + \beta \Delta T}$.

$\rho = \dfrac{1}{1 + \beta \Delta T} \rho_0 = \dfrac{1}{1 + (1.8 \times 10^{-4}\ \text{C}^{\circ -1})(100^\circ\text{C} - 0^\circ\text{C})} \times (13.6 \times 10^3\ \text{kg/m}^3)$

$= \boxed{13.4 \times 10^3\ \text{kg/m}^3}$.

64. (a) The cavity gets $\boxed{\text{larger}}$ as it expands.

(b) $V_0 = \dfrac{4\pi}{3} r_0^3 = \dfrac{4\pi}{3}(0.050\ \text{m})^3 = 5.24 \times 10^{-4}\ \text{m}^3$.

$\Delta V = 3\alpha V_0 \Delta T = 3(17 \times 10^{-6}\ \text{C}^{\circ -1})(5.24 \times 10^{-4}\ \text{m}^3)(500\ \text{K} - 293\ \text{K})] = \boxed{5.5 \times 10^{-6}\ \text{m}^3}$.

65. (a) At 20°C, $A_{ob} = \pi(0.500\ \text{cm})^2 = 0.78540\ \text{cm}^2$ and $A_{oc} = \pi(0.501\ \text{cm})^2 = 0.81713\ \text{cm}^2$.

At a temperature T, both will have the same area or radius, $A_b = A_c$.

$\Delta A = 2\alpha L_0 \Delta T$, ☞ $A = A_0 + \Delta A = A_0(1 + 2\alpha \Delta T)$. So $A_{ob}(1 + 2\alpha_b \Delta T) = A_{oc}(1 + 2\alpha_c \Delta T)$,

$\Delta T = \dfrac{A_{oc} - A_{ob}}{2(A_{ob}\alpha_b - A_{oc}\alpha_c)} = \dfrac{0.81713\ \text{cm}^2 - 0.78540\ \text{cm}^2}{2[(0.78540\ \text{cm}^2)(19 \times 10^{-6}\ \text{C}^{\circ -1}) - (0.81713\ \text{cm}^2)(17 \times 10^{-6}\ \text{C}^{\circ -1})]}$

$= 1.543 \times 10^4\ \text{C}^\circ$.

Thus the temperature is $1.543 \times 10^4\ \text{C}^\circ + 20^\circ\text{C} = \boxed{1.54 \times 10^4\ ^\circ\text{C}}$.

(b) $\boxed{\text{No}}$, since brass has a higher α, the hole will be even larger at a higher temperature.

66. At 20°C, $V_{ob} = 1000\ \text{cm}^3$ and $V_{om} = 990\ \text{cm}^3$.

At a temperature T, both the beaker and the mercury have the same volume, $V_b = V_m$.

$V = V_0 + \Delta V = V_0(1 + 3\alpha \Delta T) = V_0(1 + \beta \Delta T)$, ☞ $V_{ob}(1 + 3\alpha_b \Delta T) = V_{om}(1 + \beta \Delta T)$.

$\Delta T = \dfrac{V_{ob} - V_{om}}{V_{om}\beta_m - 3V_{ob}\alpha_b} = \dfrac{1000\ \text{cm}^3 - 990\ \text{cm}^3}{(990\ \text{cm}^3)(1.8 \times 10^{-4}\ \text{C}^{\circ -1}) - 3(1000\ \text{cm}^3)(3.3 \times 10^{-6}\ \text{C}^{\circ -1})} = 59.4\ \text{C}^\circ$.

So the temperature is $T = 20^\circ\text{C} + 59.4\ \text{C}^\circ = \boxed{79.4^\circ\text{C}}$. So the answer is $\boxed{\text{yes}}$.

67. (c), because 20°C = 293 K and 2 × 293 K = 586 K = 313°C.

68. (a). Internal energy is directly proportional to the Kelvin temperature.

69. The gases diffuse through the porous membrane, but the helium gas diffuses faster because its atoms have a smaller mass. Eventually, there will be equal concentrations of gases on both sides of the container.

70.   Since the average speed of the additive is greater than that of the gas, $\boxed{m_{\text{additive}} < m_{\text{gas}}}$.

71.   (a) $K = \frac{3}{2}k_{B}T = \frac{3}{2}(1.38 \times 10^{-23} \text{ J/K})(293 \text{ K}) = \boxed{6.1 \times 10^{-21} \text{ J}}$.

            (b) $K = \frac{3}{2}(1.38 \times 10^{-23} \text{ J/K})(373 \text{ K}) = \boxed{7.7 \times 10^{-21} \text{ J}}$.

72.   (a) The internal energy will $\boxed{\text{increase by less than a factor of 2}}$. This is because the internal energy is directly proportional to the Kelvin temperature, and doubling the Celsius temperature will increase but not double the Kelvin temperature.

            (b) $U = \frac{3}{2}nRT$,   ☞ $\Delta U = \frac{3}{2}nR\Delta T = \frac{3}{2}(2.0 \text{ mol})[8.31 \text{ J/(mol·K)}](40°C - 20°C) = \boxed{5.0 \times 10^{2} \text{ J}}$.

73.   (a) $K = \frac{3}{2}k_{B}T = \frac{3}{2}(1.38 \times 10^{-23} \text{ J/K})(300 \text{ K}) = \boxed{6.21 \times 10^{-21} \text{ J}}$.

            (b) $v_{\text{rms}} = \sqrt{\dfrac{3k_{B}T}{m_{o}}} = \sqrt{\dfrac{3(1.38 \times 10^{-23} \text{ J/K})(300 \text{ K})}{6.65 \times 10^{-27} \text{ kg}}} = \boxed{1.37 \times 10^{3} \text{ m/s}}$.

74. $v_{\text{rms}} = \sqrt{\dfrac{3k_{B}T}{m}} = \sqrt{\dfrac{3(1.38 \times 10^{-23} \text{ J/K})(273 \text{ K})}{5.31 \times 10^{-26} \text{ kg}}} = \boxed{4.61 \times 10^{2} \text{ m/s}}$.

75. $v_{\text{rms}} = \sqrt{\dfrac{3k_{B}T}{m}}$,   ☞ $\dfrac{v_{\text{rms}}}{(v_{\text{rms}})_{o}} = \sqrt{\dfrac{T}{T_{o}}} = \sqrt{\dfrac{600 \text{ K}}{300 \text{ K}}} = \boxed{\sqrt{2}}$.

76. O_2 has a greater rms speed because it has a smaller mass.

            $v_{\text{rms}} = \sqrt{\dfrac{3k_{B}T}{m}}$,   ☞ $\dfrac{(v_{\text{rms}})_{2}}{(v_{\text{rms}})_{3}} = \sqrt{\dfrac{m_{3}}{m_{2}}} = \sqrt{\dfrac{3}{2}} = 1.22$.

            So $\boxed{v_{\text{oxygen}} = 1.22 v_{\text{ozone}}}$.

77. $v_{\text{rms}} = \sqrt{\dfrac{3k_{B}T}{m_{o}}}$,   ☞ $\dfrac{(v_{\text{rms}})_{2}}{(v_{\text{rms}})_{1}} = \sqrt{\dfrac{T_{2}}{T_{1}}} = \sqrt{\dfrac{373 \text{ K}}{298 \text{ K}}} = \boxed{1.12 \text{ times}}$.

78. $T_{2} = 2T_{1} = 2(273 \text{ K}) = 546 \text{ K} = \boxed{273°C}$.

79.   (a).

80.   (b).

81. $\boxed{\text{It has more degrees of freedom}}$ than the sample consisting of monatomic molecules, and the internal energy is proportional to the number of degrees of freedom.

82. For monatomic gas, $U_1 = \frac{3}{2}nRT$.

For diatomic gas, $U_2 = \frac{5}{2}nRT$. So $U_2 = \frac{5}{3}U_1 = \frac{5}{3}(5.0 \times 10^3 \text{ J}) = \boxed{8.3 \times 10^3 \text{ J}}$.

83. For diatomic gas, $U = \frac{5}{2}nRT = \frac{5}{2}(1.0 \text{ mol})[8.31 \text{ J/(mol·K)}](293 \text{ K}) = \boxed{6.1 \times 10^3 \text{ J}}$.

84. (a) $U_t = \frac{3}{2}k_B T = \frac{3}{2}(1.38 \times 10^{-23} \text{ J/K})(273 \text{ K}) = \boxed{5.65 \times 10^{-21} \text{ J}}$.

(b) $U_r = \frac{2}{2}k_B T = \frac{2}{2}(1.38 \times 10^{-23} \text{ J/K})(273 \text{ K}) = \boxed{3.77 \times 10^{-21} \text{ J}}$.

(c) $U_{total} = U_t + U_r = 5.65 \times 10^{-21} \text{ J} + 3.77 \times 10^{-21} \text{ J} = \boxed{9.42 \times 10^{-21} \text{ J}}$.

85. $\Delta V_{gas} = \beta V_0 \Delta T = (9.5 \times 10^{-4} \text{ C}^{\circ -1})(25 \text{ gal})(30°\text{C} - 10°\text{C}) = 0.48 \text{ gal}$.

$\Delta V_{tank} = 3\alpha V_0 \Delta T = 3(12 \times 10^{-6} \text{ C}^{\circ -1})(25 \text{ gal})(30°\text{C} - 10°\text{C}) = 0.018 \text{ gal}$.

So the spilled volume is $\Delta V_{gas} - \Delta V_{tank} = 0.48 \text{ gal} - 0.018 \text{ gal} = \boxed{0.46 \text{ gal}}$.

86. $T_C = \frac{5}{9}(T_F - 32) = \frac{5}{9}(78 - 32) = \boxed{26°\text{C}}$.

$T_C = \frac{5}{9}(65 - 32) = \boxed{18°\text{C}}$.

87. $\Delta L = \alpha L_0 \Delta T = (17 \times 10^{-6} \text{ C}^{\circ -1})(0.500 \text{ m})(100°\text{C} - 20°\text{C}) = \boxed{6.8 \times 10^{-4} \text{ m}}$.

88. First find the temperature of the gas.

$pV = nRT$, ☞ $T = \frac{pV}{nR} = \frac{6.0(1.01 \times 10^5 \text{ Pa})(0.010 \text{ m}^3)}{(2.0 \text{ mol})[8.31 \text{ J/mol·K}]}) = 364.6 \text{ K}$.

$K = \frac{3}{2}k_B T = \frac{3}{2}(1.38 \times 10^{-23} \text{ J/K})(364.6 \text{ K}) = \boxed{7.5 \times 10^{-21} \text{ J}}$.

89. $\Delta V = \beta V_0 \Delta T = (1.8 \times 10^{-4} \text{ C}^{\circ -1})(0.130 \text{ cm}^3)(50°\text{C} - 10°\text{C}) = 9.36 \times 10^{-4} \text{ cm}^3$.

Also $V = Ah$, ☞ $\Delta h = \frac{\Delta V}{A} = \frac{9.36 \times 10^{-4} \text{ cm}^3}{0.012 \times 10^{-2} \text{ cm}^2} = \boxed{7.8 \text{ cm}}$.

90. $v_{rms} = \sqrt{\frac{3k_B T}{m}}$, ☞ $\frac{T}{T_o} = \left(\frac{v_{rms}}{(v_{rms})_o}\right)^2 = (2)^2 = 4$.

So $T = 4T_o = 4[(273 + 20) \text{ K}] = 1172 \text{ K} = \boxed{899°\text{C}}$.

91. $\Delta L = \alpha L_0 \Delta T$, ☞ $\dfrac{\Delta L}{L_0} = \alpha \Delta T$. So $\dfrac{F}{A} = Y \dfrac{\Delta L}{L_0} = Y\alpha\Delta T$.

Therefore $\Delta T = \dfrac{F/A}{Y\alpha} = \dfrac{8.0 \times 10^7 \text{ N/m}^2}{(20 \times 10^{10} \text{ N/m}^2)(12 \times 10^{-6} \text{ C}^{\circ-1})} = \boxed{33 \text{ C}^\circ}$.

92. $\dfrac{p_0 V_0}{T_0} = \dfrac{pV}{T}$, ☞ $\dfrac{V}{V_0} = \dfrac{Tp_0}{T_0 p}$.

Also $V = V_0 + \Delta V = V_0(1 + \beta\Delta T)$, ☞ $\dfrac{V}{V_0} = 1 + \beta\Delta T = 1 + \beta(T - T_0)$.

So $1 + \beta(T - T_0) = \dfrac{Tp_0}{T_0 p}$, or $\beta = \boxed{\dfrac{Tp_0 - T_0 p}{T_0 p(T - T_0)}}$.

93. (a) One mole occupies 22.4 L.

So $n = \dfrac{0.75 \text{ L}}{22.4 \text{ L}} = \boxed{3.3 \times 10^{-2} \text{ moles}}$.

(b) $N = nN_A = (3.35 \times 10^{-2} \text{ moles})(6.02 \times 10^{23} \text{ /mole}) = \boxed{2.0 \times 10^{22}}$.

(c) CO has a molar mass of $12 + 16 = 28$ g/mole.

So the mass is $(3.35 \times 10^{-2} \text{ moles})(28 \text{ g/mole}) = \boxed{0.94 \text{ g}}$.

94. Steel: $L = L_0(1 + \alpha\Delta T) = (1.0 \text{ m})[1 + (12 \times 10^{-6} \text{ C}^{\circ-1})(40^\circ\text{C} - 0^\circ\text{C}) = 1.00048 \text{ m}$.

Aluminum: $L = (1.0 \text{ m})[(1 + (24 \times 10^{-6} \text{ C}^{\circ-1})(40^\circ\text{C} - 0^\circ\text{C}) = 1.00096 \text{ m}$.

On the aluminum tape it still reads 1.0 m for 1.00096 m of true length. The true length of the steel is 1.00048 m, so its reading is $\dfrac{1.00048 \text{ m}}{1.00096 \text{ m}} \times (1.0 \text{ m}) = \boxed{0.999\,52 \text{ m}}$.

95. (a) $T_F = \tfrac{9}{5}T_C + 32$, ☞ $\Delta T_F = \tfrac{9}{5}\Delta T_F = \tfrac{9}{5}(10) = \boxed{18 \text{ F}^\circ}$.

(b) $\Delta T_C = \tfrac{5}{9}\Delta T_F = \tfrac{5}{9}(10) = \boxed{5.6 \text{ C}^\circ}$.

96. $\Delta L = \alpha L_0 \Delta T$, ☞ $\alpha = \dfrac{\Delta L}{L_0 \Delta T} = \dfrac{0.044 \text{ cm}}{(50 \text{ cm})(250^\circ\text{C} - 20^\circ\text{C})} = \boxed{3.8 \times 10^{-6} \text{ C}^{\circ-1}}$.

$\boxed{\text{Yes}}$, it is a very good alloy with a very low coefficient of linear expansion.

97. $pV = Nk_B T$, ☞ $N = \dfrac{pV}{k_B T} = \dfrac{(20 \text{ Pa})(0.20 \text{ m}^3)}{(1.38 \times 10^{-23} \text{ J/K})(293 \text{ K})} = \boxed{9.9 \times 10^{20}}$.

98. $T_K = T_C + 273 = \frac{5}{9}(T_F - 32) + 273.15 = \frac{5}{9}T_F + 255.37.$

Since $T_K = T_F = T,$ we have $T = \dfrac{255.37}{1 - 5/9} = \boxed{574.58 \text{ K}}$.

99.   Assuming a rectangular block. $L = L_o + \Delta L = L_0(1 + \alpha\Delta T),$

so $A = L^2 = L_0^2(1 + \alpha\Delta T)^2 = V_0(1 + 2\alpha\Delta T + \alpha^2\Delta T^2).$

Since $\alpha\Delta T$ is small, $\alpha^2\Delta T^2$ is even smaller. It can be ignored.

Therefore $A = A_0(1 + 2\alpha\Delta T).$ So the coefficient of area expansion is equal to $\boxed{2\alpha}$.

100.   (a) The temperature is $T = 20°C - (6.5 \text{ C°/km})(11 \text{ km}) = \boxed{-51.5°C}$.

(b) $T = 20°C - (6.5 \text{ C°/km})(34\,000 \text{ ft}) \times \dfrac{1 \text{ m}}{3.28 \text{ ft}} \times \dfrac{1 \text{ km}}{1000 \text{ m}} = \boxed{-47.4°C}$.

101. $\Delta V = \beta V_0 \Delta T = (1.8 \times 10^{-4} \text{ C°}^{-1})(0.200 \text{ cm}^3)(30 \text{ C°}) = 1.08 \times 10^{-3} \text{ cm}^3.$

$V = Ah = \pi r^2 h,$ ☞ $\Delta h = \dfrac{\Delta V}{\pi r^2} = \dfrac{1.08 \times 10^{-3} \text{ cm}^3}{\pi(0.0325 \text{ cm})^2} = \boxed{3.3 \text{ cm}}$.

102. $\Delta L = \alpha L_0 \Delta T = (17 \times 10^{-6} \text{ C°}^{-1})(150 \text{ m})[40°C - (-10°C)] = \boxed{0.13 \text{ m}}$.

103. $\dfrac{p_1 V_1}{T_1} = \dfrac{p_2 V_2}{T_2}.$

Since $T_2 = T_1,$ we have $p_2 = \dfrac{V_1}{V_2}p_1 = 2(1 \text{ atm}) = 2 \text{ atm} = 2(1.013 \times 10^5 \text{ Pa}) = \boxed{2.026 \times 10^5 \text{ Pa}}$.

CHAPTER 11

1. (d).

2. (b).

3. 240 Btu = (240 Btu)(252 cal/Btu)(4.186 J/cal) = $\boxed{2.54 \times 10^5 \text{ J}}$.

4. 1500 Cal = 1500×10^3 cal = $(1500 \times 10^3 \text{ cal})(4.186 \text{ J/cal})$ = $\boxed{6.279 \times 10^6 \text{ J}}$.

5. $P = \dfrac{Q}{\Delta t} = \dfrac{20\,000 \text{ Btu}}{1 \text{ h}} = \dfrac{(20\,000 \text{ Btu})(252 \text{ cal/Btu})(4.186 \text{ J/cal})}{3600 \text{ s}} = \boxed{5.86 \times 10^3 \text{ W}}$.

6. 1 Btu = 252 cal = (252 cal)(4.186 J/cal) = 1.055×10^3 J. So it is $\boxed{1 \text{ Btu} = 1.06 \times 10^3 \text{ J}}$.

7. (a) Work done in each lift: $W = Fd = (20 \text{ kg})(9.80 \text{ m/s}^2)(1.0 \text{ m}) = 196$ J.

    Energy input: $E = 2800$ Cal = 2800×10^3 cal = $(2800 \times 10^3 \text{ cal})(4.186 \text{ J/cal}) = 1.17 \times 10^7$ J.

    So the number of lifts is $\dfrac{1.17 \times 10^7 \text{ J}}{196 \text{ J}} = \boxed{60\,000 \text{ times}}$.

    (b) $t = 60\,000(5.0 \text{ s}) = 3.0 \times 10^5 \text{ s} = \boxed{83 \text{ h}}$.

8. (a).

9. $\boxed{\text{Water has higher specific heat so it takes longer to cool off}}$.

10. $\boxed{\text{No}}$. A negative specific heat corresponds to an increase in temperature when heat is removed.

11. $\boxed{\text{Yes}}$. A negative heat corresponds to $\boxed{\text{losing heat}}$.

12. It will be $\boxed{\text{toward the water}}$, because the water cools slower due to its specific heat. The "warmer" air above the water rises, and the cooler air above the water moves in to fill the void. See Fig. 11.12 in the textbook.

13. Heat flow depends on $\boxed{\text{just the temperature difference}}$ ($Q = cm\Delta T$).

14. This question is wrong because water has no weight in space (zero or negligible gravity). 3 lb of water on the Earth weighs 0 lb in space. This illustrates the limitation of the British system. Had the question been asked as "How many joules does it take to increase the temperature of 3 kg of ...", we would have an answer for it.

15. Since $Q = cm\Delta T = cm(T_f - T_i)$, $\boxed{\text{specific heat and mass}}$ can cause the final temperature of the two objects to be different.

16. If object A cools off faster, then $\boxed{\text{object A has a smaller specific heat}}$. From $Q = cm\Delta T$, if c is smaller, then ΔT is greater for the same Q. Or it takes less Q for an object with a smaller c to cool by the same ΔT.

17, $\boxed{\text{Yes}}$, c_p is always greater than c_v for gases. At constant volume, no work is done when adding heat to the gases. Under constant pressure, more heat is needed because of the work done as the gas expands.

18. $Q = mc\Delta T$, ☞ $\Delta T = \dfrac{Q}{cm} = \dfrac{(200\text{ J})}{[920\text{ J/(kg·C°)}](5.0 \times 10^{-3}\text{ kg})} = 43\text{ C°}$.

    So the final temperature is $20°C + 43\text{ C°} = \boxed{63°C}$.

19. $Q = cm\Delta T = [4186\text{ J/(kg·C°)}](5.0\text{ kg})(100°C - 20°C) = \boxed{1.7 \times 10^6\text{ J}}$.

20. (a) Copper requires $\boxed{\text{more}}$ heat $\boxed{\text{as it has a higher specific heat}}$.

    $c_{copper} = 390\text{ J/(kg·C°)} > c_{lead} = 130\text{ J/(kg·C°)}$.

    (b) $Q = cm\Delta T$, ☞ $\Delta Q = \Delta cm\Delta T = [390\text{ J/(kg·C°)} - 130\text{ J/(kg·C°)}](1.0\text{ kg})(190\text{ K} - 110\text{ K})$

    $$= \boxed{2.1 \times 10^4\text{ J more}}.$$

21. $Q = cm\Delta T$, ☞ $m = \dfrac{Q}{c\Delta T}$. So $\dfrac{m_a}{m_c} = \dfrac{\dfrac{Q}{c_a\Delta T}}{\dfrac{Q}{c_c\Delta T}} = \dfrac{c_c}{c_a} = \dfrac{390\text{ J/(kg·C°)}}{920\text{ J/(kg·C°)}} = 0.424$.

    Therefore: $m_a = 0.424(3.00\text{ kg}) = \boxed{1.27\text{ kg}}$.

22. The heat gained by the cup is $Q_{gained} = c_c m_c \Delta T_c = c_c(0.250\text{ kg})(80°C - 20°C) = (15\text{ kg·C°})c_c$.

    The heat lost by the coffee is $Q_{lost} = [4186\text{ J/(kg·C°)}](0.250\text{ kg})(80°C - 100°C) = -2.093 \times 10^4\text{ J}$.

    From calorimetry: $\Sigma Q_i = Q_{gained} + Q_{lost} = 0$, or $-Q_{lost} = Q_{gained}$.

    So $-(-2.093 \times 10^4\text{ J})\text{ J} = (15\text{ kg·C°})c_c$, therefore $c_c = \boxed{1.40 \times 10^3\text{ J/(kg·C°)}}$.

23.   The heat lost by the spoon is $Q_{lost} = c_s m_s \Delta T_s = [920 \text{ J/(kg·C°)}]m(30°C - 100°C) = -(6.44 \times 10^4)m$ J/kg.

The heat gained by water is $Q_{gained} = [4186 \text{ J/(kg·C°)}](0.200 \text{ kg})(30°C - 20°C) = 8.37 \times 10^3$ J.

From calorimetry: $\Sigma Q_i = Q_{gained} + Q_{lost} = 0$,   or $-Q_{lost} = Q_{gained}$.

So $-[-(6.44 \times 10^4)m \text{ J/kg}] = 8.37 \times 10^3$ J,   therefore $m = \boxed{0.13 \text{ kg}}$.

24.   (a) Lead has a $\boxed{\text{greater}}$ mass than copper. $c_{copper} = 390 \text{ J/(kg·C°)}$ and $c_{lead} = 130 \text{ J/(kg·C°)}$.

$$Q = cm\Delta T, \quad \text{☞} \quad \frac{m_{Pb}}{m_{Cu}} = \frac{Q/(c_{Pb}\Delta T_{Pb})}{Q/(C_{Cu}\Delta T_{Cu})} = \frac{c_{Cu}\Delta T_{Cu}}{c_{Pb}\Delta T_{Pb}} = \frac{[390 \text{ J/(kg·C°)}](5.0 \text{ C°})}{[130 \text{ J/(kg·C°)}](10 \text{ C°})} = 1.5.$$

(b) As in (a), $\frac{m_{Pb}}{m_{Cu}} = \boxed{1.5}$.

25.   The heat lost by the boiling water is $Q_1 = cm_1 \Delta T_1 = c(30 \text{ kg})(45°C - 100°C) = -(1650 \text{ kg·C°})c$.

The heat gained by the stream water is $Q_2 = cm_2 \Delta T_2 = cm_2(45°C - 15°C) = (30 \text{ C°})cm_2$.

From calorimetry: $\Sigma Q_i = Q_{gained} + Q_{lost} = 0$,   or $-Q_{lost} = Q_{gained}$.

So $(1650 \text{ kg·C°})c = (30 \text{ C°})cm_2$.   Solving, $m_2 = 55$ kg.   Therefore $\boxed{55 \text{ L}}$ must be added.

26.   The metal loses heat, and the water and the cup gain heat.

The heat lost by the metal is $Q_{lost} = cm\Delta T = c(0.150 \text{ kg})(30.5°C - 400°C) = -(55.43 \text{ kg·C°})c$.

The heat gained by the water and the cup is

$Q_{gained} = [4186 \text{ J/(kg·C°)}](0.400 \text{ kg})(30.5°C - 10.0°C) + [920 \text{ J/(kg.C°)}](0.200 \text{ kg})(30.5°C - 10.0°C)$

$\qquad = 3.810 \times 10^4$ J.

From calorimetry: $\Sigma Q_i = Q_{gained} + Q_{lost} = 0$,   or $-Q_{lost} = Q_{gained}$.

So $(55.43 \text{ kg·C°})c = 3.810 \times 10^4$ J.   Solving, $c = \boxed{687 \text{ J/(kg·C°)}}$.

27.   (a) If some water splashed out, there will be less water to absorb the heat. So the final temperature will be

higher and the measured specific heat value will be in error and appear to be $\boxed{\text{higher}}$ than accepted value.

(b) The metal loses heat and the water and the cup gain heat.

The heat lost by the metal is $Q_{lost} = cm\Delta T = c (0.50 \text{ kg})(25°C - 100°C) = -(37.5 \text{ kg·C°})c$.

The heat gained by the water and the cup is

$Q_{gained} = [4186 \text{ J/(kg·C°)}](0.50 \text{ kg})(25°C - 20°C) + [920 \text{ J/(kg.C°)}](0.250 \text{ kg})(25°C - 20°C)$

$\qquad = 1.162 \times 10^4$ J.

From calorimetry: $\Sigma Q_i = Q_{gained} + Q_{lost} = 0$,   or $-Q_{lost} = Q_{gained}$.

So $-(-37.5 \text{ kg·C°})c = 1.162 \times 10^4$ J.   Solving, $c = \boxed{3.1 \times 10^2 \text{ J/(kg·C°)}}$.

28. First calculate the heat required. 1-L water has a mass of 1 kg.

$$Q = cm\Delta T = [4186 \text{ J/(kg·C°)}](1.0 \text{ kg})(100°C - 20°C) = 3.35 \times 10^5 \text{ J}.$$

Then: $P = \dfrac{Q}{\Delta t}$ ☞ $\Delta t = \dfrac{Q}{P} = \dfrac{3.35 \times 10^5 \text{ J}}{1500 \text{ W}} = 223 \text{ s} = \boxed{3.72 \text{ min}}$.

29. Assume the final temperature is T. We use $Q = cm\Delta T$.

The heat lost by aluminum is $Q_{\text{lost}} = [920 \text{ J/(kg·C°)}](0.100 \text{ kg})(T - 90.0°C) = (92 \text{ J/C°})(T - 90.0°C)$.

The heat gained by water is $Q_{\text{gained}} = [4186 \text{ J/(kg·C°)}](1.00 \text{ kg})(T - 20°C) = (4186 \text{ J/C°})(T - 20°C)$.

From calorimetry: $\Sigma Q_i = Q_{\text{gained}} + Q_{\text{lost}} = 0$, or $-Q_{\text{lost}} = Q_{\text{gained}}$.

So $-92(T - 90.0°C) = 4186(T - 20°C)$. Solving, $T = \boxed{21.5°C}$.

30. (a) First calculate the heat required. 1-L water has a mass of 1 kg.

$$Q = cm\Delta T = [4186 \text{ J/(kg·C°)}](1.5 \text{ kg})(0°C - 20°C) = -1.26 \times 10^5 \text{ J}.$$

So: $P = \dfrac{-Q}{\Delta t} = \dfrac{1.26 \times 10^5 \text{ J}}{3.0(60 \text{ s})} = \boxed{7.0 \times 10^2 \text{ W}}$.

(b) 1-L mercury has a mass of 13.6 kg (the density of mercury is 13.6 times that of water).

$$Q = [140 \text{ J/(kg·C°)}](1.5)(13.6 \text{ kg}))(-39°C - 20°C) = -1.69 \times 10^5 \text{ J}.$$

$P = \dfrac{1.69 \times 10^5 \text{ J}}{3.0(60 \text{ s})} . = \boxed{9.4 \times 10^2 \text{ W}}$.

31. (d).

32. (d).

33. Different substances have different internal energies, different molecular structures, and different intrinsic heat properties. These quantities affect the temperature at which phase changes take place due to the different effects the addition or removal of heat has on different substances. Latent heats will also be different for different substances because of different molecular structures or bonds. The latent heat energy goes into breaking these bonds.

34. $\boxed{\text{No}}$, nothing is wrong with the thermometer. Extra heat is needed to melt the ice (latent heat of fusion). Once the ice is completely melted, the temperature of water increases.

35. This is due to the $\boxed{\text{high value of the latent heat of vaporization}}$. When steam condenses, it releases 2.26×10^6 J/kg of heat. When 100°C water drops its temperature by 1 C°, it releases only 4186 J/kg.

36. $\boxed{\text{The water molecules in the breath condens to water droplets}}$, which look like steam.

37. $\boxed{\text{The fan blows relatively dry air, promoting evaporation, and thereby keeping you cool}}$.

38. $Q = mL_v = (0.500 \text{ kg})(22.6 \times 10^5 \text{ J/kg}) = \boxed{1.13 \times 10^6 \text{ J}}$.

39.   (a) Converting 1.0 kg of water at 100°C to steam at 100°C required $\boxed{\text{more}}$ heat because the heat of vaporization L_v is greater than the heat of fusion, L_f.

(b) Heat needed to vaporize is $Q_1 = mL_v = (1.0 \text{ kg})((22.6 \times 10^5 \text{ J/kg}) = 2.26 \times 10^6 \text{ J}$.

Heat needed to raise T is: $Q_2 = cm\Delta T = [4186 \text{ J/(kg·C°)}](1.0 \text{ kg})(100°C - 0°C) = 4.186 \times 10^5 \text{ J}$.

So $\Delta Q = Q_1 - Q_2 = 2.26 \times 10^6 \text{ J} - 4.186 \times 10^5 \text{ J} = \boxed{1.8 \times 10^6 \text{ J more}}$.

40.   The melting point of lead is 328°C. So the temperature of the lead has to be increased to 328°C first. The total heat required is then

$Q = cm\Delta T + mL_f = [130 \text{ J/(kg.C°)}](0.75 \text{ kg})(328°C - 20°C) + (0.75 \text{ kg})(0.25 \times 10^5 \text{ J/kg}) = \boxed{4.9 \times 10^4 \text{ J}}$.

41.   1-L nitrogen has a mass of 0.80 kg (the density of nitrogen is 0.80 times that of water).

$Q = mL_v = 0.50(0.80 \text{ kg})(2.0 \times 10^5 \text{ J/kg}) = \boxed{8.0 \times 10^4 \text{ J}}$.

42. $Q = cm\Delta T + mL_v = [4186 \text{ J/(kg·C°)}](0.50 \text{ kg})(100°C - 50°C) + (0.50 \text{ kg})(22.6 \times 10^5 \text{ J/kg}) = \boxed{1.2 \times 10^6 \text{ J}}$.

43.   The boiling point of mercury is 357°C = 630 K. So $Q = mL_v = (0.015 \text{ kg})(2.7 \times 10^5 \text{ J/kg}) = \boxed{4.1 \times 10^3 \text{ J}}$.

44.   (a) The heat needed to raise the temperature of ice from −20°C to 0°C is

$Q_1 = cm\Delta T = [2100 \text{ J/(kg.C°)}](0.500 \text{ kg})[0°C - (-20°C)] = 2.1 \times 10^4 \text{ J}$;

the heat needed to melt the ice at 0°C is $Q_2 = mL_f = (0.500 \text{ kg})(3.3 \times 10^5 \text{ J/kg}) = 1.65 \times 10^5 \text{ J}$;

the heat needed to raise the temperature of water from 0°C to 100°C is

$Q_3 = [4186 \text{ J/(kg.C°)}](0.500 \text{ kg})(100°C - 0°C) = 2.09 \times 10^5 \text{ J}$;

the heat needed to evaporate the water at 100°C is $Q_4 = (0.500 \text{ kg})(22.6 \times 10^5 \text{ J/kg}) = 1.13 \times 10^6 \text{ J}$;

the heat needed to raise the temperature of the steam from 100°C to 115°C is

$Q_5 = [2010 \text{ J/(kg·C°)}](0.500 \text{ kg})(115°C - 100°C) = 1.51 \times 10^4 \text{ J}$.

So the total heat required is $\Sigma Q = \boxed{1.54 \times 10^6 \text{ J}}$.

(b) The heat required to increase the temperature of ice from −20°C to −5°C is

$Q = (2100 \text{ J/kg.C°})(0.500 \text{ kg})[-5°\text{C} - (-20°\text{C})] = 1.58 \times 10^4 \text{ J}.$

So the heat needed to be removed is $1.54 \times 10^6 \text{ J} - 1.58 \times 10^4 \text{ J} = \boxed{1.52 \times 10^6 \text{ J}}$.

45. The heat needed to be removed from water is

$Q_{\text{lost}} = mc\Delta T = [4186 \text{ J/(kg·C°)}](1.0 \text{ kg})(20°\text{C} - 100°\text{C}) = -3.35 \times 10^5 \text{ J}.$

The ice and the melt water have to absorb that much heat. Let the mass of ice be m.

$Q_{\text{gained}} = mL_f + mc\Delta T = m(3.3 \times 10^5 \text{ J/kg}) + m[4186 \text{ J/(kg.C°)}](20°\text{C} - 0°\text{C}) = (4.14 \times 10^5)m \text{ J/kg}.$

From calorimetry: $\Sigma Q_i = Q_{\text{gained}} + Q_{\text{lost}} = 0,$ or $-Q_{\text{lost}} = Q_{\text{gained}}.$

So $-(-3.35 \times 10^5 \text{ J}) = (4.14 \times 10^5)m \text{ J/kg}.$ Solving, $m = \dfrac{3.35 \times 10^5 \text{ J}}{4.14 \times 10^5 \text{ J/kg}} = \boxed{0.81 \text{ kg}}.$

46. To completely melt the ice to water at 0°C it requires

$Q_1 = cm\Delta T + mL_f = [2100 \text{ J/(kg·C°)}](0.60 \text{ kg})[0°\text{C} - (-10°\text{C})] + (0.60 \text{ kg})(3.3 \times 10^5 \text{ J/kg})$

$= 2.11 \times 10^5 \text{ J}.$

For 0.30 kg of water not to freeze into ice, it can only release

$Q_2 = [4186 \text{ J/(kg)}](0.30 \text{ kg})(0°\text{C} - 50°\text{C}) = -6.28 \times 10^4 \text{ J} < Q_1.$

So the temperature of the ice will increase to 0°C, and then a portion of it will be melted.

Let the amount of ice melted be M.

From calorimetry: $\Sigma Q_i = Q_{\text{gained}} + Q_{\text{lost}} = 0,$ or $-Q_{\text{lost}} = Q_{\text{gained}}.$

So $-(-6.28 \times 10^4 \text{ J}) = [2100 \text{ J/(kg·C°)}](0.60 \text{ kg})[0°\text{C} - (-10°\text{C})] + M(3.3 \times 10^5 \text{ J/kg}),$

therefore $M = 0.15 \text{ kg}.$ Hence, the total amount of water is $0.30 \text{ kg} + 0.15 \text{ kg} = \boxed{0.45 \text{ kg}}$.

47. Ice gains heat and water and the cup loses heat. Let T be the final temperature. There is a phase change (fusion for ice).   The heat gained by ice is

$Q_{\text{gained}} = m_i L_f + c_w m_i \Delta T_i = (0.050 \text{ kg})(3.3 \times 10^5 \text{ J/kg}) + [4186 \text{ J/(kg·C°)}](0.050 \text{ kg})(T - 0°\text{C})$

$= 1.65 \times 10^4 \text{ J} + (209 \text{ J/C°})T.$

The heat lost by the water and the aluminum cup is

$Q_{\text{lost}} = [4186 \text{ J/(kg.C°)}](0.300 \text{ kg})(T - 25°\text{C}) + [920 \text{ J/(kg·C°)}](0.100 \text{ kg})(T - 25°\text{C})$

$= (1348 \text{ J/C°})(T - 25°\text{C}).$

From calorimetry: $\Sigma Q_i = Q_{\text{gained}} + Q_{\text{lost}} = 0,$ or $-Q_{\text{lost}} = Q_{\text{gained}}.$

So $-(1348 \text{ J/C°})(T - 25°\text{C}) = 1.65 \times 10^4 \text{ J} + (209 \text{ J/C°})T.$ Solving, $T = \boxed{11°\text{C}}.$

48. The heat required to raise the temperature of water to 60°C is

$$Q_{\text{gained}} = cm\Delta T = [4186 \text{ J/(kg·C°)}](0.250 \text{ kg})(60°C - 20°C) = 4.19 \times 10^4 \text{ J}.$$

Let the mass of steam be M.

The steam condensates first and then lowers its temperature to 60°C.

$$Q_{\text{lost}} = -ML_v + cM\Delta T = -M(22.6 \times 10^5 \text{ J/kg}) + M[4186 \text{ J/(kg·C°)}](60°C - 100°C) = -(2.43 \times 10^6)M \text{ J/kg}.$$

From calorimetry: $\Sigma Q_i = Q_{\text{gained}} + Q_{\text{lost}} = 0$, or $-Q_{\text{lost}} = Q_{\text{gained}}$.

So $-[-(2.43 \times 10^6)M \text{ J/kg}] = 4.19 \times 10^4 \text{ J}$. Solving, $M = \dfrac{4.19 \times 10^4 \text{ J}}{2.34 \times 10^6 \text{ J/kg}} = \boxed{1.79 \times 10^{-2} \text{ kg}}$.

49. If enough ice is added, the equilibrium temperature is 0°C. Note 1-L water has a mass of 1 kg.

The heat lost by the tea is $Q_{\text{lost}} = cm\Delta T = [4186 \text{ J/(kg·C°)}](0.75 \text{ kg})(0°C - 20°C) = -6.279 \times 10^4 \text{ J}$.

Let the mass of ice melted be M. $Q_{\text{gained}} = ML_f = (3.3 \times 10^5)M \text{ J/kg}$.

From calorimetry: $\Sigma Q_i = Q_{\text{gained}} + Q_{\text{lost}} = 0$, or $-Q_{\text{lost}} = Q_{\text{gained}}$.

So $-(-6.279 \times 10^4 \text{ J}) = 3.3 \times 10^5)M \text{ J/kg}$. Solving, $M = \dfrac{6.279 \times 10^4 \text{ J}}{3.3 \times 10^5 \text{ J/kg}} = 0.190 \text{ kg}$.

So the total amount of liquid is $0.75 \text{ kg} + 0.19 \text{ kg} = \boxed{0.94 \text{ kg or } 0.94 \text{ L}}$.

50. 0.50 L of water has a mass of 0.50 kg. The heat removed from water is

$$Q_w = c_w m\Delta T_w - mL_f + c_i m\Delta T_i = [4186 \text{ J/(kg·C°)}](0.50 \text{ kg})(0°C - 16°C) - (0.50 \text{ kg})(3.33 \times 10^5 \text{ J/kg})$$
$$+ [2100 \text{ J/(kg·C°)}](0.50 \text{ kg})(-8.0°C - 0°C) = -2.083 \times 10^5 \text{ J}.$$

The heat removed from the aluminum tray is

$$Q_a = [920 \text{ J/(kg·C°)}](0.250 \text{ kg})(-8.0°C - 16°C) = -5.52 \times 10^3 \text{ J}.$$

So the total heat that must be removed is $Q = 2.083 \times 10^5 \text{ J} + 5.52 \times 10^3 \text{ J} = \boxed{2.14 \times 10^5 \text{ J}}$.

51. (a) This is because $\boxed{\text{water has high heat of vaporization}}$.

(b) $Q = mL_v = (0.50 \text{ kg})(2.26 \times 10^6 \text{ J/kg}) = \boxed{1.1 \times 10^6 \text{ J}}$.

52. (a) $\boxed{110°C \text{ and } 140°C}$.

(b) For solid: $c_1 = \dfrac{Q}{m\Delta T} = \dfrac{(0.20 - 0.10) \times 10^4 \text{ J}}{(1.0 \text{ kg})(110°C - 100°C)} = \boxed{1.0 \times 10^2 \text{ J/(kg·C°)}}$,

for liquid: $c_2 = \dfrac{(1.2 - 0.60) \times 10^4 \text{ J}}{(1.0 \text{ kg})(140°C - 110°C)} = \boxed{2.0 \times 10^2 \text{ J/(kg·C°)}}$,

for gas: $c_3 = \dfrac{(2.0 - 1.8) \times 10^4 \text{ J}}{(1.0 \text{ kg})(160°C - 140°C)} = \boxed{1.0 \times 10^2 \text{ J/(kg·C°)}}$.

(c) For fusion: $L_f = \dfrac{Q}{m} = \dfrac{(0.60 - 0.20) \times 10^4 \text{ J}}{1.0 \text{ kg}} = \boxed{4.0 \times 10^3 \text{ J/kg}}$,

for vaporization: $L_v = \dfrac{(1.8 - 1.2) \times 10^4 \text{ J}}{1.0 \text{ kg}} = \boxed{6.0 \times 10^3 \text{ J/kg}}$.

53.   The heat lost by the ceramic is

$Q_{lost} = cm\Delta T = [840 \text{ J/(kg·C°)}](0.150 \text{ kg})(-196°C - 20°C) = -2.72 \times 10^4 \text{ J}$.

Let the mass of nitrogen boiled be M. The heat gained is

$Q_{gained} = ML_v = (2.0 \times 10^5)M \text{ J/kg}$.

From calorimetry: $\Sigma Q_i = Q_{gained} + Q_{lost} = 0$,   or $-Q_{lost} = Q_{gained}$.

So $-(-2.72 \times 10^4 \text{ J}) = (2.0 \times 10^5)M \text{ J/kg}$.   Solving, $M = \dfrac{2.72 \times 10^4 \text{ J}}{2.0 \times 10^5 \text{ J/kg}} = 0.136 \text{ kg}$.

Note that 1-L liquid nitrogen has a mass of 0.80 kg (the density of liquid nitrogen is 0.80 kg/L).

$\rho = \dfrac{m}{V}$,   ☞ $V = \dfrac{m}{\rho} = \dfrac{0.136 \text{ kg}}{0.80 \text{ kg/L}} = \boxed{0.17 \text{ L}}$.

54.   (d).

55.   Water can be heated relatively quickly because of $\boxed{\text{convection}}$. The warm (less dense) water rises to the top and the cooler (more dense) water sinks to the bottom.

56.   Metal has a higher heat conductivity, so $\boxed{\text{metal conducts heat away from your hand more quickly}}$.

57.   (a) This convects the heat from the hot soup to the cooler air.
(b) No. The ice blocks airflow and cooling of the air. (Also, the air conditioner is less efficient and runs more, increasing electric cost.) Also, ice is a poor conductor.

58.   The bridge is exposed to the cold air above and below, while the road is exposed only above. Thus more heat is removed from the bridge than the road. This results in a fast freeze of the water on the bridge.

59.   It is to increase the surface area for better conduction and radiation.

60. $\boxed{\text{Cu has a higher thermal conductivity than Al}}$, so the heat transfers faster to the food.

61. The double-walled and partially evacuated container is to counteract conduction and convection because both processes depend on a medium to transfer the heat (the double-walls are more for holding the partially evacuated region than for reducing conduction and convection). The mirrored interior minimizes the loss by radiation.

62. This is because the $\boxed{\text{pan is a much better heat conductor than air}}$, so more heat is transferred to your hand more quickly through the pan.

63. $\boxed{\text{Air is a poor heat conductor}}$ so the hollow hair minimizes heat loss.

64. The temperature would have been $\boxed{\text{hotter because white is not a good emitter}}$. Painting it black means that it emits heat more efficiently.

65. (a) The tile floor will conduct heat from your bare feet $\boxed{\text{faster}}$ becauae tile has a higher thermal conductivity.

(b) $\dfrac{\Delta Q}{\Delta t} = \dfrac{kA\Delta T}{d}$, ☞ $\dfrac{(\Delta Q/\Delta t)_t}{(\Delta Q/\Delta t)_o} = \dfrac{k_t}{k_o} = \dfrac{0.67\ \text{J/(m·s·C°)}}{0.15\ \text{J/(m·s·C°)}} = \boxed{4.5}$.

66. $P_{net} = \sigma A e(T_s^4 - T^4) = [5.67 \times 10^{-8}\ \text{W/(m}^2\text{·K}^4)](0.25\ \text{m}^2)(0.70)\{[(273 + 34)\ \text{K}]^4 - [273 + 22)\ \text{K}]^4\}$

    $= 13\ \text{J/s}$.   So in 1 s, the heat energy is $\boxed{13\ \text{J}}$.

67. $\dfrac{\Delta Q}{\Delta t} = \dfrac{kA\Delta T}{d} = \dfrac{[0.84\ \text{J/(m·s·C°)}](2.00\ \text{m})(1.50\ \text{m})(2\ \text{C°})}{4.00 \times 10^{-3}\ \text{m}} = 1260\ \text{J/s}$.

So $\Delta Q = (1.36 \times 10^3\ \text{W})(3600\ \text{s}) = \boxed{4.54 \times 10^6\ \text{J}}$.

68. The normal body temperature is 37°C.

$\dfrac{\Delta Q}{\Delta t} = \dfrac{kA\Delta T}{d} = \dfrac{[0.20\ \text{J/(m·s·C°)}](0.30\ \text{m}^2)(37°\text{C} - 33°\text{C})}{0.010\ \text{m}} = \boxed{24\ \text{J/s}}$.

69. (a) $\dfrac{\Delta Q}{\Delta t} = \dfrac{kA\Delta T}{d} = \dfrac{[390\ \text{J/(m·s·C°)}](\pi)(0.15\ \text{m})^2(150°\text{C} - 100°\text{C})}{2.5 \times 10^{-3}\ \text{m}} = \boxed{5.5 \times 10^5\ \text{J/s}}$.

(b) In 5.0 min, the heat supplied to the water is

$\Delta Q = (5.5 \times 10^5\ \text{J/s})(5.0)(60\ \text{s}) = 1.65 \times 10^8\ \text{J}$.

The mass boiled away by ΔQ is $m = \dfrac{\Delta Q}{L_v} = \dfrac{1.65 \times 10^8\ \text{J}}{22.6 \times 10^5\ \text{kg}} = \boxed{73\ \text{kg}}$.

$\boxed{\text{No}}$, this answer is not reasonable because a lot of heat does not go into the water.

70. (a) The copper bar is [longer] because copper has a higher thermal conductivity.

(b) $\dfrac{\Delta Q}{\Delta t} = \dfrac{kA\Delta T}{d}$, ☞ $d = \dfrac{kA\Delta T}{(\Delta Q/\Delta t)}$. $\dfrac{d_{cu}}{d_{al}} = \dfrac{k_{Cu}}{k_{Ai}} = \dfrac{390 \text{ J/(m·s·C°)}}{240 \text{ J/(m·s·C°)}} = \boxed{1.6}$.

71. The heat required to melt the ice is $Q = mL_f = (5.0 \text{ kg})(3.3 \times 10^5 \text{ J/kg}) = 1.65 \times 10^6 \text{ J}$.

$\dfrac{\Delta Q}{\Delta t} = \dfrac{kA\Delta T}{d} = \dfrac{[0.042 \text{ J/(m·s·C°)}](1.0 \text{ m}^2)(35\ °C - 0°C)}{0.025 \text{ m}}) = 58.8 \text{ J/s}$.

So the time is $\dfrac{1.65 \times 10^6 \text{ J}}{58.8 \text{ J/s}} = 2.8 \times 10^4 \text{ s} = \boxed{7.8 \text{ h}}$.

72. (a) [Larger R-value means greater insulation].

(b)   (1) $R = \dfrac{L}{k}$, ☞ $L = R\,k$.

$\dfrac{L_{\text{fiberboard}}}{L_{\text{foam plastic}}} = \dfrac{k_{\text{fiberboard}}}{k_{\text{foam plastic}}} = \dfrac{0.059 \text{ J/(m·s·C°)}}{0.042 \text{ J/(m·s·C°)}} = 1.40$.

So $L_{\text{fiberboard}} = (1.40)(3.0 \text{ in}) = \boxed{4.2 \text{ in}}$.

(2) $\dfrac{L_{\text{brick}}}{L_{\text{foam plastic}}} = \dfrac{0.71 \text{ J/(m·s·C°)}}{0.042 \text{ J/(m·s·C°)}} = 16.9$.

Thus $L_{\text{brick}} = 16.9(3.0 \text{ in}) = \boxed{51 \text{ in}}$.

73. $R = \dfrac{L}{k}$, ☞ $L = Rk$.

(a) $\dfrac{L_{\text{glass wool}}}{L_{\text{pine wood}}} = \dfrac{k_{\text{glass wool}}}{k_{\text{pine wood}}} = \dfrac{0.042 \text{ J/(m·s·C°)}}{0.12 \text{ J/(m·s·C°)}} = 0.35$.   So $L_{\text{glass wool}} = 0.35(14 \text{ in.}) = \boxed{4.9 \text{ in.}}$.

(b) $\dfrac{L_{\text{fiberboard}}}{L_{\text{pine wood}}} = \dfrac{0.059 \text{ J/(m·s·C°)}}{0.12 \text{ J/(m·s·C°)}} = 0.492$.   So $L_{\text{fiberboard}} = \boxed{6.9 \text{ in.}}$.

74. (a) $\dfrac{\Delta Q}{\Delta t} = \dfrac{k\,A\,\Delta T}{d} = \dfrac{(0.84 \text{ J/m·s.C°})(2.0 \text{ m})(3.0 \text{ m})(20°C - 0°C)}{4.0 \times 10^{-3} \text{ m}} = \boxed{2.5 \times 10^4 \text{ J/s}}$.

(b) From Example 11.8, $\dfrac{\Delta Q}{\Delta t} = \dfrac{A(T_2 - T_1)}{d_1/k_1 + d_2/k_2 + d_3/k_3}$

$= \dfrac{(2.0 \text{ m})(3.0 \text{ m})(20°C - 0°C)}{(2.0 \times 10^{-3} \text{ m})/[0.84 \text{ J/(m·s·C°)}] + (1.0 \times 10^{-3} \text{ m})/[0.024 \text{ J/(m·s·C°)}] + (2.0 \times 10^{-3} \text{ m})/[0.84 \text{ J/(m·s·C°)}]}$

$= \boxed{2.6 \times 10^3 \text{ J/s}}$. [No], because of losses due to radiation and convection. Also, the temperature gradient

across the window is usually not as great as that given by ambient temperatures.

75. (a) This object would have $\boxed{\text{less}}$ power radiated since $P \propto e$ as in $P = \sigma A e T^4$.

(b) $P = \sigma A e T^4$, ☞ $\dfrac{P_b}{P_o} = \dfrac{e_b}{e_o} = \dfrac{1}{0.60} = \boxed{1.7}$.

76. From Example 11.8, $\dfrac{\Delta Q}{\Delta t} = \dfrac{A(T_2 - T_1)}{d_1/k_1 + d_2/k_2 + d_3/k_3}$

$= \dfrac{(3.5 \text{ m})(5.0 \text{ m})[20°C - (-10°C)]}{(0.020 \text{ m})/[0.059 \text{ J}/(\text{m·s·C°})] + (0.150 \text{ m})/[1.3 \text{ J}/(\text{m·s·C°})] + (0.070 \text{ m})/[0.71 \text{ J}/(\text{m·s·C°})]} = 949 \text{ J/s}$.

In 1 h $\Delta Q = (949 \text{ J/s})(3600 \text{ s}) = \boxed{3.4 \times 10^6 \text{ J}}$.

77. $\dfrac{\Delta Q}{\Delta t} = \dfrac{949 \text{ H/s}}{2} = 474.5 \text{ J/s} =$

$\dfrac{(3.5 \text{ m})(5.0 \text{ m})[20°C-(-10°C)]}{(0.020 \text{ m})/[0.059 \text{ J}/(\text{m·s·C°})]+d/[0.042 \text{ J}/(\text{m·s·C°})]+(0.150 \text{ m})/[1.3 \text{ J}/(\text{m·s·C°})]+(0.070 \text{ m})/[0.71 \text{ J}/(\text{m·s·C°})]}$

Solving, $d = 0.023 \text{ m} = \boxed{2.3 \text{ cm}}$.

78. (a) The power radiated increases by $\boxed{16}$ times because $P = \sigma A e T^4$.

(b) $P = \sigma A e T^4$, ☞ $\dfrac{P}{P_o} = \dfrac{T^4}{T_o^4} = \dfrac{(273 + 40)^4}{(273 + 20)^4} = 1.3$. So $\boxed{\text{increases to 1.3 times}}$.

79. From Example 11.8,

$\dfrac{\Delta Q}{\Delta t} = \dfrac{A(T_2 - T_1)}{d_1/k_1 + d_2/k_2} = \dfrac{\pi(0.050 \text{ m})^2 (95°C - 15°C)}{(0.040 \text{ m})/[46 \text{ J}/(\text{m·s·C°})] + (0.040 \text{ m})/[390 \text{ J}/(\text{m·s·C°})]} = 646 \text{ J/s}$.

In 10 min, $\Delta Q = (646 \text{ J/s})(20)(60 \text{ s}) = \boxed{7.8 \times 10^5 \text{ J}}$.

80. Let the temperature at the interface be T and consider steel.

$\dfrac{\Delta Q}{\Delta t} = \dfrac{\pi(0.050 \text{ m})^2 (95°C - T)}{(0.040 \text{ m})/[46 \text{ J}/(\text{m·s·C°})]} = 646 \text{ J/s}$, solving, $T = \boxed{23°C}$.

81. Although the surface area of the collector is $\pi r L$, the sunlight is exposed to a rectangular cross-sectional area of $A = dL = 2\pi L = 2(0.50 \text{ m})(4.0 \text{ m}) = 4.0 \text{ m}^2$.

$E = IAt = 0.50[1400 \text{ J}/(\text{m}^2\text{·s})](4.0 \text{ m}^2)(10)(3600 \text{ s}) = \boxed{1.0 \times 10^8 \text{ J}}$.

82. $Q = Q_a + Q_i = c_a m_a \Delta T = c_i m_i \Delta T$

$= [920 \text{ J}/(\text{kg·C°})](25 \text{ kg})(120°C - 20°C) + [460 \text{ J}/(\text{kg·C°})](80 \text{ kg})(120°C - 20°C) = \boxed{6.0 \times 10^6 \text{ J}}$.

83. Let the final temperature be T. The heat lost by water is

$$Q_{\text{lost}} = cm\Delta T = [4186\ \text{J/(kg·C°)}](0.40\ \text{kg})(T - 90°\text{C}) = (1674\ \text{J/C°})(T - 90°\text{C}).$$

The heat gained by the cup is

$$Q_{\text{gained}} = [840\ \text{J/(kg·C°)}](0.200\ \text{kg})(T - 20°\text{C}) = (168\ \text{J/C°})(T - 20°\text{C}).$$

From calorimetry: $\Sigma Q_i = Q_{\text{gained}} + Q_{\text{lost}} = 0$, or $-Q_{\text{lost}} = Q_{\text{gained}}$.

So $-(1674\ \text{J/C°})(T - 90°\text{C}) = (168\ \text{J/C°})(T - 20°\text{C})$. Solving, $T = \boxed{84°\text{C}}$.

84. $P_{\text{net}} = \sigma A e(T_s^4 - T^4)$, ☞ $\dfrac{100\ \text{W}}{99.5\ \text{W}} = \dfrac{T_s^4 - (293\ \text{K})^4}{T_s^4 - (303\ \text{K})^4}$,

or $1.005 T_s^4 - 8.47 \times 10^9\ \text{K}^4 = T_s^4 - 7.37 \times 10^9\ \text{K}^4$. Solving, $T_s = 684\ \text{K} = \boxed{411°\text{C}}$.

85. Let the initial temperature of the shot be T. The heat lost by the copper shot is

$$Q_{\text{lost}} = cm\Delta T = [390\ \text{J/(kg·C°)}](0.150\ \text{kg})(28°\text{C} - T) = (58.5\ \text{J/C°})(28°\text{C} - T),$$

The heat gained by water is

$$Q_{\text{gained-water}} = [4186\ \text{J/(kg·C°)}](0.200\ \text{kg})(28°\text{C} - 25°\text{C}) = 2512\ \text{J},$$

The heat gained by the cup is

$$Q_{\text{gained-cup}} = [920\ \text{J/(kg·C°)}](0.375\ \text{kg})(28°\text{C} - 25°\text{C}) = 1035\ \text{J}.$$

From calorimetry: $\Sigma Q_i = Q_{\text{gained-water}} + Q_{\text{gained-cup}} + Q_{\text{lost}} = 0$, or $-Q_{\text{lost}} = Q_{\text{gained-water}} + Q_{\text{gained-cup}}$.

So $-(58.5\ \text{J/C°})(28°\text{C} - T) = 2512\ \text{J} + 1035\ \text{J}$. Solving, $T = \boxed{88.7°\text{C}}$.

86. Let the final temperature of the mixture be T. 1.0 L of water has a mass of 1.0 kg and 1.0 L of ethyl alcohol has a mass of 0.79 kg, because the density of ethyl alcohol is 790 kg/m^3.

The heat lost by water is

$$Q_{\text{lost}} = cm\Delta T = [4186\ \text{J/(kg·C°)}](1.0\ \text{kg})(T - 40°\text{C}) = (4186\ \text{J/C°})(T - 40°\text{C}).$$

The heat gained by alcohol is

$$Q_{\text{gained}} = [2430\ \text{J/(kg·C°)}](0.79\ \text{kg})(T - 20°\text{C}) = (1920\ \text{J/C°})(T - 20°\text{C}).$$

From calorimetry: $\Sigma Q_i = Q_{\text{gained}} + Q_{\text{lost}} = 0$, or $-Q_{\text{lost}} = Q_{\text{gained}}$.

So $-(4186\ \text{J/C°})(T - 40°\text{C}) = (1920\ \text{J/C°})(T - 20°\text{C})$. Solving, $T = \boxed{34°\text{C}}$.

87. 25 km/h = 6.95 m/s. The kinetic energy is $K = \frac{1}{2}mv^2 = \frac{1}{2}(65\ \text{kg})(6.95\ \text{m/s})^2 = 1.57 \times 10^3\ \text{J}$.

So $Q = 0.40K = 627\ \text{J}$. $m = \dfrac{Q}{L_f} = \dfrac{627\ \text{J}}{3.3 \times 10^5\ \text{J/kg}} = 1.9 \times 10^{-3}\ \text{kg} = \boxed{1.9\ \text{g}}$.

The rest of the energy goes $\boxed{\text{into heating the skates and loss to the environment}}$.

88.　The kinetic energy of the bullet is $K = \frac{1}{2}mv^2$.

The heat that goes to melting the bullet is then $Q = 0.80K = 0.40mv^2$.

This heat goes into raising the temperature of lead and melting it.

$Q = cm\Delta T + mL_f = [130 \text{ J/(kg·C)}]m(328°C - 20°C) + m(0.25 \times 10^5 \text{ J/kg}) = 0.40mv^2$.

Solving,　$v = \boxed{4.0 \times 10^2 \text{ m/s}}$.

89.　(a) Aluminum (Al) gains $\boxed{\text{more}}$ heat than iron (Fe) because aluminum has a higher specific heat.

(b) $Q_{Al} = cm\Delta T = [920 \text{ J/(kg·C°)}](0.50 \text{ kg})(100°C - 20°C) = 3.68 \times 10^4$ J,

$Q_{Fe} = [460 \text{ J/(kg·C°)}](0.50 \text{ kg})(100°C - 20°C) = 1.84 \times 10^4$ J.

So the difference is 1.84×10^4 J, or $\boxed{\text{Al by } 1.8 \times 10^4 \text{ J}}$.

90.　The gravitational energy of m kg of water at the top of the waterfall is $U = mgy$.

$$U = Q = cm\Delta T, \quad \text{☞} \quad \Delta T = \frac{U}{cm} = \frac{mgy}{cm} = \frac{gy}{c} = \frac{(9.80 \text{ m/s}^2)(75 \text{ m})}{4186 \text{ J/(kg·C°)}} = \boxed{0.18 \text{ C°}}.$$

91.　The heat needed to raise the temperature of ice from $-10°C$ to $0°C$ is

$Q_1 = cm\Delta T = [2100 \text{ J/(kg.C°)}](0.75 \text{ kg})[0°C - (-10°C)] = 1.575 \times 10^4$ J.

The heat needed to melt the ice at $0°C$ is $Q_2 = mL_f = (0.75 \text{ kg})(3.3 \times 10^5 \text{ J/kg}) = 2.475 \times 10^5$ J.

The heat needed to raise the temperature of water from $0°C$ to $100°C$ is

$Q_3 = [4186 \text{ J/(kg.C°)}](0.75 \text{ kg})(100°C - 0°C) = 3.140 \times 10^5$ J.

The heat needed to evaporate the water at $100°C$ is $Q_4 = (0.75 \text{ kg})(22.6 \times 10^5 \text{ J/kg}) = 1.695 \times 10^6$ J.

The heat needed to raise the temperature of the steam from $100°C$ to $120°C$ is

$Q_5 = [2010 \text{ J/(kg·C°)}](0.75 \text{ kg})(120°C - 100°C) = 3.015 \times 10^4$ J.

So the total heat required is $\Sigma Q = \boxed{2.3 \times 10^6 \text{ J}}$.

92.　Since water cooler than 4°C is less dense than water at 4°C, the cooler water convects upward to the surface of the lake while the warmer water at or near 4°C stays at the bottom of the lake. Eventually the surface may freeze, but the bottom of the lake is still around 4°C.

93.　$\boxed{\text{It will stay hot longer if cream is added right away}}$ because the heat loss is proportional to the temperature difference. By adding the cream right away, the temperature difference is less and so is the heat loss.

CHAPTER 12

1.   (c).

2.   (d).

3.   (a).

4.   For an ideal gas, $pV = nRT$. If T is a constant, $p \propto 1/V$. That is, pressure varies inversely with volume. Therefore, a plot of p vs. V should look like the one on the left.

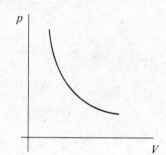

5.

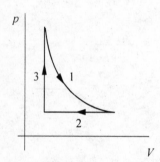

6.   (a) isothermal

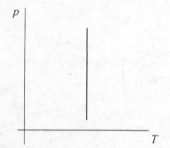

(b) isobaric

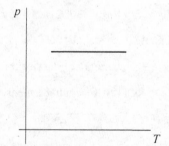

(c) isometric

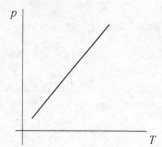

(d) adiabatic

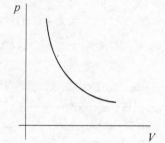

7.   (b).

8.   (c).

9.   (d).

10.   (a) A force is exerted to pump the air and does work on the system. After one cycle, the internal energy of the system returns to its original value so heat must leave the system. This causes the body of the pump to heat up.

(b) The rapid "expansion" is almost adiabatic. Work is done at the expense of the internal energy of the gas. This lowers the temperature and cools the valve.

11.   This is an adiabatic compression. When the plunger is pushed in, the work done goes into increasing of the internal energy of the air. The increase in internal energy increases the temperature of the air and causes the paper to catch fire.

12.   When you play a game of basketball, you $\boxed{\text{lost heat, did work, and decreased internal energy}}$.

13.   This is possible $\boxed{\text{through work}}$. Since $\Delta U = Q - W$, $\Delta U = -W$ when $Q = 0$.

14.   Work is equal to the area under the curve in a p-V diagram. So the ranking is $\boxed{1, 2, 3}$.

15.   From the ideal gas law, $pV = nRT$, T depends on the product of pV. Since all three have the same volume, the one with the higher pressure gets the higher temperature. So the ranking is $\boxed{3, 2, 1}$.

16.   (a) The work done by the gas is $\boxed{\text{zero}}$, because there the volume is constant for a rigid container.

(b) Since the container is rigid, $\Delta V = 0$, so $W = 0$. $Q = \Delta U + W = \Delta U = \boxed{2.0 \times 10^4 \text{ J}}$.

17.   (a) For a cyclic process, $\Delta U = 0$.   So the temperature of the gas remains $\boxed{\text{the same}}$.

(b) $Q = \Delta U + W = W = 400$ J. Therefore $\boxed{400 \text{ J added}}$.

18. $Q = \Delta U + W$, ☞ $W = Q - \Delta U = -6.5 \times 10^5 \text{ J} - (-1.2 \times 10^6 \text{ J}) = \boxed{5.3 \times 10^5 \text{ J}}$.

19.   (a) For an adiabatic process, $Q = 0$.

So $Q = \Delta U + W$,   ☞ $\Delta U = -W$.

Since $\Delta V > 0$ (gas expands), $W > 0$, or $\Delta U < 0$.

Also because ΔU is proportional to temperature for an ideal gas, the temperature $\boxed{\text{decreases}}$.

(b) For an adiabatic process, $Q = \boxed{0}$,   so $\Delta U = -W = \boxed{-500 \text{ J}}$.

20.   (a) $Q = \Delta U + W$. The heat absorbed is equal to the sum of ΔU and W so we cannot definitively say

anything. Therefore, the answer is $\boxed{\text{none of the above}}$.

(b) $W_{\text{isobar}} = p\Delta V = (1.01 \times 10^5 \text{ Pa})(3.0 \text{ m}^3 - 1.0 \text{ m}^3) = 2.02 \times 10^5 \text{ J}$.

$\Delta U = Q - W = 5.0 \times 10^4 \text{ J} - 2.02 \times 10^5 \text{ J} = \boxed{-1.5 \times 10^5 \text{ J}}$.

21.   (a) $W_{\text{isobar}} = p\Delta V = (1.65 \times 10^4 \text{ Pa})(0.40 \text{ m}^3 - 0.20 \text{ m}^3) = \boxed{3.3 \times 10^3 \text{ J}}$.

(b) $\boxed{\text{Yes}}$, the internal energy of the system changes.

$Q = \Delta U + W$,   ☞ $\Delta U = Q - W = 8.4 \times 10^3 \text{ J} - 3.3 \times 10^3 \text{ J} = \boxed{5.1 \times 10^3 \text{ J}}$.

22. $Q = \Delta U + W = \Delta U + mgy = -6.0 \times 10^4 \text{ J} + (145 \text{ kg})(9.80 \text{ m/s}^2)(2.1 \text{ m}) = \boxed{-5.7 \times 10^4 \text{ J, out (lost)}}$.

23.   (a) From the ideal gas law, $pV = nRT$, we have $T \propto pV = 2p_1(V_1/2) = p_1V_1$. So the initial and final

temperatures are the same, therefore $\Delta T = 0$. Therefore the overall change in the internal energy is $\boxed{\text{zero}}$

(b) $W_{\text{isobar}} = p\Delta V = 2p_1(V_1/2 - V_1) = \boxed{-p_1V_1 \text{ (on the gas)}}$.

(c) $Q = \Delta U + W = 0 + (-p_1V_1) = \boxed{-p_1V_1 \text{ (out of the gas)}}$.

24.   (a) From $U = \frac{3}{2}nRT$,

$\Delta U = \frac{3}{2}nR\Delta T = \frac{3}{2}(2.0 \text{ mole})(8.31 \text{ J/K·mole})(100 \text{ K}) = \boxed{2.5 \times 10^3 \text{ J}}$, independent of heat Q.

(b) $Q = \Delta U + W$,   ☞ $W = Q - \Delta U$.

So $W_1 = 2500 \text{ J} - 2500 \text{ J} = 0$, $W_2 = 3000 \text{ J} - 2500 \text{ J} = 5.0 \times 10^2 \text{ J}$.

Therefore, the $\boxed{\text{second pass by } 5.0 \times 10^2 \text{ J more}}$.

25.   (a) The work is done $\boxed{\text{by the gas}}$ because it expands.

       (b) $W_{\text{isothermal}} = nRT \ln \left| \dfrac{V_2}{V_1} \right| = (2.0 \text{ mol})[8.31 \text{ J/(mol·K)}](300 \text{ K}) \ln \left| \dfrac{40}{20} \right| = (4.99 \times 10^3 \text{ J}) \ln 2$

                    $= \boxed{3.5 \times 10^3 \text{ J}}$

26.   Work equals the area under the curve.

       From 1–2, $W = \boxed{0}$;   from 2–3, $W = (0.50 \times 10^5 \text{ Pa})(0.50 \text{ m}^3) = \boxed{2.5 \times 10^4 \text{ J}}$;

       from 3–4, $W = \boxed{0}$;   from 4–5, $W = (1.00 \times 10^5 \text{ Pa})(0.25 \text{ m}^3) = \boxed{2.5 \times 10^4 \text{ J}}$.

27.   The work in addition to that in Exercise 12.26 is:

       for isometric, $W = 0$, since $\Delta V = 0$;   for isobaric, $W = (0.70 \times 10^5 \text{ Pa})(-0.20 \text{ m}^3) = -1.4 \times 10^4 \text{ J}$.

       So the total work done is $\Sigma W = 0 + 2.5 \times 10^4 \text{ J} + 0 + 2.5 \times 10^4 \text{ J} + 0 - 1.4 \times 10^4 \text{ J} = \boxed{3.6 \times 10^4 \text{ J}}$.

28.   (a) The work done equals the area under the curve (the area of the trapezoid). The work is $\boxed{\text{negative}}$ for compression.

       (b) $|W| = \frac{1}{2}(2.0 \times 10^5 \text{ Pa} + 5.0 \times 10^5 \text{ Pa})(0.50 \text{ m}^3) = \boxed{1.8 \times 10^5 \text{ J}}$.

29.   (a) First, find the volumes from the ideal gas law. $pV = nRT$,   ☞ $V = \dfrac{nRT}{p}$.

       $V_1 = \dfrac{(1.0 \text{ mole})[8.31 \text{ J/(K·mole)}](200 \text{ K})}{1.01 \times 10^5 \text{ Pa}} = 0.0165 \text{ m}^3$;

       $V_2 = \dfrac{(1.0 \text{ mole})[8.31 \text{ J/(K·mole)}](400 \text{ K})}{1.01 \times 10^5 \text{ Pa}} = 0.0329 \text{ m}^3$.

       Path AB, $W = p\Delta V = (1.01 \times 10^5 \text{ Pa})(0.0165 \text{ m}^3 - 0.0329 \text{ m}^3) = \boxed{-1.66 \times 10^3 \text{ J}}$;

       path BC, $W = \boxed{0}$ ($\Delta V = 0$ for isometric);

       path CD, $W = (2 \times 1.01 \times 10^5 \text{ Pa})(0.0329 \text{ m}^3 - 0.0165 \text{ m}^3) = \boxed{3.31 \times 10^3 \text{ J}}$;

       path DA, $W = \boxed{0}$.

       (b) For a cyclic process, $\Delta U = \boxed{0}$. $Q = W = 3.31 \times 10^3 \text{ J} - 1.66 \times 10^3 \text{ J} = \boxed{1.65 \times 10^3 \text{ J}}$.

       (c) $T_3 = \dfrac{(2 \times 1.01 \times 10^5 \text{ Pa})(0.0329 \text{ m}^3)}{(1.0 \text{ mole})[8.31 \text{ J/(K·mole)}]} = \boxed{800 \text{ K}}$.

30.   (c).

31.   (b).

32.   (a) $\boxed{\text{Increases}}$ since heat is added.   (b) $\boxed{\text{Decreases}}$ since heat is removed.

        (c) $\boxed{\text{Increases}}$ since heat is added.   (d) $\boxed{\text{Decreases}}$ since heat is removed.

33.   There would be $\boxed{\text{energy created}}$ if the change in entropy had been negative.

34.   From the second law of thermodynamics, the entropy $\boxed{\text{increases}}$. The cold water gains more entropy than that lost by the hot water.

35. $\boxed{\text{No}}$, this is not a valid challenge, because $\boxed{\text{ice or water itself is not an isolated system}}$. When water freezes into ice, it gives off heat and that causes the entropy of the surroundings to increase. This increase actually is more than the decrease that occurred in the water-ice phase change. So the net change in entropy still increases.

36.   The entropy $\boxed{\text{increases as heat is required to be added for the expansion}}$. For isothermal, T = constant so $\Delta U = 0$. In an expansion, the work done by the gas is positive, so $Q = \Delta U + W = W$.

37. $\Delta S = \dfrac{Q}{T} = \dfrac{mL_f}{T} = \dfrac{(1.0 \text{ kg})(3.3 \times 10^5 \text{ J/kg})}{273 \text{ K}} = \boxed{1.2 \times 10^3 \text{ J/K}}$.

38.   (a) The change in entropy of the process is $\boxed{\text{negative}}$ because heat is removed in the process (negative heat).

        (b) $\Delta S = \dfrac{Q}{T} = \dfrac{-mL_v}{T} = \dfrac{-(0.50 \text{ kg})(22.6 \times 10^5 \text{ J/kg})}{373 \text{ K}} = \boxed{-3.0 \times 10^3 \text{ J/K}}$.

39. $\Delta S = \dfrac{Q}{T} = \dfrac{-mL_v}{T} = \dfrac{-(0.50 \text{ kg})(2.7 \times 10^5 \text{ J/kg})}{630 \text{ K}} = \boxed{-2.1 \times 10^2 \text{ J/K}}$.

40. $\Delta S_i = \dfrac{Q}{T} = \dfrac{mL_f}{T} = \dfrac{(0.75 \text{ kg})(3.3 \times 10^5 \text{ J/kg})}{273 \text{ K}} = \boxed{9.1 \times 10^2 \text{ J/K}}$;

        $\Delta S_s = \dfrac{(0.25 \text{ kg})(22.6 \times 10^5 \text{ J/kg})}{373 \text{ K}} = \boxed{1.5 \times 10^3 \text{ J/K}}$.

        So $\boxed{\text{steam}}$ has the greater change in entropy because steam has the most disorder and ice has the most order.

41. For isothermal, U = constant or $\Delta U = 0$. $Q = \Delta U + W = W = -7.5 \times 10^3$ J (work done on system).

Therefore $\Delta S = \dfrac{Q}{T} = \dfrac{-7.5 \times 10^3 \text{ J}}{293 \text{ K}} = \boxed{-26 \text{ J/K}}$.

42. (a) The entropy of the gas $\boxed{\text{increases as } Q > 0}$. For isothermal, T = constant so $\Delta U = 0$. In an expansion, the work done by the gas is positive, so $Q = \Delta U + W = W$.

(b) $Q = \Delta U + W = W = 3.0 \times 10^3$ J.   So $\Delta S = \dfrac{Q}{T} = \dfrac{3.0 \times 10^3 \text{ J}}{273 \text{ K}} = \boxed{11 \text{ J/K}}$.

43. $\Delta S = \dfrac{Q}{T}$,   ☞ $T = \dfrac{Q}{\Delta S} = \dfrac{-1.67 \times 10^6 \text{J}}{-4.19 \times 10^3 \text{ J/K}} = 399 \text{ K} = \boxed{126°\text{C}}$.

44. (a) $\Delta S_\text{h} = \dfrac{Q_\text{h}}{T_\text{h}} = \dfrac{1000 \text{ J}}{373 \text{ K}} = \boxed{2.68 \text{ J/K}}$.

(b) $\Delta S_\text{c} = \dfrac{-1000 \text{ J}}{273 \text{ K}} = \boxed{-3.66 \text{ J/K}}$.

(c) $\Delta S = \Delta S_\text{h} + \Delta S_\text{c} = 2.68 \text{ J/K} - 3.66 \text{ J/K} = \boxed{-0.98 \text{ J/K}}$.

(d) $\boxed{\text{No}}$ because the entropy decreased, and this is a violation of the second law of thermodynamics.

45. $\Delta S = \Delta S_1 + \Delta S_2 = \dfrac{Q_1}{T_1} + \dfrac{Q_2}{T_2} = \dfrac{-1.5 \times 10^3 \text{ J}}{473 \text{ K}} + \dfrac{1.5 \times 10^3 \text{ J}}{333 \text{ K}} = \boxed{1.33 \text{ J/K}}$.

46. For an isometric process, $\Delta V = 0$, so $W = 0$.   Therefore $Q = \Delta U + W = \Delta U = -2.0 \times 10^4$ J.

$\Delta S = \dfrac{Q}{T} = \dfrac{-2.0 \times 10^4 \text{ J}}{(273 + 18) \text{ K}} = -\boxed{69 \text{ J/K}}$.

47. (a) The vertical line has $\Delta S = 0$.   The horizontal line has $\Delta S = 100$ J/K.

So $\Delta S = \dfrac{Q}{T}$,   ☞ $Q = T\Delta S = (273 \text{ K})(100 \text{ J/K}) = \boxed{2.73 \times 10^4 \text{ J}}$.

(b) From b to c, $\Delta S = 0$,   so $Q = 0$. Therefore it is adiabatic or $\boxed{\text{isotropic}}$.

48. Since the process returns to its original state, $\Delta S = \boxed{0}$.

Heat equals the area under the curve (the area of the triangle).

$Q = -\frac{1}{2}(100 \text{ J/K})(100 \text{ K}) = \boxed{-5.0 \times 10^3 \text{ J}}$.

49.   (a) $\Delta S = \dfrac{Q}{T} = \dfrac{mL_f}{T} = \dfrac{(0.0500\ \text{kg})(3.33 \times 10^5\ \text{J/kg})}{273\ \text{K}} = \boxed{61.0\ \text{J/K}}$.

        (b) From calorimetry, the heat lost by water is also $(0.0500\ \text{kg})(3.33 \times 10^5\ \text{J/kg}) = 1.67 \times 10^4\ \text{J}$.

        The temperature change of the water is $\Delta T = \dfrac{Q}{cm} = \dfrac{-1.67 \times 10^4\ \text{J}}{[4186\ \text{J/(kg·C°)}](0.500\ \text{kg})} = -7.98\ \text{C°}$.

        So the final temperature of the water is 12.0°C. The average water temperature is $(20 + 12)/2 = 16°\text{C}$.

        Use the average temperature of the water in entropy calculation. $\Delta S = \dfrac{-1.67 \times 10^4\ \text{J}}{289\ \text{K}} = \boxed{-57.8\ \text{J/K}}$.

        (c) The total change in entropy is $\Delta S = 61.0\ \text{J/K} - 57.8\ \text{J/K} = \boxed{3.2\ \text{J/K}}$.

50.   (d).

51.   (b).

52.   (b). Since $\varepsilon = 1 - \dfrac{Q_c}{Q_h}$, $\boxed{\dfrac{Q_c}{Q_h}}$ determines the thermal efficiency of a heat engine.

53. $\boxed{\text{It is unchanged since it returns to its original value}}$ for a cyclic process. This is true for any parameter or quantity.

54. $\boxed{\text{No}}$, this is not a practical way to air-condition a room. As a matter of fact, the room will be heated. The heat expelled to the room by the refrigerator is more than the heat removed by the refrigerator from the room.

55.   This is important because heat can be completely converted to work for a single process (not a cycle), such as an isothermal expansion process of an ideal gas.

56. $\boxed{\text{No}}$, this is not a violation. The heat output to the hot reservoir is the sum of the energy input and heat input from the cold reservoir.

57. $\boxed{\text{No}}$, as the warm air rises to the higher altitude, both gravity and buoyancy forces do work. Since it is a natural process with work input, the entropy increases and the second law is not violated.

58.   (a) $\varepsilon = \dfrac{W_{net}}{Q_h}$,   ☞ $W_{net} = \varepsilon Q_h = 0.28(2000\ \text{J}) = \boxed{560\ \text{J}}$.

        (b) $Q_c = Q_h - W_{net} = 2000\ \text{J} - 560\ \text{J} = \boxed{1440\ \text{J}}$.

59. $Q_h = Q_c + W_{net} = 600 \text{ J} + 200 \text{ J} = 800 \text{ J}.$ $\varepsilon = \dfrac{W_{net}}{Q_h} = \dfrac{200 \text{ J}}{800 \text{ J}} = \boxed{25\%}$.

60. $\varepsilon = \dfrac{W_{net}}{Q_h}$,   ☞ $Q_{in} = \dfrac{W_{net}}{\varepsilon} = \dfrac{800 \text{ J}}{0.20} = 4000 \text{ J}.$

     So $Q_c = Q_h - W_{net} = 4000 \text{ J} - 800 \text{ J} = \boxed{3.2 \times 10^3 \text{ J}}$.

61. $\varepsilon = \dfrac{W_{net}}{Q_h}$,   ☞ $Q_{in} = \dfrac{W_{net}}{\varepsilon} = \dfrac{2.60 \times 10^4 \text{ J}}{0.150} = 1.73 \times 10^5 \text{ J}.$

     So $Q_c = Q_h - W_{net} = 1.73 \times 10^5 \text{ J} - 2.60 \times 10^4 \text{ J} = \boxed{1.47 \times 10^5 \text{ J}}$.

62. $Q_h = W_{net} + Q_c = 4.0 \times 10^3 \text{ J} + 7.5 \times 10^3 \text{ J} = 11.5 \times 10^3 \text{ J}.$

     So $\varepsilon = \dfrac{W_{net}}{Q_h} = \dfrac{4.0 \times 10^3 \text{ J}}{11.5 \times 10^3 \text{ J}} = \boxed{35\%}$.

63. $\varepsilon = \dfrac{W_{net}}{Q_h}$,   ☞ $Q_h = \dfrac{W_{net}}{\varepsilon} = \dfrac{4500 \text{ J}}{0.1000} = 4.5 \times 10^4 \text{ J}.$

     $Q_h = W_{net} + Q_c,$ ☞ $Q_c = Q_h - W_{net} = 4.5 \times 10^4 \text{ J} - 4500 \text{ J} = \boxed{4.05 \times 10^4 \text{ J}}.$

64.   (a) $\varepsilon = 1 - \dfrac{Q_c}{Q_h}$. When ε increases, the ratio of $\dfrac{Q_c}{Q_h}$ $\boxed{\text{decreases}}$.

     (b) $\dfrac{Q_c}{Q_h} = 1 - \varepsilon,$ so the change in $\dfrac{Q_c}{Q_h}$ is $\Delta\varepsilon = (1 - 0.25) - (1 - 0.20) = \boxed{-0.05}$.

65.   (a) $E = 2(3.3 \times 10^8 \text{ J}) = \boxed{6.6 \times 10^8 \text{ J}}$.

     (b) In 1 h, $W = Pt = (25 \times 10^3 \text{ J/s})(3600 \text{ s}) = 9.0 \times 10^7 \text{ J}.$

     So $\varepsilon = \dfrac{W_{net}}{Q_h} = \dfrac{9.0 \times 10^7 \text{ J}}{3.3 \times 10^8 \text{ J}} = \boxed{27\%}$.

66.   Since $Q_h = W_{net} + Q_c,$ ☞ $P_h = P_{net} + P_c = 2.5 \text{ kW} + 7.5 \text{ kW} = \boxed{10 \text{ kW}}$.

67.   (a) $\text{COP}_{ref} = \dfrac{Q_c}{Q_h - Q_c},$ ☞ $Q_{hot} = Q_c\left(1 + \dfrac{1}{\text{COP}_{ref}}\right) = (4.2 \times 10^5 \text{ J})\left(1 + \dfrac{1}{2.2}\right) = \boxed{6.1 \times 10^5 \text{ J}}$.

     (b) $W_{in} = Q_h - Q_c = 6.1 \times 10^5 \text{ J} - 4.2 \times 10^5 \text{ J} = 1.9 \times 10^5 \text{ J}.$

     So in 10 cycles the total work is $10(1.9 \times 10^5 \text{ J}) = \boxed{1.9 \times 10^6 \text{ J}}$.

68. (a) $W_{in} = Q_h - Q_c = 3.5 \times 10^3$ J $- 2.0 \times 10^3$ J $= \boxed{1.5 \times 10^3 \text{ J}}$.

(b) $COP_{hp} = \dfrac{Q_h}{W_{in}} = \dfrac{3.5 \times 10^3 \text{ J}}{1.5 \times 10^3 \text{ J}} = \boxed{2.3}$.

69. $COP_{ref} = \dfrac{Q_c}{W_{in}}$, ☞ $W_{in} = \dfrac{Q_c}{COP_{ref}} = \dfrac{1.0 \times 10^7 \text{ J}}{2.75} = 3.64 \times 10^6$ J.

So $P = \dfrac{W}{\Delta t} = \dfrac{3.64 \times 10^6 \text{ J}}{(20 \text{ min})(60 \text{ s/min})} = \boxed{3.0 \text{ kW}}$.

70. (a) $Q_h = mL_v = (8.00 \text{ kg})(22.6 \times 10^5 \text{ J/kg}) = 1.81 \times 10^7$ J.

$\varepsilon = \dfrac{W_{net}}{Q_h}$, ☞ $W_{net} = \varepsilon Q_h = 0.300(1.81 \times 10^7 \text{ J}) = \boxed{5.42 \times 10^6 \text{ J}}$.

(b) $Q_c = Q_h - W_{net} = 1.81 \times 10^7$ J $- 5.42 \times 10^6$ J $= \boxed{1.27 \times 10^7 \text{ J}}$.

71. (a) $Q_h = W_{in} + Q_c = 3.0 \times 10^4$ J $+ 2.1 \times 10^5$ J $= \boxed{2.4 \times 10^5 \text{ J}}$.

(b) Water's heat loss is $Q_{in} = -2.1 \times 10^5$ J $= cm\Delta T$.

So $\Delta T = \dfrac{-2.1 \times 10^5 \text{ J}}{[4186 \text{ J/(kg·C°)}](5.0 \text{ kg})} = -\boxed{10 \text{ C°}}$.

72. (a) $\varepsilon = \dfrac{W_{net}}{Q_h} = \dfrac{P_{net}}{P_h}$, ☞ $P_h = \dfrac{P_{net}}{\varepsilon} = \dfrac{900 \text{ MW}}{0.25} = \boxed{3.6 \times 10^3 \text{ MW}}$.

(b) $P_c = P_h - P_{net} = 3.6 \times 10^3$ MW $- 900$ MW $= \boxed{2.7 \times 10^3 \text{ MW}}$.

(c) This is to $\boxed{\text{minimize thermal pollution of the river}}$.

73. (a) There are two revolutions in each cycle so 3600 rpm is $\boxed{1800}$ cycles in 1 minute.

(b) $P_{net} = 150$ hp $= (150 \text{ hp})(746 \text{ W/hp}) = 1.12 \times 10^5$ W $= 1.12 \times 10^5$ J/s.

So in 1 minute, $W_{net} = (1.12 \times 10^5 \text{ J/s})(60 \text{ s}) = 6.72 \times 10^6$ J.

$\varepsilon = \dfrac{W_{net}}{Q_h}$, ☞ $Q_h = \dfrac{W_{net}}{\varepsilon} = \dfrac{6.72 \times 10^6 \text{ J}}{0.20} = \boxed{3.4 \times 10^7 \text{ J}}$.

(c) $Q_h = W_{net} + Q_c$, ☞ $Q_c = Q_h - W_{net} = 3.36 \times 10^7$ J $- 6.72 \times 10^6$ J $= \boxed{2.7 \times 10^7 \text{ J}}$.

74. (c).

75. (a), since $\varepsilon = 1 - \dfrac{Q_c}{Q_h}$.

76. (a).

77.   (a) $\boxed{\text{No}}$, the product of p and V has to be a constant for T to be constant. $\boxed{Q_h = +Q_4}$.

(b) $\boxed{\text{No, } Q_c = -Q_2}$.

(c) Expansion, positive work.   Compression, negative work.   Net work

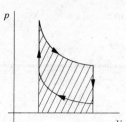 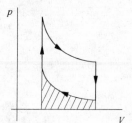 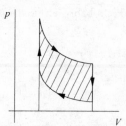

78.   (a) No, this change does not make the cycle a Carnot cycle because a Carnot cycle consists of two adiabatic and two isothermal processes.

(b) There are heat transfers for all four legs. There are heat inputs for Q_1 and Q_4 and heat outputs for Q_2 and Q_3. The transfers at legs 1 and 3 occur at constant temperatures, because the processes are isothermal.

79.   Water-cooled is more effective. The $\boxed{\text{efficiency of cooling depends on the temperature difference}}$, and $\boxed{\text{water can have higher temperature differences}}$. Also water has high specific heat so it can absorb more heat.

80. $\varepsilon_C = 1 - \dfrac{T_c}{T_h}$.

For 100°C and 300°C, $\varepsilon_C = 1 - \dfrac{273 + 100}{273 + 300} = 0.35 = 35\%$.

For 50°C and 250°C, $\varepsilon_C = 1 - \dfrac{273 + 50}{273 + 250} = 0.38 = 38\%$.

You would chose $\boxed{50°\text{C and }250°\text{C}}$ for $\boxed{\text{higher efficiency}}$.

81. $\boxed{\text{Diesel}}$ engines run hotter because diesel fuel has a higher spontaneous combustion temperature.

According to Carnot efficiency, the higher the hot reservoir temperature, and the higher the efficiency, for a fixed low temperature reservoir.

82. $\varepsilon_C = 1 - \dfrac{T_c}{T_h} = 1 - \dfrac{(273 + 30) \text{ K}}{(273 + 100) \text{ K}} = \boxed{19\%}$.

83. $\varepsilon_C = 1 - \dfrac{T_c}{T_h}$, ☞ $T_c = (1 - \varepsilon_C)T_h = (1 - 0.35)(273 + 147) \text{ K} = 273 \text{ K} = \boxed{0°\text{C}}$.

84. $\varepsilon_C = 1 - \dfrac{T_c}{T_h}$, ☞ $T_h = \dfrac{T_c}{1 - \varepsilon_C} = \dfrac{(273 + 20)\ \text{K}}{1 - 0.30} = 419\ \text{K} = \boxed{146°\text{C}}$.

85. (a) $\varepsilon_C = 1 - \dfrac{T_c}{T_h} = 1 - \dfrac{(273 + 5)\ \text{K}}{(273 + 25)\ \text{K}} = \boxed{6.7\%}$.

(b) $\boxed{\text{Probably not}}$ at the moment, due to low efficiency and relatively cheap fossil fuels.

86. $\varepsilon_C = 1 - \dfrac{T_c}{T_h}$, ☞ $T_c = (1 - \varepsilon_c)T_h = (1 - 0.40)(273 + 350)\ \text{K} = 374\ \text{K} = \boxed{101°\text{C}}$.

87. First find the Carnot efficiency. $\varepsilon_C = 1 - \dfrac{T_c}{T_h} = 1 - \dfrac{(273 + 120\ )\ \text{K}}{(273 + 320)\ \text{K}} = 0.338$.

Also $\varepsilon = \dfrac{W_{net}}{Q_{in}}$, ☞ $W_{net} = \varepsilon Q_{in} = 0.338(2.7 \times 10^4\ \text{J}) = \boxed{9.1 \times 10^3\ \text{J}}$.

88. (a) $\varepsilon = 1 - \dfrac{Q_{out}}{Q_{in}}$, ☞ $Q_{in} = \dfrac{Q_{out}}{1 - \varepsilon} = \dfrac{1200\ \text{J}}{1 - 0.40} = \boxed{2000\ \text{J}}$.

(b) $\varepsilon_C = 1 - \dfrac{T_c}{T_h}$, ☞ $T_h = \dfrac{T_c}{1 - \varepsilon_C} = \dfrac{(273 + 50)\ \text{K}}{1 - 0.40} = 538\ \text{K} = \boxed{265°\text{C}}$.

89. $\varepsilon_C = 1 - \dfrac{T_c}{T_h}$, ☞ $T_h = \dfrac{T_c}{1 - \varepsilon_C}$. So $\dfrac{T'_h}{T_h} = \dfrac{1 - \varepsilon_C}{1 - \varepsilon'_C} = \dfrac{1 - 0.30}{1 - 0.40} = 1.17$.

Therefore $\Delta T_h = \dfrac{T'_h - T_h}{T_h} = 0.17 T_h = 0.17(273 + 327)\ \text{K} = \boxed{100\ \text{C}°}$.

90. $\varepsilon_C = 1 - \dfrac{T_c}{T_h} = 1 - \dfrac{(273 + 125)\ \text{K}}{(273 + 400)\ \text{K}} = 59.1\%$. $\varepsilon = 1 - \dfrac{Q_{out}}{Q_{in}} = 1 - \dfrac{2.0 \times 10^5\ \text{J}}{5.0 \times 10^5\ \text{J}} = 60\%$.

$\boxed{\text{No, not possible}}$, because the claimed efficiency is higher than the Carnot efficiency (upper limit).

91. (a) You should chose $\boxed{\text{lowering the low-temperature reservoir temperature}}$.

(b) If T_h is raised by ΔT, $\varepsilon_{C1} = 1 - \dfrac{T_c}{T_h + \Delta T}$;

if T_{cold} is lowered by ΔT, $\varepsilon_{C2} = 1 - \dfrac{T_c - \Delta T}{T_h}$.

$\varepsilon_{C1} - \varepsilon_{C2} = (1 - \dfrac{T_c}{T_h + \Delta T}) - (1 - \dfrac{T_c - \Delta T}{T_h}) = \dfrac{T_c - \Delta T}{T_h} - \dfrac{T_c}{T_h + \Delta T}$

$= \dfrac{(T_c - \Delta T)(T_h + \Delta T) - T_h T_c}{T_h (T_h + \Delta T)} = \dfrac{(T_c - T_h)\Delta T + (\Delta T)^2}{T_h (T_h + \Delta T)} < 0$.

So $\varepsilon_{C1} < \varepsilon_{C2}$.

92. The ideal efficiency is $\varepsilon_C = 1 - \dfrac{T_c}{T_h} = 1 - \dfrac{(273 + 100)\text{ K}}{(273 + 400)\text{ K}} = \boxed{44.6\%}$.

So the thermal efficiency is $\varepsilon = 0.45\varepsilon_C = 0.45(44.6\%) = \boxed{20.1\%}$.

93. (a) $\varepsilon_C = 1 - \dfrac{T_c}{T_h} = 1 - \dfrac{(273 + 100)\text{ K}}{(273 + 375)\text{ K}} = 0/424 = \boxed{42\%.}$

(b) So $\varepsilon = 0.50\varepsilon_C = 0.50(42.4\%) = 0.212 = 1 - \dfrac{Q_{out}}{Q_{in}} = 1 - \dfrac{P_{out}}{P_{in}}$,

$P_{out} = (1 - \varepsilon)P_{in} = (1 - 0.212)(50\text{ kW}) = \boxed{39\text{ kW}}$.

94. From ideal gas law, $pV = nRT$, ☞ $T = \dfrac{pV}{nR}$.

$T_{hot} = \dfrac{(250 \times 10^3\text{ Pa})(2.25 \times 10^{-2}\text{ m}^3)}{nR} = \dfrac{5625\text{ N·m}}{nR}$,

$T_{cold} = \dfrac{(150 \times 10^3\text{ Pa})(1.75 \times 10^{-2}\text{ m}^3)}{nR} = \dfrac{2625\text{ N·m}}{nR}$.

So $\varepsilon_C = 1 - \dfrac{T_c}{T_h} = 1 - \dfrac{2625}{5625} = 0.53\ (\times 100\%) = \boxed{53\%}$.

95. (a) $\varepsilon_C = 1 - \dfrac{Q_{out}}{Q_{in}} = 1 - \dfrac{600\text{ J}}{800\text{ J}} = \boxed{25\%}$.

(b) $\varepsilon_C = 0.25 = 1 - \dfrac{T_c}{T_h}$, ☞ $\dfrac{T_h}{T_c} = \dfrac{1}{1 - 0.25} = 4/3$. So $\boxed{T_h = 1.3T_c}$.

96. (a) $\varepsilon_C = 1 - \dfrac{T_c}{T_h} = 1 - \dfrac{(273 + 27)\text{ K}}{(273 + 227)\text{ K}} = \boxed{40\%}$.

(b) For a cyclic process, everything such as pressure, volume, and temperature, etc., returns to their original

values. So $\Delta S = \boxed{0;\text{ returns to original entropy value}}$.

97. (a) $\varepsilon_C = 1 - \dfrac{T_c}{T_h} = 1 - \dfrac{(273 + 20)\text{ K}}{(273 + 540)\text{ K}} = \boxed{64\%}$.

(b) ε_C is the upper limit of efficiency. In reality, $\boxed{\text{a lot more energy is lost than in the ideal situation}}$.

98. (a) $\text{COP}_C = \dfrac{Q_h}{Q_h - Q_c} = \dfrac{T_h}{T_h - T_c}$.

(b) The efficiency improves as the temperature difference between the two reservoirs decreases. The COP_C

of a refrigerator should be $\dfrac{T_c}{T_h - T_c}$.

99. (a) $COP_{ref} = \dfrac{Q_c}{Q_h - Q_c} = \dfrac{2.6 \times 10^3 \text{ J}}{2.8 \times 10^3 \text{ J} - 2.6 \times 10^3 \text{ J}} = \boxed{13}$.

(b) From Exercise 12.98, $COP_C = \dfrac{T_h}{T_h - T_c} = \dfrac{(273 + 5.0) \text{ K}}{30°C - 5.0°C} = 11 < 13.$ $\boxed{\text{No, } COP_C = 11}$.

100. Since $\varepsilon_C = \dfrac{T_h - T_c}{T_h}$, and from Exercise 12.98, $COP_C = \dfrac{T_h}{T_h - T_c}$.

So $COP_C = \dfrac{T_h}{T_h - T_c} = \dfrac{1}{\varepsilon_C} = \dfrac{1}{0.40} = \boxed{2.5}$.

101. $\varepsilon_C = 1 - \dfrac{T_c}{T_h} = 1 - \dfrac{Q_c}{Q_h}$, ☞ $Q_h = Q_c \dfrac{T_h}{T_c}$.

So $W = Q_h - Q_c = Q_c \dfrac{T_h}{T_c} - Q_c = Q_c \left(\dfrac{T_h}{T_c} - 1 \right)$.

102. $W = p\Delta V$, ☞ $\Delta V = \dfrac{W}{p} = \dfrac{-900 \text{ J}}{300 \times 10^3 \text{ Pa}} = -3.0 \times 10^{-3} \text{ m}^3 = -3.0 \text{ L}.$

So $V_f = V_i + \Delta V = \boxed{7.0 \text{ L}}$.

103. For the hot reservoir, $\Delta S_h = \dfrac{-Q}{T_h}$; for the cold reservoir, $\Delta S_c = \dfrac{Q}{T_c}$.

For the universe, $\Delta S = \Delta S_h + \Delta S_c = Q \left(\dfrac{1}{T_c} - \dfrac{1}{T_h} \right)$. Since $T_h > T_c$, $\Delta S > 0$.

104. For the hot reservoir, $\Delta S_h = \dfrac{-Q_h}{T_h}$; for the cold reservoir, $\Delta S_c = \dfrac{Q_c}{T_c}$.

Also $\Delta S_h = -\Delta S_c$ for a cyclic process (everything returns to its original value, so $\Delta S = 0$).

Therefore $\varepsilon = \dfrac{W_{net}}{Q_h} = \dfrac{Q_h - Q_c}{Q_h} = 1 - \dfrac{Q_c}{Q_h} = 1 - \dfrac{\Delta S_c \, T_c}{-\Delta S_h \, T_h} = 1 - \dfrac{T_c}{T_h} = \varepsilon_C.$

105. (a) It is an $\boxed{\text{isobaric expansion}}$.

(b) $Q = \Delta U + W$, ☞ $\Delta U = Q - W = Q - p\Delta V = Q - pA\Delta x$

$= 420 \text{ J} - (1.01 \times 10^5 \text{ Pa})(\pi)(0.120 \text{ m})^2 (0.0600 \text{ m}) = \boxed{146 \text{ J}}$.

106. $\varepsilon_C = 1 - \dfrac{T_c}{T_h} = 1 - \dfrac{(273 + 20) \text{ K}}{(273 + 250) \text{ K}} = \boxed{44\%}$.

$\boxed{\text{No, Carnot efficiency is the upper limit}}$, and it could never be achieved.

107.   (a) For a monatomic ideal gas, $\gamma = 1.67$.

$$p_1 V_1^{\gamma} = p_2 V_2^{\gamma}, \quad \text{☞} \quad p_2 = p_1 \frac{V_2^{\gamma}}{V_1^{\gamma}} = p_1 \left(\frac{V_1}{V_2}\right)^{\gamma} = (1.00 \times 10^5 \text{ Pa}) \left(\frac{240}{40}\right)^{1.67} = \boxed{1.99 \times 10^6 \text{ Pa}}.$$

(b) $W_{\text{adiabatic}} = \dfrac{p_1 V_1 - p_2 V_2}{\gamma - 1} = \dfrac{(1.00 \times 10^5 \text{ Pa})(240 \times 10^{-3} \text{ m}^3) - (1.99 \times 10^6 \text{ Pa})(40 \times 10^{-3} \text{ m}^3)}{1.67 - 1}$

$= \boxed{-8.30 \times 10^4 \text{ J}}.$

108.   (a) $\Delta S_u = \Delta S_h + \Delta S_c = \dfrac{-Q}{T_h} + \dfrac{Q}{T_c} = Q\left(\dfrac{1}{T_c} - \dfrac{1}{T_h}\right), \quad \text{so} \quad W = T_c\, \Delta S_u = Q\left(1 - \dfrac{T_c}{T_h}\right).$

(b) It is $\boxed{\text{Carnot efficiency}}$.

109.   In an isothermal process, $\Delta U = 0$ for an ideal gas.   So $Q = \Delta U + W = W = 30$ J.

$\Delta S = \dfrac{Q}{T} = \dfrac{30 \text{ J}}{(273 + 27) \text{ K}} = \boxed{0.10 \text{ J/K}}.$

110.   For an adiabatic process, $Q = 0$.   So $\Delta U = Q - W = -W = -(-1500 \text{ J}) = \boxed{1500 \text{ J}}.$

The temperature $\boxed{\text{increases}}$ since U increases.

111. $\Delta U = Q - W = (2500 \text{ J}) - (-1000 \text{ J}) = \boxed{3500 \text{ J}}.$

112. $\varepsilon_C = 1 - \dfrac{T_c}{T_h} = 1 - \dfrac{(273 + 70) \text{ K}}{(273 + 400) \text{ K}} = 0.49 = \varepsilon.$

$\varepsilon = \dfrac{W_{\text{net}}}{Q_h}, \quad \text{☞} \quad Q_h = \dfrac{W_{\text{net}}}{\varepsilon} = \dfrac{5.0 \times 10^4 \text{ J}}{0.49} = 1.02 \times 10^5 \text{ J}.$

$Q_h = W_{\text{net}} + Q_c, \quad \text{☞} \quad Q_c = Q_h - W_{\text{net}} = 1.02 \times 10^5 \text{ J} - 5.0 \times 10^4 \text{ J} = \boxed{5.2 \times 10^4 \text{ J}}.$

113.   (a) $W = p\Delta V = (1.01 \times 10^5 \text{ Pa})(1671 \text{ cm}^3 - 1.00 \text{ cm}^3) \times (10^{-6} \text{ m}^3/\text{cm}^3) = \boxed{169 \text{ J}}.$

(b) The heat required in the process is $Q = mL_v = (1.00 \times 10^{-3} \text{ kg})(22.6 \times 10^5 \text{ J/kg}) = 2260$ J.

$Q = \Delta U + W, \quad \text{☞} \quad \Delta U = Q - W = 2260 \text{ J} - 169 \text{ J} = \boxed{2.09 \times 10^3 \text{ J}}.$

114.   The process is an adiabatic free expansion. There is no transfer of heat and the gas does no work. So the internal energy of the gas remains unchanged, according to the first law of thermodynamics.

CHAPTER 13

VIBRATIONS AND WAVES

1.   (b).

2.   (d).

3.   (b), because $f = \dfrac{1}{T}$.

4.   (a), because $U = \frac{1}{2}kx^2$.

5.   (a) $E = \frac{1}{2}kA^2$, so $\boxed{\text{four times as large}}$.   (b) $v_{max} = \sqrt{\dfrac{k}{m}}\, A$, so $\boxed{\text{twice as large}}$.

6.   At the equilibrium position the elastic potential energy is zero, and so all the energy is kinetic. Therefore the speed $\boxed{\text{increases}}$ as it approaches the equilibrium position.

7.   In one period T, the mass goes through a distance equal to $4A$. So the time is $\boxed{T/4}$ for distance A and $\boxed{T/2}$ for $2A$.

8. $\boxed{\text{No}}$, this is not a simple harmonic motion because the $\boxed{\text{restoring force does not obey Hooke's law}}$. Once the ball is in the air, the gravitational force is always constant and downward.

9.   In each T, it travels $A + A + A + A = \boxed{4A}$.

10. $f = \dfrac{1}{T} = \dfrac{1}{0.50 \text{ s}} = \boxed{2.0 \text{ Hz}}$.

11. $T = \dfrac{1}{f} = \dfrac{1}{40 \text{ Hz}} = \boxed{0.025 \text{ s}}$.

12. $T = \dfrac{1}{f}$, ☞ $\Delta T = \dfrac{1}{f_2} - \dfrac{1}{f_1} = \dfrac{1}{0.50 \text{ s}} - \dfrac{1}{0.25 \text{ s}} = -2.0 \text{ s} = \boxed{\text{decrease of 2.0 s}}$.

13. $k = \dfrac{F}{x} = \dfrac{mg}{x} = \dfrac{(0.25 \text{ kg})(9.80 \text{ m/s}^2)}{0.060 \text{ m}} = \boxed{41 \text{ N/m}}$.

14. $v_{max} = \sqrt{\dfrac{k}{m}}\, A = \sqrt{\dfrac{10 \text{ N/m}}{0.50 \text{ kg}}}\, (0.050 \text{ m}) = \boxed{0.22 \text{ m/s}}$.

Chapter 13 Vibrations and Waves

15. (a) $T = \dfrac{1}{f} = \dfrac{1}{10^{12}\text{ Hz}} = \boxed{10^{-12}\text{ s}}$.

   (b) $v_{\max} = \sqrt{\dfrac{k}{m}}\,A = \omega A = 2\pi f A = 2\pi(10^{12}\text{ Hz})(10^{-11}\text{ m}) = \boxed{63\text{ m/s}}$.

16. (a) Since $|F_s| = kx$, maximum x corresponds to maximum F_s. So the answer is $\boxed{x = \pm A}$.

   (b) $F_s = kx = (150\text{ N/m})(0) = \boxed{0\text{ N}}$; $\quad a = \dfrac{F_s}{m} = \boxed{0\text{ m/s}^2}$.

   $F_s = (150\text{ N/m})(0.050\text{ m}) = \boxed{7.50\text{ N}}$; $\quad a = \dfrac{7.50\text{ N}}{0.500\text{ kg}} = \boxed{15.0\text{ m/s}^2}$.

   $F_s = (150\text{ N/m})(0.150\text{ m}) = \boxed{22.5\text{ N}}$; $\quad a = \dfrac{22.5\text{ N}}{0.500\text{ kg}} = \boxed{45.0\text{ m/s}^2}$.

17. (a) The speed is maximum at $\boxed{x = 0}$, because $v = \sqrt{\dfrac{k}{m}(A^2 - x^2)}$. At $x = 0$, there is no elastic potential energy so all the energy of the system is kinetic, thus maximum speed.

   (b) $v_{\max} = \sqrt{\dfrac{k}{m}(A^2 - 0^2)} = \sqrt{\dfrac{k}{m}}\,A = \sqrt{\dfrac{100\text{ N/m}}{0.250\text{ kg}}}\,(0.10\text{ m}) = \boxed{2.0\text{ m/s}}$.

18. (a) $v_{\max} = \sqrt{\dfrac{k}{m}}\,A = \sqrt{\dfrac{12\text{ N/m}}{0.25\text{ kg}}}\,(0.15\text{ m}) = \boxed{1.0\text{ m/s}}$.

   (b) $\boxed{\text{At the equilibrium position}}$ where $x = 0$.

   (c) $v = \sqrt{\dfrac{k}{m}(A^2 - x^2)} = \sqrt{\dfrac{12\text{ N/m}}{0.25\text{ kg}}[(0.15\text{ m})^2 - (0.075\text{ m})^2]} = \boxed{0.90\text{ m/s}}$.

19. (a) $v = \sqrt{\dfrac{k}{m}(A^2 - x^2)} = \sqrt{\dfrac{12\text{ N/m}}{0.25\text{ kg}}[(0.15\text{ m})^2 - (0.10\text{ m})^2]} = \boxed{0.77\text{ m/s}}$.

   (b) $F = kx = (12\text{ N/m})(0.10\text{ m}) = \boxed{1.2\text{ N}}$.

20. (a) The total mechanical energy is $E = \tfrac{1}{2}kA^2 = \tfrac{1}{2}(80\text{ N/m})(0.15\text{ m})^2 = \boxed{0.90\text{ J}}$.

   (b) $\boxed{\text{No}}$, it does not. It depends only on the spring constant and amplitude.

21. (a) $v = \sqrt{\dfrac{k}{m}(A^2 - x^2)} = \sqrt{\dfrac{80\text{ N/m}}{0.25\text{ kg}}[(0.15\text{ m})^2 - (0.050\text{ m})^2]} = \boxed{2.5\text{ m/s}}$.

   (b) $v = \sqrt{\dfrac{80\text{ N/m}}{0.25\text{ kg}}[(0.15\text{ m})^2 - (-0.050\text{ m})^2]} = \boxed{2.5\text{ m/s}}$.

   (c) $v_{\max} = \sqrt{\dfrac{k}{m}}\,A = \sqrt{\dfrac{80\text{ N/m}}{0.25\text{ kg}}}\,(0.15\text{ m}) = \boxed{2.7\text{ m/s, equilibrium position}}$.

22. The total energy is $E = \frac{1}{2}kA^2$.

At $x = A/2$, the potential energy is $U = \frac{1}{2}kx^2 = \frac{1}{2}k(A/2)^2 = \frac{1}{2}\frac{1}{4}kA^2 = E/4$. So the fraction is $\boxed{1/4}$.

$E = K + U$, ☞ $K = E - U = E - E/4 = 3E/4$. So the fraction is $\boxed{3/4}$.

23. (a) From conservation of energy (choose the bottom of the trampoline when stretched as $U = 0$):

$$E = \frac{1}{2}kA^2 = U = mgy, \quad ☞ \quad k = \frac{2mgy}{A^2} = \frac{2(75 \text{ kg})(9.80 \text{ m/s}^2)(5.0 \text{ m} + 0.30 \text{ m})}{(0.30 \text{ m})^2} = 8.66 \times 10^4 \text{ N/m}.$$

For the jump from 8.0 m high, $\frac{1}{2}(8.66 \times 10^4 \text{ N/m})A^2 = (75 \text{ kg})(9.80 \text{ m/s}^2)(8.0 \text{ m} + A)$.

Reduce to a quadratic equation: $4.33 \times 10^4 A^2 - 735A - 5880 = 0$.

Solve for $A = \boxed{0.38 \text{ m}}$ or -0.36 m, which is discarded.

(b) From Hooke's law, $x = \dfrac{F}{k} = \dfrac{mg}{k} = \dfrac{(75 \text{ kg})(9.80 \text{ m/s}^2)}{8.66 \times 10^4 \text{ N/m}} = \boxed{8.5 \times 10^{-3} \text{ m}}$.

24. (a) From conservation of energy (choose the position of the object when the spring is compressed as $U_g = 0$): $E = \frac{1}{2}kA^2 = U = mgh$, ☞ $\frac{1}{2}(60.0 \text{ N/m})A^2 = (0.250 \text{ kg})(9.80 \text{ m/s}^2)(0.100 \text{ m} + A)$.

Reduce to a quadratic equation: $30.0A^2 - 2.45A - 0.245 = 0$.

Solve for $A = \boxed{0.14 \text{ m}}$ or -0.058 m, which is discarded.

(b) From energy conservation, the object will go to a height of $\boxed{10.0 \text{ cm (original position)}}$.

25. (d).

26. $T = 2\pi\sqrt{\dfrac{L}{g}} \propto \sqrt{L}$, so the period is $\boxed{\sqrt{2} \text{ times as large}}$.

27. This could be done by tracing out the path of the object on a scrolling horizontal paper.

28. $\boxed{\text{No, } \tan 90° \text{ goes to } \infty}$.

29. In an upward accelerating elevator, the effective gravitational acceleration increases.

According to $T = 2\pi\sqrt{\dfrac{L}{g}}$, the period would be $\boxed{\text{decreased}}$.

30. Since $f = \dfrac{1}{T} = \dfrac{1}{2\pi}\sqrt{\dfrac{k}{m}}$, frequency is higher if mass is smaller.

So the $\boxed{\text{driver alone has higher frequency}}$.

31.　Since $T = 2\pi \sqrt{\dfrac{m}{k}}$ for a mass-spring system, the period is independent on the gravitational acceleration.

So the answer is $\boxed{\text{no}}$.

Since $T = 2\pi \sqrt{\dfrac{L}{g}}$ for a pendulum, the period depends on the gravitational acceleration. The period

actually increases on the Moon due to the smaller gravitational acceleration. The answer is then $\boxed{\text{yes}}$.

32.　(a) $T = 2\pi \sqrt{\dfrac{m}{k}} = 2\pi \sqrt{\dfrac{0.50 \text{ kg}}{200 \text{ N/m}}} = \boxed{0.31 \text{ s}}$.

(b) $f = \dfrac{1}{T} = \dfrac{1}{0.31 \text{ s}} = \boxed{3.2 \text{ Hz}}$.

33.　(a) $T = 2\pi \sqrt{\dfrac{L}{g}} = 2\pi \sqrt{\dfrac{1 \text{ m}}{9.80 \text{ m/s}^2}} = \boxed{2.0 \text{ s}}$.

(b) $f = \dfrac{1}{T} = \dfrac{1}{2.0 \text{ s}} = \boxed{0.50 \text{ Hz}}$.

34.　$T = 2\pi \sqrt{\dfrac{m}{k}}$, ☞ $m = \dfrac{T^2 k}{4\pi^2} = \dfrac{(2.0 \text{ s})^2 (100 \text{ N/m})}{4\pi^2} = \boxed{10 \text{ kg}}$.

35.　$T = 2\pi \sqrt{\dfrac{L}{g}}$, ☞ $L = \dfrac{T^2 g}{4\pi^2} = \dfrac{(1.0 \text{ s})^2 (9.80 \text{ m/s}^2)}{4\pi^2} = \boxed{0.25 \text{ m}}$.

36.　(a) The position right after the push is positive and the initial position is zero.

So　　$x = A \sin \omega t$.

(b) The initial position is at $x = A$.　So　$x = A \cos \omega t$.

37.　(a) Compare to $y = A \sin \omega t$.　$A = \boxed{0.10 \text{ m}}$.

(b) $\omega = 2\pi f = 100 \text{ rad/s}$,　☞　$f = \dfrac{100}{2\pi} = \boxed{16 \text{ Hz}}$.

(c) $T = \dfrac{1}{f} = \dfrac{1}{16 \text{ Hz}} = \boxed{0.063 \text{ s}}$.

38.　(a) Compare to $y = A \sin 2\pi f t$.　$A = \boxed{5.0 \text{ cm}}$.

(b) $\omega = 2\pi f = 20\pi \text{ rad/s}$,　☞　$f = \boxed{10 \text{ Hz}}$.

(c) $T = \dfrac{1}{f} = \dfrac{1}{10 \text{ Hz}} = \boxed{0.10 \text{ s}}$.

39. (a) $y = (025\text{ m}) \cos 314t = (0.25\text{ m}) \cos 0 = \boxed{0.25\text{ m}}$.

   (b) $y = (0.25\text{ m}) \cos[(314\text{ rad/s})(5.0\text{ s})] = \boxed{0.17\text{ m}}$.

   (c) $y = (0.25\text{ m}) \cos[(314\text{ rad/s})(15\text{ s})] = \boxed{-0.18\text{ m}}$.

40. (a) Since $T = \dfrac{1}{2\pi}\sqrt{\dfrac{m}{k}}$ and $E = \frac{1}{2}kA^2 = \dfrac{1}{8\pi^2}\dfrac{mA^2}{T^2}$.

   System A has 4 times the mass, but that is cancelled by the $\frac{1}{2}$ amplitude squared. So $E \propto \dfrac{1}{T^2}$.

   Since System A has a larger period, it has $\boxed{\text{less}}$ energy.

   (b) $\dfrac{E_b}{E_a} = \dfrac{m_b T_a^2 A_b^2}{m_a T_b^2 A_a^2} = \frac{1}{4} \times \dfrac{(8.0\text{ s})^2}{(0.60\text{ s})^2} \times \dfrac{10^2}{5.0^2} = \boxed{1.8 \times 10^2}$.

41. $\omega = \sqrt{\dfrac{k}{m}}$, ☞ $k = \omega^2 m$. So $E = \frac{1}{2}kA^2 = \frac{1}{2}m\omega^2 A^2$.

42. (a) $T = 2\pi\sqrt{\dfrac{m}{k}}$, ☞ $\dfrac{T_2}{T_1} = \sqrt{\dfrac{m_2}{m_1}} = \sqrt{\dfrac{2}{1}} = \boxed{\sqrt{2}}$.

   (b) $T_2 = \sqrt{\dfrac{m_2}{m_1}}\,T_1 = \sqrt{\dfrac{1}{3}}\,(3.0\text{ s}) = \boxed{1.7\text{ s}}$.

43. (a) $T = 2\pi\sqrt{\dfrac{m}{k}}$, ☞ $\dfrac{T_2}{T_1} = \sqrt{\dfrac{k_1}{k_2}} = \sqrt{\dfrac{1}{3}} = \boxed{1/\sqrt{3}}$.

   (b) $T_2 = \sqrt{\dfrac{k_1}{k_2}}\,T_1 = \sqrt{\dfrac{1}{1/2}}\,(2.0\text{ s}) = \sqrt{2}\,(2.0\text{ s}) = \boxed{2.8\text{ s}}$

44. $T = 2\pi\sqrt{\dfrac{m}{k}} = 2\pi\sqrt{\dfrac{L}{g}}$, ☞ $L = \dfrac{mg}{k}$.

45. $T = 2\pi\sqrt{\dfrac{m}{k}}$, ☞ $m = \dfrac{T^2 k}{4\pi^2} = \dfrac{(0.91\text{ s})^2(12\text{ N/m})}{4\pi^2} = \boxed{0.25\text{ kg}}$.

46. (a) They can $\boxed{\text{use the period of vibration}}$ of a mass-spring system.

   Since $T = 2\pi\sqrt{\dfrac{m}{k}}$, $m = \dfrac{T^2 k}{4\pi^2}$.

   (b) $m = \dfrac{(1.0\text{ s})^2(3000\text{ N/m})}{4\pi^2} = \boxed{76\text{ kg}}$.

47. $T = 2\pi \sqrt{\dfrac{L}{g}}$, ☞ $g = \dfrac{4\pi^2 L}{T^2} = \dfrac{4\pi^2 (0.3690 \text{ m})}{(1.220 \text{ s})^2} = \boxed{9.787 \text{ m/s}^2}$.

48. (a) $y = (10 \text{ cm}) \sin 0.50t = (10 \text{ cm}) \sin[(0.50 \text{ rad/s})(1.0 \text{ s})] = \boxed{4.8 \text{ cm}}$.

   (b) $v = A\omega \cos \omega t = (10 \text{ cm})(0.50 \text{ rad/s}) \cos[(0.50 \text{ rad/s})(1.0 \text{ s})] = \boxed{4.4 \text{ cm/s}}$.

   (c) $a = -\omega^2 y = -(0.50 \text{ rad/s})^2 (4.8 \text{ cm}) = \boxed{-1.2 \text{ cm/s}^2}$.

49. (a) $\omega = \sqrt{\dfrac{k}{m}} = \sqrt{\dfrac{6.0 \text{ N/m}}{0.15 \text{ kg}}} = 6.3 \text{ rad/s}$.

   $y = A \sin(\omega t + \delta)$.   At $t = 0$, $y = 8.0$ cm,   so $\delta = 90°$ or $\pi/2$ rad.

   Therefore $y = (8.0 \text{ cm}) \sin[(6.3 \text{ rad/s})t + 90°] = \boxed{(8.0 \text{ cm}) \cos(6.3 \text{ rad/s})t}$.

   (b) $y = (8.0 \text{ cm}) \cos[(6.3 \text{ rad/s})(0.50 \text{ s})] = \boxed{-8.0 \text{ cm, or at the other amplitude}}$.

50. $f = 1/T = \dfrac{1}{2\pi} \sqrt{\dfrac{k}{m}}$, ☞ $\dfrac{f_2}{f_1} = \sqrt{\dfrac{k_2}{k_1}} = \sqrt{2}$. So $\boxed{f_2 = \sqrt{2} f_1}$.

51. (a) Since $T = 2\pi \sqrt{\dfrac{L}{g}}$, a smaller g will have a greater T. So the period will $\boxed{\text{increase}}$.

   (b) $\dfrac{T_M}{T_E} = \sqrt{\dfrac{g_E}{g_M}} = \sqrt{\dfrac{g}{g/6}} = \sqrt{6} = 2.4$. $T_M = 2.4 T_E = 2.4(2.0 \text{ s}) = \boxed{4.8 \text{ s}}$.

52. $T = 2\pi \sqrt{\dfrac{L}{g}} = 2\pi \sqrt{\dfrac{m}{k}}$, ☞ $k = \dfrac{mg}{L} = \dfrac{(0.075 \text{ kg})(9.80 \text{ m/s}^2)}{0.30 \text{ m}} = \boxed{2.5 \text{ N/m}}$.

53. $T = 8.0 \text{ s}$, $A = 5.0 \text{ cm}$,   and $y = 5.0 \text{ cm at } t = 0$. $\omega = 2\pi f = \dfrac{2\pi}{T} = \dfrac{2\pi}{8.0 \text{ s}} = \dfrac{\pi}{4}$ rad/s.

   So $y = A \cos(\omega t + \delta) = \boxed{(5.0 \text{ cm}) \cos(\pi t/4)}$.

54. (a) $T = 0.60 \text{ s}$, $A = 10 \text{ cm} = 0.10 \text{ m}$,   and $y = 0$ and v is negative when $t = 0$.

   $\omega = 2\pi f = \dfrac{2\pi}{T} = \dfrac{2\pi}{0.60 \text{ s}} = \dfrac{10\pi}{3}$ rad/s.

   So $y = A \sin(\omega t + \delta) = \boxed{(-0.10 \text{ m}) \sin(10\pi/3) t}$.

   (b) $T = 2\pi \sqrt{\dfrac{m}{k}}$, ☞ $k = \dfrac{4\pi^2 m}{T^2} = \dfrac{4\pi^2 (0.35 \text{ kg})}{(0.60 \text{ s})^2} = \boxed{38 \text{ N/m}}$.

55.   (a) In the tangential direction, $\Sigma F = mg \sin\theta \approx mg\,\theta = mg\dfrac{x}{L} = \dfrac{mg}{L}x = kx$.

(b) Since the effective spring constant is $k = \dfrac{mg}{L}$,

then $T = 2\pi\sqrt{\dfrac{m}{k}} = 2\pi\sqrt{\dfrac{m}{mg/L}} = 2\pi\sqrt{\dfrac{L}{g}}$.

56.   (a) Since $T = 2\pi\sqrt{\dfrac{L}{g}}$ and the length is shorter, T is smaller.

So the clock runs faster or $\boxed{\text{gains time}}$.

(b) $\Delta T = 2\pi\sqrt{\dfrac{0.7500 \text{ m}}{9.80 \text{ m/s}^2}} - 2\pi\sqrt{\dfrac{0.7480 \text{ m}}{9.80 \text{ m/s}^2}} = 2.32 \times 10^{-3}$ s.

$T = 2\pi\sqrt{\dfrac{0.7500 \text{ m}}{9.80 \text{ m/s}^2}} = 1.7382$ s. In one day, there are 24 h = 86 400 s (or 4.9707×10^4 periods).

Therefore, the time difference is $(2.32 \times 10^{-3} \text{ s})(4.9707 \times 10^4) = 115 \text{ s} = \boxed{1.9 \text{ min}}$.

(c) $\boxed{\text{Yes}}$. Because of linear thermal expansion, the length depends on the temperature.

57.   (d).

58.   (a).

59.   (c). A water wave is a combination of transverse and longitudinal.

60.   (a) $\boxed{\text{Transverse and longitudinal}}$.   (b) $\boxed{\text{Longitudinal}}$.   (c) $\boxed{\text{Longitudinal}}$.

61.   The one on the left is $\boxed{\text{transverse}}$ and the one on the right is $\boxed{\text{longitudinal}}$.

62.   This is a $\boxed{\text{longitudinal}}$ wave because the direction of the wave motion (horizontal across the field) is parallel to the direction of the wheat plant vibration.

63. $\lambda = \dfrac{v}{f} = \dfrac{340 \text{ m/s}}{1000 \text{ Hz}} = \boxed{0.34 \text{ m}}$.

64. $v = \lambda f = (0.50 \text{ m})(20 \text{ Hz}) = \boxed{10 \text{ m/s}}$.

65. $v = \dfrac{2.4 \text{ m}}{1.6 \text{ s}} = \boxed{1.5 \text{ m/s}}$.

66. $\lambda = \dfrac{v}{f} = \dfrac{3.00 \times 10^8 \text{ m/s}}{5 \times 10^{14} \text{ Hz}} = \boxed{6 \times 10^{-7} \text{ m}}$.

67. $f = \dfrac{v}{\lambda} = \dfrac{3.00 \times 10^8 \text{ m/s}}{633 \times 10^{-9} \text{ m}} = \boxed{4.7 \times 10^{14} \text{ Hz}}$.

68. $\lambda_{\min} = \dfrac{345 \text{ m/s}}{20 \times 10^3 \text{ Hz}} = 0.017 \text{ m} = \boxed{1.7 \text{ cm}}$. $\quad \lambda_{\max} = \dfrac{v}{f} = \dfrac{345 \text{ m/s}}{20 \text{ Hz}} = \boxed{17 \text{ m}}$.

69. (a) From $v = \lambda f$, low frequency corresponds to longer wavelength. The AM frequencies have $\boxed{\text{longer}}$ wavelength.

   (b) AM: $\qquad \lambda_{\min} = \dfrac{3.00 \times 10^8 \text{ m/s}}{1600 \times 10^3 \text{ Hz}} = \boxed{188 \text{ m}}, \quad \lambda_{\max} = \dfrac{v}{f} = \dfrac{3.00 \times 10^8 \text{ m/s}}{550 \times 10^3 \text{ Hz}} = \boxed{545 \text{ m}}$.

   (b) FM: $\qquad \lambda_{\min} = \dfrac{3.00 \times 10^8 \text{ m/s}}{108 \times 10^6 \text{ Hz}} = \boxed{2.78 \text{ m}}, \quad \lambda_{\max} = \dfrac{3.00 \times 10^8 \text{ m/s}}{88.0 \times 10^6 \text{ Hz}} = \boxed{3.41 \text{ m}}$.

70. $v = \lambda f = (4.80 \times 10^{-4} \text{ m})(2.50 \times 10^6 \text{ Hz}) = 1200 \text{ m/s}$.

   So the depth is $\frac{1}{2}(1200 \text{ m/s})(10 \text{ s}) = 6.00 \times 10^3 \text{ m} = \boxed{6.00 \text{ km}}$.

71. In between 13 crests, there are only 12 wavelengths. So the frequency is $f = \dfrac{12}{3.0 \text{ s}} = 4.0 \text{ Hz}$.

   Therefore $\quad v = \lambda f = (0.75 \text{ m})(4.0 \text{ Hz}) = \boxed{3.0 \text{ m/s}}$.

72. (a) 15 cm $= \boxed{0.15 \text{ m}}$.

   (b) $T = 0.80 \text{ s}$, $\quad \mathcal{F} \quad f = \dfrac{1}{T} = \dfrac{1}{0.80 \text{ s}} = 1.25 \text{ Hz}$. So $\quad v = \lambda f = (0.12 \text{ m})(1.25 \text{ Hz}) = \boxed{0.15 \text{ m/s}}$.

73. (a) 90° in latitude covers one quarter of the Earth's circumference. The straight line distance between the locations is $d = \sqrt{R^2 + R^2} = \sqrt{2}\,R = \sqrt{2}\,(6.4 \times 10^3 \text{ km}) = 9.05 \times 10^3 \text{ km}$.

   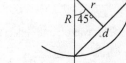

   $\Delta t = \dfrac{d}{v_S} - \dfrac{d}{v_P} = \dfrac{9.05 \times 10^3 \text{ km}}{6.0 \text{ km/s}} - \dfrac{9.05 \times 10^3 \text{ km}}{8.0 \text{ km/s}} = \boxed{3.8 \times 10^2 \text{ s}}$.

   (b) $r = R \cos 45°$. So the depth under the surface is

   $R - r = R(1 - \cos 45°) = (6.4 \times 10^3 \text{ km})(1 - \cos 45°) = 1.9 \times 10^3 \text{ km} > 30 \text{ km}$.

   So the answer is $\boxed{\text{yes}}$.

   (c) $t = \dfrac{2(6.4 \times 10^3 \text{ km})}{8.0 \text{ km/s}} = \boxed{1.6 \times 10^3 \text{ s; S waves do not go through the liquid core}}$.

74.   (a) $v = \sqrt{\dfrac{Y}{\rho}} = \sqrt{\dfrac{7.0 \times 10^{10}\ \text{N/m}^2}{2.7 \times 10^3\ \text{kg/m}^3}} = 5091\ \text{m/s}.$ $\lambda = \dfrac{v}{f} = \dfrac{5091\ \text{m/s}}{40\ \text{Hz}} = \boxed{1.3 \times 10^2\ \text{m}}.$

       (b) $v = \sqrt{\dfrac{11 \times 10^{10}\ \text{N/m}^2}{8.9 \times 10^3\ \text{kg/m}^3}} = 3516\ \text{m/s}.$ $\lambda = \dfrac{3516\ \text{m/s}}{40\ \text{Hz}} = \boxed{88\ \text{m}}.$

75.   (a) $v = \sqrt{\dfrac{Y}{\rho}} = \sqrt{\dfrac{20 \times 10^{10}\ \text{N/m}^2}{7.8 \times 10^3\ \text{kg/m}^3}} = 5064\ \text{m/s}.$ $t = \dfrac{1.0 \times 10^3\ \text{m}}{5064\ \text{m/s}} = \boxed{0.20\ \text{s}}.$

       (b) $T = \dfrac{1}{f} = \dfrac{1}{0.50\ \text{Hz}} = \boxed{2.0\ \text{s}}.$

76.   (d).

77.   (b).

78.   (d).

79.   Only $\boxed{\text{waveform}}$ is destroyed. Energy is not destroyed, but redistributed.

80. $\boxed{\text{Reflection (this is called echolocation)}}$, because the sound is reflected by the prey.

81. $\boxed{\text{Sound from different frequencies would arrive at different times}}$.

82.   (d).

83.   (c).

84.   At a frequency of $f_0/2$ (or a period of $2T_0$), the swing is pushed every other oscillation. So only half the energy is going into the swing, but it is pushed smoothly.

85. $\boxed{5}$.

86.   The wavelength $\boxed{\text{decreases}}$ if the frequency is increased as $v = \lambda f$.

       There is $\boxed{\text{no change}}$ in the speed of the wave because it is independent of wavelength or frequency. It depends only on the tension and the mass per unit length of the string.

87. $\boxed{\text{Increase the string tension to increase the speed, therefore, frequency}}$.

88. A $\boxed{\text{thinner}}$ string will sound higher frequency. Since $v = \sqrt{\dfrac{F_T}{\mu}}$, a thinner string will have a small μ, thus the $\boxed{\text{speed is higher, as is frequency}}$, because $v = \lambda f$.

89. (a) $L = \dfrac{\lambda_1}{2}$, ☞ $\lambda_1 = 2L = 2(3.0 \text{ m}) = \boxed{6.0 \text{ m}}$.

   (b) $L = 1.5\lambda_3$, ☞ $\lambda_3 = \dfrac{L}{1.5} = \dfrac{3.0 \text{ m}}{1.5} = \boxed{2.0 \text{ m}}$.

90. (a) $f_2 = 2f_1 = 2(100 \text{ Hz}) = \boxed{200 \text{ Hz}}$.

   (b) $f_3 = 3f_1 = 3(100 \text{ Hz}) = \boxed{300 \text{ Hz}}$.

91. $f_3 = 3f_1$, ☞ $f_1 = \dfrac{f_3}{3} = \dfrac{450 \text{ Hz}}{3} = \boxed{150 \text{ Hz}}$.

92. (a) $f_1 = \dfrac{v}{2L} = \dfrac{12 \text{ m/s}}{2(4.0 \text{ m})} = 1.5 \text{ Hz}$. So the answer is $\boxed{\text{yes}}$, 15 Hz is the 10th harmonic.

   (b) $\boxed{\text{No}}$, 20 Hz is not a harmonic.

93. $f = \dfrac{v}{\lambda} = \dfrac{250 \text{ m/s}}{0.80 \text{ m}} = 312.5 \text{ Hz}$. $f_1 = \dfrac{v}{2L} = \dfrac{250 \text{ m/s}}{2(2.0 \text{ m})} = 62.5 \text{ Hz}$.

   So $n = \dfrac{f}{f_o} = \dfrac{312.5 \text{ Hz}}{62.5 \text{ Hz}} = \boxed{5}$.

94. (a) $v = \sqrt{\dfrac{F_T}{\mu}}$, ☞ $\dfrac{v_2}{v_1} = \sqrt{\dfrac{F_{T2}}{F_{T1}}} = \sqrt{\dfrac{2}{1}} = \sqrt{2}$.

   So the speed $\boxed{\text{increases by } \sqrt{2}}$.

   (b) $v = \sqrt{\dfrac{9.00 \text{ N}}{0.125 \text{ kg/m}}} = \boxed{8.49 \text{ m/s}}$.

   (b) $f_n = \dfrac{nv}{2L} = n\dfrac{8.49 \text{ m/s}}{2(10.0 \text{ m})} = \boxed{(0.425)n \text{ Hz}; \; n = 1, 2, 3, \dots}$.

95. $v = \sqrt{\dfrac{F_T}{\mu}} = \sqrt{\dfrac{40 \text{ N}}{2.5 \times 10^{-2} \text{ kg/m}}} = 40 \text{ m/s}$.

   $f_n = \dfrac{nv}{2L} = \dfrac{40 \text{ m/s}}{2(2.0 \text{ m})} n = 10n \text{ Hz}$.

   So the frequencies of the first four harmonics are $\boxed{10 \text{ Hz, } 20 \text{ Hz, } 30 \text{ Hz, and } 40 \text{ Hz}}$.

96. (a) The wave speeds in the two strings are the same.

Since $f_n = \dfrac{v}{2L}$, $\dfrac{(f_n)_{1.0}}{(f_n)_{3.0}} = \dfrac{3.0 \text{ m}}{1.0 \text{ m}} = 3$, the $\boxed{\text{3rd harmonic of 3.0 m} = \text{1st harmonic of 1.0}}$

and the $\boxed{\text{6th harmonic of 3.0 m} = \text{2nd harmonic of 1.0 m}}$.

(b) $\dfrac{(f_n)_{1.5}}{(f_n)_{2.0}} = \dfrac{2.0 \text{ m}}{1.5 \text{ m}} = \dfrac{4}{3}$. So the $\boxed{\text{3rd harmonic of 2.0 m} = \text{4th harmonic of 1.5 m}}$.

97. (a) The length of the string should be $\boxed{\text{shortened}}$ because a shorter string has a shorter wavelength, therefore a higher frequency given the speed is a constant.

(b) There is a node where the finger is placed. So the longest possible wavelength is $\dfrac{\lambda}{2} = \dfrac{7}{8}L$.

$f = \dfrac{v}{\lambda} = \dfrac{v}{7L/4} = \dfrac{4v}{7L} = \dfrac{8}{7}\dfrac{v}{2L} = \dfrac{8}{7}f_1 = \dfrac{8}{7}(440 \text{ Hz}) = \boxed{503 \text{ Hz}}$.

98. The first harmonic, $\lambda_1 = 4L$. $\quad f_1 = \dfrac{v}{\lambda} = \dfrac{v}{4L} = 1 \times \dfrac{v}{4L}$;

the next harmonic (3rd), $\lambda_3 = \dfrac{4L}{3}$, $\quad f_3 = \dfrac{3\,v}{4L} = 3 \times \dfrac{v}{4L}$;

the next harmonic (5th), $\lambda_5 = \dfrac{4L}{5}$, $\quad f_5 = \dfrac{5\,v}{4L} = 5 \times \dfrac{v}{4L}$;

Therefore $f_m = \dfrac{mv}{4L} = m\,\dfrac{3.5 \times 10^3 \text{ m/s}}{4(1.0 \text{ m})} = \boxed{m(8.8 \times 10^2 \text{ Hz}), \; m = 1, 3, 5, \ldots}$.

99. $v = \lambda f = \sqrt{\dfrac{F_T}{\mu}} = \sqrt{\dfrac{Mg}{m/L}}$, ☞ $M = \dfrac{m\lambda^2 f^2}{gL} = \dfrac{(0.10 \times 10^{-3} \text{ kg})(60 \text{ Hz})^2}{(9.80 \text{ m/s}^2)(1.5 \text{ m})}\lambda^2 = 0.0245\lambda^2$.

$\lambda_1 = 2L = 2(1.5 \text{ m}) = 3.0 \text{ m},\quad \lambda_2 = L = 1.5 \text{ m},\quad \lambda_3 = \dfrac{2L}{3} = 1.0 \text{ m},\quad \lambda_4 = \dfrac{L}{2} = 0.75 \text{ m}.$

So $M_1 = \boxed{0.22 \text{ kg}},\quad M_2 = \boxed{0.055 \text{ kg}},\quad M_3 = \boxed{0.024 \text{ kg}},\quad M_4 = \boxed{0.014 \text{ kg}}$.

100. $v_{max} = \sqrt{\dfrac{k}{m}}\, A = \omega A$.

$v = \sqrt{\dfrac{k}{m}(A^2 - x^2)} = \omega A \sqrt{1 - \dfrac{x^2}{A^2}} = v_{max}\sqrt{1 - \dfrac{x^2}{A^2}}$

$= (0.40 \text{ m/s})\sqrt{1 - \dfrac{(0.040 \text{ m})^2}{(0.080 \text{ m})^2}} = \boxed{0.35 \text{ m/s}}$.

101. (a) The distance between two successive nodes is $\frac{\lambda}{2}$. So $\lambda = 2(6.0 \text{ cm}) = \boxed{12 \text{ cm}}$.

(b) The anti-nodes are halfway between the nodes. So they are at $\boxed{3.0 \text{ cm, 9.0 cm, 15 cm}}$.

102. (a) $T = \dfrac{10 \text{ s}}{5} = \boxed{2.0 \text{ s}}$. $f = \dfrac{1}{T} = \dfrac{1}{2.0 \text{ s}} = \boxed{0.50 \text{ Hz}}$.

(b) $T = 2\pi \sqrt{\dfrac{L}{g}}$, $\Rightarrow$ $L = \dfrac{T^2 g}{4\pi^2} = \dfrac{(2.0 \text{ s})^2 (9.80 \text{ m/s}^2)}{4\pi^2} = \boxed{0.99 \text{ m}}$.

103. $x = A \cos\omega t = A \sin(\omega t + 90°)$.

So $v = \omega A \cos(\omega t + 90°) = -\omega A \sin\omega t$

and $a = -\omega^2 x = -\omega^2 A \cos\omega t$.

$v_{max} = \omega A = (50 \text{ rad/s})(0.10 \text{ m}) = \boxed{5.0 \text{ m/s}}$.

$a_{max} = \omega^2 A = (50 \text{ rad/s})^2 (0.10 \text{ m}) = \boxed{2.5 \times 10^2 \text{ m/s}^2}$.

104. $v = \sqrt{\dfrac{F_T}{\mu}} = \sqrt{\dfrac{550 \text{ N}}{(3.0 \times 10^{-3} \text{ kg})/(0.60 \text{ m})}} = 332 \text{ m/s}$.

$f_1 = \dfrac{v}{2L} = \dfrac{332 \text{ m/s}}{2(0.60 \text{ m})} = \boxed{2.8 \times 10^2 \text{ Hz}}$.

$\lambda_1 = \dfrac{v}{f_1} = \dfrac{332 \text{ m/s}}{276 \text{ Hz}} = \boxed{1.2 \text{ m}}$, or $\lambda_1 = 2L = 1.2 \text{ m}$.

105. The 4th harmonic and the 2nd harmonic vibrate in 4 and 2 loops, respectively.

So $f_2 = \dfrac{f_4}{2} = \dfrac{420 \text{ Hz}}{2} = \boxed{210 \text{ Hz}}$.

106. $f_n = \dfrac{n}{2L} \sqrt{\dfrac{F_T}{\mu}}$, $\Rightarrow$ $\dfrac{F_T'}{F_T} = \dfrac{(f_1')^2}{(f_1)^2} = \dfrac{(440 \text{ Hz})^2}{(450 \text{ Hz})^2} = 0.956$.

So $F_T' = 0.956(500 \text{ N}) = \boxed{478 \text{ N}}$.

107. Since $v = \sqrt{\dfrac{F_T}{\mu}}$, doubling the tension will make the speed $\sqrt{2}$ times as large.

(a) The wavelength is $\boxed{\text{unchanged}}$ because it is determined by the length of the string and the mode of vibration.

(b) However, the frequency $\boxed{\text{increases by } \sqrt{2} \text{ times}}$ due to the speed increase ($v = \lambda f$).

108.   The dimension of F_T is $[M][L]/[T]^2$ (think $F = ma$).

The dimension of μ is $[M]/[L]$ (mass per unit length).

So the dimension of $\sqrt{\dfrac{F_T}{\mu}}$ is $\sqrt{\dfrac{[M][L]/[T]^2}{[M]/[L]}} = \sqrt{\dfrac{[M][L]^2}{[M][T]^2}} = \sqrt{\dfrac{[L]^2}{[T]^2}} = [L]/[T]$.

$[L]/[T]$ is the dimension of speed v.

109. $y = A \sin(\omega t + \delta) = (0.20 \text{ cm}) \sin 1.8\pi t$.

$v = \omega A \cos(\omega t + \delta) = (1.8\pi \text{ rad/s})(0.20 \text{ cm}) \cos[(1.8\pi \text{ rad/s})(10 \text{ s})] = \boxed{1.1 \text{ cm/s}}$.

110.   (a) $\boxed{20 \text{ cm from the equilibrium position}}$ according to the definition of amplitude.

(b) $v_{max} = \omega A = 2\pi f A = 2\pi(0.50 \text{ Hz})(0.20 \text{ m}) = \boxed{0.63 \text{ m/s}}$.

(c) $a_{max} = \omega^2 A = (2\pi f)^2 A = 4\pi^2 f^2 A = 4\pi^2 (0.50 \text{ Hz})^2 (0.20 \text{ m}) = \boxed{2.0 \text{ m/s}^2}$.

111.   The equation of motion is $x = A \sin(\omega t + \delta) = (16 \text{ cm}) \sin(\omega t + 90°) = (16 \text{ cm}) \cos \omega t$.

So $8.0 \text{ cm} = (16 \text{ cm}) \cos[\omega(0.50 \text{ s})]$, $\omega(0.50 \text{ s}) = \dfrac{2\pi}{T}(0.50 \text{ s}) = \cos^{-1} 0.50 = 1.05 \text{ rad}$.

Therefore $T = \dfrac{2\pi(0.50 \text{ s})}{1.05 \text{ rad}} = \boxed{3.0 \text{ s}}$.

CHAPTER 14

1.   (b).

2.   (a).

3.   (a).

4.   (d).

5.   Some insects produce sounds that are $\boxed{\text{not in our audible range}}$.

6.   Sound is a traveling disturbance like any other wave. $\boxed{\text{Warmer air molecules vibrate faster}}$ so they can pass the disturbance along faster.

7.   They arrive at the $\boxed{\text{same time}}$ because sound is not dispersive, i.e., speed does not depend on frequency.

8.   At the same temperature and pressure, water vapor has a smaller density than air. The speed of sound is inversely proportional to the square root of the density of the medium. Generally, the less dense air (O_2 and N_2 molecules replaced by H_2O molecules), the faster sound travels.
So $\boxed{\text{the speed increases with increasing humidity}}$.

9.   Sound travels considerably faster in solids than in air. Dogs can hear better by putting their ear on the floor. Yes, it is related to people putting their ears on railroad tracks.

10.   (a) $v = (331 + 0.6T_C)$ m/s $= [331 + 0.6(10)]$ m/s $= \boxed{337 \text{ m/s}}$.

       (b) $v = [331 + 0.6(20)]$ m/s $= \boxed{343 \text{ m/s}}$.

11. $v = (331 + 0.6T_C)$ m/s, ☞ $T_C = \dfrac{v - 331 \text{ m/s}}{0.6} = \dfrac{350 \text{ m/s} - 331 \text{ m/s}}{0.6} = \boxed{32°C}$.

12.   (a) Neglect the time taken by the lightning since light travels at a much faster speed.

       $t \approx (1/3 \text{ km/s})(3.0 \text{ s}) = \boxed{1.0 \text{ km}}$.

       (b) $t \approx (1/5 \text{ mi/s})(3.0 \text{ s}) = \boxed{0.60 \text{ mi}}$.

13. The sound travels through the distance twice. $d = \dfrac{vt}{2} = \dfrac{(1.5 \times 10^3 \text{ m/s})(2.0 \text{ s})}{2} = \boxed{1.5 \times 10^3 \text{ m}}$.

14. The unit of v in a liquid is $\sqrt{\dfrac{\text{N/m}^2}{\text{kg/m}^3}} = \sqrt{\dfrac{\text{N}\cdot\text{m}}{\text{kg}}} = \sqrt{\dfrac{\text{kg}\cdot\text{m}^2/\text{s}^2}{\text{kg}}} = \sqrt{\dfrac{\text{m}^2}{\text{s}^2}} = \text{m/s}$.

   Y has the same unit as B, so the unit of v in a solid is also m/s.

15. (a) The wavelength $\boxed{\text{increases}}$ when the air temperature increases. The speed of sound increases with

   temperature and $v = \lambda f$. So if v increases and f remains the same, λ increases.

   (b) At 0°C: $\lambda = \dfrac{v}{f} = \dfrac{331 \text{ m/s}}{256 \text{ Hz}} = 1.293$ m.

   At 20°C, $\lambda = \dfrac{(331 + 0.6T_C) \text{ m/s}}{f} = \dfrac{[331 + 0.6(20)] \text{ m/s}}{256 \text{ Hz}} = 1.340$ m.

   So $\Delta\lambda = 1.340 \text{ m} - 1.293 \text{ m} = \boxed{+0.047 \text{ m}}$.

16. $f = \dfrac{v}{\lambda} = \dfrac{1500 \text{ m/s}}{3.0 \times 10^{-4} \text{ m}} = \boxed{5.0 \times 10^6 \text{ Hz}}$, where $v = 1500$ m/s is the speed of sound in water.

17. (a) The smallest detectable object is in the order of the wavelength.

   $\lambda = \dfrac{v}{f} = \dfrac{1500 \text{ m/s}}{20 \times 10^6 \text{ Hz}} = \boxed{7.5 \times 10^{-5} \text{ m}}$.

   (b) Depth $= 200(7.5 \times 10^{-5} \text{ m}) = \boxed{1.5 \times 10^{-2} \text{ m}}$

18. From Table 14.1, the speed of sound in copper is 3500 m/s, while the speed of sound in zinc is 3200 m/s.

   So adding zinc to copper will $\boxed{\text{decrease}}$ the speed of sound in the alloy, i.e., brass.

19. (a) $\Delta t = \dfrac{d}{v_a} - \dfrac{d}{v_s} = \dfrac{300 \text{ m}}{343 \text{ m/s}} - \dfrac{300 \text{ m}}{4500 \text{ m/s}} = \boxed{0.81 \text{ s}}$.

   (b) 36 km/h = 10 m/s.   So $\Delta t = \dfrac{300 \text{ m}}{343 \text{ m/s} + 10 \text{ m/s}} - \dfrac{300 \text{ m}}{4500 \text{ m/s}} = \boxed{0.78 \text{ s}}$.

20. $v = (331 + 0.6T_C) \text{ m/s} = [331 + 0.6(16)] \text{ m/s} = 341 \text{ m/s}$. $d = vt = (341 \text{ m/s})(0.25 \text{ s}) = \boxed{85 \text{ m}}$.

21. $\lambda_{20} = \dfrac{v_{20}}{f} = \dfrac{[331 + 0.6(20)] \text{ m/s}}{2000 \text{ Hz}} = 0.1715$ m, $\lambda_{10} = \dfrac{[331 + 0.6(10)] \text{ m/s}}{2000 \text{ Hz}} = 0.1685$ m.

   So the percentage difference is $\dfrac{0.1685 \text{ m} - 0.1715 \text{ m}}{0.1715 \text{ m}} = \boxed{-1.75\%}$.

22. $T_C = \frac{5}{9}(T_F - 32) = \frac{5}{9}(72 - 32) = 22.22°C.$ $v_s = (331 + 0.6T_C) \text{ m/s} = [331 + 0.6(22.22)] \text{ m/s} = 344.3 \text{ m/s}.$

$$\Delta t = \frac{d}{v_b} + \frac{d}{v_s} = d\left(\frac{1}{v_b} + \frac{1}{v_s}\right). \quad \text{So} \quad d = \frac{\Delta t}{\dfrac{1}{v_b} + \dfrac{1}{v_s}} = \frac{1.00 \text{ s}}{\dfrac{1}{200 \text{ m/s}} + \dfrac{1}{344.3 \text{ m/s}}} = \boxed{127 \text{ m}}.$$

23. The sound travels twice through the distance (to and from).

$$d = \frac{vt}{2} = \frac{(1500 \text{ m/s})(0.12 \text{ s})}{2} = \boxed{90 \text{ m}}.$$

24. $v = (331 + 0.6T_C) \text{ m/s} = (331 + 0.6 \times 20) \text{ m/s} = 343 \text{ m/s}.$ $d = \frac{\lambda}{2} = \frac{v}{2f}.$

$$d_1 = \frac{343 \text{ m/s}}{2(20\,000 \text{ Hz})} = 8.6 \times 10^{-3} \text{ m} = 0.86 \text{ cm}.$$

$$d_2 = \frac{343 \text{ m/s}}{2(16\,000 \text{ Hz})} = 1.1 \times 10^{-2} \text{ m} = 1.1 \text{ cm}.$$

So the range is $\boxed{8.6 \times 10^{-3} \text{ m} - 1.1 \times 10^{-2} \text{ m}}$. $\boxed{\text{Yes}}$, the answer is $\boxed{\text{reasonable}}$.

25. (a) The answer is $\boxed{\text{less than double}}$. This is because the total time is the sum of the time it takes for the stone to hit the ground (free fall motion) and the time it takes sound to travel back that distance. While the time for sound is directly proportional to the distance, the time for free fall is not. Since $d = \frac{1}{2}gt^2$ or $t = \sqrt{\dfrac{2d}{g}}$ (see Chapter 2), doubling the distance d will only increase the time by a factor of $\sqrt{2}$, i.e., an increase, but not double.

(b) $v = (331 + 0.6T_C) \text{ m/s} = (331 + 0.6 \times 20) \text{ m/s} = 343 \text{ m/s}.$

$$4.80 \text{ s} = \frac{d}{343 \text{ m/s}} + \sqrt{\frac{2d}{g}} = \frac{d}{343 \text{ m/s}} + \sqrt{\frac{2d}{9.80 \text{ m/s}^2}}.$$

Or $(2.915 \times 10^{-3})(\sqrt{d})^2 + 0.4518(\sqrt{d}) - 4.8 = 0.$

Solving, $\sqrt{d} = 9.98$, that is $d = (\sqrt{d})^2 = (9.98)^2 = \boxed{1.0 \times 10^2 \text{ m}}.$

(c) $t = \dfrac{3(99.6 \text{ m})}{343 \text{ m/s}} + \sqrt{\dfrac{2(3 \times 99.6 \text{ m})}{9.80 \text{ m/s}^2}} = \boxed{8.7 \text{ s}}.$

26. Since $\lambda = \dfrac{v}{f}$ and $v = (331 + 0.6T_C) \text{ m/s}$, the percentage change in wavelength is

$$\frac{\lambda_{30} - \lambda_{4.0}}{\lambda_{30}} = \frac{0.6(4.0 - 30)}{331 + 0.6(30)} = -\boxed{4.5\%}.$$

27. (c).

28.   (b).

29.   They are used $\boxed{\text{to compress a large range into a smaller numerical scale}}$. For example, the range from
10^{-12} W/m^2 to 1 W/m^2 is 12 orders of magnitude (a big range). After converting them to the decibel scale,
it is from 0 to 120, a compressed scale.

30. $\boxed{\text{Yes}}$. Since $\beta = 10 \log \dfrac{I}{I_o}$ and $\log x < 0$ for $x < 1$, if $I < I_o$.

So for $\boxed{\text{an intensity below the intensity of threshold of hearing}}$, β is negative.

31.   (a) Threshold of hearing: $P = IA = (10^{-12}$ W/m$^2)[\pi \times (0.005\text{ m})^2] = \boxed{8 \times 10^{-17}\text{ W}}$.

Threshold of pain: $P = (1\text{ W/m}^2)[\pi \times (0.005\text{ m})^2] = \boxed{8 \times 10^{-5}\text{ W}}$

32.   (a) $I = \dfrac{P}{4\pi R^2} = \dfrac{1.0\text{ W}}{4\pi(3.0\text{ m})^2} = \boxed{8.8 \times 10^{-3}\text{ W/m}^2}$.

(b) $I = \dfrac{1.0\text{ W}}{4\pi(6.0\text{ m})^2} = \boxed{2.2 \times 10^{-3}\text{ W/m}^2}$.

33.   (a) Since $I = \dfrac{P}{4\pi R^2}$, I is inversely proportional to the square of R. Tripling R will reduce I to $1/3^2 = 1/9$.

Or $\dfrac{I_2}{I_1} = \dfrac{R_1^{\,2}}{R_2^{\,2}} = \dfrac{1^2}{3^2} = \boxed{1/9}$.

(b) $I_2 = \frac{1}{2} I_1$. $\dfrac{R_2}{R_1} = \sqrt{\dfrac{I_1}{I_2}} = \sqrt{2} = \boxed{1.4\text{ times}}$.

34.   (a) $\beta = 10 \log \dfrac{I}{I_o} = 10 \log \dfrac{10^{-12}\text{ W/m}^2}{10^{-12}\text{ W/m}^2} = 10 \log 1 = \boxed{0}$.

(b) $\beta = 10 \log \dfrac{1\text{ W/m}^2}{10^{-12}\text{ W/m}^2} = 10 \log 10^{12} = 10(12) = \boxed{120\text{ dB}}$.

35.   (a) $\beta = 10 \log \dfrac{I}{I_o} = 10 \log \dfrac{10^{-2}}{10^{-12}} = \boxed{100\text{ dB}}$.

(b) $\beta = 10 \log \dfrac{10^{-6}}{10^{-12}} = \boxed{60\text{ dB}}$.

(c) $\beta = 10 \log \dfrac{10^{-15}}{10^{-12}} = \boxed{-30\text{ dB}}$.

36. $\beta = 10 \log \frac{I}{I_o}$, ☞ $\Delta\beta = 10\left(\log \frac{I_2}{I_o} - \log \frac{I_1}{I_o}\right) = 10 \log \frac{I_2}{I_1} = 10 \log \frac{10^{-2}}{10^{-4}} = \boxed{20 \text{ dB}}$.

$(\log x - \log y = \log \frac{x}{y})$.

37. (a) The intensity level $\boxed{\text{increases}}$ but will not double. Doubling the power will double the intensity.

However, it will not generate twice as much intensity level (decibel level) because

$\log 2x = \log 2 + \log x = 0.3 + \log x \neq 2(\log x)$.

(b) 5.0 W: $I = \frac{P}{4\pi R^2} = \frac{5.0 \text{ W}}{4\pi(10 \text{ m})^2} = 3.98 \times 10^{-3} \text{ W/m}^2$.

$\beta_5 = 10 \log \frac{I}{I_o} = 10 \log \frac{3.98 \times 10^{-3} \text{ W/m}^2}{10^{-12} \text{ W/m}^2} = \boxed{96 \text{ dB}}$

10 W: $\beta_{10} = 10 \log \frac{2I}{10^{-12} \text{ W/m}^2} = 10 \log 2 + 10 \log \frac{I}{10^{-12} \text{ W/m}^2} = 3 + 96 = \boxed{99 \text{ dB}}$.

38. (a) $\beta = 10 \log \frac{I}{I_o}$, ☞ $\frac{I}{I_o} = 10^{\beta/10}$,

so $I = 10^{\beta/10} I_o = 10^5 (10^{-12} \text{ W/m}^2) = \boxed{10^{-7} \text{ W/m}^2}$.

(b) $I = 10^9 (10^{-12} \text{ W/m}^2) = \boxed{10^{-3} \text{ W/m}^2}$.

39. (a) $\beta = 10 \log \frac{I}{I_o}$, ☞ $\frac{I}{I_o} = 10^{\beta/10}$,   so $I = 10^{\beta/10} I_o$.

Therefore $I_{min} = 10^{8.57} (10^{-12} \text{ W/m}^2) = \boxed{3.72 \times 10^{-4} \text{ W/m}^2}$,

$I_{max} = 10^{11.0} (10^{-12} \text{ W/m}^2) = \boxed{1.00 \times 10^{-1} \text{ W/m}^2}$.

(b) $I_{min} = 10^{9.98} (10^{-12} \text{ W/m}^2) = \boxed{9.55 \times 10^{-3} \text{ W/m}^2}$,

$I_{max} = 10^{10.78} (10^{-12} \text{ W/m}^2) = \boxed{6.03 \times 10^{-2} \text{ W/m}^2}$.

40. (a) Since $I = \frac{P}{4\pi R^2}$, I varies inversely proportional to the square of R. So halving R will make I four times

as large. However, $\log 4x = \log 4 + \log x = 0.6 + \log x$. Therefore, the intensity level will not increase by a

factor of either 2 or 4. The answer is $\boxed{\text{none of the above}}$.

(b) $\beta = 10 \log 4x = 10 \log 4 + 10 \log x = 10(0.6) + 10 \log x = 6 \text{ dB} + 10 \log x$.

So it $\boxed{\text{increases by 6 dB}}$.

41.   (a) $\beta = 10 \log \dfrac{10{,}000\,I}{I_0} = 10 \log 10{,}000 + 10 \log \dfrac{I}{I_0} = 40 + 23 = \boxed{63\ \text{dB}}$.

   $(\log xy = \log x + \log y)$.

   (b) $\beta = 10 \log \dfrac{10^6\,I}{I_0} = 10 \log 10^6 + 10 \log \dfrac{I}{I_0} = 60 + 23 = \boxed{83\ \text{dB}}$.

   (c) $\beta = 10 \log \dfrac{10^9\,I}{I_0} = 10 \log 10^9 + 10 \log \dfrac{I}{I_0} = 90 + 23 = \boxed{113\ \text{dB}}$.

42. $\beta = 10 \log \dfrac{I_s}{I_n}$, ☞ $\dfrac{I_s}{I_n} = 10^{\beta/10} = 10^{5.3} = \boxed{2.0 \times 10^5\ \text{times larger}}$.

43.   (a) $\beta = 10 \log \dfrac{I}{I_0}$, ☞ $\dfrac{I}{I_0} = 10^{\beta/10}$, so $I = 10^{\beta/10}\,I_0$.

   $I_M = 10^9\,(10^{-12}\ \text{W/m}^2) = \boxed{10^{-3}\ \text{W/m}^2}$ and $I_L = 10^4\,(10^{-12}\ \text{W/m}^2) = \boxed{10^{-8}\ \text{W/m}^2}$.

   (b) $\dfrac{I_M}{I_L} = \dfrac{10^{-3}}{10^{-8}} = \boxed{10^5}$.

44.   (a) The intensity level is $\boxed{\text{between 40 dB and 80 dB}}$. First of all, the intensity level increases due to the increased intensity. However, doubling the intensity (two dogs) will not double the intensity level due to the logarithm scale. $\log 2x = \log 2 + \log x = 0.3 + \log x \neq 2(\log x)$.

   (b) $\beta_2 = 10 \log \dfrac{2I}{I_0} = 10 \log 2 \dfrac{I}{I_0} = 10 \left(\log 2 + \log \dfrac{I}{I_0}\right) = 10\,(0.3)\ \text{dB} + 40\ \text{dB} = \boxed{43\ \text{dB}}$.

   (because $\log xy = \log x + \log y$).

45.   Assume n bands. $\beta_n = 10 \log \dfrac{n\,I}{I_0} = 10 \log n + 10 \log \dfrac{I}{I_0} = 10 \log n + 110\ \text{dB}$.

   (because $\log xy = \log x + \log y$).

   So $10 \log n = 120\ \text{dB} - 110\ \text{dB} = 10\ \text{dB}$, ☞ $\log n = 1$, so $n = \boxed{10\ \text{bands}}$.

46. $\beta = 10 \log \dfrac{I}{I_0}$, ☞ $\Delta\beta = \beta_2 - \beta_1 = 10 \log \dfrac{I_2}{I_0} - 10 \log \dfrac{I_1}{I_0} = 10 \log \dfrac{I_2}{I_1}$

   (because $\log x - \log y = \log \dfrac{x}{y}$).

   So $\dfrac{I_2}{I_1} = 10^{\Delta\beta/10} = 10^{-3}$.

   Also $\dfrac{I_2}{I_1} = \dfrac{R_1{}^2}{R_2{}^2}$, ☞ $R_2 = \sqrt{\dfrac{I_1}{I_2}}\,R_1 = \sqrt{10^3}\,(10.0\ \text{m}) = \boxed{316\ \text{m}}$.

47. $\dfrac{I_B}{I_A} = \dfrac{R_A^2}{R_B^2} = \dfrac{(150 \text{ m})^2}{(200 \text{ m})^2} = 0.56.$ So $\boxed{I_B = 0.56 I_A}$;

$\dfrac{I_C}{I_A} = \dfrac{R_A^2}{R_C^2} = \dfrac{(150 \text{ m})^2}{(300 \text{ m})^2} = 0.25.$ So $\boxed{I_C = 0.25 I_A}$;

$\dfrac{I_D}{I_A} = \dfrac{R_A^2}{R_D^2} = \dfrac{(150 \text{ m})^2}{(200 \text{ m})^2 + (300 \text{ m})^2} = 0.17.$ So $\boxed{I_D = 0.17 I_A}$.

48. Just before reflection, $\beta_1 = 10 \log \dfrac{I_1}{I_o} = 10 \log \dfrac{2.5 \times 10^{-4} \text{ W/m}^2}{10^{-12} \text{ W/m}^2} = \boxed{84 \text{ dB}}$.

Just after reflection, $\beta_2 = 10 \log \dfrac{0.80(2.0 \times 10^{-4} \text{ W/m}^2)}{10^{-12} \text{ W/m}^2} = \boxed{83 \text{ dB}}$.

49. (a) $\beta = 10 \log \dfrac{I}{I_o}$, ☞ $I = 10^{\beta/10} I_o = 10^{9.5} (10^{-12} \text{ W/m}^2) = \boxed{3.2 \times 10^{-3} \text{ W/m}^2}$.

(b) From Exercise 14.46, $\dfrac{I_2}{I_1} = 10^{\Delta\beta/10} = 10^{1.2} = \boxed{16}$.

50. (a) From Exercise 14.46, $\dfrac{I_2}{I_1} = 10^{\Delta\beta/10} = 10^{-4.0} = 10^{-4}$.

Also $\dfrac{I_2}{I_1} = \dfrac{R_1^2}{R_2^2}$, ☞ $R_2 = \sqrt{\dfrac{I_1}{I_2}} \, R_1 = 10^2 (2.5 \text{ m}) = \boxed{2.5 \times 10^2 \text{ m}}$.

(b) The threshold of hearing is at 0 dB. $\dfrac{I_2}{I_1} = 10^{-10.0}$.

$R_2 = \sqrt{10^{10.0}} \, R_1 = 10^{5.0} (2.5 \text{ m}) = \boxed{2.5 \times 10^5 \text{ m}}$.

This number is a bit unrealistic because we ignored loss of sound during propogation.

51. For one bee, $I = I_o$. Assume it takes n bees.

$\beta = 10 \log \dfrac{nI}{I_o} = 10 \log n$, ☞ $n = 10^{\beta/10} = 10^{5.0} = \boxed{10^5 \text{ bees}}$.

52. (a).

53. (b).

54. $\boxed{\text{No}}$. The beat of music has to do with tempo. Beats are physical phenomena related to the frequency difference between two tones.

55.   (a) $\boxed{\text{No}}$, there is no relative velocity between the observer and the source.

(b) An $\boxed{\text{increasing sound frequency}}$ is observed since the source is moving toward the observer, and its speed increases.

56.   It must be $\boxed{\text{faster than the speed of sound in water, around 1500 m/s}}$.

57.   The varying sound intensity is caused by the interference effect. At certain locations there is constructive interference and at other locations, there is destructive interference.

58.   It uses $\boxed{\text{echolocation}}$ to measure the location and $\boxed{\text{Doppler effect}}$ to measure the motion of the clouds (direction and speed).

59.   It can be concluded that the star is $\boxed{\text{moving away from us}}$ due to the lower observed frequency. The velocity of the star can be determined by measuring the frequency difference between the true frequency of the star and the observed frequency, using the Doppler effect.

60.   (a) $\Delta L = 3.75 \text{ m} - 2.50 \text{ m} = 1.25 \text{ m} = 2.5 \,(0.50 \text{ m}) = 2.5\lambda$. So $\boxed{\text{destructive}}$.

(b) $\Delta L = 8.25 \text{ m} - 3.25 \text{ m} = 5.00 \text{ m} = 10(0.50 \text{ m}) = 10\lambda$. So $\boxed{\text{constructive}}$.

61.   At the first destructive point, $\Delta L = \tfrac{1}{2}\lambda = \tfrac{1}{2}\dfrac{v}{f} = \dfrac{343 \text{ m/s}}{2(1000 \text{ Hz})} = \boxed{0.172 \text{ m}}$.

62.   The beat frequency is $f_b = |f_2 - f_1| = 440 \text{ Hz} - 436 \text{ Hz} = \boxed{4 \text{ Hz}}$.

63.   (a) The answer is $\boxed{\text{both (1) and (3)}}$ because the beat frequency measures only the frequency difference between the two, and it does not specify which frequency is higher. So the frequency of the violin can be either higher or lower than that of the instrument.

(b) $f_2 = f_1 \pm f_b = 264 \text{ Hz} \pm 3 \text{ Hz} = \boxed{267 \text{ Hz or } 261 \text{ Hz}}$.

64.   The observer moves with a speed of 50 km/h = 13.9 m/s.

So $f_o = \dfrac{v + v_o}{v} f_s = \dfrac{331 \text{ m/s} + 13.9 \text{ m/s}}{331 \text{ m/s}} (800 \text{ Hz}) = \boxed{834 \text{ Hz}}$.

65. (a) Since the heard frequency is higher than the siren frequency, the person is moving $\boxed{\text{toward}}$ the siren.

(b) $f_o = \dfrac{v + v_o}{v} f_s$, ☞ $v_o = \dfrac{f_o - f_s}{f_s} v = \dfrac{520\ \text{Hz} - 500\ \text{Hz}}{500\ \text{Hz}} (343\ \text{m/s}) = \boxed{13.7\ \text{m/s}}$.

66. $v = (331 + 0.6 T_C)\ \text{m/s} = [331 + 0.6(25)]\ \text{m/s} = 346\ \text{m/s}$, $v_s = 90\ \text{km/h} = 25\ \text{m/s}$. Source is in motion.

(a) $f_o = \dfrac{v}{v - v_s} f_s = \dfrac{346\ \text{m/s}}{346\ \text{m/s} - 25\ \text{m/s}} (400\ \text{Hz}) = \boxed{431\ \text{Hz}}$.

(b) $f_o = \dfrac{v}{v + v_s} f_s = \dfrac{346\ \text{m/s}}{346\ \text{m/s} + 25\ \text{m/s}} (400\ \text{Hz}) = \boxed{373\ \text{Hz}}$.

67. $f = \dfrac{v}{\lambda} = \dfrac{\sqrt{\dfrac{F}{\mu}}}{\lambda}$, ☞ $\dfrac{f_2}{f_1} = \sqrt{\dfrac{F_2}{F_1}} = \sqrt{0.985} = 0.9925$.

So $f_2 = 0.9925 f_1$, or $f_b = |f_1 - f_2| = f_1 - f_2 = 0.0075 f_1 = (0.0075)(440\ \text{Hz}) = \boxed{3.3\ \text{Hz}}$.

68. The source is in motion. $f_o = \dfrac{v}{v - v_s} f_s$, ☞ $1.050 = \dfrac{v}{v - v_s}$.

So $v_s = \dfrac{0.050 v}{1.050} = \dfrac{0.050(340\ \text{m/s})}{1.050} = 16.2\ \text{m/s} = \boxed{58\ \text{km/h}}$.

69. $\sin\theta = \dfrac{v}{v_s}$, ☞ $\theta = \sin^{-1}\left(\dfrac{v}{v_s}\right) = \sin^{-1} 1 = \boxed{90°}$.

70. (a) Since $M = \dfrac{1}{\sin\theta}$, M is inversely proportional to $\sin\theta$. So the half angle $\boxed{\text{decreases}}$ as M increases.

(b) $M = \dfrac{1}{\sin\theta}$, ☞ $\theta = \sin^{-1}\left(\dfrac{1}{M}\right) = \sin^{-1}\left(\dfrac{1}{1.5}\right) = \sin^{-1} 0.667 = \boxed{42°}$.

71. (a) $M = \dfrac{1}{\sin\theta} = \dfrac{1}{\sin 35°} = \boxed{1.74}$.

(b) $M = \dfrac{v_s}{v}$, ☞ $v_s = Mv = 1.74\{[331 + 0.6(-20)]\ \text{m/s}\} = \boxed{555\ \text{m/s}}$.

72. The minimum separation for destructive interference corresponds to $\Delta L = \dfrac{\lambda}{2}$.

$\Delta L = d - 12\ \text{m} = \sqrt{x^2 + (12.0\ \text{m})^2} - 12.0\ \text{m}$

$= \dfrac{\lambda}{2} = \dfrac{v}{2f} = \dfrac{340\ \text{m/s}}{2(1000\ \text{Hz})} = 0.170\ \text{m}$.

So $x^2 + (12.0\ \text{m})^2 = (12.17\ \text{m})^2$, ☞ $x = \boxed{2.03\ \text{m}}$.

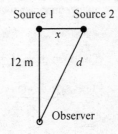

73.   When the source is approaching, $f_{oA} = \dfrac{v}{v - v_s} f_s$,   Eq. (1)

When the source is moving away, $f_{oM} = \dfrac{v}{v + v_s} f_s$ Eq. (2)

$\dfrac{\text{Eq. (2)}}{\text{Eq. (1)}}$ gives $\dfrac{f_{oM}}{f_{oA}} = \dfrac{v - v_s}{v + v_s}$, ☞ $f_{oM}(v + v_s) = f_{oA}(v - v_s)$.

So $v_s = \dfrac{(f_{oA} - f_{oM})v}{f_{oA} + f_{oM}} = \dfrac{(476 \text{ Hz} - 404 \text{ Hz})(343 \text{ m/s})}{476 \text{ Hz} + 404 \text{ Hz}} = \boxed{28 \text{ m/s}}$.

74.   (a) $v = (331 + 0.6 \times 20.0)$ m/s $= 343$ m/s. This is a case of the source moving.

$f_o = \dfrac{v}{v - v_s} f_s = \dfrac{343 \text{ m/s}}{343 \text{ m/s} - 12.0 \text{ m/s}} (35.0 \text{ kHz}) = \boxed{36.3 \text{ kHz}}$.

(b) Upon reflection, the insect acts as a source of sound with a frequency of 36.3 kHz, so this is a case of

the observer moving. $f_o = \dfrac{v + v_o}{v} f_s = \dfrac{343 \text{ m/s} + 12.0 \text{ m/s}}{343 \text{ m/s}} (36.3 \text{ kHz}) = \boxed{37.6 \text{ kHz}}$

(c) $\boxed{\text{Yes}}$ as can be seen in the calculations. The speed of the bat (12.0 m/s) is used in both calculations.

75.   (b).

76.   (a).

77.   (a) The snow absorbs sound so there is little reflection.

(b) In an empty room, there is less absorption. So the reflections die out more slowly; and therefore, the

sound sounds hollow and echoing.

(c) Sound is reflected by the shower walls, and standing waves are set up, giving rise to more harmonics and

therefore richer sound quality.

78. $f_1 = \dfrac{v}{2L}$, ☞ $L = \dfrac{v}{2f_1}$.   For two notes A and B, the spacing between the frets is

$\Delta L = f_{1B} - f_{1A} = \dfrac{v}{2f_{1B}} - \dfrac{v}{2f_{1A}} = \dfrac{v}{2f_{1A}f_{1B}} (f_{1A} - f_{1B}) = \dfrac{v}{2f_{1A}f_{1B}} \Delta f$.

So the spacing (change in length) depends not only on the frequency difference Δf, but also on the values of

the frequencies themselves. For different frequencies, ΔL is therefore different.

79.   For open pipe, $f_n = \dfrac{nv}{2L}$ for $n = 1, 2, 3, \ldots$.   For closed pipe, $f_m = \dfrac{mv}{4L}$ for $m = 1, 3, 5, \ldots$.

So $\dfrac{f_n}{f_m} = \dfrac{n/2}{m/4} = \dfrac{2n}{m}$.   For $f_n = f_m$, $2n = m$.

$\boxed{\text{No}}$, this is not possible because $2n$ is an even integer and m is an odd integer.

80.   As the level of water increases in the bottle, the length of the air column above the water decreases. This decrease in length of the air column decreases the wavelength and increases the frequency.

81.   For a pipe closed at one end, $\boxed{\text{the closed end must be a node}}$. So only odd harmonics are possible.

82.   (a) 378 Hz = 3(126 Hz) and 630 Hz = 5(126 Hz), so it is a $\boxed{\text{closed pipe}}$.

(b) $f_n = \dfrac{mv}{4L}$,   ☞ $L = \dfrac{v}{4f_1} = \dfrac{340 \text{ m/s}}{4(126 \text{ Hz})} = \boxed{0.675 \text{ m}}$; here we take $m = 1$.

83. $f = \dfrac{v}{\lambda}$,   ☞ $\dfrac{f_2}{f_1} = \dfrac{v_2}{v_1} = \dfrac{331 \text{ m/s}}{343 \text{ m/s}} = 0.965$.   So $f_2 = 0.965(528 \text{ Hz}) = \boxed{510 \text{ Hz}}$.

84.   (a) The ear can be considered as a closed pipe,

$f_1 = \dfrac{v}{4L} = f_n = \dfrac{343 \text{ m/s}}{4(0.025 \text{ m})} = \boxed{3.4 \text{ kHz}}$.

(b) The ear is also the most sensitive to this frequency, $\boxed{3.4 \text{ kHz}}$.

(c) The frequency is $\boxed{\text{lower}}$ because it is inversely proportional to the length.

85.   (a) Since $f_m = \dfrac{mv}{4L}$,   for $m = 1, 3, 5, \ldots, f_2 \boxed{\text{does not exist, only odd harmonics}}$.

(b) $f_3 = \dfrac{3v}{4L} = \dfrac{3(343 \text{ m/s})}{4(0.900 \text{ m})} = 285.8 \text{ Hz}$. The distance between a node and an anti-node is $\lambda/4$.

$\lambda = \dfrac{v}{f} = \dfrac{343 \text{ m/s}}{285.8 \text{ Hz}} = 1.20 \text{ m}$. So the distance is $(1.20 \text{ m})/4 = \boxed{0.30 \text{ m}}$.

86.   For the open pipe, $(f_1)_o = \dfrac{(1)v}{2L} = \dfrac{343 \text{ m/s}}{2(0.52 \text{ m})} = \boxed{330 \text{ Hz}}$.

For the closed pipe, $(f_1)_c = \dfrac{(1)v}{4L} = \dfrac{(f_1)_o}{2} = \boxed{165 \text{ Hz}}$.

87.   (a) The position at the mouthpiece is an $\boxed{\text{antinode}}$ because it has the maximum vibration.

(b) $f_n = \dfrac{mv}{2L}$,   ☞ $L = \dfrac{mv}{2f_n} = \dfrac{(1)(343 \text{ m/s})}{2(262 \text{ Hz})} = \boxed{0.655 \text{ m}}$.

(c) $L = \dfrac{(1)(343 \text{ m/s})}{2(440 \text{ Hz})} = \boxed{0.390 \text{ m}}$.

88. The distance between node–antinode is $\lambda/4$, and the distance between node–node is $\lambda/2$.

So for the mth ($m = 1, 3, 5, \ldots$) resonant position, $L_m = \dfrac{m\lambda}{4} = \dfrac{mv/f}{4} = \dfrac{mv}{4f}$.

So $\quad L_1 = \dfrac{(1)(342 \text{ m/s})}{4(440 \text{ Hz})} = \boxed{0.194 \text{ m}}, \quad L_3 = 3L_1 = \boxed{0.583 \text{ m}}, \quad$ and $\quad L_5 = 5L_1 = \boxed{0.972 \text{ m}}, \ldots$

89. $f_1 = \dfrac{(1)\,v}{4L}, \quad \mathscr{F} \quad \dfrac{(f_1)_{\text{He}}}{(f_1)_{\text{air}}} = \dfrac{v_{\text{He}}}{v_{\text{air}}} = \dfrac{965 \text{ m/s}}{331 \text{ m/s}} = 2.915. \quad (f_1)_{\text{He}} = 2.915(660 \text{ Hz}) = \boxed{1.92 \times 10^3 \text{ Hz}}$.

90. $\lambda = \dfrac{v}{f} = \dfrac{[331 + 0.6(15)] \text{ m/s}}{440 \text{ Hz}} = 0.773 \text{ m}. \quad \Delta L = 8.90 \text{ m} - 6.97 \text{ m} = 1.93 \text{ m} = 2.5\,(0.773) = 2.5\lambda.$

So they will interfere $\boxed{\text{destructively}}$.

91. $\dfrac{I_2}{I_1} = \dfrac{R_1^{\,2}}{R_2^{\,2}} = \dfrac{(30.0 \text{ m})^2}{(25.0 \text{ m})^2} = 1.44. \quad$ So $\boxed{I_2 = 1.44 I_1}$.

92. $\boxed{\text{No}}$, the manager does achieve his goal. Removing 25 computers will cut the intensity in half, but won't cut the intensity level in half.

With $\beta = 10 \log \dfrac{I}{I_0}$, $\beta_{1/2} = \beta_1 - 10(\log 2)$ because $\log x = \log 2 + \log x/2$.

So $\beta_2 = 40 \text{ dB} - 10(\log 2) \text{ dB} = 40\text{dB} - 10(0.3) \text{ dB} = \boxed{37 \text{ dB}}$.

93. $f_0 = \dfrac{v + v_0}{v} f_s, \quad \mathscr{F} \quad v_0 = \dfrac{f_0 - f_s}{f_s}\, v = \dfrac{2f_s - f_s}{f_s} = v,$ which is at the $\boxed{\text{speed of sound}}$.

94. $\beta = 10 \log \dfrac{I}{I_0}, \quad \mathscr{F} \quad \dfrac{I}{I_0} = 10^{\beta/10}. \quad$ So $\dfrac{I_1}{I_0} = 10^{6.00} \quad$ and $\quad \dfrac{I_2}{I_0} = 10^{6.50}$.

Therefore, the intensity level heard by another person is

$\beta_{\text{tot}} = 10 \log \dfrac{I_1 + I_2}{I_0} = 10 \log (10^{6.00} + 10^{6.50}) = \boxed{66.2 \text{ dB}}$.

95. $\beta = 10 \log \dfrac{I}{I_0}, \quad \mathscr{F} \quad \dfrac{I}{I_0} = 10^{\beta/10}. \quad$ So $\quad I = 10^{9.0}\,(10^{-12} \text{ W/m}^2) = 10^{-3} \text{ W/m}^2$.

In 5.0 s, the energy is $E = IAt = (10^{-3} \text{ W/m}^2)[\pi(0.005 \text{ m})^2](5.0 \text{ s}) = \boxed{3.9 \times 10^{-7} \text{ J}}$.

96. $M = \dfrac{1}{\sin\theta}, \quad \mathscr{F} \quad \theta = \sin^{-1}\left(\dfrac{1}{M}\right) = \sin^{-1}\left(\dfrac{1}{2.0}\right) = \sin^{-1} 0.50 = \boxed{30°}$.

$\boxed{\text{Yes}}$, you can tell its speed if you know the air temperature or the speed of sound.

97.   The period (time for one vibration) is $T = \dfrac{1}{f} = \dfrac{1}{440 \text{ Hz}} = 2.273 \times 10^{-3}$ s.

The time taken for sound to travel 30 m is $t = \dfrac{d}{v} = \dfrac{30 \text{ m}}{343 \text{ m/s}} = 0.08746$ s.

So the number of vibrations is $n = \dfrac{t}{T} = \dfrac{0.08746 \text{ s}}{2.273 \times 10^{-3} \text{ s}} = \boxed{38 \text{ vibrations}}$.

98. $v_s = (331 + 0.6T_C)$ m/s $= [331 + 0.6(10)]$ m/s $= 337$ m/s. Assume the depth is d. The stone first free falls to the bottom and then the sound travels up to the person. The time taken for the free fall is

$\sqrt{\dfrac{2d}{g}}$ $(y = d = \tfrac{1}{2}gt^2)$.   So $3.16 \text{ s} = \sqrt{\dfrac{2d}{g}} + \dfrac{d}{v_s} = \sqrt{\dfrac{2d}{9.80 \text{ m/s}^2}} + \dfrac{d}{337 \text{ m/s}}$.

Reducing to a quadratic equation: $d^2 - 2.531 \times 10^4 d + 1.134 \times 10^6 = 0$.   Solving, $d = \boxed{45 \text{ m}}$.

99.   90.0 km/h = 25 m/s.   Approaching: $f_o = \dfrac{v}{v - v_s} f_s = \dfrac{343 \text{ m/s}}{343 \text{ m/s} - 25 \text{ m/s}} (700 \text{ Hz}) = \boxed{755 \text{ Hz}}$.

Moving away: $f_o = \dfrac{v}{v + v_s} f_s = \dfrac{343 \text{ m/s}}{343 \text{ m/s} + 25 \text{ m/s}} (700 \text{ Hz}) = \boxed{652 \text{ Hz}}$.

100.   Neglect the time taken by the light since light travels at a much faster speed.

$t = \dfrac{d}{v} = \dfrac{d}{(331 + 0.6T_C) \text{ m/s}} = \dfrac{300 \text{ m}}{[331 + 0.6(5)] \text{ m/s}} = \boxed{0.90 \text{ s}}$.

101.   For the open pipe, $(f_1)_o = \dfrac{(1)v}{2L_o}$.   For the closed pipe, $(f_3)_c = \dfrac{(3)v}{4L_c}$.

If $(f_1)_o = (f_3)_c$, $L_c = \tfrac{3}{2}L_o = \tfrac{3}{2}(0.75 \text{ m}) = \boxed{1.1 \text{ m}}$.

102.   (a) If the observer were stationary, the frequency heard by the observer would have been

$(f_o)_1 = \dfrac{v}{v \mp v_s} f_s$, which would be the frequency of the "source" to the moving observer.

$(f_s)_2 = (f_o)_1$.   So $(f_o)_2 = f_o = \dfrac{v \pm v_o}{v} (f_s)_2 = \dfrac{v \pm v_o}{v} \dfrac{v}{v \mp v_s} f_s = \dfrac{v \pm v_o}{v \mp v_s} f_s$.

103.   (a) $v_s = 90$ km/h $= -25$ m/s and $v_o = 65$ km/h $= 18.1$ m/s. Both the source and the observer are moving toward each other. From Exercise 14.102 and according to the sign conventions:

$f_o = \dfrac{v + v_o}{v - v_s} f_s = \dfrac{354 \text{ m/s} + 18.1 \text{ m/s}}{354 \text{ m/s} - 25 \text{ m/s}} (500 \text{ Hz}) = \boxed{566 \text{ Hz}}$.

(b) Both the source and the observer are moving away from each other.

So $f_o = \dfrac{354 \text{ m/s} - 18.1 \text{ m/s}}{354 \text{ m/s} + 25 \text{ m/s}} (500 \text{ Hz}) = \boxed{443 \text{ Hz}}$.

CHAPTER 15

ELECTRIC CHARGE, FORCE, AND FIELD

1.   (c).

2.   (b).

3.   (a) We know there are two types of charges because attractive and repulsive forces can be produced by
       different combinations of just two types of charges.
       (b) There would be no effect as it is simply a sign convention.

4. $\boxed{\text{No}}$. Charges are simply moved from the object to another object, which will have opposite charge.

5.   If an object is positively charged, its mass $\boxed{\text{decreases}}$ because it loses electrons. If an object is negatively

       charged, its mass $\boxed{\text{increases}}$ because it gains electrons.

6.   We can $\boxed{\text{use a known charge}}$. For example, if a known positive charge experiences a repulsive force, then

       the type of charge on an object is also positive and vice versa.

7. $\boxed{\text{Yes}}$, both objects are charged with the same type of charge if they repel each other.

       However, if two objects attract each other, both are $\boxed{\text{not necessarily}}$ charged. For example, through

       polarization and polarization by induction, a charged object can attract a neutral object, but the neutral

       object has a nonuniform charge distribution.

8. $q = -ne = -(10^6)(1.60 \times 10^{-19}\text{ C}) = \boxed{-1.60 \times 10^{-13}\text{ C}}$.

9. $q = -ne,$ ☞ $n = -\dfrac{q}{e} = -\dfrac{-50 \times 10^{-6}\text{ C}}{1.60 \times 10^{-19}\text{ C}} = \boxed{3.1 \times 10^{14}\text{ electrons}}$.

10.   (a) The charge on the silk must be $\boxed{\text{negative}}$ because of the conservation of charge. When one object

       becomes positively charged, it loses electrons. These same electrons must be gained by another object, and

       therefore it is negatively charged.

       (b) $\boxed{-8.0 \times 10^{-10}\text{ C}}$ according to charge conservation.

       $q = -ne,$ ☞ $n = -\dfrac{q}{e} = \dfrac{-8.0 \times 10^{-10}\text{ C}}{1.6 \times 10^{-19}\text{ C}} = \boxed{5.0 \times 10^9\text{ electrons}}$.

11.   (a) The charge on the fur must be $\boxed{\text{positive}}$ because of the conservation of charge. When one object

becomes negatively charged, it gains electrons. These same electrons must be lost by another object, and

therefore it is positively charged.

(b) $\boxed{+4.8 \times 10^{-9}\ \text{C}}$ according to charge conservation.

$$q = +ne, \qquad \text{☞} \qquad n = \frac{q}{e} = \frac{4.8 \times 10^{-9}\ \text{C}}{1.6 \times 10^{-19}\ \text{C}} = 3.0 \times 10^{10}\ \text{electrons}.$$

So the mass is $(3.0 \times 10^{10})(9.11 \times 10^{-31}\ \text{kg}) = \boxed{2.7 \times 10^{-20}\ \text{kg}}$.

12.   There are two protons in each α particle.

So the charge is $q = +ne = (2)(2)(1.60 \times 10^{-19}\ \text{C}) = \boxed{+6.40 \times 10^{-19}\ \text{C}}$.

13.   When the positively charged fur is brought near an electroscope, the leaves are charged by polarization. So

the charges on the leaves are $\boxed{\text{positive}}$.

14.   The $\boxed{\text{water is polarized}}$. The water molecules reorient in such a direction that the end nearer the charged

object carries an opposite charge to that on the charged object, and the end far from the charged object

carries the same charge as the charged object. The attractive force between water and the object is greater

than the repulsive force because the distance for the attractive force is smaller, resulting in a net attractive

force.

15. $\boxed{\text{No, the wall is neutral but polarized}}$. That is why there is a *net* attractive force between the balloon and

the wall.

16.   This is $\boxed{\text{to remove excess charge due to friction of rubber on road}}$. If the charges are not removed, they

could result in sparks if enough of them accumulate.

17. $\boxed{\text{No, charges simply reorient}}$. There is no gain or loss of electrons.

18.   If you bring a $\boxed{\text{negatively charged object}}$ near the electroscope, the induction process will charge the

electroscope with positive charges. You can prove the charges are positive by bringing the negatively

charged object near the leaves and seeing if the leaves fall.

19.   The spheres can be charged through polarization by $\boxed{\text{induction}}$. For example, if you bring a positively charged object near one of the two spheres, the sphere near the charged object will have a net negative charge and the other sphere will have a net positive charge (polarization by induction). Then you separate the two spheres (while keeping the positively charged object nearby) and the spheres will have $\boxed{\text{opposite charges}}$ according to charge conservation.

20.   (c).

21.   (d).

22.   Although the electric force is fundamentally much stronger than the gravitational force, both the Earth, our bodies, and other $\boxed{\text{objects are electrically neutral}}$ so there are no noticeable electric forces.

23. $\boxed{\text{Both the Sun and the planets are electrically neutral}}$.

24. $\boxed{\text{Yes}}$, the third charge will also exert forces on the other two charges, so the net force on the other two charges will be affected.

25.   That tells us that the $\boxed{\text{force depends on the inverse square of the distance between the charges}}$.

26.   (a) Since $F_e = \dfrac{kq_1q_2}{r^2}$, F is inversely proportional to the square of the distance, r. If r doubles, F_e becomes $\boxed{1/4}$ times the original force.

(b) $\dfrac{F_e}{F_{eo}} = \dfrac{r_o^{\,2}}{r^2} = \dfrac{1^2}{(1/3)^2} = 9.$ So $F_e = \boxed{9F}$.

27.   (a) Since $F_e = \dfrac{kq_1q_2}{r^2} \propto q_1q_2$, F_e is $2 \times \frac{1}{2} = \boxed{1}$, i.e., the same.

(b) $F_e = \frac{1}{2} \times \frac{1}{2} = \boxed{1/4}$.

(c) $F_e = \frac{1}{2} \times 1 = \boxed{1/2}$.

28. $F_e = \dfrac{kq_1q_2}{r^2} = \dfrac{k(6e)(6e)}{r^2} = \dfrac{(9.0 \times 10^9 \text{ N·m}^2/\text{C}^2)(6)^2(1.6 \times 10^{-19} \text{ C})^2}{(0.25 \times 10^{-9} \text{ m})^2} = \boxed{1.3 \times 10^{-7} \text{ N}}$.

29. (a) $F_e = \dfrac{kq_1q_2}{r^2} = \dfrac{(9.0 \times 10^9 \ \text{N·m}^2/\text{C}^2)(1.6 \times 10^{-19} \ \text{C})^2}{(2.0 \times 10^{-9} \ \text{m})^2} = \boxed{5.8 \times 10^{-11} \ \text{N}}$.

(b) $\boxed{\text{Zero}}$, because they are internal forces of the system.

30. (a) Since $F_e = \dfrac{kq_1q_2}{r^2}$, r is proportional to $1/\sqrt{F_e}$. If F_e decreases by a factor of 10, r will increase but not

by a factor of 10. So the answer is $\boxed{\text{less than 10}}$ times the original distance.

(b) $F_e = \dfrac{kq_1q_2}{r^2}$, ☞ $\dfrac{F_2}{F_1} = \dfrac{r_1^{\ 2}}{r_2^{\ 2}}$, so $r_2 = \sqrt{\dfrac{F_1}{F_2}} \ r_1 = \sqrt{10} \ (30 \ \text{cm}) = \boxed{95 \ \text{cm}}$.

31. $F_e = \dfrac{kq_1q_2}{r^2}$, ☞ $\dfrac{F_2}{F_1} = \dfrac{r_1^{\ 2}}{r_2^{\ 2}}$, so $r_1 = \sqrt{\dfrac{F_2}{F_1}} \ r_2 = \sqrt{5} \ (100 \ \text{cm}) = \boxed{2.24 \ \text{m}}$.

32. $F_e = \dfrac{kq_1q_2}{r^2} = \dfrac{(9.00 \times 10^9 \ \text{N·m}^2/\text{C}^2)(1.6 \times 10^{-19} \ \text{C})^2}{(2.82 \times 10^{-10} \ \text{m})^2} = \boxed{2.9 \times 10^{-9} \ \text{N}}$.

33. (a) By symmetry, the electron has to be at the $\boxed{50\text{-cm}}$ mark since both forces are repulsive and opposite.

(b) By symmetry, the proton has to be at the $\boxed{50\text{-cm}}$ mark since both forces are attractive and opposite.

34. (a) $\boxed{\text{Nowhere}}$, since both forces are in the same direction.

(b) $\boxed{\text{Nowhere}}$, since both forces are in the same direction.

35. (a) If q_1 and q_2 are like charges, the third charge must be placed between q_1 and q_2 for it to be in

electrostatic equilibrium. Also, q_1 and q_2 have the same magnitude; it must be at $\boxed{0.25 \ \text{m}}$ from symmetry.

(b) If q_1 and q_2 are unlike charges, the third charge could be

placed outside q_1 and q_3 ($x < 0$ and $x > 0.50$ m). However, since

the magnitudes of q_1 and q_2 are equal, there will be $\boxed{\text{nowhere}}$

for it to happen according to Coulomb's law.

(c) Since $q_1 = +3.0 \ \mu C$ and $q_2 = -7.0 \ \mu C$, a third charge of either type can be placed outside q_1 ($x < 0$) for it to be in electrostatic equilibrium. It cannot be placed to the right of q_2 ($x > 0.50$ m) since the force by q_2 will always be larger due to the closer distance from it. Assume q_3 is placed at d from q_1 (or $x = -d$).

From Coulomb's law, we have $\dfrac{kq_1q_3}{r_{13}^2} = \dfrac{k|q_2|q_3}{r_{23}^2}, \quad \text{☞} \quad \dfrac{q_1}{d^2} = \dfrac{|q_2|}{(d + 0.50 \text{ m})^2}.$

Taking the square root on both sides gives $\dfrac{\sqrt{3.0}}{d} = \dfrac{\sqrt{7.0}}{d + 0.50}, \quad$ so $\quad 1.73(d + 0.50) = 2.65d.$

Solving, $\quad d = 0.94$ m. Thus $\quad \boxed{x = -0.94 \text{ m for } \pm q_3}$.

36.   (a) $F_e = \dfrac{kq_1q_2}{r^2} = \dfrac{(9.0 \times 10^9 \text{ N·m}^2/\text{C}^2)(1.6 \times 10^{-19} \text{ C})^2}{(5.3 \times 10^{-11} \text{ m})^2} = \boxed{8.2 \times 10^{-8} \text{ N}}.$

(b) The electric force provides the required centripetal force. $\quad F_e = F_c = m\dfrac{v^2}{r},$

so $\quad v = \sqrt{\dfrac{F_c r}{m}} = \sqrt{\dfrac{(8.2 \times 10^{-8} \text{ N})(5.3 \times 10^{-11} \text{ m})}{9.11 \times 10^{-31} \text{ kg}}} = \boxed{2.2 \times 10^6 \text{ m/s}}.$

(c) $a_c = \dfrac{v^2}{r} = \dfrac{F}{m} = \dfrac{8.2 \times 10^{-8} \text{ N}}{9.11 \times 10^{-31} \text{ kg}} = 9.0 \times 10^{22} \text{ m/s}^2 = \boxed{9.2 \times 10^{21} \text{ g}}$, where $g = 9.80 \text{ m/s}^2$.

37.   From Exercise 36(a), $F_e = 8.2 \times 10^{-8}$ N.

$F_g = \dfrac{Fm_1m_2}{r^2} = \dfrac{(6.67 \times 10^{-11} \text{ N·m}^2/\text{kg}^2)(9.11 \times 10^{-31} \text{ kg})(1.67 \times 10^{-27} \text{ kg})}{(5.3 \times 10^{-11} \text{ m})^2} = \boxed{3.6 \times 10^{-47} \text{ N}}.$

So $\quad \dfrac{F_e}{F_g} = \dfrac{8.2 \times 10^{-8} \text{ N}}{3.6 \times 10^{-47} \text{ N}} = \boxed{2.3 \times 10^{39}}.$

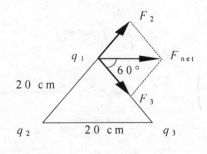

38. $F_2 = F_3 = \dfrac{kq_1q_2}{r^2} = \dfrac{(9.0 \times 10^9 \text{ N·m}^2/\text{C}^2)(4.0 \times 10^{-6} \text{ C})^2}{(0.20 \text{ m})^2} = 3.6$ N.

According to symmetry, the net force on q_1 points in the $+x$ direction.

$F_{net} = F_x = F_2 \cos 60° + F_3 \cos 60°$

$= 2(3.6 \text{ N}) \cos 60° = \boxed{3.6 \text{ N in the } +x \text{ direction}}.$

39.   (a) From Coulomb's law: $F_1 = \dfrac{kq_1q_2}{r^2} = \dfrac{(9.0 \times 10^9 \text{ N·m}^2/\text{C}^2)(10 \times 10^{-6} \text{ C})(10 \times 10^{-6} \text{ C})}{(0.10 \text{ m})^2} = 90$ N.

So $\quad \mathbf{F}_1 = (90 \text{ N}) \ \hat{\mathbf{x}}.$

$F_3 = \dfrac{(9.0 \times 10^9 \text{ N·m}^2/\text{C}^2)(5.0 \times 10^{-6} \text{ C})(10 \times 10^{-6} \text{ C})}{(0.10 \text{ m})^2} = 45$ N.

So $\quad \mathbf{F}_3 = (-45 \text{ N}) \ \hat{\mathbf{y}}.$

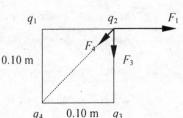

$$F_4 = \frac{(9.0 \times 10^9 \text{ N·m}^2/\text{C}^2)(5.0 \times 10^{-6} \text{ C})(10 \times 10^{-6} \text{ C})}{(0.10 \text{ m})^2 + (0.10 \text{ m})^2} = 22.5 \text{ N}.$$

So $\quad \mathbf{F}_4 = -F_4 (\cos 45°) \, \hat{\mathbf{x}} + (\sin 45°) \, \hat{\mathbf{y}} = (-15.9 \text{ N}) \, (\hat{\mathbf{x}} + \hat{\mathbf{y}}).$

Therefore the net force is $\mathbf{F}_2 = \mathbf{F}_1 + \mathbf{F}_3 + \mathbf{F}_4 = (74.1 \text{ N}) \, \mathbf{x} + (-60.9 \text{ N}) \, \hat{\mathbf{y}}.$

Thus $\quad F_2 = \sqrt{(74.1 \text{ N})^2 + (60.9 \text{ N})^2} = \boxed{96 \text{ N}}, \quad \theta = \tan^{-1}\left(\frac{60.9}{74.1}\right) = \boxed{39° \text{ below the } +x \text{ axis}}.$

(b) $F_1 = \frac{(9.0 \times 10^9 \text{ N·m}^2/\text{C}^2)(10 \times 10^{-6} \text{ C})(5.0 \times 10^{-6} \text{ C})}{(0.10 \text{ m})^2} = 45 \text{ N}.$

So $\quad \mathbf{F}_1 = (45 \text{ N}) \, \hat{\mathbf{y}}.$

$$F_2 = \frac{(9.0 \times 10^9 \text{ N·m}^2/\text{C}^2)(10 \times 10^{-6} \text{ C})(5.0 \times 10^{-6} \text{ C})}{(0.10 \text{ m})^2 + (0.10 \text{ m})^2} = 22.5 \text{ N}.$$

So $\quad \mathbf{F}_2 = F_2 (\cos 45°) \, \hat{\mathbf{x}} + (\sin 45°) \, \hat{\mathbf{y}} = (15.9 \text{ N}) \, (\hat{\mathbf{x}} + \hat{\mathbf{y}}).$

$$F_3 = \frac{(9.0 \times 10^9 \text{ N·m}^2/\text{C}^2)(5.0 \times 10^{-6} \text{ C})(5.0 \times 10^{-6} \text{ C})}{(0.10 \text{ m})^2} = 22.5 \text{ N}. \quad \text{So} \quad \mathbf{F}_3 = (-22.5 \text{ N}) \, \hat{\mathbf{x}}.$$

Therefore the net force is $\mathbf{F}_4 = \mathbf{F}_1 + \mathbf{F}_2 + \mathbf{F}_3 = (-6.6 \text{ N}) \, \hat{\mathbf{x}} + (60.9 \text{ N}) \, \hat{\mathbf{y}}.$

Thus $\quad F_2 = \sqrt{(6.6 \text{ N})^2 + (60.9 \text{ N})^2} = \boxed{61 \text{ N}}, \quad \theta = \tan^{-1}\left(\frac{60.9}{6.6}\right) = \boxed{84° \text{ above the } -x \text{ axis}}.$

40. $\quad F_e = \frac{k q_1 q_2}{r^2} = \frac{k q^2}{r^2}. \quad \sin \theta = \frac{9.0 \text{ cm}}{30 \text{ cm}}, \quad \text{☞} \quad \theta = 17.5°.$

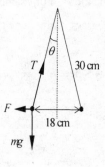

In the vertical direction, $\quad T \cos\theta = mg, \quad \text{☞} \quad T = \frac{mg}{\cos\theta}.$

In the horizontal direction, $\quad F = T \sin\theta = \frac{mg}{\cos\theta} \sin\theta = mg \tan\theta.$

Therefore $\quad \frac{k q^2}{r^2} = mg \tan\theta, \quad \text{☞} \quad q = \sqrt{\frac{mg \tan\theta}{k}} \, r.$

Thus $\quad q = \sqrt{\frac{(0.10 \times 10^{-3} \text{ kg})(9.80 \text{ m/s}^2) \tan 17.5°}{9.0 \times 10^9 \text{ N·m}^2/\text{C}^2}} \, (0.18 \text{ m}) = \boxed{3.3 \times 10^{-8} \text{ C}}.$

41. (c).

42. (b).

43. (b), because the electron has negative charge.

44. It is determined $\boxed{\text{from the relative lengths of the electric field vectors}}$ (the lengths of the arrows).

45. It is determined by the relative density or spacing of the field lines . The closer the lines, the greater the magnitude.

46. No . Electric field is defined as the ratio of force to charge at a given point in space. The force on a charge can only point in one direction, and so does the electric field. Therefore, the field lines never cross, since that would indicate two different directions at the crossing point.

47. If a positive charge is at center of the spherical shell, the electric field is *not* zero inside. The field lines run radially outward to the inside surface of the shell where they stop at the induced negative charges on this surface. The field lines reappear on the outside shell surface (positively charged) and continue radially outward as if emanating from the point charge at the center. If the charge were negative, the field lines would reverse their directions.

48. The Earth carries negative as the electric fields terminate at negative charges.

49. Yes , this is possible, for example, when the electric fields created by the two charges are equal in magnitude and opposite in direction at some locations. For example, midway in between and along a line joining two charges of the same type and magnitude, the electric field is zero.

50. (a) Since $E = \dfrac{kq}{r^2}$, E is inversely proportional to the square of the distance.

So if r doubles, E becomes 1/4 as large .

(b) $\dfrac{E}{E_o} = \dfrac{r_o^2}{r^2} = \dfrac{1^2}{(1/3)^2} = 9$.

Therefore $E = 9E_o = 9(1.0 \times 10^{-4} \text{ N/C}) = \boxed{9.0 \times 10^{-4} \text{ N/C}}$.

51. $E = \dfrac{F}{q} = \dfrac{3.2 \times 10^{-14} \text{ N}}{1.6 \times 10^{-19} \text{ C}} = \boxed{2.0 \times 10^5 \text{ N/C}}$.

52. $E = \dfrac{kq}{r^2} = \dfrac{(9.0 \times 10^9 \text{ N·m}^2/\text{C}^2)(2.0 \times 10^{-6} \text{ C})}{(0.25 \times 10^{-2} \text{ m})^2} = \boxed{2.9 \times 10^9 \text{ N/C}}$.

53. $E = \dfrac{kq}{r^2}$, ☞ $r = \sqrt{\dfrac{kq}{E}} = \sqrt{\dfrac{(9.00 \times 10^9 \text{ N·m}^2/\text{C}^2)(1.67 \times 10^{-27} \text{ kg })}{1.0 \times 10^5 \text{ N/C}}} = \boxed{1.2 \times 10^{-7} \text{ m}}$.

54. (a) The net field is directed $\boxed{\text{toward the } -5.0\text{-}\mu C \text{ charge}}$. The electric fields by the two charges are

opposite in direction but the one by the -5.0-μC charge has a greater magnitude.

(b) $E_{4.0} = \dfrac{kq}{r^2} = \dfrac{(9.0 \times 10^9 \text{ N·m}^2/\text{C}^2)(4.0 \times 10^{-6} \text{ C})}{(0.10 \text{ m})^2} = 3.6 \times 10^6$ N/C,

$E_{5.0} = \dfrac{(9.0 \times 10^9 \text{ N·m}^2/\text{C}^2)(5.0 \times 10^{-6} \text{ C})}{(0.10 \text{ m})^2} = 4.5 \times 10^6$ N/C.

So the net field is $E = E_{5.0} - E_{4.0} = \boxed{9.0 \times 10^5 \text{ N/C}}$.

55. Proton: $E = \dfrac{F}{q} = \dfrac{mg}{q} = \dfrac{(1.67 \times 10^{-27} \text{ kg })(9.80 \text{ m/s}^2)}{1.6 \times 10^{-19} \text{ C}} = \boxed{1.0 \times 10^{-7} \text{ N/C upward}}$.

Electron: $E = \dfrac{(9.11 \times 10^{-31} \text{ kg })(9.80 \text{ m/s}^2)}{1.6 \times 10^{-19} \text{ C}} = \boxed{5.6 \times 10^{-11} \text{ N/C downward}}$.

56. (a) Since both charges are negative, a point between the

two charges could have zero electric field. The location is

$\boxed{\text{nearer the } -3.0\text{-}\mu C \text{ charge}}$ because it has the smaller

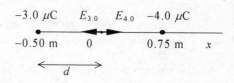

magnitude. The distance from it has to be smaller to

match the field by the bigger charge.

(b) Assume the point is d from the -3.0-μC charge. For the electric field to be zero, $E_{3.0} = E_{4.0}$.

So $E_{3.0} = \dfrac{kq}{r^2} = \dfrac{k(3.0 \ \mu C)}{d^2} = E_{4.0} = \dfrac{k(4.0 \ \mu C)}{(1.25 - d)^2}$.

Taking the square root on both sides gives $\dfrac{\sqrt{3.0}}{d} = \dfrac{\sqrt{4.0}}{1.25 - d}$. Or $1.73(1.25 - d) = 2.0d$.

Solving for $d = 0.580$ m. Therefore the coordinates of the point are $\boxed{(0.080 \text{ m, } 0)}$.

57. $r = \sqrt{x^2 + y^2}$, and $\theta = \tan^{-1}\left(\dfrac{y}{x}\right)$.

The electric field by the +2.5-μC charge is

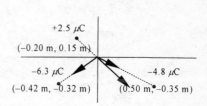

$E_{2.5} = \dfrac{kq}{r^2} = \dfrac{(9.0 \times 10^9 \text{ N·m}^2/\text{C}^2)(2.5 \times 10^{-6} \text{ C})}{(0.20 \text{ m})^2 + (0.15 \text{ m})^2} = 3.6 \times 10^5$ N/C,

$\theta_{2.5} = 36.9°$,

so $\mathbf{E}_{2.5} = (3.6 \times 10^5 \text{ N/C})[(\cos 36.9°) \ \hat{\mathbf{x}} - (\sin 36.9°) \ \hat{\mathbf{y}}] = (2.88 \times 10^5 \text{ N/C}) \ \hat{\mathbf{x}} + (-2.16 \times 10^5 \text{ N/C}) \ \hat{\mathbf{y}}$;

the electric field by the -4.8-μC charge is

$E_{4.8} = \dfrac{(9.0 \times 10^9 \text{ N·m}^2/\text{C}^2)(4.8 \times 10^{-6} \text{ C})}{(0.50 \text{ m})^2 + (0.35 \text{ m})^2} = 1.16 \times 10^5$ N/C, $\theta_{4.8} = 35.0°$, so $\mathbf{E}_{4.8} = (1.16 \times 10^5 \text{ N/C})[(\cos 35.0°)\,\hat{\mathbf{x}} - (\sin 35.0°)\,\hat{\mathbf{y}}] = (9.50 \times 10^4 \text{ N/C})\,\hat{\mathbf{x}} + (-6.65 \times 10^4 \text{ N/C})\,\hat{\mathbf{y}}$;

the electric field by the -6.3-μC charge is

$$E_{6.3} = \text{c}\frac{(9.0 \times 10^9 \text{ N·m}^2/\text{C}^2)(6.3 \times 10^{-6} \text{ C})}{(0.42 \text{ m})^2 + (0.32 \text{ m})^2} = 2.03 \times 10^5 \text{ N/C}, \quad \theta_{6.3} = 37.3°,$$

so $\mathbf{E}_{6.3} = [(2.03 \times 10^5 \text{ N/C})(-\cos 37.3°)\,\hat{\mathbf{x}} - (\sin 37.3°)\,\hat{\mathbf{y}}] = -[(1.61 \times 10^5 \text{ N/C})\,\hat{\mathbf{x}} + (1.23 \times 10^5 \text{ N/C})\,\hat{\mathbf{y}}]$.

Therefore the net electric field is $\mathbf{E} = \mathbf{E}_{2.5} + \mathbf{E}_{4.8} + \mathbf{E}_{6.3} = \boxed{(2.2 \times 10^5 \text{ N/C})\,\hat{\mathbf{x}} + (-4.1 \times 10^5 \text{ N/C})\,\hat{\mathbf{y}}}$.

Or $\quad E = \sqrt{(2.22 \times 10^5 \text{ N/C})^2 + (4.06 \times 10^5 \text{ N/C})^2} = \boxed{4.6 \times 10^5 \text{ N/C}}$,

$$\theta = \tan^{-1}\left(\frac{4.06}{2.22}\right) = \boxed{61° \text{ below } +x \text{ axis}}.$$

58.   The point has to be between the two charges. Assume it is d from the $+4.0$ μC charge.

For the electric field to be zero, $\quad \dfrac{kq_1}{r_1^2} = \dfrac{kq_2}{r_2^2}, \quad \Longrightarrow \quad \dfrac{4.0 \ \mu\text{C}}{d^2} = \dfrac{9.0 \ \mu\text{C}}{(0.30 \text{ m} - d)^2}$.

Taking the square root on both sides gives $\quad \dfrac{2}{d} = \dfrac{3}{0.30 - d}$.

Therefore $\quad 3d = 2(0.30 - d)$.

Solving, $\quad d = 0.12 \text{ m} = \boxed{12 \text{ cm from the } 4.0 \ \mu\text{C charge (between the charges)}}$.

59. $r = \dfrac{0.10 \text{ m}}{\cos 30°} = 0.115 \text{ m}$.

$$E_1 = E_2 = E_3 = \frac{kq}{r^2} = \frac{(9.0 \times 10^9 \text{ N·m}^2/\text{C}^2)(4.0 \times 10^{-6} \text{ C})}{(0.115 \text{ m})^2} = 2.72 \times 10^6 \text{ N/C}.$$

Due to symmetry, the resultant of $\mathbf{E}_1$ and $\mathbf{E}_2$ will point toward q_3.

So the net electric field

$E = E_3 + E_1 \cos 60° + E_2 \cos 60°$

$= 2.72 \times 10^6 \text{ N/C} + 2(2.72 \times 10^6 \text{ N/C}) \cos 60°$

$= \boxed{5.4 \times 10^6 \text{ N/C toward } -4.0 \ \mu\text{C charge}}$.

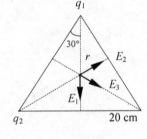

60.   Due to symmetry, E_1 and E_2 cancel out.

So the net electric field is the electric field by q_3.

$$E = E_3 = \frac{kq_3}{r^2} = \frac{(9.0 \times 10^9 \text{ N·m}^2/\text{C}^2)(4.0 \times 10^{-6} \ \mu\text{C})}{[(0.20 \text{ m}) \cos 30°]^2}$$

$= \boxed{1.2 \times 10^6 \text{ N/C toward the } -4.0 \ \mu\text{C-charge}}$.

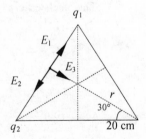

61. $E_1 = E_2 = \dfrac{kq}{r^2} = \dfrac{(9.0 \times 10^9 \text{ N·m}^2/\text{C}^2)(10 \times 10^{-6} \text{ C})}{(0.05 \text{ m})^2 + (0.05 \text{ m})^2} = 1.8 \times 10^7 \text{ N/C}.$

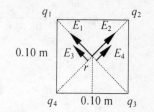

$E_3 = E_4 = \dfrac{(9.0 \times 10^9 \text{ N·m}^2/\text{C}^2)(5.0 \times 10^{-6} \text{ C})}{(0.05 \text{ m})^2 + (0.05 \text{ m})^2} = 9.0 \times 10^6 \text{ N/C}.$

Due to symmetry, the net electric field will be upward and it is equal to

$E = (E_1 + E_3) \cos 45° + (E_2 + E_3) \cos 45°$

$= 2(1.8 \times 10^7 \text{ N/C} + 9.0 \times 10^6 \text{ N/C}) \cos 45° = \boxed{3.8 \times 10^7 \text{ N/C in the } +y \text{ direction}}.$

62. (a) First find the acceleration. $a = \dfrac{F}{m} = \dfrac{qE}{m} = \dfrac{(2.0 \times 10^{-6} \text{ C})(12 \text{ N/C})}{2.0 \times 10^{-5} \text{ kg}} = 1.2 \text{ m/s}^2.$

$x = v_0 t + \frac{1}{2} at^2 = \frac{1}{2}(1.2 \text{ m/s}^2)(0.50 \text{ s})^2 = \boxed{0.15 \text{ m}}.$

(b) $v = v_0 + at = (1.2 \text{ m/s}^2)(0.50 \text{ s}) = \boxed{0.60 \text{ m/s}}.$

(c) $E = \dfrac{4\pi kQ}{A},$ so $Q = \dfrac{EA}{4\pi k} = \dfrac{(12 \text{ N/C})(0.050 \text{ m})^2}{4\pi(9.00 \times 10^9 \text{ N·m}^2/\text{C}^2)} = 2.7 \times 10^{-13} \text{ C}.$

The plates carry opposite charge so they are $\boxed{\pm 0.27 \text{ pC}}.$

63. (a) Since $E = \dfrac{4\pi kQ}{A}$, E does not depend on $\boxed{\text{the separation of the plates}}.$

(b) $E = \dfrac{4\pi kQ}{A},$ ☞ $\dfrac{Q}{A} = \dfrac{E}{4\pi k} = \dfrac{1.7 \times 10^6 \text{ N/C}}{4\pi(9.00 \times 10^9 \text{ N·m}^2/\text{C}^2)} = \boxed{15 \ \mu\text{C/m}^2}.$

64. (a) $E = \dfrac{4\pi kQ}{A} = \dfrac{4\pi(9.00 \times 10^9 \text{ N·m}^2/\text{C}^2)(4.0 \times 10^{-9} \text{ C})}{(0.20 \text{ m})^2} = \boxed{1.1 \times 10^4 \text{ N/C}}.$

(b) $F = qE = (1.60 \times 10^{-19} \text{ C})(1.1 \times 10^4 \text{ N/C}) = \boxed{1.8 \times 10^{-15} \text{ N to positive plate}}.$

65. $E_1 = \dfrac{kq}{r^2} = \dfrac{(9.0 \times 10^9 \text{ N·m}^2/\text{C}^2)(10 \times 10^{-6} \text{ C})}{(0.10 \text{ m})^2 + (0.040 \text{ m})^2} = 7.76 \times 10^6 \text{ N/C},$

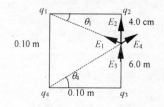

$\theta_1 = \tan^{-1}\left(\dfrac{4.0}{10}\right) = 21.8°,$ so

$\mathbf{E}_1 = (7.76 \times 10^6 \text{ N/C})[(-\cos 21.8°) \, \hat{\mathbf{x}} + (\sin 21.8°) \, \hat{\mathbf{y}}]$

$= (-7.20 \times 10^6 \text{ N/C}) \, \hat{\mathbf{x}} + (2.88 \times 10^6 \text{ N/C}) \, \hat{\mathbf{y}};$

$E_2 = \dfrac{(9.0 \times 10^9 \text{ N·m}^2/\text{C}^2)(10 \times 10^{-6} \text{ C})}{(0.040 \text{ m})^2} = 5.63 \times 10^7 \text{ N/C},$ so $\mathbf{E}_2 = (5.63 \times 10^7 \text{ N/C}) \, \hat{\mathbf{y}};$

$E_3 = \dfrac{(9.0 \times 10^9 \text{ N·m}^2/\text{C}^2)(5.0 \times 10^{-6} \text{ C})}{(0.060 \text{ m})^2} = 1.25 \times 10^7 \text{ N/C},$ so $\mathbf{E}_3 = (1.25 \times 10^7 \text{ N/C}) \, \hat{\mathbf{y}};$

$$E_4 = \frac{(9.0 \times 10^9 \text{ N·m}^2/\text{C}^2)(5.0 \times 10^{-6} \text{ C})}{(0.10 \text{ m})^2 + (0.060 \text{ m})^2} = 3.31 \times 10^6 \text{ N/C}, \quad \theta_4 = \tan^{-1}\left(\frac{6.0}{10}\right) = 31.0°,$$

Therefore $\mathbf{E}_4 = (3.31 \times 10^6 \text{ N/C})[(\cos 31.0°)\,\hat{\mathbf{x}} + (\sin 31.0°)\,\hat{\mathbf{y}}] = (2.84 \times 10^6 \text{ N/C})\,\hat{\mathbf{x}} + (1.70 \times 10^6 \text{ N/C})\,\hat{\mathbf{y}}.$

Thus $\quad \mathbf{E} = \mathbf{E}_1 + \mathbf{E}_2 + \mathbf{E}_3 + \mathbf{E}_4 = \boxed{(-4.4 \times 10^6 \text{ N/C})\,\hat{\mathbf{x}} + (7.3 \times 10^7 \text{ N/C})\,\hat{\mathbf{y}}}.$

Or $\quad E = \sqrt{(4.36 \times 10^6 \text{ N/C})^2 + (7.34 \times 10^7 \text{ N/C})^2} = \boxed{7.4 \times 10^7 \text{ N/C}},$

$$\theta = \tan^{-1}\left(\frac{73.4}{4.36}\right) = \boxed{87°}.$$

66. (a) From symmetry, the net electric field is in the $\boxed{-y}$ direction.

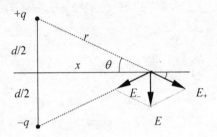

(b) $r = \sqrt{(d/2)^2 + x^2}, \quad \sin\theta = \dfrac{d/2}{r} = \dfrac{d/2}{\sqrt{(d/2)^2 + x^2}}.$

$$E_- = E_+ = \frac{kq}{r^2} = \frac{kq}{(d/2)^2 + x^2}.$$

$$E = E_y = E_- \sin\theta + E_+ \sin\theta = 2E_+ \sin\theta = \frac{2kq}{(d/2)^2 + x^2}\frac{d/2}{\sqrt{(d/2)^2 + x^2}}$$

$$= \boxed{\frac{kqd}{[(d/2)^2 + x^2]^{3/2}}}.$$

(c) If $x \gg d$, we can ignore the term $(d/2)^2$ in $(d/2)^2 + x^2$.

So $\quad E = \dfrac{kqd}{[(d/2)^2 + x^2]^{3/2}} \approx \dfrac{kqd}{(x^2)^{3/2}} = \dfrac{kqd}{x^3}.$

67. (b) since there is no electric field inside a conductor in electrostatic equilibrium.

68. (a) since there is no electric field inside a conductor in electrostatic equilibrium.

69. (b).

70. $\boxed{\text{Yes}}$, because the car (a metal frame) keeps the electric field from reaching you.

71. $\boxed{\text{No}}$. There are conduction electrons inside a conductor. However, the protons inside neutralize these conduction electrons.

72. This is because $\boxed{\text{charges accumulate at sharp points, and lightening hits the tall rods first}}$ with it higher than the building.

73.   (a) The inner surface of the shell will have $\boxed{\text{negative}}$ charge due to induction.

(b) $\boxed{\text{Zero}}$ since all excess charge resides on the surface of the conductor in electrostatic equilibrium.

(c) $\boxed{+Q}$ since all excess charge resides on the surface of the conductor in electrostatic equilibrium.

(d) $\boxed{-Q}$ by induction and the conservation of charge.

(e) $\boxed{+Q}$ by induction and the conservation of charge.

74.   (a) There is $\boxed{\text{none}}$ since the electric field is zero in the interior of the solid sphere.

(b) $\boxed{\text{Outward}}$ from the center of the sphere since the charge on the surface of the sphere is positive.

(c) There is $\boxed{\text{none}}$ since the electric field is zero. The field by the sphere cancels out the field by the inner surface of the shell.

(d) $\boxed{\text{Outward}}$ from the center of the sphere. The net excess charge is positive on the outer surface of the shell.

75.   (a) Again, it is $\boxed{\text{zero}}$ since there is no electric field inside a conductor in electrostatic equilibrium.

(b) The charge on the surface of the sphere can be considered as if it were concentrated at the center.

So $E = \dfrac{k(-Q)}{r^2} = \boxed{-\dfrac{kQ}{r^2}}$, the negative sign indicates it is toward the center.

(c) Again, it is $\boxed{\text{zero}}$.

(d) All charges can be considered as if they were concentrated at the center.

So $E = \dfrac{k(-Q)}{r^2} + \dfrac{kQ}{r^2} + \dfrac{k(-Q)}{r^2} = \boxed{-\dfrac{kQ}{r^2}}$, the negative sign indicates it is toward the center.

76.   More charges accumulate at sharper points, and the electric field lines are perpendicular to the surface.

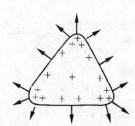

77.   See the diagram below.

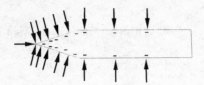

78.   (a) Since field lines point away from positive charge.

79. $\boxed{\text{Zero}}$, since the number of lines going into the surface equals the number of lines coming out of the surface.

80.   The $\boxed{\text{same}}$, since both enclose the same charge.

81.   Since the number of lines is proportional to charge, $\boxed{\text{the net charges are equal and opposite in sign}}$.

82.   (a) The magnitude of the unknown charge is $\boxed{\text{greater than } 10.0 \ \mu C}$ because the number of field lines is proportional to the magnitude of the charge inside the Gaussian surface.

       (b) $q_2 = -\dfrac{75}{16} (+10.0 \ \mu C) = \boxed{-46.9 \ \mu C}$.

83.   A dipole consists of a pair of equal and opposite charges.
       There will be $\boxed{\text{10 field lines entering (negative)}}$.

84.   The net number of field lines is $+6 - 2 \times 6 = \boxed{-6 \text{ lines}}$ or $\boxed{\text{net of 6 entering it}}$.

85. $\boxed{\text{No}}$. All it means is that there is $\boxed{\text{just more positive charge than negative charge}}$ or there is a
       $\boxed{\text{net positive charge}}$. A special case would be no negative charge and only positive charge.

86.   (a) $F = qE = (-1.6 \times 10^{-19} \text{ C})(3.5 \times 10^3 \text{ N/C}) = -5.6 \times 10^{-16} \text{ N} = \boxed{5.6 \times 10^{-16} \text{ N in } +y \text{ direction}}$.

       (b) First find the acceleration. $a = \dfrac{F}{m}$,   and $v^2 = v_o^2 + 2ax = \dfrac{2Fx}{m}$ (since $v_o = 0$).

       So $K = \tfrac{1}{2}mv^2 = Fx = (5.6 \times 10^{-16} \text{ N})(0.10 \text{ m}) = \boxed{5.6 \times 10^{-17} \text{ J}}$.

87. (a) $n = \dfrac{q}{e} = \dfrac{-0.50 \times 10^{-6}\ \text{C}}{-1.60 \times 10^{-19}\ \text{C/electron}} = \boxed{3.1 \times 10^{12}\ \text{electrons}}$.

(b) The percentage is $\dfrac{(3.1 \times 10^{12})(9.11 \times 10^{-31}\ \text{kg})}{2.5 \times 10^{-3}\ \text{kg}} \times 100\% = \boxed{1.1 \times 10^{-13}\ \%}$.

88. (a) The charge has to be placed between the two charges. Assume it is d from the -3.0-μC charge.

So $\dfrac{kq(3.0\ \mu\text{C})}{d^2} = \dfrac{k\,q\,(5.0\ \mu\text{C})}{(0.40\ \text{m} - d)^2}$.

Taking the square root on both sides gives $\dfrac{\sqrt{3}}{d} = \dfrac{\sqrt{5}}{0.40\ \text{m} - d}$.   Or $2.24d = 1.73(0.40 - d)$.

Solve for $d = \boxed{0.17\ \text{m from the } -3.0\ \mu\text{C charge in between the charges}}$.

(b) In (a), the result is independent of q. So the answer is still $\boxed{0.17\ \text{m from the } -3.0\text{-}\mu\text{C charge}}$.

89. (a) First find the acceleration. $a = \dfrac{F}{m} = \dfrac{eE}{m}$. $x = v_0 t + \tfrac{1}{2} at^2 = \tfrac{1}{2} at^2$,

so $t = \sqrt{\dfrac{2x}{a}} = \sqrt{\dfrac{2x}{eE/m}} = \sqrt{\dfrac{2xm}{eE}} = \sqrt{\dfrac{2(1.0\ \text{m})(9.11 \times 10^{-31}\ \text{kg})}{(1.6 \times 10^{-19}\ \text{C})(450\ \text{N/C})}} = \boxed{1.6 \times 10^{-7}\ \text{s}}$.

(b) $x = \tfrac{1}{2} at^2 = \tfrac{1}{2}\dfrac{(-1.6 \times 10^{-19}\ \text{C})(450\ \text{N/C})}{9.11 \times 10^{-31}\ \text{kg}} \times (7.95 \times 10^{-8}\ \text{s})^2 = -0.25\ \text{m},\ y = 0.$

So it is at $\boxed{(-0.25\ \text{m}, 0)}$.

90. $E_x = \dfrac{kq}{r^2} = \dfrac{(9.00 \times 10^9\ \text{N·m}^2/\text{C}^2)(4.0 \times 10^{-6}\ \text{C})}{(4.0\ \text{m})^2} = (2.25 \times 10^3\ \text{N/C})\ \hat{\text{x}}.$

$E_y = -\dfrac{(9.00 \times 10^9\ \text{N·m}^2/\text{C}^2)(5.0 \times 10^{-6}\ \text{C})}{(3.0\ \text{m})^2} = -(5.00 \times 10^3\ \text{N/C})\ \hat{\text{y}}.$

So $E = \sqrt{(2.25 \times 10^3\ \text{N/C})^2 + (5.00 \times 10^3\ \text{N/C})^2} = \boxed{5.5 \times 10^3\ \text{N/C}}$.

$\theta = \tan^{-1}\left(\dfrac{-5.00}{2.25}\right) = \boxed{66^\circ\ \text{below } +x \text{ axis}}$.

91. $F = \dfrac{kq_1 q_2}{r^2},$ ☞ $q_2 = \dfrac{Fr^2}{kq_1} = \dfrac{(1.8\ \text{N})(0.30\ \text{m})^2}{(9.0 \times 10^9\ \text{N·m}^2/\text{C}^2)(6.0 \times 10^{-6}\ \text{C})} = 3.0 \times 10^{-6}\ \text{C} = 3.0\ \mu\text{C}.$

So the charge could be $\boxed{+3.0\ \mu\text{C on the } -y \text{ axis or } -3.0\ \mu\text{C on the } +y \text{ axis}}$ from the charge-force law.

92. $E_1 = \dfrac{kq}{r^2} = \dfrac{(9.0 \times 10^9 \text{ N·m}^2/\text{C}^2)(10 \times 10^{-6} \text{ C})}{(0.050 \text{ m})^2} = 3.6 \times 10^7$ N/C,

so $\quad \mathbf{E}_1 = (3.6 \times 10^7$ N/C$) \hat{\mathbf{y}}$;

$E_2 = \dfrac{(9.0 \times 10^9 \text{ N·m}^2/\text{C}^2)(10 \times 10^{-6} \text{ C})}{(0.050 \text{ m})^2 + (0.10 \text{ m})^2} = 7.2 \times 10^6$ N/C,

$\theta = \tan^{-1}\left(\dfrac{0.05}{0.10}\right) = 26.6°$,

so $\quad \mathbf{E}_2 = (7.2 \times 10^6$ N/C$)[(\cos 26.6°)\,\hat{\mathbf{x}} + (\sin 26.6°)\,\hat{\mathbf{y}}] = (6.44 \times 10^6$ N/C$)\,\hat{\mathbf{x}} + (3.22 \times 10^6$ N/C$)\,\hat{\mathbf{y}}$,

$E_3 = \dfrac{(9.0 \times 10^9 \text{ N·m}^2/\text{C}^2)(5.0 \times 10^{-6} \text{ C})}{(0.050 \text{ m})^2 + (0.10 \text{ m})^2} = 3.6 \times 10^6$ N/C,

so $\quad \mathbf{E}_3 = (3.6 \times 10^6$ N/C$)[(-\cos 26.6°)\,\hat{\mathbf{x}} + (\sin 26.6°)\,\hat{\mathbf{y}}] = (-3.22 \times 10^6$ N/C$)\,\hat{\mathbf{x}} + (1.61 \times 10^6$ N/C$)\,\hat{\mathbf{y}}$,

$E_4 = \dfrac{(9.0 \times 10^9 \text{ N·m}^2/\text{C}^2)(5.0 \times 10^{-6} \text{ C})}{(0.050 \text{ m})^2} = 1.8 \times 10^7$ N/C, $\quad$ so $\quad \mathbf{E}_4 = (1.8 \times 10^7$ N/C$)\,\hat{\mathbf{y}}$.

Therefore $\quad \mathbf{E} = \mathbf{E}_1 + \mathbf{E}_2 + \mathbf{E}_3 + \mathbf{E}_4 = \boxed{(3.2 \times 10^6 \text{ N/C})\,\hat{\mathbf{x}} + (5.9 \times 10^7 \text{ N/C})\,\hat{\mathbf{y}}}$, $\quad$ or

$E = \sqrt{(3.22 \times 10^6 \text{ N/C})^2 + (5.88 \times 10^7 \text{ N/C})^2} = \boxed{5.9 \times 10^7 \text{ N/C}}$,

$\theta = \tan^{-1}\left(\dfrac{5.8.8}{3.22}\right) = \boxed{87° \text{ above } +x \text{ axis}}$.

93. See diagram below.

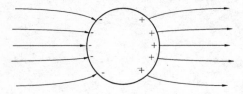

94. $Q_{\text{net}} = -10 \times 10^{-6} \text{ C} - 10 \times 10^{-6} \text{ C} + 5.0 \times 10^{-6} \text{ C} + 5.0 \times 10^{-6} \text{ C} = -10 \times 10^{-6} \text{ C}$.

The net lines are $\boxed{\text{negative}}$.

95.

96. It will still rotate, but be drawn into region of higher electric field, negative end first.

97. If d is zero, two charges (+ and −) would produce equal and opposite electric fields that cancel out.

98. 　$\boxed{\text{Same field except zero inside the slab}}$. Induced charges on slab create exactly opposite field and cancel the original field the to create zero net field inside the slab.

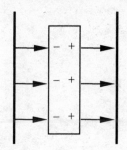

99. 　$t = \dfrac{x}{v_x} = \dfrac{0.10\text{ m}}{6.0 \times 10^7\text{ m/s}} = 1.67 \times 10^{-9}\text{ s}.$

$a_y = \dfrac{F}{m} = \dfrac{qE}{m} = \dfrac{(1.60 \times 10^{-19}\text{ C})(2.0 \times 10^4\text{ N/C})}{9.11 \times 10^{-31}\text{ kg}} = 3.51 \times 10^{15}\text{ m/s}^2.$

$d = \tfrac{1}{2}a_y t^2 = \tfrac{1}{2}(3.51 \times 10^{15}\text{ m/s}^2)(1.67 \times 10^{-9}\text{ s})^2 = 4.9 \times 10^{-3}\text{ m} = \boxed{4.9\text{ mm}}.$

CHAPTER 16

ELECTRIC POTENTIAL, ELECTRIC ENERGY, AND CAPACITORS

1. (d).

2. (a).

3. (a) Electrical potential is the electrostatic potential energy *per unit charge*, i.e., $V = \dfrac{U}{q_0}$.

    (b) $\boxed{\text{No difference}}$.

4. The potential energy $\boxed{\text{increases}}$ because potential energy is inversely proportional to the distance between the charges.

5. Approaching a negative charge means moving toward a region of lower electric potential that is losing potential. Positive charges tend to move toward regions of lower potential, thus losing potential energy and gaining kinetic energy (speeding up).

6. It will move toward the $\boxed{\text{higher potential region}}$ because the electron has negative charge. The higher potential region, for the electron, has a lower potential energy.

7. The electric field is then $\boxed{\text{zero}}$. Electric field is related to the change in potential in space. If there is no change in potential, the electric field is zero.

8. (b).

9. $\boxed{\text{No}}$, it does not. Since $W = q_0 \Delta V$, if $\Delta V = 0$, $W = 0$.

10. $W = q\Delta V = (-4.0 \times 10^6 \text{ C})(-24 \text{ V}) = \boxed{+9.6 \times 10^{-5} \text{ J}}$.

11. (a) $W = q\Delta V$,   ☞ $q = \dfrac{W}{\Delta V} = \dfrac{1.6 \times 10^{-5} \text{ J}}{6 \text{ V}} = 2.7 \times 10^{-6} \text{ C} = \boxed{2.7 \ \mu\text{C}}$.

    (b) For a negative charge, it moves from $\boxed{\text{positive to negative}}$ since work is done by an external source, or the electric field does negative work.

12.	From $W = q\Delta V = qEd$,

$$E = \frac{W}{qd} = \frac{\Delta V}{d} = \frac{6.0 \text{ V}}{4.0 \times 10^{-3} \text{ m}} = \boxed{1.5 \times 10^3 \text{ V/m from positive to negative}}.$$

13.	$W = q\Delta V = \Delta K = K - K_o = K = \frac{1}{2}mv^2$,

So	$v = \sqrt{\dfrac{2q\Delta V}{m}} = \sqrt{\dfrac{2(1.60 \times 10^{-19} \text{ C})(10 \times 10^3 \text{ V})}{1.67 \times 10^{-27} \text{ kg}}} = \boxed{1.4 \times 10^6 \text{ m/s}}.$

14.	The electron will accelerate downward because it is negatively charged.

$$a = \frac{F}{m} = \frac{qE}{m}, \quad \text{and} \quad v^2 = v_o^2 + 2ax = 2ax.$$

$$v = \sqrt{2ax} = \sqrt{\frac{2qEx}{m}} = \sqrt{\frac{2(1.6 \times 10^{-19} \text{ C})(1000 \text{ V/m})(0.0050 \text{ m})}{9.11 \times 10^{-31} \text{ kg}}} = \boxed{1.3 \times 10^6 \text{ m/s down}}.$$

15.	(a) The electron will accelerate downward because it is negatively charged.

From the work-energy theorem:	$|W| = q\Delta V = eE\Delta x = \Delta K = K - K_o = K = \frac{1}{2}mv^2$,

$$v = \sqrt{\frac{2eE\Delta x}{m}} = \sqrt{\frac{2(1.6 \times 10^{-19} \text{ C})(1000 \text{ V/m})(0.0050 \text{ m})}{9.11 \times 10^{-31} \text{ kg}}} = \boxed{1.3 \times 10^6 \text{ m/s downward}}.$$

(b) The electron does not move from high to low potential.	$\boxed{\text{It loses potential energy}}$.

16.	(a) The point closer to the charge has a $\boxed{\text{higher potential}}$ because electric potential is inversely

proportional to the distance, $V = \dfrac{kq}{r}$.

(b) $\Delta V = \dfrac{kq}{r_B} - \dfrac{kq}{r_A} = \dfrac{(9.0 \times 10^9 \text{ N·m}^2/\text{C}^2)(5.5 \times 10^{-6} \text{ C})}{0.20 \text{ m}} - \dfrac{(9.0 \times 10^9 \text{ N·m}^2/\text{C}^2)(5.5 \times 10^{-6} \text{ C})}{0.40 \text{ m}}$

$= \boxed{1.2 \times 10^5 \text{ V}}$.

17.	(a) The electric potential will change by a factor of $\boxed{3}$ because electric potential is inversely proportional

to the distance, $V = \dfrac{kq}{r}$.

(b) $V = \dfrac{kq}{r}$, ☞ $r = \dfrac{kq}{V} = \dfrac{(9.0 \times 10^9 \text{ N·m}^2/\text{C}^2)(1.0 \times 10^{-6} \text{ C})}{10 \times 10^3 \text{ V}} = \boxed{0.90 \text{ m}}$.

(c) $\Delta V = \dfrac{kq}{r_B} - \dfrac{kq}{r_A} = \dfrac{(9.0 \times 10^9 \text{ N·m}^2/\text{C}^2)(1.0 \times 10^{-6} \text{ C})}{3(0.90 \text{ m})} - \dfrac{(9.0 \times 10^9 \text{ N·m}^2/\text{C}^2)(1.0 \times 10^{-6} \text{ C})}{0.90 \text{ m}}$

$= \boxed{-6.7 \times 10^3 \text{ V}}$. Since the potential difference is negative, it is a potential decrease.

18. (a) A large orbit will have a $\boxed{\text{lower potential}}$ because electric potential is inversely proportional to the

distance, $V = \dfrac{kq}{r}$.

(b) $\Delta V = \dfrac{kq}{r_{\mathrm{B}}} - \dfrac{kq}{r_{\mathrm{A}}} = \dfrac{(9.0 \times 10^9 \text{ N·m}^2/\text{C}^2)(1.6 \times 10^{-19} \text{ C})}{0.48 \times 10^{-9} \text{ m}} - \dfrac{(9.0 \times 10^9 \text{ N·m}^2/\text{C}^2)(1.6 \times 10^{-19} \text{ C})}{0.21 \times 10^{-9} \text{ m}}$

$= -3.9 \text{ V}.$ So the difference is $\boxed{3.9 \text{ V}}$.

19. (a) $\Delta U_{\mathrm{e}} = q\Delta V_{\text{L-H}} = (-1.6 \times 10^{-19} \text{ C})(-3.86 \text{ V}) = \boxed{+6.2 \times 10^{-19} \text{ J}}$. The electron gains potential energy.

(b) $\Delta U_{\mathrm{e}} = q\Delta V_{\text{H-L}} = q(-\Delta V_{\text{L-H}}) = (-1.6 \times 10^{-19} \text{ C})(3.86 \text{ V}) = \boxed{-6.2 \times 10^{-19} \text{ J}}$.

The electron loses potential energy.

(c) $\Delta V = \dfrac{kq}{\infty} - \dfrac{(9.0 \times 10^9 \text{ N·m}^2/\text{C}^2)(1.6 \times 10^{-19} \text{ C})}{0.48 \times 10^{-9} \text{ m}} = -3.0 \text{ V}.$

$\Delta U = (-1.6 \times 10^{-19} \text{ C})(-3.0 \text{ V}) = \boxed{+4.8 \times 10^{-19} \text{ J}}$. The electron gains potential energy.

20. Field does work. $W_{\text{elec}} = -U_{\mathrm{t}} = -\dfrac{kq_1 q_2}{r} = -\dfrac{(9.0 \times 10^9 \text{ N·m}^2/\text{C}^2)(-1.4 \times 10^{-6} \text{ C})^2}{8.0 \times 10^{-3} \text{ m}} = \boxed{-2.2 \text{ J}}$.

21. From conservation of energy, each will have half of the total potential energy. The kinetic energy is $\boxed{1.1 \text{ J}}$.

22. (a) External source does work. $W_{\text{ext}} = U_{\mathrm{t}} = \dfrac{kq_1 q_2}{r} = \dfrac{kq^2}{r}$,

so $q = \sqrt{\dfrac{Wr}{k}} = \sqrt{\dfrac{(5.5 \text{ J})(0.010 \text{ m})}{9.0 \times 10^9 \text{ N·m}^2/\text{C}^2}} = 2.5 \times 10^{-6} \text{ C} = \boxed{2.5 \ \mu\text{C}}$.

(b) Since q^2 is a positive quantity, all you know is that the charges are of the $\boxed{\text{same sign}}$.

23. (a) $W = \Delta U_{\mathrm{e}} = \dfrac{kq_1 q_2}{r_2} - \dfrac{kq_1 q_2}{r_1} = \dfrac{(9.0 \times 10^9 \text{ N·m}^2/\text{C}^2)(-5.0 \times 10^{-6} \text{ C})(2.0 \times 10^{-6} \text{ C})}{0.50 \text{ m}}$

$- \dfrac{(9.0 \times 10^9 \text{ N·m}^2/\text{C}^2)(-5.0 \times 10^{-6} \text{ C})(2.0 \times 10^{-6} \text{ C})}{0.20 \text{ m}} = \boxed{+0.27 \text{ J}}$.

(b) $\boxed{\text{No}}$, since electric force is a conservative force.

24. (a) $W = \Delta U_{\text{A-C}} = q\Delta V = qEd = (-1.60 \times 10^{-19} \text{ C})(15 \text{ V/m})(0.25 \text{ m}) = -\boxed{6.0 \times 10^{-19} \text{ J}}$.

(b) $\Delta V_{\text{A-C}} = \dfrac{\Delta U_{\text{A-C}}}{q} = \dfrac{-6.0 \times 10^{-19} \text{ J}}{-1.60 \times 10^{-19} \text{ C}} = \boxed{3.8 \text{ V}}$.

(c) Since $\Delta V_{\text{A-C}}$ is positive, $\boxed{\text{point C}}$ is at a higher potential.

25. $$W_{ext} = U_t = \frac{(9.0 \times 10^9 \text{ N} \cdot \text{m}^2/\text{C}^2)(4.0 \times 10^{-6} \text{ C})(-4.0 \times 10^{-6} \text{ C})}{0.20 \text{ m}}$$

$$+ \frac{(9.0 \times 10^9 \text{ N} \cdot \text{m}^2/\text{C}^2)(4.0 \times 10^{-6} \text{ C})(4.0 \times 10^{-6} \text{ C})}{0.20 \text{ m}}$$

$$+ \frac{(9.0 \times 10^9 \text{ N} \cdot \text{m}^2/\text{C}^2)(4.0 \times 10^{-6} \text{ C})(-4.0 \times 10^{-6} \text{ C})}{0.20 \text{ m}} = \boxed{-0.72 \text{ J}}.$$

26. $$W_{ext} = U_t = \frac{(9.0 \times 10^9 \text{ N} \cdot \text{m}^2/\text{C}^2)(-10 \times 10^{-6} \text{ C})(-10 \times 10^{-6} \text{ C})}{0.10 \text{ m}}$$

$$+ \frac{(9.0 \times 10^9 \text{ N} \cdot \text{m}^2/\text{C}^2)(-10 \times 10^{-6} \text{ C})(5.0 \times 10^{-6} \text{ C})}{0.10 \text{ m}}$$

$$+ \frac{(9.0 \times 10^9 \text{ N} \cdot \text{m}^2/\text{C}^2)(-10 \times 10^{-6} \text{ C})(5.0 \times 10^{-6} \text{ C})}{0.10 \text{ m}}$$

$$+ \frac{(9.0 \times 10^9 \text{ N} \cdot \text{m}^2/\text{C}^2)(5.0 \times 10^{-6} \text{ C})(5.0 \times 10^{-6} \text{ C})}{0.10 \text{ m}}$$

$$+ \frac{(9.0 \times 10^9 \text{ N} \cdot \text{m}^2/\text{C}^2)(-10 \times 10^{-6} \text{ C})(5.0 \times 10^{-6} \text{ C})}{\sqrt{(0.10 \text{ m})^2 + (0.10 \text{ m})^2}}$$

$$+ \frac{(9.0 \times 10^9 \text{ N} \cdot \text{m}^2/\text{C}^2)(-10 \times 10^{-6} \text{ C})(5.0 \times 10^{-6} \text{ C})}{\sqrt{(0.10 \text{ m})^2 + (0.10 \text{ m})^2}}$$

$$= \boxed{-4.1 \text{ J}}.$$

27. The distance from the center to the corner is $r = \dfrac{10 \text{ cm}}{\cos 30°} = 11.5 \text{ cm}.$

$$V = \Sigma \frac{kq}{r} = \frac{(9.0 \times 10^9 \text{ N} \cdot \text{m}^2/\text{C}^2)(4.0 \times 10^{-6} \text{ C})}{0.115 \text{ m}} + \frac{(9.0 \times 10^9 \text{ N} \cdot \text{m}^2/\text{C}^2)(4.0 \times 10^{-6} \text{ C})}{0.115 \text{ m}}$$

$$+ \frac{(9.0 \times 10^9 \text{ N} \cdot \text{m}^2/\text{C}^2)(-4.0 \times 10^{-6} \text{ C})}{0.115 \text{ m}} = \boxed{3.1 \times 10^5 \text{ V}}.$$

28. The distance from q_1 to the point is $r = (20 \text{ cm}) \cos 30° = 17.3 \text{ cm}.$

$$V = \Sigma \frac{kq}{r} = \frac{(9.0 \times 10^9 \text{ N} \cdot \text{m}^2/\text{C}^2)(4.0 \times 10^{-6} \text{ C})}{0.173 \text{ m}} + \frac{(9.0 \times 10^9 \text{ N} \cdot \text{m}^2/\text{C}^2)(-4.0 \times 10^{-6} \text{ C})}{0.10 \text{ m}}$$

$$+ \frac{(9.0 \times 10^9 \text{ N} \cdot \text{m}^2/\text{C}^2)(4.0 \times 10^{-6} \text{ C})}{0.10 \text{ m}} + \frac{(9.0 \times 10^9 \text{ N} \cdot \text{m}^2/\text{C}^2)(5.0 \times 10^{-6} \text{ C})}{0.112 \text{ m}} = \boxed{2.1 \times 10^5 \text{ V}}.$$

29. The distance from the charges to the center of the square is

$$r = \sqrt{(0.05 \text{ m})^2 + (0.05 \text{ m})^2} = 0.0707 \text{ m}.$$

$$V = \Sigma \frac{kq}{r} = 2\frac{(9.0 \times 10^9 \text{ N} \cdot \text{m}^2/\text{C}^2)(-10 \times 10^{-6} \text{ C})}{0.0707 \text{ m}} + 2\frac{(9.0 \times 10^9 \text{ N} \cdot \text{m}^2/\text{C}^2)(5.0 \times 10^{-6} \text{ C})}{0.0707 \text{ m}}$$

$$= \boxed{-1.3 \times 10^6 \text{ V}}.$$

30.   The distance from q_2 and q_3 to the point is $r = \sqrt{(0.10 \text{ m})^2 + (0.05 \text{ m})^2} = 0.112$ m.

$$V = \Sigma \frac{kq}{r} = \frac{(9.0 \times 10^9 \text{ N·m}^2/\text{C}^2)(-10 \times 10^{-6} \text{ C})}{0.05 \text{ m}} + \frac{(9.0 \times 10^9 \text{ N·m}^2/\text{C}^2)(-10 \times 10^{-6} \text{ C})}{0.112 \text{ m}}$$

$$+ \frac{(9.0 \times 10^9 \text{ N·m}^2/\text{C}^2)(5.0 \times 10^{-6} \text{ C})}{0.112 \text{ m}} + \frac{(9.0 \times 10^9 \text{ N·m}^2/\text{C}^2)(5.0 \times 10^{-6} \text{ C})}{0.05 \text{ m}} = \boxed{-1.3 \times 10^6 \text{ V}}.$$

31.   (a) The left side of the gun should be at a $\boxed{\text{lower}}$ potential because electrons have a negative charge. They

move toward higher potential regions where they have lower potential energy.

(b) $\Delta K = K - K_o = K = \frac{1}{2} mv^2,$

also from work-energy theorem: $W = \Delta K = -\Delta U_e = -q\Delta V = e\Delta V.$

So $v = \sqrt{\dfrac{2e\Delta V}{m}} = \dfrac{2(1.6 \times 10^{-19} \text{ C})(10 \times 10^3 \text{ V})}{9.11 \times 10^{-31} \text{ kg}} = \boxed{5.9 \times 10^7 \text{ m/s}}.$

(c) $t = \dfrac{\Delta x}{v} = \dfrac{0.35 \text{ m}}{5.93 \times 10^7 \text{ m/s}} = \boxed{5.9 \times 10^{-9} \text{ s}}.$

32.   The distance from q_2 to the point is $r_2 = \sqrt{(0.10 \text{ m})^2 + (0.06 \text{ m})^2} = 0.117$ m.

The distance from q_3 to the point is $r_3 = \sqrt{(0.10 \text{ m})^2 + (0.04 \text{ m})^2} = 0.108$ m.

$$V = \Sigma \frac{kq}{r} = \frac{(9.0 \times 10^9 \text{ N·m}^2/\text{C}^2)(-10 \times 10^{-6} \text{ C})}{0.06 \text{ m}} + \frac{(9.0 \times 10^9 \text{ N·m}^2/\text{C}^2)(-10 \times 10^{-6} \text{ C})}{0.117 \text{ m}}$$

$$+ \frac{(9.0 \times 10^9 \text{ N·m}^2/\text{C}^2)(5.0 \times 10^{-6} \text{ C})}{0.108 \text{ m}} + \frac{(9.0 \times 10^9 \text{ N·m}^2/\text{C}^2)(5.0 \times 10^{-6} \text{ C})}{0.04 \text{ m}} = \boxed{-7.3 \times 10^5 \text{ V}}.$$

33.   (a).

34.   (b).

35.

Higher gravitational potential energy

Beach _____

_____

_____ | Ball accelerating

_____ ↓

Ocean _____

Lower gravitational potential energy

36.   A point in space can have only one potential value. If two equipotential surfaces intersect in space, the intersection will have two different potential values. Therefore, the equipotential surfaces cannot intersect.

37. $\boxed{\text{Yes}}$, because there is no change in kinetic or potential energy. So the net work done is zero.

38.   They are planes, parallel to the plate surfaces .

39.   (a) The surfaces are cylindrical in shape due to symmetry.

        (b) The electric potential is higher near the inner surface .

        (c) Then the electric potential is higher near the outer surface .

40.   Since $V = \dfrac{kq}{r}$ and V = constant, r = constant.

        So the equipotential surfaces are concentric spheres centered on the charge .

41.   Since $V = \dfrac{kq}{r}$, V increases as r decreases. So it increases to a larger positive value .

42. $\text{V/m} = \dfrac{\text{J/C}}{\text{m}} = \dfrac{\text{J}}{\text{C·m}} = \dfrac{\text{N·m}}{\text{C·m}} = \text{N/C}$.

43.   The electron volt unit is gotten from $e\Delta V = q\Delta V = \Delta U_e$. It is also the kinetic energy gained by an electron when it goes through a potential difference of 1 V. So it is a unit of energy. A GeV is larger than a MeV by 1000 times.

44.   (b) since $W = -qE\Delta x$, ☞ $E = -\dfrac{W}{q\,\Delta x} = -\dfrac{\Delta V}{\Delta x}$.

45.   From Exercise 16.36, equipotential surfaces cannot cross. Since electric field lines are perpendicular to the equipotential surfaces, electric field lines cannot cross either.

46.   Yes . Electric field is a measure of the change in electric potential over a distance. Inside a conductor in electrostatic equilibrium, the electric field is zero, yet the electrical potential could be at a *constant* value.

47. $V = \dfrac{kq}{r}$, ☞ $r = \dfrac{kq}{V} = \dfrac{(9.0 \times 10^9 \text{ N·m}^2/\text{C}^2)(3.50 \times 10^{-6} \text{ C})}{2.50 \times 10^3 \text{ V}} = \boxed{12.6 \text{ m}}$.

48. $E = \dfrac{\Delta V}{\Delta x}$, ☞ $\Delta x = \dfrac{\Delta V}{E} = \dfrac{10 \text{ V}}{100 \text{ V/m}} = 10^{-2} \text{ m} = \boxed{1.0 \text{ cm}}$.

49. $\Delta x = \dfrac{7.0 \times 10^3 \text{ V}}{10 \times 10^3 \text{ V/m}} = 0.70 \text{ m} = \boxed{70 \text{ cm}}$.

50. $E = -\dfrac{\Delta V}{\Delta x}$, ☞ $\dfrac{E_2}{E_1} = \dfrac{\Delta x_2}{\Delta x_1}$ since E is constant.

So $E_2 = \dfrac{\Delta x_2}{\Delta x_1} E_1 = \dfrac{2.5\text{ mm}}{10\text{ mm}}(24\text{ V}) = 6.0\text{ V}.$

If we choose the negative plate as the reference point ($V = 0$), then $V = \boxed{+6.0\text{ V}}$.

51. From Exercise 16.50, $\Delta x_2 = \dfrac{E_2}{E_1}\Delta x_1 = \dfrac{20\text{ V}}{24\text{ V}}(10\text{ mm}) = 8.3\text{ mm}$ from the negative plate.

So it is $10\text{ mm} - 8.3\text{ mm} = \boxed{1.7\text{ mm away from the positive plate, toward the negative plate}}$.

52. $V = \dfrac{kq}{r}$, ☞ $q = \dfrac{Vr}{k} = \dfrac{(2.20 \times 10^3\text{ V})(14.3\text{ m})}{9.0 \times 10^9\text{ N·m}^2/\text{C}^2} = \boxed{3.50\ \mu\text{C}}$.

53. (a) The equipotential surfaces are $\boxed{\text{concentric spheres}}$ because the electric potential depends only on the

distance from the charge, $V = \dfrac{kq}{r}$. So it is radially symmetric.

(b) $W = q_0\Delta V$

$= (1.6 \times 10^{-19}\text{ C}) \times \dfrac{(9.00 \times 10^9\text{ N·m}^2/\text{C}^2)(3.50 \times 10^{-6}\text{ C})}{12.6\text{ m}} - \dfrac{(9.00 \times 10^9\text{ N·m}^2/\text{C}^2)(3.50 \times 10^{-6}\text{ C})}{14.3\text{ m}}$

$= \boxed{+4.76 \times 10^{-17}\text{ J}} = (+4.76 \times 10^{-10}\text{ J}) \times \dfrac{1.60 \times 10^{-19}\text{ J}}{1\text{ eV}} = \boxed{+297\text{ eV}}$

54. (a) $W = \Delta K = K - K_o = K = -\Delta U_e = -q\Delta V = e\Delta V = e(100 \times 10^6\text{ V})$

$= \boxed{1.00 \times 10^8\text{ eV}}$.

(b) $(1.00 \times 10^8\text{ eV}) \times \dfrac{1.60 \times 10^{-19}\text{ J}}{1\text{ eV}} = \boxed{1.60 \times 10^{-11}\text{ J}}$.

55. (a) $W = \Delta K = K - K_o = K = -\Delta U_e = -q\,(-\Delta V) = e\Delta V = e(20\text{ MV}) = \boxed{2.0 \times 10^7\text{ eV}}$.

(b) $2.0 \times 10^7\text{ eV} = \boxed{2.0 \times 10^4\text{ keV}}$.

(c) $2.0 \times 10^7\text{ eV} = \boxed{20\text{ MeV}}$.

(d) $2.0 \times 10^7\text{ eV} = \boxed{2.0 \times 10^{-2}\text{ GeV}}$.

(e) $(2.0 \times 10^7\text{ eV}) \times \dfrac{1.6 \times 10^{-19}\text{ J}}{1\text{ eV}} = \boxed{3.2 \times 10^{-12}\text{ J}}$.

56. $\boxed{\text{They are all doubled}}$ since $K \propto q$.

57. From the work-energy theorem: $W = \Delta K = \frac{1}{2}mv^2 = q\Delta V$, ☞ $v = \sqrt{\dfrac{2q\Delta V}{m}}$.

So $v_p = \sqrt{\dfrac{2(1.6 \times 10^{-19}\ \text{C})(20 \times 10^6\ \text{V})}{1.67 \times 10^{-27}\ \text{kg}}} = \boxed{6.2 \times 10^7\ \text{m/s (proton)}}$;

$v_\alpha = \sqrt{\dfrac{2[2(1.6 \times 10^{-19}\ \text{C})](20 \times 10^6\ \text{V})}{4(1.67 \times 10^{-27}\ \text{kg})}} = \boxed{4.4 \times 10^7\ \text{m/s (alpha)}}$.

58. (a) $\Delta V = \dfrac{\Delta U_e}{q} = \dfrac{\Delta U_e}{e} = \dfrac{3.5\ \text{eV}}{e} = \boxed{3.5\ \text{V}}$.

$\frac{1}{2}mv^2 = K = |\Delta U_e|$, ☞ $v = \sqrt{\dfrac{2|\Delta U_e|}{m}} = \sqrt{\dfrac{2(3.5\ \text{eV})(1.6 \times 10^{-19}\ \text{J/eV})}{1.67 \times 10^{-27}\ \text{kg}}} = \boxed{2.6 \times 10^4\ \text{m/s}}$.

(b) $\Delta V = \boxed{4.1\ \text{kV}}$. $v = \sqrt{\dfrac{2(4.1 \times 10^3\ \text{eV})(1.6 \times 10^{-19}\ \text{J/eV})}{1.67 \times 10^{-27}\ \text{kg}}} = \boxed{8.9 \times 10^5\ \text{m/s}}$.

(c) $8.0 \times 10^{-16}\ \text{J} = (8.0 \times 10^{-16}\ \text{J}) \times \dfrac{1\ \text{eV}}{1.60 \times 10^{-19}\ \text{J}} = 5.0 \times 10^3\ \text{eV} = 5.0\ \text{keV}$.

So $\Delta V = \boxed{5.0\ \text{kV}}$. $v = \sqrt{\dfrac{2(5.0 \times 10^3\ \text{eV})(1.6 \times 10^{-19}\ \text{J/eV})}{1.67 \times 10^{-27}\ \text{kg}}} = \boxed{9.8 \times 10^5\ \text{m/s}}$.

59. (a) $\Delta V = \boxed{3.5\ \text{V}}$ $v = \sqrt{\dfrac{2|\Delta U_e|}{m}} = \sqrt{\dfrac{2(3.5\ \text{eV})(1.6 \times 10^{-19}\ \text{J/eV})}{9.11 \times 10^{-31}\ \text{kg}}} = \boxed{1.1 \times 10^6\ \text{m/s}}$.

(b) $\Delta V = \boxed{4.1\ \text{kV}}$. $v = \sqrt{\dfrac{2(4.1 \times 10^3\ \text{eV})(1.6 \times 10^{-19}\ \text{J/eV})}{9.11 \times 10^{-31}\ \text{kg}}} = \boxed{3.8 \times 10^7\ \text{m/s}}$.

(c) $\Delta V = \boxed{5.0\ \text{kV}}$. $v = \sqrt{\dfrac{2(5.0 \times 10^3\ \text{eV})(1.6 \times 10^{-19}\ \text{J/eV})}{9.11 \times 10^{-31}\ \text{kg}}} = \boxed{4.2 \times 10^7\ \text{m/s}}$.

60. $\Delta V = E\Delta x \cos\theta = \dfrac{12\ \text{V}}{0.030\ \text{m}}(0.010\ \text{m})\cos 45° = \boxed{+2.8\ \text{V}}$.

61. If it is moved parallel to the plates, $\theta = 90°$, so $\Delta V = 0$ for this move. Therefore it is still $\boxed{+2.8\ \text{V}}$.

62. (d).

63. Since $C = \dfrac{\varepsilon_o A}{d}$, we can $\boxed{\text{increase plate area and/or decrease plate separation}}$. The greater the capacitance, the greater the energy-storing capability.

64. Charge Q remains constant. $U_C = \dfrac{1}{2}\dfrac{Q^2}{C} = \dfrac{1}{2}\dfrac{Q^2}{\varepsilon A/d} = \dfrac{1}{2}\dfrac{Q^2}{\varepsilon A}d \propto d$. So $\boxed{\text{it decreases}}$.

65. (a) Since $Q = CV$, $\boxed{\text{it doubles}}$.

(b) Since $U_C = \frac{1}{2}CV^2$, $\boxed{\text{it quadruples}}$.

66. Since $C = \dfrac{\varepsilon_0 A}{d}$, C decreases as d increases. Also $U_C = \frac{1}{2}CV^2$, $\boxed{\text{it decreases}}$ when V remains constant and

C is decreasing.

67. $Q = CV = (2.0 \times 10^{-6}\ \text{F})(12\ \text{V}) = \boxed{2.4 \times 10^{-5}\ \text{C}}$.

68. $C = \dfrac{\varepsilon_0 A}{d} = \dfrac{(8.85 \times 10^{-12}\ \text{F/m})(0.50\ \text{m}^2)}{2.0 \times 10^{-3}\ \text{m}} = \boxed{2.2 \times 10^{-9}\ \text{F}}$.

69. $C = \dfrac{\varepsilon_0 A}{d}$, ☞ $d = C = \dfrac{\varepsilon_0 A}{C} = \dfrac{(8.85 \times 10^{-12}\ \text{F/m})(0.40\ \text{m}^2)}{5.0 \times 10^{-9}\ \text{F}} = \boxed{0.71\ \text{mm}}$.

70. (a) A large plate area results in a $\boxed{\text{larger}}$ capacitance because capacitance is directly proportional to the

plate area, $C = \dfrac{\varepsilon_0 A}{d}$.

(b) A larger plate separation results in a $\boxed{\text{smaller}}$ capacitance because capacitance is inversely proportional

to the plate separation.

(c) $C = \dfrac{\varepsilon_0 A}{d}$, ☞ $A = \dfrac{Cd}{\varepsilon_0} = \dfrac{(2.5 \times 10^{-9}\ \text{F})(3.0 \times 10^{-3}\ \text{m})}{8.85 \times 10^{-12}\ \text{F/m}} = \boxed{0.85\ \text{m}^2}$.

71. (a) $Q = CV = \dfrac{\varepsilon_0 A}{d}V = \dfrac{\varepsilon_0 AV}{d} = \dfrac{(8.85 \times 10^{-12}\ \text{C}^2/\text{N·m}^2)(0.20\ \text{m}^2)(12\ \text{V})}{5.0 \times 10^{-3}\ \text{m}} = \boxed{4.2 \times 10^{-9}\ \text{C}}$.

(b) $U_C = \frac{1}{2}CV^2 = \frac{1}{2}QV = \frac{1}{2}(4.25 \times 10^{-9}\ \text{C})(12\ \text{V}) = \boxed{2.5 \times 10^{-8}\ \text{J}}$.

72. (a) Charge remains constant and so it is the $\boxed{\text{same}}$.

(b) $U_C = \frac{1}{2}\dfrac{Q^2}{C}$. Now C is only half as large because d doubles.

So the energy stored $\boxed{\text{doubles to } 5.0 \times 10^{-8}\ \text{J}}$.

73. The energy supplied is $E = U = Pt = (0.50\ \text{W})(5.0\ \text{s}) = 2.5\ \text{J}$.

Also $U_C = \frac{1}{2}CV^2$, ☞ $V = \sqrt{\dfrac{2U_C}{C}} = \sqrt{\dfrac{2(2.5\ \text{J})}{1.0\ \text{F}}} = \boxed{2.2\ \text{V}}$.

74.   (b).

75.   (d), because the dielectric increases the capacitance and, therefore, the charge.

76.   We cannot maintain a nonzero voltage on a conductor; charges will move from the positive to the negative immediately so they cannot be stored.

77.   (a) The capacitance $\boxed{\text{increases}}$ because $C = \kappa C_\text{o}$.

        (b) The voltage $\boxed{\text{remains the same}}$ because it is connected to a battery that has a constant voltage.

78. $\kappa = \dfrac{C}{C_\text{o}} = \dfrac{150 \text{ pF}}{50 \text{ pF}} = \boxed{3.0}$.

79. $Q = CV = \kappa C_\text{o} V = 2.6(50 \times 10^{-12} \text{ F})(24 \text{ V}) = \boxed{3.1 \times 10^{-9} \text{ C}}$,

        $U_C = \frac{1}{2} CV^2 = \frac{1}{2} \kappa C_\text{o} V^2 = \frac{1}{2} 2.6(50 \times 10^{-12} \text{ C})(24 \text{ V})^2 = \boxed{3.7 \times 10^{-8} \text{ J}}$.

80.   (a) $C = \dfrac{\kappa \varepsilon_\text{o} A}{d}$, ☞ $d = \dfrac{\kappa \varepsilon_\text{o} A}{C} = \dfrac{4.6(8.85 \times 10^{-12} \text{ F/m})(0.50 \text{ m}^2)}{0.10 \times 10^{-6} \text{ F}} = \boxed{020 \text{ mm}}$.

        (b) $Q = CV = (0.10 \times 10^{-6} \text{ F})(12 \text{ V}) = \boxed{1.2 \ \mu\text{C}}$.

81.   The charge Q remains constant.

        $\kappa = \dfrac{C}{C_\text{o}} = \dfrac{Q/V}{Q/V_\text{o}} = \dfrac{V_\text{o}}{V} = \dfrac{12 \text{ V}}{5.0 \text{ V}} = \boxed{2.4}$.

82. $C = \dfrac{\kappa \varepsilon_\text{o} A}{d} = \dfrac{2.1(8.85 \times 10^{-12} \text{ F/m})(0.060 \text{ m})(0.080 \text{ m})}{1.5 \times 10^{-3} \text{ m}} = 5.95 \times 10^{-11} \text{ F}$.

        $U_1 = \frac{1}{2} CV^2 = \frac{1}{2}(5.95 \times 10^{-11} \text{ F})(12 \text{ V})^2 = \boxed{4.3 \times 10^{-9} \text{ J}}$.

83.   (b).

84.   (a).

85.   They have the same voltage when they are $\boxed{\text{equal in capacitance}}$.

86.   They have the same charge when they are $\boxed{\text{equal in capacitance}}$

87.   (a) Connect them in $\boxed{\text{parallel}}$ to get maximum equivalent capacitance.

    (b) Connect them in $\boxed{\text{series}}$ to get minimum equivalent capacitance.

88.   (a) $\dfrac{1}{C_s} = \dfrac{1}{C_1} + \dfrac{1}{C_2}$, ☞ $C_s = \dfrac{C_1 C_2}{C_1 + C_2} = \dfrac{(0.40\ \mu\text{F})(0.60\ \mu\text{F})}{0.40\ \mu\text{F} + 0.60\ \mu\text{F}} = \boxed{0.24\ \mu\text{F}}$.

    (b) $C_p = C_1 + C_2 = 0.40\ \mu\text{F} + 0.60\ \mu\text{F} = \boxed{1.0\ \mu\text{F}}$.

89.   (a) The parallel combination will draw $\boxed{\text{more}}$ energy from the battery because the equivalent capacitance is higher and the energy drawn is proportional to capacitance.

    (b) $U_{\text{total}} = \frac{1}{2} C_s V^2$, ☞ $C_s = \dfrac{2 U_{\text{total}}}{V^2} = \dfrac{2(173\ \mu\text{J})}{(12\ \text{V})^2} = 2.40\ \mu\text{F}$.

    Also $\dfrac{1}{C_s} = \dfrac{1}{C_1} + \dfrac{1}{C_2}$, ☞ $C_2 = \dfrac{C_1 C_s}{C_1 - C_s} = \dfrac{(4.0\ \mu\text{C})(2.40\ \mu\text{F})}{4.0\ \mu\text{F} - 2.40\ \mu\text{F}} = \boxed{6.0\ \mu\text{F}}$.

90.   All three are in parallel.   So $C_p = C_1 + C_2 + C_3 = 1.7\ \mu\text{F}$.

    Therefore $C_1 = 1.7\ \mu\text{F} - 0.20\ \mu\text{F} - 0.30\ \mu\text{F} = \boxed{1.2\ \mu\text{F}}$.

91.   (a) The charge on each capacitor will be $\boxed{Q/3}$ because $Q_{\text{total}} = Q_1 + Q_2 + Q_3$.

    Also $Q_1 = Q_2 = Q_3$ because the capacitors have the same capacitance.

    (b) The voltage is the same for all three capacitors.

    $Q_1 = Q_2 = Q_3 = C_1 V = (0.25\ \mu\text{F})(12\ \text{V}) = \boxed{3.0\ \mu\text{C}}$.

    (c) $Q_{\text{total}} = Q_1 + Q_2 + Q_3 = 3(3.0\ \mu\text{C}) = \boxed{9.0\ \mu\text{C}}$.

92.   (a) You can obtain $\boxed{7}$ different values.

    (b) Three in series: $\dfrac{1}{C_s} = \dfrac{1}{C_1} + \dfrac{1}{C_2} + \dfrac{1}{C_2} = \dfrac{3}{1.0\ \mu\text{F}}$,   so $C_s = \boxed{0.33\ \mu\text{F}}$.

    Two in series: $\dfrac{1}{C_s} = \dfrac{1}{C_1} + \dfrac{1}{C_2} = \dfrac{2}{1.0\ \mu\text{F}}$,   so $C_s = \boxed{0.50\ \mu\text{F}}$.

    Two parallel, then series: $C_p = C_1 + C_2 = 2.0\ \mu\text{F}$.

    So $C_s = \dfrac{C_p C_3}{C_p + C_3} = \dfrac{(2.0\ \mu\text{F})(1.0\ \mu\text{F})}{2.0\ \mu\text{F} + 1.0\ \mu\text{F}} = \boxed{0.67\ \mu\text{F}}$.

    Just one: $C = \boxed{1.0\ \mu\text{F}}$.

Two in series, then parallel: $C_p = 0.50\ \mu F + 1.0\ \mu F = \boxed{1.5\ \mu F}$.

Two in parallel: $C_p = 1.0\ \mu F + 1.0\ \mu F = \boxed{2.0\ \mu F}$.

Three in parallel: $C_p = 1.0\ \mu F + 1.0\ \mu F + 1.0\ \mu F = \boxed{3.0\ \mu F}$.

93. Parallel combination gives maximum.

$C_p = C_1 + C_2 + C_3 = 1.5\ \mu F + 2.0\ \mu F + 3.0\ \mu F = \boxed{6.5\ \mu F}$.

Series combination gives minimum.

$$\frac{1}{C_s} = \frac{1}{C_1} + \frac{1}{C_2} + \frac{1}{C_3} = \frac{1}{1.5\ \mu F} + \frac{1}{2.0\ \mu F} + \frac{1}{3.0\ \mu F} = \frac{1}{1.5\ \mu F}.$$

So $C_s = \boxed{0.67\ \mu F}$.

94. The voltage is the same for all capacitors in parallel.

$Q_1 = C_1\,V = (0.10\ \mu F)(6.0\ V) = \boxed{0.60\ \mu C}$,

$Q_2 = (0.20\ \mu F)(6.0\ V) = \boxed{1.2\ \mu C}$, $\quad Q_3 = (0.30\ \mu F)(6.0\ V) = \boxed{1.8\ \mu C}$.

95. (a) Charge is the same for series combination, and voltage is the same for parallel combination.

C_1 and C_2 are in parallel: $\quad C_{p1} = C_1 + C_2 = 0.40\ \mu F + 0.40\ \mu F = 0.80\ \mu F$.

C_3 and C_4 are in parallel: $\quad C_{p3} = C_3 + C_4 = 0.20\ \mu F + 0.60\ \mu F = 0.80\ \mu F$.

C_{p1} and C_{p3} are in series: $\quad \dfrac{1}{C_s} = \dfrac{1}{C_{p1}} + \dfrac{1}{C_{p3}}$,

$C_s = \dfrac{C_{p1}\,C_{p3}}{C_{p1} + C_{p3}} = \dfrac{(0.80\ \mu F)(0.80\ \mu F)}{0.80\ \mu F + 0.80\ \mu F} = 0.40\ \mu F$.

So the total charge on C_s is $Q_s = C_s\,V = (0.40\ \mu F)(12\ V) = 4.8\ \mu C$.

Therefore, C_{p1} and C_{p3} have the same charge as C_s, which is $4.8\ \mu C$.

The voltage across C_{p1} (C_1 and C_2) is $V_1 = \dfrac{Q_{p1}}{C_{p1}} = \dfrac{4.8\ \mu C}{0.80\ \mu F} = 6.0\ V$.

Thus, the charge on C_1 and C_2 is $Q_1 = C_2 = (0.40\ \mu F)(6.0\ V) = 2.4\ \mu C$.

The voltage across C_{p3} (C_3 and C_4) is $V_3 = \dfrac{Q_{p3}}{C_{p3}} = \dfrac{4.8\ \mu C}{0.80\ \mu F} = 6.0\ V$.

Thus, the charges on C_3 and C_4 are $Q_3 = (0.20\ \mu F)(6.0\ V) = 1.2\ \mu F$, $\quad Q_4 = (0.60\ \mu F)(6.0\ V) = 3.6\ \mu C$.

Hence, the answers are $\boxed{2.4\ \mu C \text{ for } C_1,\ 2.4\ \mu C \text{ for } C_2,\ 1.2\ \mu C \text{ for } C_3,\ 3.6\ \mu C \text{ for } C_4}$.

(b) As found in (a), the voltages are $\boxed{6.0\ V \text{ for all the capacitors}}$.

96.   The direction of the field is $\boxed{\text{up}}$.

$$E = -\frac{\Delta V}{\Delta x} = -\frac{-200 \text{ V}}{10.0 \times 10^{-3} \text{ m}} = 2.00 \times 10^4 \text{ V/m} = \boxed{20.0 \text{ kV/m}}.$$

Since the ground is below, its potential should be higher than your location because it increases as you go up.

$$V = |E\Delta x| = (20.0 \text{ kV/m})(0.100 \text{ m}) = 2.00 \text{ kV}.$$

So the potential 10.0 cm below is $\boxed{\text{higher by 2.00 kV}}$ than your location.

97. $$W = \Delta U_e = U - U_o = \frac{kq_1 q_2}{r} = \frac{k(+q)(-q)}{d} = \boxed{-\frac{kq^2}{d}}.$$

98.   Electric field lines are pointing toward the wire.

Looking at the end of the wire   Side view

 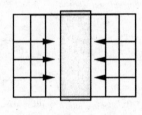

99. $$U_e = \frac{kq_1 q_2}{r} = \frac{(9.0 \times 10^9 \text{ N·m}^2/\text{C}^2)[2(1.6 \times 10^{-19} \text{ C})](-e)}{0.027 \times 10^{-9} \text{ m}} = -107 \text{ eV} = \boxed{-1.1 \times 10^2 \text{ eV}}.$$

100.   (a) C_1 and C_2 are in parallel: $C_p = C_1 + C_2 = 0.15 \ \mu\text{F} + 0.25 \ \mu\text{F} = 0.40 \ \mu\text{F}.$

This C_p and C_3 are in series: $\dfrac{1}{C_s} = \dfrac{1}{C_p} + \dfrac{1}{C_3},$

so $C_s = \dfrac{C_p C_3}{C_p + C_3} = \dfrac{(0.40 \ \mu\text{F})(0.30 \ \mu\text{F})}{0.40 \ \mu\text{F} + 0.30 \ \mu\text{F}} = \boxed{0.17 \ \mu\text{F}}.$

(b) $Q = C_s V = (0.171 \ \mu\text{F})(12 \text{ V}) = \boxed{2.1 \ \mu\text{C}}.$

(c) Charge is the same for series combination, and voltage is the same for parallel combination.

So the charge on C_3 is 2.1 μC.

Therefore, $V_3 = \dfrac{Q_3}{C_3} = \dfrac{2.06 \ \mu\text{F}}{0.30 \ \mu\text{F}} = 6.9 \text{ V}.$

Thus, the voltage on C_1 and C_2 is 12 V − 6.9 V = 5.1 V.

Hence, the answers are $\boxed{V_1 = V_2 = 5.1 \text{ V and } V_3 = 6.9 \text{ V}}.$

101. (a) The top plate should be at a $\boxed{\text{higher}}$ potential because the electron has negative charge. It will

experience an upward force if the potential is higher at the top.

(b) The electric force must balance the gravitational force.

$$F_e = qE = q\,\frac{\Delta V}{\Delta x} = w = mg,$$

So $\quad \Delta V = \dfrac{mg\Delta x}{q} = \dfrac{(9.11 \times 10^{-31}\ \text{kg})(9.80\ \text{m/s}^2)(0.015\ \text{m})}{1.6 \times 10^{-19}\ \text{C}} = \boxed{8.4 \times 10^{-13}\ \text{V}}.$

102. (a) $C_0 = \dfrac{\varepsilon_0 A_0}{d}, \quad \text{☞} \quad A_0 = \dfrac{Cd}{\varepsilon_0} = \dfrac{(1.0\ \text{F})(0.50 \times 10^{-3}\ \text{m})}{8.85 \times 10^{-12}\ \text{C}^2/\text{N·m}^2} = \boxed{5.6 \times 10^{7}\ \text{m}^2}.$

(b) $C = C_0 = K\dfrac{\varepsilon_0 A}{d}, \quad \text{☞} \quad A = \dfrac{A_0}{K} = \dfrac{5.65 \times 10^{7}\ \text{m}^2}{2.6} = \boxed{2.2 \times 10^{7}\ \text{m}^2}.$

103. $\Delta U_e = -q\Delta V = eE\Delta x = (1.6 \times 10^{-19}\ \text{C})(5.5 \times 10^{4}\ \text{V/m})(0.030\ \text{m}) = \boxed{2.6 \times 10^{-16}\ \text{J}}.$

104. (a) The direction of the electric field is $\boxed{\text{radially inward}}$.

(b) The resting membrane potential is -70 mV (typical value).

$$E = \frac{\Delta V}{d} = \frac{70 \times 10^{-3}\ \text{V}}{10 \times 10^{-9}\ \text{m}} = \boxed{7.0 \times 10^{6}\ \text{V/m}}.$$

CHAPTER 17

ELECTRIC CURRENT AND RESISTANCE

1.   (b).

2.   (d).

3.   (a).

4.   The chemical membrane is to $\boxed{\text{prevent the two ions from each electrode from mixing}}$. If the ions mix, one ion can be attracted to the other electrode along with that electrode's ion. The result is that it could "coat" the other electrode, and then essentially the two electrodes are identical.

5. $\boxed{\text{No}}$, this is not possible. Any battery has internal resistance, and there will be a voltage across the internal resistance when the battery is in use. The terminal voltage is always smaller than the emf of the battery when it is in use.

6.   EMF is the potential difference across the terminals of a battery when it is not connected to a circuit or there is no current in the battery. Terminal voltage is the potential difference across the terminals of a battery when it is connected to a circuit or there is a current in the battery. All batteries have internal resistance. When there is a current, the internal resistance of the battery will also have a potential difference. So $\boxed{\text{EMF}}$ is always greater.

7.   (a) $V = V_1 + V_2 = 1.5 \text{ V} + 1.5 \text{ V} = \boxed{3.0 \text{ V}}$.

      (b) $V = V_1 = V_2 = \boxed{1.5 \text{ V}}$.

8.   (a) $V = V_1 + V_2 + \ldots = 6(1.5 \text{ V}) = \boxed{9.0 \text{ V}}$.

      (b) $V = V_1 = V_2 = \ldots = \boxed{1.5 \text{ V}}$.

9.   (a) $V = V_1 + V_2 + V_3 = 2(6.0 \text{ V}) + 12 \text{ V} = \boxed{24 \text{ V}}$.

      (b) The $\boxed{\text{two 6.0-V in series, together in parallel with the 12-V}}$.

10. Using just one battery at a time gives three voltages: 1.0 V, 3.0 V, and 12 V.

Using just two batteries at a time gives six voltages:

two in series at a time, 4.0 V, 13 V, and 15 V;

two in parallel at a time, 1.0 V, 3.0 V, 1.0 V;

so three more different voltages of 4.0 V, 13 V, and 15 V.

Using three batteries at a time gives eight voltages:

two in parallel, then in series with the third, 13 V, 4.0 V, and 4.0 V;

all three in series, 16 V; all three in parallel, 1.0 V;

two in series, then parallel to the third, 4.0 V, 3.0 V, 1.0 V;

so there is one new different voltage of 16 V.

Therefore there are $\boxed{\text{7 different voltages}}$ and they are

$\boxed{\text{1.0 V, 3.0 V, 4.0 V, 12 V, 13 V, 15 V, and 16 V}}$.

11. (a) They have $\boxed{\text{the same}}$ total voltage. The total voltage of identical batteries in parallel is the same as the voltage of each individual battery, and the total voltage of the batteries in series is the sum of the voltages of each individual battery. Each arrangement has one parallel and one series so they have the same total voltage.

(b) Arrangement A: Series gives 1.5 V + 1.5 V = 3.0 V for each group.

Parallel gives the same $\boxed{\text{3.0 V}}$ for the total.

Arrangement B: Parallel gives the same 1.5 V for each group.

Series gives 1.5 V + 1.5 V = $\boxed{\text{3.0 V}}$ for the total.

12. (d).

13. The current inside the battery is from $\boxed{\text{negative to positive}}$. The current has to complete a loop. Outside the battery the current goes from positive to negative, so it has to be from negative to positive inside the battery.

14. This is because the $\boxed{\text{electric field travels close to the speed of light}}$. Although the electron moves slowly, there are immediate movements of electrons as soon as a voltage is applied because there are free electrons everywhere in the circuit.

15. $I = \dfrac{q}{t} = \dfrac{30 \text{ C}}{120 \text{ s}} = \boxed{0.25 \text{ A}}$.

16. $I = \dfrac{q}{t}$, ☞ $t = \dfrac{q}{I} = \dfrac{2.5 \text{ C}}{5.0 \times 10^{-3} \text{ A}} = 500 \text{ s} = \boxed{8.3 \text{ min}}$.

17. (a) $q = It = (0.50 \times 10^{-3} \text{ A})(600 \text{ s}) = \boxed{0.30 \text{ C}}$.

    (b) $E = \Delta U = q\Delta V = (0.30 \text{ C})(3.0 \text{ V}) = \boxed{0.90 \text{ J}}$.

18. $q = It = (50 \text{ A})(1.5 \text{ s}) = 75 \text{ C}$. $n = \dfrac{q}{e} = \dfrac{75 \text{ C}}{1.60 \times 10^{-19} \text{ C}}) = \boxed{4.7 \times 10^{20}}$ electrons.

19. (a) The answer is $\boxed{\text{none of the preceding}}$, since current depends on both the charge and the time interval the charge flows past a certain location.

    (b) $I_1 = \dfrac{q_1}{t_1} = \dfrac{20 \text{ C}}{1.25(60 \text{ s})} = 0.267 \text{ A}$, $I_2 = \dfrac{30 \text{ C}}{1.52(60 \text{ s})} = 0.329 \text{ A}$.

    So $\Delta I = I_2 - I_1 = 0.061 \text{ A}$. Therefore, the $\boxed{\text{2nd wire by 0.062 A}}$.

20. $q = It = (5.0 \text{ A})(20 \text{ h})(3600 \text{ s/h}) = \boxed{3.6 \times 10^5 \text{ C}}$.

21. (a) The net current will be $\boxed{\text{to the left}}$. The current due to the protons will be to the left, and the current due to the electrons will also be to the left because electrons have negative charge.

    (b) $I = \dfrac{q_{net}}{t} = \dfrac{-6.7 \text{ C} - (+8.3 \text{ C})}{4.5 \text{ s}} = -\boxed{3.3 \text{ A}}$.

22. (a) In each second.

    $q = It = (9.5 \times 10^{-3} \text{ A})(1.0 \text{ s}) = 9.5 \times 10^{-3} \text{ C} = (9.5 \times 10^{-3} \text{ C}) \times \dfrac{1 \, e}{1.6 \times 10^{-19} \text{ C}} = \boxed{5.9 \times 10^{16} \text{ protons}}$.

    (b) $P = \dfrac{E}{t} = \dfrac{(5.9 \times 10^{16} \text{ protons})(20 \times 10^6 \text{ eV/proton})(1.6 \times 10^{-19} \text{ J/eV})}{1.0 \text{ s}} = \boxed{1.9 \times 10^5 \text{ J/s}}$.

23. (a).

24. (d).

25. From $V = (R)I$ ($y = mx$ is the equation for a straight line where m is the slope) we conclude that $\boxed{\text{the one with the smaller slope}}$ is less resistive.

26. This is because the $\boxed{\text{resistance is low and the current is high at turn-on}}$. Once the lamp is hot, its resistance increases and current decreases, so there is less chance of burning out.

27.   Because nichrome has a small temperature coefficient of resistivity and a high resistivity, its

       $\boxed{\text{performance is more temperature independent and compact in size}}$.

28.   (a) $R = \dfrac{\rho L}{A}$, ☞ $\dfrac{R_2}{R_1} = \dfrac{L_2}{L_1}\dfrac{A_1}{A_2} = (2)\left(\tfrac{1}{2}\right) = 1$.   Also $I = \dfrac{V}{R}$.

       So the current is the $\boxed{\text{same}}$.

       (b) Since $A = \dfrac{\pi d^2}{4}$, half the diameter means 1/4 the area, so $\dfrac{A_2}{A_1} = 1/4$.

       Therefore $\dfrac{R_2}{R_1} = (1)(4) = 4$.   Thus $\dfrac{I_2}{I_1} = \dfrac{R_1}{R_2} = 1/4$, i.e., $\boxed{\text{one-quarter the current}}$.

29. $\boxed{\text{The number rises with temperature}}$. There are also more collisions (more resistance) among the charge

       carriers as temperature increases. However, the former dominates.

30.   The $\boxed{\text{current decreases as internal resistance increases so the terminal voltage decreases}}$.

31.   (a) $V = IR = (1.9\ \text{A})(6.0\ \Omega) = \boxed{11.4\ \text{V}}$.

       (b) $\mathscr{E} = V + I\,r$, ☞ $r = \dfrac{\mathscr{E} - V}{I} = \dfrac{12\ \text{V} - 11.4\ \text{V}}{1.9\ \text{A}} = \boxed{0.32\ \Omega}$.

32. $\mathscr{E} = V + Ir = IR + Ir = I(R + r) = (1.5\ \text{A})(5.0\ \Omega + 0.15\ \Omega) = \boxed{7.7\ \text{V}}$.

33.   (a) Aluminum wire would have to have $\boxed{\text{a greater diameter}}$. Since aluminum has a higher resistivity, its

       area (diameter) must be greater, if the length of the wire is the same, to have the same resistance as copper

       according to $R = \dfrac{\rho L}{A}$.

       (b) $R = \dfrac{\rho L}{A}$, ☞ $A = \pi r^2 = \dfrac{\rho L}{R}$. So $\dfrac{r_{\text{Al}}}{r_{\text{Cu}}} = \sqrt{\dfrac{\rho_{\text{Al}}}{\rho_{\text{Cu}}}} = \sqrt{\dfrac{2.82 \times 10^{-8}\ \Omega\cdot\text{m}}{1.70 \times 10^{-8}\ \Omega\cdot\text{m}}} = \boxed{1.29}$.

34. $I = \dfrac{V}{R} = \dfrac{12\ \text{V}}{15\ \Omega} = \boxed{0.80\ \text{A}}$.

35. $V = IR = (0.50\ \text{A})(2.0\ \Omega) = \boxed{1.0\ \text{V}}$.

36. $R = \dfrac{V}{I} = \dfrac{100 \times 10^{-3}\ \text{V}}{12.5 \times 10^{-3}\ \text{A}} = \boxed{8.00\ \Omega}$.

37. $R = \dfrac{\rho L}{A} = \dfrac{\rho L}{\pi r^2} = \dfrac{(1.70 \times 10^{-8}\ \Omega\cdot\text{m})(0.60\ \text{m})}{\pi (0.05 \times 10^{-2}\ \text{m})^2} = \boxed{1.3 \times 10^{-2}\ \Omega}$.

38. $V = IR = (1.5\ \text{A})(100\ \Omega) = 150\ \text{V}$.

The terminal voltage of one battery is $\dfrac{150\ \text{V}}{2} = \boxed{75\ \text{V}}$ since they are in series.

39. $I = \dfrac{V}{R} = \dfrac{12\ \text{V}}{2.5\ \Omega} = 4.8\ \text{A} = (4.8\ \text{C/s}) \times \dfrac{1\ \text{electron}}{1.6 \times 10^{-19}\ \text{C}} = \boxed{3.0 \times 10^{19}\ \text{electrons/s}}$.

40. (a) $R = \dfrac{V}{I} = \dfrac{\rho L}{A}$, $\quad\text{\reflectbox{$\to$}}\quad$ $\rho = \dfrac{VA}{IL} = \dfrac{(100\ \text{V})(0.50 \times 10^{-2}\ \text{m})^2}{(5.0\ \text{A})(20\ \text{m})} = \boxed{2.5 \times 10^{-5}\ \Omega\cdot\text{m}}$.

(b) This is $\boxed{\text{likely a semiconductor}}$.

41. $I = \dfrac{V}{R} = \dfrac{V}{\rho L/A} = \dfrac{VA}{\rho L}$, $\quad\text{\reflectbox{$\to$}}\quad$ $I \propto \dfrac{1}{L}$.

$\dfrac{I_{0.50}}{I_{2.0}} = \dfrac{L_{2.0}}{L_{0.50}} = \dfrac{2.0\ \text{m}}{0.50\ \text{m}} = 4$. That is, $\boxed{\text{the shorter wire carries 4 times the current}}$.

42. (a) The resistance of the thinner wire is $\boxed{9\ \text{times}}$ that of the resistance of the thicker wire. Since $R = \dfrac{\rho L}{A}$

and A is proportional to the diameter squared, having 1/3 of the diameter means 1/9 of the area and therefore 9 times the resistance.

(b) $R = \dfrac{\rho L}{A} = \dfrac{\rho L}{\pi d^2/4} = \dfrac{4\rho}{\pi d^2}$, $\quad\text{\reflectbox{$\to$}}\quad$ $R \propto \dfrac{1}{d^2}$.

$\dfrac{R_{\text{thin}}}{R_{\text{thick}}} = \dfrac{R^2_{\text{thick}}}{R^2_{\text{thin}}} = 3^2 = 9$. So $R_{\text{thin}} = 9 R_{\text{thick}} = 9(1.0\ \Omega) = \boxed{9.0\ \Omega}$.

43. $R = R_0 (1 + \alpha \Delta T) = \dfrac{\rho_0 L (1 + \alpha \Delta T)}{A}$

$= \dfrac{(10 \times 10^{-8}\ \Omega\cdot\text{m})(0.75\ \text{m})[1 + (6.51 \times \times 10^{-3}\ \text{C}^{\circ -1})(360\ \text{C}^\circ)]}{2.0 \times 10^{-6}\ \text{m}^2} = \boxed{0.13\ \Omega}$.

44. $\rho = \rho_0 (1 + \alpha \Delta T) = \rho_0 [1 + (6.80 \times 10^{-3}\ \text{C}^{\circ -1})(80\ \text{C}^\circ)] = 1.544 \rho_0$.

So the percentage variation is $\dfrac{\rho - \rho_0}{\rho_0} = \dfrac{\rho}{\rho_0} - 1 = 0.544 = \boxed{54\%\ \text{increase}}$.

45. $\Delta R = R_0\, \alpha \Delta T = (25\ \text{m}\Omega)(6.80 \times 10^{-3}\ \text{C}^{\circ -1})(27\ \text{C}^\circ) = \boxed{4.6\ \text{m}\Omega}$.

46. $\Delta R = R_0\,\alpha\Delta T = (10.00\ \Omega)(4.29 \times 10^{-3}\ \mathrm{C^{\circ -1}})(100\ \mathrm{C^{\circ}}) = \boxed{4.29\ \Omega}$.

47. $R_1 = \dfrac{V_1}{I_1} = \dfrac{12\ \mathrm{V}}{0.185\ \mathrm{A}} = 65\ \Omega, \quad R_2 = \dfrac{90\ \mathrm{V}}{1.25\ \mathrm{A}} = 72\ \Omega.$

     So it is $\boxed{\text{not ohmic}}$ since $R \neq$ constant.

48. $R = \dfrac{\rho L}{A}, \quad \text{☞} \quad L = \dfrac{RA}{\rho} = \dfrac{(20\ \Omega)(\pi)(2.588 \times 10^{-3}\ \mathrm{m})^2/4}{100 \times 10^{-8}\ \Omega\cdot\mathrm{m}} = \boxed{105\ \mathrm{m}}.$

49.   (a) The resistance after the stretch will be $\boxed{\text{greater}}$. After the stretch, the length L increases and the cross-

     sectional area A decreases, so R increases according to $R = \dfrac{\rho L}{A}$.

     (b) The volume (material) of the wire remains constant. $\quad A_1 L_1 = A_2 L_2, \quad \text{☞} \quad \dfrac{A_1}{A_2} = \dfrac{L_2}{L_1}.$

     $R = \dfrac{\rho L}{A}, \quad \text{☞} \quad \dfrac{R_2}{R_1} = \dfrac{L_2}{L_1}\dfrac{A_1}{A_2} = \left(\dfrac{L_2}{L_1}\right)^2 = \left(\dfrac{1.25}{1}\right)^2 = \boxed{1.6}.$

50. $R = \dfrac{\rho L}{A}, \quad \text{☞} \quad A = \dfrac{\pi d^2}{4} = \dfrac{\rho L}{R}.$

     So $\quad d = \sqrt{\dfrac{4\rho L}{\pi R}} = \sqrt{\dfrac{4(2.82 \times 10^{-8}\ \Omega\cdot\mathrm{m})(20\ \mathrm{m})}{\pi(0.25 \times 10^{-3}\ \Omega)}} = \boxed{5.4 \times 10^{-2}\ \mathrm{m}}.$

51. $\Delta R = R_0\,\alpha\Delta T, \quad \text{☞} \quad \Delta T = \dfrac{\Delta R}{R_0\,\alpha} = \dfrac{\Delta R}{R_0}\dfrac{1}{\alpha} = \pm 0.050\,\dfrac{1}{\alpha} = \pm 0.050\,\dfrac{1}{4.29 \times 10^{-3}\ \mathrm{C^{\circ -1}}} = \pm 11.7\ \mathrm{C^{\circ}}.$

     So $\quad T_{max} = 20^{\circ}\mathrm{C} + 11.7\ \mathrm{C^{\circ}} = 32^{\circ}\mathrm{C} \quad$ and $\quad T_{min} = 20^{\circ}\mathrm{C} - 11.7\ \mathrm{C^{\circ}} = 8.3^{\circ}\mathrm{C}.$

     Therefore the range is from $\boxed{8.2^{\circ}\mathrm{C} \text{ to } 32^{\circ}\mathrm{C}}$.

52.   (a) $\boxed{\text{Yes}}$, the resistor is an ohmic resistor because the V vs. I graph is a straight line (constant slope).

     (b) $R = \text{slope} = \dfrac{\Delta V}{\Delta I} = \dfrac{40\mathrm{V} - 10\ \mathrm{V}}{20\ \mathrm{A} - 5.0\ \mathrm{A}} = \boxed{2.0\ \Omega}.$

53. $I = \dfrac{V}{R} = \dfrac{V}{R_0\,(1 + \alpha\Delta T)}, \quad \text{☞} \quad \dfrac{I}{I_0} = \dfrac{1}{1 + \alpha\Delta T}.$

     So $\quad I = \dfrac{1}{1 + \alpha\Delta T}\,I_0 = \dfrac{1}{1 + (-7.0 \times 10^{-2}\ \mathrm{C^{\circ -1}})(5\ \mathrm{C^{\circ}})}\,(0.50\ \mathrm{A}) = \boxed{0.77\ \mathrm{A}}.$

54.   (a) The current will ⌈decrease⌉ if the temperature increases. Platinum has a positive temperature coefficient of resistivity, so its resistivity, and therefore resistance, increases with temperature. The increased resistance causes a decrease in current according to Ohm's law.

(b) $I_0 = \dfrac{V}{R_0} = \dfrac{1.5 \text{ V}}{5.0 \ \Omega} = 0.30$ A.

$I = \dfrac{V}{R} = \dfrac{V}{R_0(1 + \alpha\Delta T)} = \dfrac{1.5 \text{ V}}{(5.0 \ \Omega)[1 + (3.93 \times 10^{-3} \ \text{C}^{\circ -1})(2000 \ \text{C}^{\circ})]} = 0.0334$ A.

So $\Delta I = 0.0334 \text{ A} - 0.30 \text{ A} = -0.27$ A, i.e., ⌈decrease by 0.27 A⌉.

55.   (d).

56.   (b), since $P = \dfrac{V^2}{R}$.

57.   (d), because $P = I^2 R$.

58. $P = \dfrac{V^2}{R}$. So its ⌈power output would quadruple, and it would overheat and burn out⌉.

59.   Since $P = \dfrac{V^2}{R}$, the bulb of higher power has smaller resistance or thicker wire.

So ⌈the wire in the 60-W bulb would be thicker⌉.

60.   The ⌈5.0 Ω⌉ consumes more power because it has the smaller resistance.

With the ⌈same voltage, more curent⌉ is through the 5.0 Ω so the power is more.

61. $P = \dfrac{V^2}{R}$,   ☞ $R = \dfrac{V^2}{P} = \dfrac{(120 \text{ V})^2}{100 \text{ W}} = \boxed{144 \ \Omega}$.

62. $P = \dfrac{V^2}{R} = \dfrac{(110 \text{ V})^2}{10 \ \Omega} = \boxed{1.2 \times 10^3 \text{ W}}$.

63. $P = I^2 R = (13 \text{ A})^2 (12 \ \Omega) = \boxed{2.0 \times 10^3 \text{ W}}$.

64. $\dfrac{V^2}{\Omega} = \dfrac{V^2}{V/A} = V \ A = \dfrac{J}{C} \dfrac{C}{s} = J/s = W$.

65. $P = \dfrac{V^2}{R}$,   ☞ $R = \dfrac{V^2}{P} = \dfrac{(240 \text{ V})^2}{50 \times 10^3 \text{ W}} = \boxed{1.2 \ \Omega}$.

66.   The heat (energy) needed is

$$Q = cm\Delta T = [4186 \text{ J/(kg·C°)}](50 \text{ gal})(3.785 \text{ kg/gal})(60 \text{ C°}) = 4.75 \times 10^7 \text{ J}.$$

At 90% efficiency, the energy input is $\dfrac{4.75 \times 10^7 \text{ J}}{0.90} = 5.28 \times 10^7 \text{ J}.$

So $t = \dfrac{E}{P} = \dfrac{5.28 \times 10^7 \text{ J}}{50 \times 10^3 \text{ W}} = 1.05 \times 10^3 \text{ s} = \boxed{18 \text{ min}}.$

67.   (a) The resistor will dissipate $\boxed{1/4}$ times the designed power if the voltage is halved. If the voltage is halved, the current is also halved. Since power is equal to voltage times current, power becomes ¼ as large.

(b) $P = IV = \dfrac{V^2}{R}$,   ☞ $\dfrac{P}{P_0} = \dfrac{V^2}{V_0^2} = \dfrac{(40 \text{ V})^2}{(120 \text{ V})^2} = 1/9.$ So $P = \dfrac{P_0}{9} = \dfrac{90 \text{ W}}{9} = \boxed{10 \text{ W}}.$

68.   (a) $I = \dfrac{V}{R} = \dfrac{1.50 \text{ V}}{2.50 \text{ }\Omega} = \boxed{0.600 \text{ A}}.$

(b) $q = It = (0.600 \text{ A})(6.00 \text{ h})(3600 \text{ s/h}) = \boxed{1.30 \times 10^4 \text{ C}}.$

(c) $E = qV = (1.30 \times 10^4 \text{ C})(1.50 \text{ V}) = \boxed{1.94 \times 10^4 \text{ J}}.$

Alternate method: $E = pt = I^2Rt = (0.600 \text{ A})^2(2.50 \text{ }\Omega)(6.00 \text{ h})(3600 \text{ s/h}) = 1.94 \times 10^4 \text{ J}.$

69.   (a) $E = Pt = IVt = (18 \text{ A})(240 \text{ V})(1.0 \text{ s}) = \boxed{4.3 \times 10^3 \text{ J}}.$

(b) $R = \dfrac{V}{I} = \dfrac{240 \text{ V}}{18 \text{ A}} = \boxed{13 \text{ }\Omega}.$

70.   (a) $E = P\,t = (4.5 \text{ kW})(2.0 \text{ h/d})(30 \text{ d}) = 270 \text{ kWh}.$

So it costs $(270 \text{ kWh})(15 \text{ ¢/kWh}) = \boxed{\$40.50}.$

(b) From Table 17.2, a water heater draws 37.5 A at 240 V.   So $R = \dfrac{V}{I} = \dfrac{240 \text{ V}}{37.5 \text{ A}} = \boxed{6.4 \text{ }\Omega}.$

71. $P = \dfrac{V^2}{R}$,   ☞ $R = \dfrac{V^2}{P} = \dfrac{(120 \text{ V})^2}{(15 \times 10^3 \text{ J/min})(1 \text{ min})/(60 \text{ s})} = \boxed{58 \text{ }\Omega}.$

72. $E = Pt = (0.200 \text{ kW})(10 \text{ h/day})(365 \text{ day/year}) = 730 \text{ kWh/year}.$

So the annual cost is $(730 \text{ kWh})(15 \text{ ¢/kWh}) = \boxed{\$110}.$

73.   (a) $E = Pt = IVt = (15 \text{ A})(120 \text{ V})(1/3 \text{ h}) = 600 \text{ Wh} = \boxed{0.60 \text{ kWh}}.$

(b) It costs $(0.60 \text{ kWh})(15 \text{ ¢/kWh}) = \boxed{\$0.09}.$

74. $P = \dfrac{V^2}{R}$, ☞ $V = \sqrt{PR}$.

For 100 Ω, $V = \sqrt{(1.5 \text{ W})(100 \ \Omega)} = \boxed{12 \text{ V}}$;

for 25 kΩ, $V = \sqrt{(0.25 \text{ W})(25 \times 10^3 \ \Omega)} = \boxed{79 \text{ V}}$.

75. (a) $I = \dfrac{V}{R} = \dfrac{15 \text{ V}}{100 \ \Omega} = \boxed{0.15 \text{ A}}$.

(b) $R = \dfrac{\rho L}{A}$, ☞ $\rho = \dfrac{RA}{L} = \dfrac{(100 \ \Omega)(\pi)(1.5 \times 10^{-3} \text{ m})^2}{5.0 \text{ m}} = \boxed{1.4 \times 10^{-4} \ \Omega \cdot \text{m}}$.

(c) $P = VI = (15 \text{ V})(0.15 \text{ A}) = \boxed{2.3 \text{ W}}$.

76. (a) The dissipated power will $\boxed{\text{decrease}}$ because the current in the wire decreases. As temperature

increases, the resistance of the wire increases. Since power is voltage times current, the power decreases.

(b) $R = R_0 (1 + \alpha \Delta T) = R_0 [1 + (4.5 \times 10^{-3} \text{ C}^{\circ -1})(150 \text{ C}^\circ)] = 1.68 R_0$.

$P = \dfrac{V^2}{R}$, ☞ $\dfrac{P}{P_0} = \dfrac{R_0}{R} = \dfrac{1}{1.68} = 0.595$.

So $P = 0.595(500 \text{ W}) = 298 \text{ W}$.

Therefore $\Delta P = 298 \text{ W} - 500 \text{ W} \approx -202 \text{ W}$. Thus it is a $\boxed{\text{decrease by 202 W}}$.

77. (a) $E = Pt = \dfrac{V^2}{R} t = \dfrac{[4(1.5 \text{ V})]^2 (60 \text{ s})}{20 \ \Omega} = \boxed{1.1 \times 10^2 \text{ J}}$.

(b) $E = \dfrac{(1.5 \text{ V})^2 (60 \text{ s})}{20 \ \Omega} = \boxed{6.8 \text{ J}}$.

78. (a) $I = \dfrac{P}{V} = \dfrac{5.5 \times 10^3 \text{ W}}{240 \text{ V}} = 23 \text{ A} > 20 \text{ A}$. So it should have a $\boxed{\text{30-A breaker}}$.

(b) The heat (energy) is $Q = cm\Delta T = [4190 \text{ J/(kg} \cdot \text{C}^\circ)](55 \text{ gal})(3.785 \text{ kg/gal})(60 \text{ C}^\circ) = 5.23 \times 10^7 \text{ J}$.

The energy input is $E = \dfrac{5.23 \times 10^7 \text{ J}}{0.85} = 6.16 \times 10^7 \text{ J}$.

$t = \dfrac{E}{P} = \dfrac{6.16 \times 10^7 \text{ J}}{5.5 \times 10^3 \text{ W}} = 1.12 \times 10^4 \text{ s} = \boxed{3.1 \text{ h}}$.

79. The heat required is $Q = cm\Delta T = [4190 \text{ J/(kg} \cdot \text{C}^\circ)](0.300 \text{ kg})(60 \text{ C}^\circ) = 7.54 \times 10^4 \text{ J}$.

The energy input is $E = \dfrac{7.54 \times 10^4 \text{ J}}{0.75} = 1.01 \times 10^5 \text{ J}$.

$P = \dfrac{E}{t} = \dfrac{V^2}{R}$, ☞ $R = \dfrac{V^2 t}{E} = \dfrac{(120 \text{ V})^2 (2.5)(60 \text{ s})}{1.01 \times 10^5 \text{ J}} = \boxed{21 \ \Omega}$.

80. $P = \dfrac{V^2}{R}$, ☞ $\dfrac{P_2}{P_1} = \left(\dfrac{V_2}{V_1}\right)^2 = \left(\dfrac{0.95 \times 120 \text{ V}}{120 \text{ V}}\right)^2 = 0.90.$

So $P_2 = 0.90 P_1 = 0.90(100 \text{ W}) = \boxed{90 \text{ W}}$.

81. $P = \dfrac{V^2}{R}$, ☞ $R = \dfrac{V^2}{P}$, so $\dfrac{R_2}{R_1} = \dfrac{V_2^{\,2}}{V_1^{\,2}}\dfrac{P_1}{P_2}.$ So $\dfrac{R_{120\text{ V}}}{R_{90\text{ V}}} = \dfrac{(120 \text{ V})^2}{(60 \text{ V})^2}\dfrac{20 \text{ W}}{60 \text{ W}} = \boxed{4/3}$.

82. (a) The input power to the pump is $P = \dfrac{2.00 \text{ kW}}{0.84} = 2.38 \text{ kW}.$

$P = VI$, ☞ $I = \dfrac{P}{V} = \dfrac{2.38 \times 10^3 \text{ W}}{240 \text{ V}} = \boxed{9.9 \text{ A}}$.

(b) $R = \dfrac{V}{I} = \dfrac{240 \text{ V}}{9.9 \text{ A}} = \boxed{24 \ \Omega}$.

83. $E = \Sigma P t = (5.0 \text{ kW})(0.30)(24 \text{ h/d})(30 \text{ d}) + (0.8 \text{ kW})(0.50 \text{ h}) + (0.625 \text{ kW})(1/4 \text{ h/d})(30 \text{ d})$

$\qquad + (0.5 \text{ kW})(0.15)(24 \text{ h/d})(30 \text{ d}) + (10.5 \text{ kW})(10 \text{ h}) + (0.1 \text{ kW})(120 \text{ h}) = 1256 \text{ kWh}.$

So it costs $(1256 \text{ kWh})(\$0.12 \text{ /kWh}) = \boxed{\$151}$.

84. (a) Since copper has a positive temperature coefficient of resistance and carbon has a negative one, copper will have a $\boxed{\text{higher resistance}}$.

(b) $R = R_o (1 + \alpha \Delta T)$, ☞ $\dfrac{R_{Cu}}{R_C} = \dfrac{1 + \alpha_{Cu} \Delta T}{1 + \alpha_C \Delta T} = \dfrac{1 + (6.80 \times 10^{-3} \text{ C}^{\circ -1})(10.0 \text{ C}^\circ)}{1 + (-5.0 \times 10^{-4} \text{ C}^{\circ -1})(10.0 \text{ C}^\circ)} = \boxed{1.07}$.

85. $\dfrac{\Delta R}{R_o} = \alpha \Delta T = 0.25$, ☞ $\Delta T = \dfrac{0.25}{3.93 \times 10^{-3} \text{ C}^{\circ -1}} = \boxed{64 \text{ C}^\circ}$.

86. $I_o = \dfrac{V}{R_o} = \dfrac{12 \text{ V}}{1.75 \ \Omega} = 6.86 \text{ A}.$ $R = R_o (1 + \alpha \Delta T) = (1.75 \ \Omega)[1 + (6.51 \times 10^{-3} \text{ C}^{\circ -1})(280 \text{ C}^\circ)] = 4.94 \ \Omega.$

So $I = \dfrac{12 \text{ V}}{4.94 \ \Omega} = 2.43 \text{ A}.$ Therefore $\Delta I = 2.43 \text{ A} - 6.86 \text{ A} = -4.4 \text{ A} = \boxed{4.4 \text{ A less}}$.

87. (a) $I = \dfrac{P}{V} = \dfrac{40 \text{ W}}{120 \text{ V}} = \boxed{0.33 \text{ A}}$.

(b) $R = \dfrac{V}{I} = \dfrac{120 \text{ V}}{0.33 \text{ A}} = \boxed{3.6 \times 10^2 \ \Omega}$.

88. $E = Pt = (0.075 \text{ kW})(8.0 \text{ h}) = 0.60 \text{ kWh}.$

So it costs $10 \times (0.60 \text{ kWh})(\$0.15/\text{KWh}) = \boxed{\$0.90}$.

89. $P = \dfrac{V^2}{R}$, ☞ $R_o = \dfrac{V^2}{P_o} = \dfrac{(120\ \text{V})^2}{1600\ \text{W}} = 9.00\ \Omega$.

Since $R = \dfrac{\rho L}{A}$, R is $0.90 R_o$. So $P = \dfrac{(120\ \text{V})^2}{0.90(9.00\ \Omega)} = 1.78 \times 10^3\ \text{W} = 1.78\ \text{kW}$.

$\boxed{\text{It increases to 1.78 kW}}$.

90. $R = R_o\,(1 + \alpha \Delta T) = (200\ \Omega)[1 + (4.5 \times 10^{-3}\ \text{C}^{\circ -1})(1580\ \text{C}^\circ)] = \boxed{1.62 \times 10^3\ \Omega}$.

91. $R = \dfrac{\rho L}{A}$. If aluminum is at room temperature, $\dfrac{R_{\text{Cu}}}{R_{\text{Al}}} = 1 = \dfrac{\rho_{\text{Cu}}(1 + \alpha_{\text{Cu}}\Delta T)}{\rho_{\text{Al}}}$.

So $\Delta T = \dfrac{\rho_{\text{Al}}/\rho_{\text{Cu}} - 1}{\alpha_{\text{Cu}}} = \dfrac{(2.82 \times 10^{-8}\ \Omega\cdot\text{m})/(1.70 \times 10^{-8}\ \Omega\cdot\text{m}) - 1}{6.80 \times 10^{-3}\ \text{C}^{\circ -1}} = 96.9^\circ\text{C}^\circ$.

Therefore $20^\circ\text{C} + 96.9\ \text{C}^\circ = 117^\circ\text{C}$, i.e., $\boxed{\text{copper at } 117^\circ\text{C}}$.

If copper is at room temperature, $\dfrac{R_{\text{Cu}}}{R_{\text{Al}}} = 1 = \dfrac{\rho_{\text{Cu}}}{\rho_{\text{Al}}(1 + \alpha_{\text{Al}}\Delta T)}$.

So $\Delta T = \dfrac{\rho_{\text{Cu}}/\rho_{\text{Al}} - 1}{\alpha_{\text{Al}}} = \dfrac{(1.70 \times 10^{-8}\ \Omega\cdot\text{m})/(2.82 \times 10^{-8}\ \Omega\cdot\text{m}) - 1}{4.29 \times 10^{-3}\ \text{C}^{\circ -1}} = -92.6^\circ\text{C}^\circ$.

So $20^\circ\text{C} - 92.6\ \text{C}^\circ = -73^\circ\text{C}$, i.e., $\boxed{\text{aluminum at } -73^\circ\text{C}}$.

92. (a) $R = \dfrac{\rho L}{A} = \dfrac{(2.82 \times 10^{-8}\ \Omega\cdot\text{m})(100\ \text{m})}{\pi(1.0 \times 10^{-3}\ \text{m})^2} = 0.898\ \Omega$. $I = \dfrac{V}{R} = \dfrac{1.5\ \text{V}}{0.898\ \Omega} = \boxed{1.7\ \text{A}}$.

(b) $E = pt = I^2 Rt = (1.67\ \text{A})^2(0.898\ \Omega)(10\ \text{min})(60\ \text{s/min}) = \boxed{1.5 \times 10^3\ \text{J}}$.

93. $E = Pt = \dfrac{V^2}{R}\,t = \dfrac{(120\ \text{V})^2(3600\ \text{s})}{15\ \Omega} = \boxed{3.5 \times 10^6\ \text{J}}$.

94. (a) $R = \dfrac{V}{I} = \dfrac{\rho L}{A}$, ☞ $\rho = \dfrac{VA}{IL} = \dfrac{(3.00\ \text{V})(\pi)(0.5 \times 10^{-3}\ \text{m})^2}{(11.8\ \text{A})(2.0\ \text{m})} = \boxed{1.0 \times 10^{-7}\ \Omega\cdot\text{m}}$.

(b) From Table 17.1, it could be $\boxed{\text{iron or platinum}}$.

95. (a) $P = I^2 R$, ☞ $I = \sqrt{\dfrac{P}{R}} = \sqrt{\dfrac{0.25\ \text{W}}{100\ \Omega}} = \boxed{5.0 \times 10^{-2}\ \text{A}}$.

(b) $V = IR = (0.05\ \text{A})(100\ \Omega) = \boxed{5.0\ \text{V}}$.

96. $I = \dfrac{q}{t} = \dfrac{ne}{t}$, ☞ $n = \dfrac{It}{e} = \dfrac{(75 \times 10^{-3}\ \text{A})(2.0\ \text{s})}{1.6 \times 10^{-19}\ \text{C}} = \boxed{9.4 \times 10^{17}\ \text{electrons}}$.

97.   (a) $R = \dfrac{V}{I} = \dfrac{40\text{ V}}{0.10\text{ A}} = \boxed{4.0 \times 10^2\ \Omega}$.

(b) $P = IV = (0.10\text{ A})(40\text{ V}) = \boxed{4.0\text{ W}}$.

(c) $E = Pt = (4.0\text{ W})(2.0)(60\text{ s}) = \boxed{4.8 \times 10^2\text{ J}}$.

98.   (a) $R = \dfrac{\rho L}{A}$, ☞ $\dfrac{R_{Cu}}{R_{Al}} = \dfrac{\rho_{Cu}}{\rho_{Al}} \dfrac{L_{Cu}}{L_{Al}} \dfrac{A_{Al}}{A_{Cu}} = \dfrac{1.70 \times 10^{-8}\ \Omega\cdot m}{2.82 \times 10^{-8}\ \Omega\cdot m}\,(1)(1) = \boxed{0.60}$.

(b) Half the diameter means $\tfrac{1}{4}$ the area $(A = \pi r^2)$, so $\dfrac{A_{Al}}{A_{Cu}} = 4$.

$\dfrac{R_{Cu}}{R_{Al}} = \dfrac{\rho_{Cu}}{\rho_{Al}}\,(2)(4) = \boxed{4.8}$.

99.   (a) $P = IV$, ☞ $I = \dfrac{P}{V} = \dfrac{5.00\text{ W}}{3.00\text{ V}} = \boxed{1.67\text{ A}}$.

(b) $q = It = (1.67\text{ A})(3.00\text{ h})(3600\text{ s/h}) = \boxed{1.80 \times 10^4\text{ C}}$.

(c) $E = pt = (5.00\text{ W})(3.00\text{ h})(3600\text{ s/h}) = \boxed{5.40 \times 10^4\text{ J}}$.

100. $V = IR = I\dfrac{\rho L}{A} = \dfrac{(3000\text{ A})(1.70 \times 10^{-8}\ \Omega\cdot m)(1.5\text{ m})}{(0.080\text{ m})(0.040\text{ m})} = \boxed{2.4 \times 10^{-2}\text{ V}}$.

101.   This is $\boxed{\text{to reduce the } I^2 R \text{ losses}}$. Since $P = IV$, a higher voltage means lower current if P is kept constant. The resistance of the transmission lines is approximately a constant. With a lower current, the power loss in the lines is reduced since joule heating varies as the square of the current $(P = I^2 R)$. For example, $P_{loss} = I^2 R = \dfrac{P^2}{V^2} R \propto \dfrac{1}{V^2}$. So if V is raised by 10 times, P_{loss} will be reduced by a factor of $1/100$.

102.   (a) $\Delta Q = nVq = nAxq = (nAx)q$.

(b) $I = \dfrac{\Delta Q}{\Delta t} = nq\,\dfrac{x}{\Delta t}\,A = nqv_d A$.

103. $1\text{ m}^3 = 10^6\text{ cm}^3$.   From Exercise 17.102, $I = nqv_d A$,

so $v_d = \dfrac{I}{nqA} = \dfrac{1.2\text{ A}}{(8.5 \times 10^{28}\ /m^3)(1.6 \times 10^{-19}\text{ C})(13.3 \times 10^{-6}\ m^2)} = \boxed{6.6 \times 10^{-6}\text{ m/s}}$.

In this chapter, the following convenient calculation of equivalent resistance for two resistors in parallel is used in many exercises. $\dfrac{1}{R_p} = \dfrac{1}{R_1} + \dfrac{1}{R_2}$, ☞ $R_p = \dfrac{R_1 R_2}{R_1 + R_2}$.

1.   (b).

2.   (a).

3. $\boxed{\text{No}}$, not generally. However $\boxed{\text{if all resistors are equal}}$, the voltages across them are the same.

4. $\boxed{\text{No}}$, not generally. However $\boxed{\text{if all resistors are equal}}$, the currents through each is the same.

5.   If they are in series, the effective resistance will be closer in value to that of the $\boxed{\text{large}}$ resistance because $R_s = R_1 + R_2$. If $R_1 \gg R_2$, then $R_s \approx R_1$.

   If they are in parallel, the effective resistance will be closer in value to that of the $\boxed{\text{small}}$ resistance because

   $R_p = \dfrac{R_1 R_2}{R_1 + R_2}$. If $R_1 \gg R_2$, then $R_p \approx \dfrac{R_1 R_2}{R_1} = R_2$.

6.   These bulbs are connected $\boxed{\text{in series}}$. If one bulb burns out in a series combination, there will be no current in the rest of the bulbs.

7.   Since $P = IV$, the $\boxed{5\ \Omega}$ resistor gets the most power because it gets the most voltage, and all resistors have the same current.

8.   Since $P = IV$, the $\boxed{1\ \Omega}$ resistor gets the most power because it gets the most current and all resistors have the same voltage.

9.   (a) They should be $\boxed{\text{in series}}$ for maximum resistance.

   $R_s = R_1 + R_2 + R_3 = 10\ \Omega + 20\ \Omega + 30\ \Omega = \boxed{60\ \Omega}$.

   (b) They should be $\boxed{\text{in parallel}}$ for minimum resistance.

   $\dfrac{1}{R_p} = \dfrac{1}{R_1} + \dfrac{1}{R_2} + \dfrac{1}{R_3} = \dfrac{1}{10\ \Omega} + \dfrac{1}{20\ \Omega} + \dfrac{1}{30\ \Omega} = \dfrac{11}{60\ \Omega}$, so $R_p = \boxed{5.5\ \Omega}$.

10. Series combination: $R_s = R_1 + R_2 = R + R = 2R.$

Parallel combination: $\dfrac{1}{R_p} = \dfrac{1}{R_s} + \dfrac{1}{R_3}$, ☞ $R_p = \dfrac{R_s R_3}{R_s + R_3} = 10\ \Omega = \dfrac{(2R)(20\ \Omega)}{2R + 20\ \Omega}$.

Simplifying, $20R + 200 = 40R.$ Solving, $R = \boxed{10\ \Omega}$.

11. Parallel combination: $\dfrac{1}{R_p} = \dfrac{1}{R_1} + \dfrac{1}{R_2}$, ☞ $R_p = \dfrac{R_1 R_2}{R_1 + R_2} = \dfrac{R\,R}{R + R} = \dfrac{R}{2}$.

Series combination: $R_s = R_p + R_3 = \dfrac{R}{2} + 40\ \Omega = 55\ \Omega$, ☞ $R = \boxed{30\ \Omega}$.

12. (a) You can get $\boxed{7}$ different values of equivalent resistance.

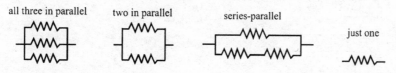

all three in parallel   two in parallel   series-parallel   just one

parallel-series   two in series   all three in series

(b) All three in parallel: $\dfrac{1}{R_p} = \dfrac{1}{R_1} + \dfrac{1}{R_2} + \dfrac{1}{R_3} = 3\,\dfrac{1}{4.0\ \Omega} = \dfrac{3}{4.0\ \Omega}$, $R_p = \boxed{1.3\ \Omega}$.

Two in parallel: $\dfrac{1}{R_p} = \dfrac{1}{R_1} + \dfrac{1}{R_2} = 2\,\dfrac{1}{4.0\ \Omega} = \dfrac{2}{4.0\ \Omega}$, $R_p = \boxed{2.0\ \Omega}$.

Two in series-parallel: $\dfrac{1}{R_p} = \dfrac{1}{R_s} + \dfrac{1}{R} = \dfrac{1}{R + R} + \dfrac{1}{R} = \dfrac{3}{2(4.0\ \Omega)}$, $R_p = \boxed{2.7\ \Omega}$.

Just one alone: $R = \boxed{4.0\ \Omega}$.

Two in parallel-series: $R_s = R + R_p = R + \dfrac{R\,R}{R + R} = \dfrac{3R}{2} = \dfrac{3(4.0\ \Omega)}{2} = \boxed{6.0\ \Omega}$.

Two in series: $R_s = R_1 + R_2 = 4.0\ \Omega + 4.0\ \Omega = \boxed{8.0\ \Omega}$.

All three in series: $R_s = R_1 + R_2 + R_3 = 3(4.0\ \Omega) = \boxed{12\ \Omega\ \text{for series}}$.

13. (a) $R_s = R_1 + R_2 + R_3 = 5.0\ \Omega + 10\ \Omega + 15\ \Omega = \boxed{30\ \Omega}$.

(b) $I = \dfrac{V}{R_s} = \dfrac{9.0\ \text{V}}{30\ \Omega} = \boxed{0.30\ \text{A}}$.

(c) $P = I^2 R = (0.30\ \text{A})^2 (15\ \Omega) = \boxed{1.4\ \text{W}}$.

14. Two or more in series: $R_s = R_1 + R_2 + R_3 = \boxed{15\ \Omega,\ 20\ \Omega,\ 25\ \Omega,\ 30\ \Omega}$.

Two or more in parallel: $\dfrac{1}{R_p} = \dfrac{1}{R_1} + \dfrac{1}{R_2} + \dfrac{1}{R_3}$, ☞ $R_p = \boxed{3.3\ \Omega,\ 3.8\ \Omega,\ 6.0\ \Omega,\ 2.7\ \Omega}$.

Parallel-series: $R_s = \dfrac{R_1 R_2}{R_1 + R_2} + R_3 = \boxed{11\ \Omega,\ 14\ \Omega,\ 18\ \Omega}$.

Series-parallel: $\dfrac{1}{R_p} = \dfrac{1}{R_1 + R_2} + \dfrac{1}{R_3}$, ☞ $R_p = \boxed{4.2\ \Omega,\ 6.7\ \Omega,\ 7.5\ \Omega}$.

15. (a) $\dfrac{1}{R_p} = \dfrac{1}{R_1} + \dfrac{1}{R_2} + \dfrac{1}{R_3} = \dfrac{1}{1.0\ \Omega} + \dfrac{1}{2.0\ \Omega} + \dfrac{1}{4.0\ \Omega} = \dfrac{7}{4.0\ \Omega}$, ☞ $R_p = \boxed{0.57\ \Omega}$.

(b) $\boxed{6.0\ \text{V}}$ for all three since they are in parallel combination.

(c) $P = \dfrac{V^2}{R} = \dfrac{(6.0\ \text{V})^2}{4.0\ \Omega} = \boxed{9.0\ \text{W}}$.

16. (a) The minimum required is $\boxed{3}$.

(b) $\boxed{\text{Two in parallel, then series with a third one}}$.

$R = \dfrac{1.0\ \Omega}{2} + 1.0\ \Omega = 0.5\ \Omega + 1.0\ \Omega = 1.5\ \Omega$.

17. (a) The resistance of the shortened conductor is $\boxed{R/4}$. Each shortened segment has a resistance of $R/2$ because resistance is proportional to length (Chapter 17). Then two $R/2$ resistors in parallel gives $R/4$.

(b) The series of three segments has a resistance of 27 $\mu\Omega$: $27\ \mu\Omega = 3R$, ☞ $R = \dfrac{27\ \mu\Omega}{3} = 9.0\ \mu\Omega$.

These three segments are in parallel now: $\dfrac{1}{R_p} = 3\ \dfrac{1}{9.0\ \mu\Omega} = \dfrac{1}{3.0\ \mu\Omega}$, ☞ $R_p = \boxed{3.0\ \mu\Omega}$.

18. (a) $\boxed{\text{Yes}}$, it is possible.

(b) $\boxed{\text{Three in series, connected in parallel to the fourth}}$.

The equivalent resistance is $R_p = \dfrac{(5.0\ \Omega + 5.0\ \Omega + 5.0\ \Omega)(5.0\ \Omega)}{(5.0\ \Omega + 5.0\ \Omega + 5.0\ \Omega) + 5.0\ \Omega} = 3.75\ \Omega$.

19. (a) $I = \dfrac{V}{R_s} = \dfrac{12\ \text{V}}{2.0\ \Omega + 4.0\ \Omega + 6.0\ \Omega} = \boxed{1.0\ \text{A}}$.

(b) In series, all have the same current, $\boxed{1.0\ \text{A}}$.

(c) $P = I^2 R$, ☞ $P_{2\,\Omega} = (1.0 \text{ A})^2 (2.0 \text{ }\Omega) = \boxed{2.0 \text{ W}}$; $P_{4\,\Omega} = (1.0 \text{ A})^2 (4.0 \text{ }\Omega) = \boxed{4.0 \text{ W}}$;

and $P_{6\,\Omega} = (1.0 \text{ A})^2 (6.0 \text{ }\Omega) = \boxed{6.0 \text{ W}}$.

(d) $P_{\text{total}} = (1.0 \text{ A})^2 (12 \text{ }\Omega) = 12 \text{ W}$, $P_{\text{sum}} = 2.0 \text{ W} + 4.0 \text{ W} + 6.0 \text{ W} = 12 \text{ W}$. $\boxed{P_{\text{sum}} = P_{\text{total}} = 12 \text{ W}}$.

20.   (a) $\dfrac{1}{R_p} = \dfrac{1}{2.0 \text{ }\Omega} + \dfrac{1}{4.0 \text{ }\Omega} + \dfrac{1}{6.0 \text{ }\Omega} = \dfrac{11}{12 \text{ }\Omega}$, ☞ $R_p = 1.09 \text{ }\Omega$.

So $I = \dfrac{V}{R_p} = \dfrac{12 \text{ V}}{1.09 \text{ }\Omega} = \boxed{11 \text{ A}}$.

(b) $I_{2\,\Omega} = \dfrac{12 \text{ V}}{2.0 \text{ }\Omega} = \boxed{6.0 \text{ A}}$; $I_{4\,\Omega} = \dfrac{12 \text{ V}}{4.0 \text{ }\Omega} = \boxed{3.0 \text{ A}}$; $I_{6\,\Omega} = \dfrac{12 \text{ V}}{6.0 \text{ }\Omega} = \boxed{2.0 \text{ A}}$.

(c) $P = I^2 R$, ☞ $P_{2\,\Omega} = (6.0 \text{ A})^2 (2.0 \text{ }\Omega) = \boxed{72 \text{ W}}$; $P_{4\,\Omega} = (3.0 \text{ A})^2 (4.0 \text{ }\Omega) = \boxed{36 \text{ W}}$;

and $P_{6\,\Omega} = (2.0 \text{ A})^2 (6.0 \text{ }\Omega) = \boxed{24 \text{ W}}$.

(d) $P_{\text{total}} = (11 \text{ A})^2 (1.09 \text{ }\Omega) = 132 \text{ W}$, $P_{\text{sum}} = 72 \text{ W} + 36 \text{ W} + 24 \text{ W} = 132 \text{ W}$.

So $\boxed{P_{\text{sum}} = P_{\text{total}} = 132 \text{ W}}$.

21. $R_s = R_{p8} + R_{p4} = \dfrac{(8.0 \text{ }\Omega)(8.0 \text{ }\Omega)}{8.0 \text{ }\Omega + 8.0 \text{ }\Omega} + \dfrac{(4.0 \text{ }\Omega)(4.0 \text{ }\Omega)}{4.0 \text{ }\Omega + 4.0 \text{ }\Omega} = 6.0 \text{ }\Omega$.

$I = \dfrac{V}{R_s} = \dfrac{12 \text{ V}}{6.0 \text{ }\Omega} = 2.0 \text{ A}$.

So the current through each resistor is $\dfrac{2.0 \text{ A}}{2} = \boxed{1.0 \text{ A for all}}$.

$V_{8.0} = (1.0 \text{ A})(8.0 \text{ }\Omega) = \boxed{8.0 \text{ V}}$, and $V_{4.0} = (1.0 \text{ A})(4.0 \text{ }\Omega) = \boxed{4.0 \text{ V}}$.

22. R_1 and R_2 are in series: $R_s = 2.0 \text{ }\Omega + 2.0 \text{ }\Omega = 4.0 \text{ }\Omega$.

R_s, R_3, and R_4 are in parallel: $\dfrac{1}{R_p} = \dfrac{1}{4.0 \text{ }\Omega} + \dfrac{1}{2.0 \text{ }\Omega} + \dfrac{1}{2.0 \text{ }\Omega} = \dfrac{5}{4.0 \text{ }\Omega}$,

so $R_p = \dfrac{4.0 \text{ }\Omega}{5} = \boxed{0.80 \text{ }\Omega}$.

23. R_2 and R_3 are in series: $R_s = 6.0 \text{ }\Omega + 4.0 \text{ }\Omega = 10 \text{ }\Omega$.

R_s, R_1, and R_4 are in parallel: $\dfrac{1}{R_p} = \dfrac{1}{10 \text{ }\Omega} + \dfrac{1}{6.0 \text{ }\Omega} + \dfrac{1}{10 \text{ }\Omega} = \dfrac{22}{60 \text{ }\Omega}$, ☞ $R_p = \boxed{2.7 \text{ }\Omega}$.

24. R_2, R_3, and R_4 are in series: $R_s = 20 \text{ }\Omega + 5.0 \text{ }\Omega + 5.0 \text{ }\Omega = 30 \text{ }\Omega$.

R_s and R_1 are in parallel: $R_p = \dfrac{(30 \text{ }\Omega)(10 \text{ }\Omega)}{30 \text{ }\Omega + 10 \text{ }\Omega} = \boxed{7.5 \text{ }\Omega}$.

25. (a) See diagram.

(b) The current through each bulb is

$$I = \frac{P}{V} = \frac{60 \text{ W}}{120 \text{ V}} = 0.50 \text{ A}.$$

So it takes $\dfrac{15 \text{ A}}{0.50 \text{ A}} = 30$ bulbs to make 15 A. Therefore $\boxed{31}$ bulbs will blow the fuse.

26. (a) Parallel consumes maximum power:

parallel

$$\frac{1}{R_p} = 3 \frac{1}{50 \text{ }\Omega} = \frac{3}{50 \text{ }\Omega}, \quad \text{☞} \quad R_p = \frac{50 \text{ }\Omega}{3} = 16.7 \text{ }\Omega.$$

So $P_{max} = \dfrac{V^2}{R_p} = \dfrac{(120 \text{ V})^2}{16.7 \text{ }\Omega} = \boxed{860 \text{ W}}$.

(b) Series consumes minimum power:

series

$$R_s = 3(50 \text{ }\Omega) = 150 \text{ }\Omega. \quad \text{So} \quad P_{min} = \frac{(120 \text{ V})^2}{150 \text{ }\Omega} = \boxed{96 \text{ W}}.$$

27. The equivalent resistance is

$$R_s = R_p + R_3 = \frac{R_1 R_2}{R_1 + R_2} + R_3 = \frac{(10 \text{ }\Omega)(2.0 \text{ }\Omega)}{10 \text{ }\Omega + 2.0 \text{ }\Omega} + 5.0 \text{ }\Omega = 6.67 \text{ }\Omega.$$

The total current is $I = \dfrac{V}{R_s} = \dfrac{10 \text{ V}}{6.67 \text{ }\Omega} = 1.5 \text{ A}.$

The voltage drop across R_3 is $V_3 = (1.5 \text{ A})(5.0 \text{ }\Omega) = 7.5 \text{ V}.$

The voltage drop across the 10 Ω is $10 \text{ V} - 7.5 \text{ V} = \boxed{2.5 \text{ V}}$, and the current is $\dfrac{2.5 \text{ V}}{10 \text{ }\Omega} = \boxed{0.25 \text{ A}}$.

28. (a) $P = IV$, $\quad \text{☞} \quad I_{50} = \dfrac{P}{V} = \dfrac{50 \text{ W}}{120 \text{ V}} = \boxed{0.42 \text{ A}}$.

$$I_{100} = \frac{100 \text{ W}}{120 \text{ V}} = \boxed{0.83 \text{ A}}, \quad I_{150} = \frac{150 \text{ W}}{120 \text{ V}} = \boxed{1.25 \text{ A}}.$$

(b) $R_{50} = \dfrac{V}{I} = \dfrac{120 \text{ V}}{0.417 \text{ A}} = \boxed{290 \text{ }\Omega}$, $\quad R_{100} = \dfrac{120 \text{ V}}{0.833 \text{ A}} = \boxed{144 \text{ }\Omega}$, $\quad R_{150} = \dfrac{120 \text{ V}}{1.25 \text{ A}} = \boxed{96 \text{ }\Omega}$.

29. (a) $I_1 = \dfrac{V}{R_1} = \dfrac{20 \text{ V}}{20 \text{ }\Omega} = \boxed{1.0 \text{ A}}$. R_2 and R_3 are in series: $R_s = 20 \text{ }\Omega + 20 \text{ }\Omega = 40 \text{ }\Omega.$

So $I_2 = I_3 = \dfrac{20 \text{ V}}{40 \text{ }\Omega} = \boxed{0.50 \text{ A}}$.

(b) $V_1 = \boxed{20 \text{ V}}$, $\quad V_2 = V_3 = I_2 R_2 = (0.50 \text{ A})(20 \text{ }\Omega) = \boxed{10 \text{ V}}$.

(c) The total power is $P = \dfrac{V^2}{R_1} + \dfrac{V^2}{R_s} = \dfrac{(20 \text{ V})^2}{20 \text{ }\Omega} + \dfrac{(20 \text{ V})^2}{40 \text{ }\Omega} = \boxed{30 \text{ W}}$.

30. $I = \dfrac{V}{R} = \dfrac{120 \text{ V}}{300 \text{ }\Omega} = 0.40 \text{ A}.$ So there can be only $(15 \text{ A})/(0.40 \text{ A}) = 37.5$ resistors.

So $\boxed{37}$ resistors could be connected in parallel without tripping the 15 A breaker.

31. $P = 2(100 \text{ W}) + 150 \text{ W} + 300 \text{ W} + 900 \text{ W} + 200 \text{ W} = 1750 \text{ W}.$

$I = \dfrac{P}{V} = \dfrac{1750 \text{ W}}{120 \text{ V}} = 14.6 \text{ A} < 15 \text{ A}.$ $\boxed{\text{No}}$, the breaker will not trip.

32. R_1 and R_2 are in series. $R_s = 2.0 \text{ }\Omega + 2.0 \text{ }\Omega = 4.0 \text{ }\Omega.$

So $I_1 = I_2 = \dfrac{V}{R_s} = \dfrac{12 \text{ V}}{4.0 \text{ }\Omega} = \boxed{3.0 \text{ A}}$,

$I_3 = \dfrac{12 \text{ V}}{2.0 \text{ }\Omega} = \boxed{6.0 \text{ A}}$, $I_4 = \dfrac{12 \text{ V}}{2.0 \text{ }\Omega} = \boxed{6.0 \text{ A}}$.

(b) $V_1 = V_2 = I_1 R_1 = (3.0 \text{ A})(2.0 \text{ }\Omega) = \boxed{6.0 \text{ V}}$, $V_3 = V_4 = \boxed{12 \text{ V}}$.

(c) From Exercise 18.22, $P = \dfrac{V^2}{R_p} = \dfrac{(12 \text{ V})^2}{0.80 \text{ }\Omega} = \boxed{1.8 \times 10^2 \text{ W}}$.

33.   The heat required is $Q = cm\Delta T = [4186 \text{ J/(kg·C°)}](0.20 \text{ kg})(80°C - 20°C) = 5.02 \times 10^4 \text{ J}.$

$P = \dfrac{E}{t}$,   ☞ $t = \dfrac{E}{P} = \dfrac{5.02 \times 10^4 \text{ J}}{500 \text{ W}} = \boxed{100 \text{ s} = 1.7 \text{ min}}$.

34.   (a) $I_1 = \dfrac{V}{R_1} = \dfrac{6.0 \text{ V}}{6.0 \text{ }\Omega} = \boxed{1.0 \text{ A}}$ R_2 and R_3 are in series. $R_s = 4.0 \text{ }\Omega + 6.0 \text{ }\Omega = 10 \text{ }\Omega.$

So $I_2 = I_3 = \dfrac{6.0 \text{ V}}{10 \text{ }\Omega} = \boxed{0.60 \text{ A}}$, $I_4 = \dfrac{6.0 \text{ V}}{10 \text{ }\Omega} = \boxed{0.60 \text{ A}}$.

(b) $P_1 = I_1^2 R_1 = (1.0 \text{ A})^2 (6.0 \text{ }\Omega) = \boxed{6.0 \text{ W}}$, $P_2 = (0.60 \text{ A})^2 (4.0 \text{ }\Omega) = \boxed{1.4 \text{ W}}$,

$P_3 = (0.60 \text{ A})^2 (6.0 \text{ }\Omega) = \boxed{2.2 \text{ W}}$, $P_4 = (0.60 \text{ A})^2 (10 \text{ }\Omega) = \boxed{3.6 \text{ W}}$.

(c) $P_{sum} = 6.0 \text{ W} + 1.44 \text{ W} + 2.16 \text{ W} + 3.6 \text{ W} = 13 \text{ W}.$ From Exercise 18.23,

$P_{total} = \dfrac{(6.0 \text{ V})^2}{2.7 \text{ }\Omega} = 13 \text{ W}.$ Therefore $\boxed{P_{sum} = P_{total} = 13 \text{ W}}$.

35.   (a) The wattage ratings are based on 120 V. $P = \dfrac{V^2}{R}$,   ☞ $R = \dfrac{V^2}{P}$.

$R_{15} = \dfrac{(120 \text{ V})^2}{15 \text{ W}} = 960 \text{ }\Omega$, $R_{40} = \dfrac{(120 \text{ V})^2}{40 \text{ W}} = 360 \text{ }\Omega$, $R_{60} = \dfrac{(120 \text{ V})^2}{60 \text{ W}} = 240 \text{ }\Omega$,

and $R_{100} = \dfrac{(120 \text{ V})^2}{100 \text{ W}} = 144 \text{ }\Omega$.   So the equivalent resistance is

$R_{eq} = 960 \text{ }\Omega + 360 \text{ }\Omega + \dfrac{(240 \text{ }\Omega)(144 \text{ }\Omega)}{240 \text{ }\Omega + 144 \text{ }\Omega} = 1410 \text{ }\Omega.$ Therefore $I = \dfrac{V}{R_{eq}} = \dfrac{120 \text{ V}}{1410 \text{ }\Omega} = \boxed{0.085 \text{ A}}$.

(b) $P_{15} = I^2 R = (0.0851 \text{ A})^2 (960 \text{ }\Omega) = \boxed{7.0 \text{ W}}$, $\quad P_{40} = (0.851 \text{ A})^2 (360 \text{ }\Omega) = \boxed{2.6 \text{ W}}$.

$V_{60} = V_{100} = 120 \text{ V} - (0.0851 \text{ A})(960 \text{ }\Omega + 360 \text{ }\Omega) = 7.67 \text{ V}$.

So $\quad P_{60} = \dfrac{V^2}{R} = \dfrac{(7.67 \text{ V})^2}{240 \text{ }\Omega} = \boxed{0.24 \text{ W}}$, $\quad P_{100} = \dfrac{(7.67 \text{ V})^2}{144 \text{ }\Omega} = \boxed{0.41 \text{ W}}$.

36. The current in through both is $I = \dfrac{7.0 \text{ V}}{2.0 \text{ }\Omega + R_2}$, so $R_2 = \dfrac{7.0 \text{ V}}{I} - 2.0 \text{ }\Omega$.

The power in R_2 is $P_2 = 6.0 \text{ W} = I^2 R_2 = I^2 (\dfrac{7.0 \text{ V}}{I} - 2.0 \text{ }\Omega) = (7.0 \text{ V})I - (2.0 \text{ }\Omega)I^2$.

Simplifying $\quad I^2 - (3.5 \text{ A})I + 3 \text{ A}^2 = 0$. $\quad$ Solving $\quad I = \boxed{1.5 \text{ A or } 2.0 \text{ A}}$.

There are two answers to this exercise because there are two values for R_2 that satisfies the conditions. $R_2 = 1.5 \text{ }\Omega$ or $2.7 \text{ }\Omega$.

37. (a) R_1 and R_2 are in series. $\quad R_{s1} = 10 \text{ }\Omega + 5.0 \text{ }\Omega = 15 \text{ }\Omega$.

So $\quad I_1 = I_2 = \dfrac{V}{R_{s1}} = \dfrac{10 \text{ V}}{15 \text{ }\Omega} = \boxed{0.67 \text{ A}}$ $\quad I_3 = \dfrac{10 \text{ V}}{10 \text{ }\Omega} = \boxed{1.0 \text{ A}}$.

R_4 and R_5 are in series. $\quad R_{s2} = 5.0 \text{ }\Omega + 20 \text{ }\Omega = 25 \text{ }\Omega$. $\quad$ So $\quad I_4 = I_5 = \dfrac{10 \text{ V}}{25 \text{ }\Omega} = \boxed{0.40 \text{ A}}$.

(b) $V_1 = I_1 R_1 = (0.667 \text{ A})(10 \text{ }\Omega) = \boxed{6.7 \text{ V}}$, $\quad V_2 = (0.667 \text{ A})(5.0 \text{ }\Omega) = \boxed{3.3 \text{ V}}$, $\quad V_3 = \boxed{10 \text{ V}}$,

$V_4 = (0.40 \text{ A})(5.0 \text{ }\Omega) = \boxed{2.0 \text{ V}}$, $\quad V_5 = (0.40 \text{ A})(20 \text{ }\Omega) = \boxed{8.0 \text{ V}}$.

38. 6.0 Ω and 4.0 Ω are in parallel. $\quad R_{p1} = \dfrac{(6.0 \text{ }\Omega)(4.0 \text{ }\Omega)}{6.0 \text{ }\Omega + 4.0 \text{ }\Omega} = 2.4 \text{ }\Omega$.

This R_{p1} and 2.0 Ω are in series. $\quad R_{s1} = 2.4 \text{ }\Omega + 2.0 \text{ }\Omega = 4.4 \text{ }\Omega$.

This R_{s1} and 12 Ω are in parallel. $\quad R_{p2} = \dfrac{(4.4 \text{ }\Omega)(12 \text{ }\Omega)}{4.4 \text{ }\Omega + 12 \text{ }\Omega} = 3.22 \text{ }\Omega$.

10 Ω (the one on the bottom) and 5.0 Ω are in parallel. $\quad R_{p3} = \dfrac{(10 \text{ }\Omega)(5.0 \text{ }\Omega)}{10 \text{ }\Omega + 5.0 \text{ }\Omega} = 3.33 \text{ }\Omega$.

Finally, R_{p2}, R_{p3}, and 10 Ω (the one on the top) are in series, $\quad R_{s2} = 3.22 \text{ }\Omega + 3.33 \text{ }\Omega + 10 \text{ }\Omega = 16.6 \text{ }\Omega$.

So $\quad P = \dfrac{V^2}{R_{s2}} = \dfrac{(24 \text{ V})^2}{16.6 \text{ }\Omega} = \boxed{35 \text{ W}}$.

39. 8.0 Ω and 4.0 Ω are in parallel. $\quad R_{p1} = \dfrac{(8.0 \text{ }\Omega)(4.0 \text{ }\Omega)}{8.0 \text{ }\Omega + 4.0 \text{ }\Omega} = 2.67 \text{ }\Omega$.

This R_{p1} and 10 W are in series. $\quad R_{s1} = 2.67 \text{ }\Omega + 10 \text{ }\Omega = 12.7 \text{ }\Omega$.

6.0 Ω, 3.0 Ω, and 2.0 Ω are in parallel. $\quad \dfrac{1}{R_{p2}} = \dfrac{1}{6.0 \text{ }\Omega} + \dfrac{1}{3.0 \text{ }\Omega} + \dfrac{1}{2.0 \text{ }\Omega} = \dfrac{1}{1.0 \text{ }\Omega}$,

so $\quad R_{p2} = 1.0 \text{ }\Omega$.

This R_{p2} and 5.0 Ω are in series. $R_{s2} = 1.0\ \Omega + 5.0\ \Omega = 6.0\ \Omega$.

R_{s1} and R_{s2} are in parallel. $R_{p3} = \dfrac{(12.7\ \Omega)(6.0\ \Omega)}{12.7\ \Omega + 6.0\ \Omega} = 4.07\ \Omega$.

Finally, this R_{p3} and 4.0 Ω are in series. $R_{s3} = 4.07\ \Omega + 4.0\ \Omega = \boxed{8.1\ \Omega}$.

40.   When it is balanced, point b and point c have the same potential, or $V_{ab} = V_{ac}$, and $V_{bd} = V_{cd}$.

So $V_{ab} = I_1 R_s = I_2 R_1$ (1)   and $V_{bd} = I_1 R_x = I_2 R_2$ (2)

$\dfrac{(2)}{(1)}$ gives $\dfrac{R_x}{R_s} = \dfrac{R_2}{R_1}$,   ☞ $R_x = \dfrac{R_2}{R_1} R_s$.

41.   (d).

42.   (c).

43.   The voltage is $\boxed{\text{positive}}$ because you traverse from low potential to high potential so the potential difference is positive.

44.   The junction theorem basically says that the current going into a junction is equal to the current leaving the junction. Since current is defined as charge per unit time, it is equivalent to the charge going into a junction being equal to the charge leaving a junction. This is essentially the conservation of charge.

45.   The loop theorem says that the total voltage around a complete loop is equal to zero. Since voltage is defined as potential energy difference per unit charge, it is equivalent to the potential energy difference around a complete loop being equal to zero. This is essentially the conservation of energy because the same point in a complete loop can only have the same potential energy value, so the potential energy difference is equal to zero.

46.   Around loop 3, $-V_1 + I_1 R_1 + I_2 R_2 = 0$, or $V_1 - I_1 R_1 - I_2 R_2 = 0$, which is the result of the equations for loop 1 plus the equation for loop 2.

47.   Around loop 1 (reverse), $-V_1 + I_3 R_3 + V_2 + I_1 R_1 = 0$.
If we multiply −1 on both sides, it is the same as the equation for loop 1 (forward).
Around loop 2 (reverse), $I_2 R_2 - V_2 - I_3 R_3 = 0$.
Again, if we multiply by −1 on both sides, it is the same as the equation for loop 2 (forward).

48.   Around the inner loop: $10\text{ V} - I_2(2.0\text{ }\Omega) - I_3(5.0\text{ }\Omega) = 0.$ Eq. (1)

Around the outer loop: $10\text{ V} - I_1(10\text{ }\Omega) - I_3(5.0\text{ }\Omega) = 0.$ Eq. (2)

From junction theorem: $I_3 = I_1 + I_2.$ Eq. (3)

Substituting Eq. (3) into Eq. (1) and Eq. (2) gives

$(5.0\text{ }\Omega)I_1 + (7.0\text{ }\Omega)I_2 = 10\text{ V}$ Eq. (3)

$(7.0\text{ }\Omega)I_1 + (5.0\text{ }\Omega)I_2 = 10\text{ V}$ Eq. (4)

Solving, $I_1 = \boxed{0.25\text{ A}}$, $I_2 = \boxed{1.25\text{ A}}$,   and $I_3 = \boxed{1.5\text{ A}}$.

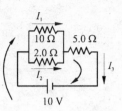

49.   Around the left loop in a clockwise direction, $20\text{ V} - I_1(20\text{ }\Omega) = 0$,   ☞ $\boxed{I_1 = 1.0\text{ A}}$ down.

Around the outer loop (without R_1) in clockwise direction, $20\text{ V} - I_2(20\text{ }\Omega) - I_2(20\text{ }\Omega) = 0$,

so $\boxed{I_2 = 0.50\text{ A}}$ right   and $\boxed{I_3 = 0.50\text{ A}}$ down.

50.   (a) The current in the resistor is $\boxed{\text{between 0 A and 1.0 A}}$. There must be a

current because the voltages of the two batteries are different. Since one is 10 V
and the other is 4 V, the net voltage is 8 V. For a 12 Ω resistor, the current is
less than 1.0 A.

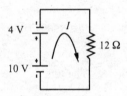

(b) Around the loop, $10\text{ V} - 4\text{ V} - I(12\text{ }\Omega) = 0$,

so $I = \boxed{0.50\text{ A}}$ and $P = I^2R = (0.50\text{ A})^2(12\text{ }\Omega) = \boxed{3.0\text{ W}}$.

(b) $P_{10} = \varepsilon I = (10\text{ V})(0.50\text{ A}) = \boxed{5.0\text{ W output}}$,

$P_4 = (-4\text{ V})(0.50\text{ A}) = -2.0\text{ W} = \boxed{2.0\text{ W input}}$.

$P_{net} = 5.0\text{ W} - 2.0\text{ W} = \boxed{3.0\text{ W to the resistor}}$.

51.   Around the loop in a counterclockwise direction, $20\text{ V} - I(20\text{ }\Omega) - 10\text{ V} - I(10\text{ }\Omega) = 0$,

so $I = I_1 = I_2 = 0.33\text{ A}$.   Therefore $\boxed{I_1 = 0.33\text{ A left}}$ and $\boxed{I_2 = 0.33\text{ A right}}$.

52.   (a) For the R_1 and R_2 connecting junction: $I = I_1 + I_2.$ Eq. (1)

Around the loop through R_1 in counterclockwise direction,

$12\text{ V} - I(2.0\text{ }\Omega) - I(8.0\text{ }\Omega) + 6.0\text{ V} - I(2.0\text{ }\Omega) - I_1(4.0\text{ }\Omega) = 0$,

or $-12I - 4I_1 + 18 = 0.$ Eq. (2)

Around the loop through R_2 in counterclockwise direction,

$12\text{ V} - I(2.0\text{ }\Omega) - I(8.0\text{ }\Omega) + 6.0\text{ V} - I(2.0\text{ }\Omega) - I_2(6.0\text{ }\Omega) = 0$,

or $-12I - 6I_1 + 18 = 0.$ Eq. (3)

Substituting Eq. (1) into Eq. (2) and Eq. (3) gives $\quad -16I_1 - 12I_2 + 18 = 0.$ $\quad$ Eq. (4)

$$-12I_1 - 18I_2 + 18 = 0. \quad \text{Eq. (5)}$$

Solving, $\quad \boxed{I_1 = 0.75 \text{ A left}}, \quad \boxed{I_2 = 0.50 \text{ A left}}, \quad I = I_3 = I_4 = I_5,$

so $\quad \boxed{I_3 = 1.25 \text{ A up}}, \quad \boxed{I_4 = 1.25 \text{ A right}}, \quad$ and $\quad \boxed{I_5 = 1.25 \text{ A down}}.$

(b) $P = I^2 R = (1.25 \text{ A})^2 (8.0 \text{ }\Omega) = \boxed{13 \text{ W}}.$

53. $\quad$ Around the left loop in clockwise direction, $\quad 10 \text{ V} - I_1(4.0 \text{ }\Omega) + 5.0 \text{ V} = 0, \quad$ ☞ $\quad I_1 = 3.75 \text{ A}.$

Around the right loop in counterclockwise direction, $\quad 5.0 \text{ V} - I_3(4.0 \text{ }\Omega) + 5.0 \text{ V} - I_2(4.0 \text{ }\Omega) = 0.$

Also $\quad I_2 = I_3.$ $\quad$ So $\quad I_2 = I_3 = 1.25 \text{ A}.$

Therefore $\quad \boxed{I_1 = 3.75 \text{ A up}}, \quad \boxed{I_2 = 1.25 \text{ A left}}, \quad$ and $\quad \boxed{I_3 = 1.25 \text{ A right}}.$

54. $\quad$ The equivalent resistance of the three 2.0 Ω in parallel is $\quad R_p = \dfrac{2.0 \text{ }\Omega}{3} = 0.667 \text{ }\Omega.$

Assume the current through the parallel combination is I. $\quad$ From junction theorem, $\quad I = I_1 + I_2 + I_3.$

Around the left loop in clockwise direction, $\quad 20 \text{ V} - I_1(5.0 \text{ }\Omega) - I(0.667 \text{ }\Omega) = 0,$

or $\quad 5.667I_1 + 0.667I_2 + 0.667I_3 = 20.$ $\qquad\qquad$ Eq. (1)

Around the middle loop in counterclockwise direction, $\quad 10 \text{ V} - I_1(5.0 \text{ }\Omega) + I_2(4.0 \text{ }\Omega) = 0,$

or $\quad 5I_1 - 4I_2 = 10,$ $\qquad\qquad$ Eq. (2)

Around the right loop in counterclockwise direction, $\quad -I_2(4.0 \text{ }\Omega) + I_3(6.0 \text{ }\Omega) = 0,$

or $\quad 4I_2 - 6I_3 = 0.$ $\qquad\qquad$ Eq. (3).

Solve the simultaneous equations for $\quad I_1 = 3.23 \text{ A}, \quad I_2 = 1.54 \text{ A}, \quad I_3 = 1.02 \text{ A}.$

$V_p = I R_p = (I_1 + I_2 + I_3)R_p = (3.23 \text{ A} + 1.54 \text{ A} + 1.02 \text{ A})(0.667 \text{ }\Omega) = 3.86 \text{ V}.$

So $\quad I_4 = I_5 = I_6 = \dfrac{3.86 \text{ V}}{2.0 \text{ }\Omega} = 1.93 \text{ A}.$

Therefore $\quad \boxed{I_1 = 3.23 \text{ A down}}, \quad \boxed{I_2 = 1.54 \text{ A down}}, \quad \boxed{I_3 = 1.02 \text{ A down}},$

and $\quad \boxed{I_4 = I_5 = I_6 = 1.93 \text{ A left}}.$

55. $\quad$ From the junction theorem, $\quad I_3 = I_1 + I_2, \quad$ and $\quad I_2 = I_4 + I_5.$ $\quad$ So $\quad I_3 = I_1 + I_4 + I_5.$

Around the left loop in counterclockwise direction,

$$6.0 \text{ V} - I_1(12 \text{ }\Omega) + 12 \text{ V} - I_3(6.0 \text{ }\Omega) - I_1(2.0 \text{ }\Omega) = 0,$$

or $\quad 14I_1 + 6I_3 = 18.$ $\qquad\qquad$ Eq. (1)

Around the middle loop in clockwise direction,

$$12 \text{ V} - I_3(6.0 \text{ }\Omega) - I_2(4.0 \text{ }\Omega) + 6.0 \text{ V} - I_4(8.0 \text{ }\Omega) = 0,$$

or $4I_2 + 6I_3 + 8I_4 = 18$,   or $-4I_1 + 10I_3 + 8I_4 = 18$.   Eq. (2)

Around the right loop in counterclockwise direction, $6.0 \text{ V} - I_4(8.0 \text{ }\Omega) + I_5(10 \text{ }\Omega) = 0$,

or $8I_4 - 10I_5 = 6$,   or $10I_1 - 10I_3 + 18I_4 = 6$.   Eq. (3)

Solving, $\boxed{I_1 = 0.664 \text{ A left}}$, $\boxed{I_2 = 0.786 \text{ A right}}$, $\boxed{I_3 = 1.450 \text{ A up}}$,

$\boxed{I_4 = 0.770 \text{ A down}}$, $\boxed{I_5 = 0.016 \text{ A down}}$,   and $\boxed{I_6 = 0.664 \text{ A down}}$.

56.   (a). The voltage across the capacitor decreases exponentially when a capacitor is discharged.

57.   (c). The current through the capacitor decreases exponentially when a capacitor is charged.

58.   You can $\boxed{\text{increase the resistance or capacitance}}$ to increase the time constant as $\tau = RC$.

59.   At the beginning of the charging process, $\boxed{\text{there is little charge on the capacitor}}$. Since $V = Q/C$ for a

capacitor, little Q means low V.

60.   As the capacitor is charged, charges accumulate on the capacitor. From the charge-force law, these

$\boxed{\text{charges on capacitor resist more charges to be transferred}}$.

61.   (a) Just after the switch is closed, the capacitor is not charged.

So $V_C = \boxed{0}$ and $V_R = V_o - V_C = \boxed{V_o}$.

(b) After one time constant, $V_C = \boxed{0.63V_o}$ and $V_R = V_o - V_C = \boxed{0.37V_o}$.

(c) After many time constants, the capacitor is fully charged.

So $V_C = \boxed{V_o}$ and $V_R = \boxed{0}$.

62.   (a) By definition, $\tau = \boxed{1.5 \text{ s}}$.

(b) $V_C = V_o\left(1 - e^{-t/\tau}\right) = V_o\left(1 - e^{-10}\right) = 0.99995$,

So the percentage is $\dfrac{V_C}{V_o} = \boxed{99.995\%}$.

63.   (a) You should $\boxed{\text{increase the capacitance}}$ to increase the time constant as $\tau = RC$.

(b) $\tau = RC$,   ☞ $R = \dfrac{\tau}{C} = \dfrac{2.0 \text{ s}}{1.0 \times 10^{-6} \text{ F}} = 2.0 \times 10^6 \text{ }\Omega = \boxed{2.0 \text{ M}\Omega}$.

64. $V_C = V_o e^{-t/\tau}$, ☞ $0.5 = e^{-t/\tau}$, or $\ln 0.5 = -\dfrac{t}{\tau}$.

So $t = \boxed{0.693\,\tau}$.

65. (a) $\tau = RC$, ☞ $R = \dfrac{\tau}{C} = \dfrac{1.50 \text{ s}}{1.00 \times 10^{-6} \text{ F}} = 1.50 \times 10^6 \ \Omega = \boxed{1.50 \text{ M}\Omega}$.

(b) $V_C = V_o\left(1 - e^{-t/\tau}\right) = (12.0 \text{ V})\left(1 - e^{-3}\right) = \boxed{11.4 \text{ V}}$.

66. (a) The potential difference on the capacitor is zero immediately after the switch is closed because the capacitor is uncharged.

$V_C = V_o\left(1 - e^{-t/\tau}\right) = V_o\left(1 - e^0\right) = 0$. So the potential difference across the resistor is $\boxed{24 \text{ V}}$.

(b) $\boxed{0}$.

(c) $I = \dfrac{\mathcal{E}}{R} = \dfrac{24 \text{ V}}{6.0 \ \Omega} = \boxed{4.0 \text{ A}}$.

67. (a) $V_C = V_o\left(1 - e^{-t/\tau}\right) = (24 \text{ V})\left(1 - e^{-4}\right) = 23.56 \text{ V}$.

So $Q = C\,V_C = (40 \times 10^{-6} \text{ F})(23.56 \text{ V}) = \boxed{9.4 \times 10^{-4} \text{ C}}$.

(b) After a long time, the capacitor is fully charged. $V_C = \boxed{24 \text{ V}}$ and $V_R = \boxed{0}$.

68. At $t = 2\tau$, $V_C = V_o\left(1 - e^{-t/\tau}\right) = (12 \text{ V})\left(1 - e^{-2}\right) = 10.38 \text{ V}$.

At $t = 4\tau$, $V_C = (12 \text{ V})\left(1 - e^{-4}\right) = 11.78 \text{ V}$.

So $\Delta V_C = 11.78 \text{ V} - 10.38 \text{ V} = \boxed{1.4 \text{ V}}$, an increase.

69. (a) At $t = 0$, $V_C = \boxed{0}$, $I = \dfrac{\mathcal{E}}{R} = \dfrac{4(1.5 \text{ V})}{3.0 \times 10^6 \ \Omega} = 2.0 \times 10^{-6} \text{ A} = \boxed{2.0 \ \mu\text{A}}$.

(b) $\tau = RC = (3.0 \times 10^6 \ \Omega)(0.28 \times 10^{-6} \text{ F}) = 0.84 \text{ s}$. $V_C = V_o\left(1 - e^{-t/\tau}\right) = (6.0 \text{ V})\left(1 - e^{-4.0/0.84}\right) = 5.95 \text{ V}$.

So $Q = CV_C = (0.28 \times 10^{-6} \text{ F})(5.95 \text{ V}) = \boxed{1.7 \times 10^{-6} \text{ C}}$.

70. (b).

71. (c).

72.　　(b).

73.　　(a) An ammeter has very low resistance, so if it were connected in parallel in a circuit, the circuit current would be very high and the galvanometer could burn out.

(b) A voltmeter has very high resistance, so if it were connected in series in a circuit, it would read the voltage of the source because it has the highest resistance (most probably) and therefore the most voltage drop among the circuit elements.

74.　　The resistance of an ideal voltmeter is $\boxed{\text{infinite}}$. A voltmeter is used to measure voltage when it is connected in parallel to a circuit element. If it has infinite resistance, there will be no current through it, so it will not affect the current through the circuit element, therefore its voltage.

75.　　The resistance of an ammeter should be $\boxed{\text{small}}$. An ammeter is used to measure current when it is connected in series to a circuit element. If it has small resistance, there will be little voltage across it, so it will not affect the voltage across the circuit element, therefore its current.

76.　　(a) You should use a $\boxed{\text{shunt}}$ resistor. Since a galvanometer cannot allow a large current through it, current has to be diverted through another branch through the shunt resistor.

(b) $I_g = \dfrac{IR_s}{r + R_s}$, ☞ $R_s = \dfrac{I_g r}{I - I_g} = \dfrac{(2000 \times 10^{-6}\text{ A})(100\ \Omega)}{30\text{ A} - 2000 \times 10^{-6}\text{ A}} = 0.00667\ \Omega = \boxed{6.7\text{ m}\Omega}$.

77.　　(a) You should use a $\boxed{\text{multipler}}$ resistor. Since a galvanometer cannot have a large voltage across it, the large voltage has to be across a series resistor (multiplier).

(b) $I_g = \dfrac{V}{r + R_m}$, ☞ $R_m = \dfrac{V}{I_g} - r = \dfrac{15\text{ V}}{2000 \times 10^{-6}\text{ A}} - 100\ \Omega = 7.4 \times 10^3\ \Omega = \boxed{7.4\text{ k}\Omega}$.

78.　　$I_g = \dfrac{IR_s}{r + R_s}$, ☞ $R_s = \dfrac{I_g r}{I - I_g} = \dfrac{(600 \times 10^{-6}\text{ A})(50\ \Omega)}{5.0\text{ A} - 600 \times 10^{-6}\text{ A}} = 6.0 \times 10^{-3}\ \Omega = \boxed{6.0\text{ m}\Omega}$.

79.　　$I_g = \dfrac{V}{r + R_m}$, ☞ $R_m = \dfrac{V}{I_g} - r = \dfrac{10\text{ V}}{200 \times 10^{-6}\text{ A}} - 20\ \Omega = 4.998 \times 10^4\ \Omega = \boxed{50\text{ k}\Omega}$.

80.　　Ammeter is connected in series. $I = \dfrac{V}{R + R_a} = \dfrac{6.0\text{ V}}{10\ \Omega + 1.0 \times 10^{-3}\ \Omega} = \boxed{0.59994\text{ A}}$.

81.　　Voltmeter is connected in parallel. $I = \dfrac{V}{R_v} = \dfrac{6.0\text{ V}}{30 \times 10^3\ \Omega} = 2.0 \times 10^{-4}\text{ A} = \boxed{0.20\text{ mA}}$.

82. (a) The internal resistance of the voltmeter should be ⟮infinite⟯. A voltmeter is connected in parallel with a circuit element. If its resistance is infinite, there will be no current through it; therefore, it does not affect the voltage across the circuit element it is measuring.
(b) The current reading I is the total current through the parallel combination R_p (R and R_v).

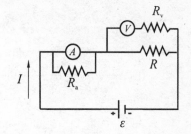

So the voltage reading is $V = IR_p = I\dfrac{R_v R}{R_v + R}$. Therefore $R = \dfrac{V}{I - (V/R_v)}$.

If R_v is ∞, $R = \dfrac{V}{I}$, i.e., the measurement is "perfect."

83. (a) The internal resistance of the ammeter should be ⟮zero⟯. An ammeter is connected in series with a circuit element. If its resistance is zero, it will not affect the current through the circuit element.
(b) The current reading I is the current through R, and the voltage reading is the total voltage across R and R_a.

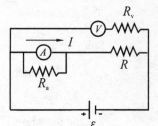

So $V = I(R + R_a)$, ☞ $R = \dfrac{V}{I} - R_a$.

If $R_a = 0$, $R = \dfrac{V}{I}$, i.e., the measurement is "perfect."

84. (a).

85. (c).

86. The fuse and the switch are on the ground side of the circuit. An open switch or blown fuse would potentially leave the motor at a high voltage if it were touched by a person.

87. No. Since current is caused by voltage (potential difference), a high voltage can produce high "harmful" current, even though the resistance of a body is high.

88. A conductor has very low resistance. The resistance of the wire between the feet is very small; the voltage between the feet is also small and so is the current through the bird, so most continues through the wire.

89. It is safer to jump. If you step off the car one foot at a time, there will be a high voltage between your feet. If you jump, the voltage between your feet is zero because your feet will be at the same potential all the time.

90. $\boxed{\text{The case is grounded so the potential of the case is always zero}}$ even if the hot wire accidentally touches the case.

91. $R_p = \dfrac{R_1 R_2}{R_1 + R_2} = \dfrac{(50\ \Omega)(50\ \Omega)}{50\ \Omega + 50\ \Omega} = 25\ \Omega.$ $R_s = R_p + R_3 = 25\ \Omega + 50\ \Omega = \boxed{75\ \Omega}.$

92. $R_s = R_1 + R_2 = 100\ \Omega + 100\ \Omega = 200\ \Omega.$ $R_p = \dfrac{R_s R_3}{R_s + R_3} = \dfrac{(200\ \Omega)(100\ \Omega)}{200\ \Omega + 100\ \Omega} = \boxed{66.7\ \Omega}.$

93. $R_s = R_1 + \dfrac{R_2 R_3}{R_2 + R_3} = 4.0\ \Omega + \dfrac{(6.0\ \Omega)R_3}{6.0\ \Omega + R_3} = 7.0\ \Omega.$

Solving, $R_3 = \boxed{6.0\ \Omega}.$

94.   From the junction theorem, $I_1 = I_2 + I_3.$

Around the upper loop in clockwise direction, $6.0\ \text{V} - I_1(2.0\ \Omega) - I_2(4.0\ \Omega) + 6.0\ \text{V} = 0,$

or $2I_1 + 4I_2 = 12.$ Eq. (1)

Around the whole circuit in clockwise direction, $6.0\ \text{V} - I_1(2.0\ \Omega) - I_3(8.0\ \Omega) + 6.0\ \text{V} = 0,$

or $10I_1 - 8I_2 = 12.$ Eq. (2)

Solving, $\boxed{I_1 = 2.6\ \text{A right}},$ $\boxed{I_2 = 1.7\ \text{A left}},$ and $\boxed{I_3 = 0.86\ \text{A left}}.$

95.   The total power is $P = \dfrac{V^2}{R_1} + \dfrac{V^2}{R_2} = \dfrac{(9.0\ \text{V})^2}{30\ \Omega} + \dfrac{(9.0\ \text{V})^2}{15\ \Omega} = 8.1\ \text{W} = \boxed{8.1\ \text{J/s}}.$

96.   (a) $\boxed{R_1 \text{ and } R_2}$ will dissipate the most power.

The current through the 10 Ω resistor is $P = \dfrac{V^2}{R} = \dfrac{(90\ \text{V})^2}{10\ \Omega} = \boxed{8.1 \times 10^2\ \text{W}}.$

(b) $\dfrac{1}{R_p} = \dfrac{1}{10\ \Omega} + \dfrac{1}{5.0\ \Omega + 10\ \Omega} + \dfrac{1}{10\ \Omega} = \dfrac{4}{15\ \Omega},$ ☞ $R_p = 3.75\ \Omega.$

So the total power is $P = \dfrac{(90\ \text{V})^2}{3.75\ \Omega} = \boxed{2.2 \times 10^3\ \text{W}}.$

97.   (a) R_2, R_3, and R_4 are in parallel combination,

$\dfrac{1}{R_p} = \dfrac{1}{25\ \Omega} + \dfrac{1}{50\ \Omega} + \dfrac{1}{25\ \Omega} = \dfrac{1}{10\ \Omega},$ so $R_p = 10\ \Omega.$

So the total current is $I = I_1 = \dfrac{110\ \text{V}}{100\ \Omega + 10\ \Omega} = \boxed{1.0\ \text{A}}.$

The voltage on R_p is $(1.0 \text{ A})(10 \ \Omega) = 10 \text{ V}$.

Therefore $\quad I_2 = I_4 = \dfrac{10 \text{ V}}{25 \ \Omega} = \boxed{0.40 \text{ A}}, \quad I_3 = \dfrac{10 \text{ V}}{50 \ \Omega} = \boxed{0.20 \text{ A}}$.

(b) $P_1 = I^2 R_1 = (1.0 \text{ A})^2 (100 \ \Omega) = \boxed{100 \text{ W}}, \quad P_2 = P_4 = (0.40 \text{ A})^2 (25 \ \Omega) = \boxed{4.0 \text{ W}}$,

$P_3 = (0.20 \text{ A})^2 (50 \ \Omega) = \boxed{2.0 \text{ W}}$.

98.   Three R's are in series, $\quad R_{s1} = 3R$.

This R_{s1} and R are in parallel, $\quad R_{p1} = \dfrac{(3R)R}{3R + R} = \dfrac{3}{4} R$.

This R_{p1} and two R are in series, $\quad R_{s2} = 2R + \dfrac{3}{4} R = \dfrac{11}{4} R$.

This R_{s2} and R are in parallel, $\quad R_{p2} = \dfrac{\frac{11}{4} R \, R}{\frac{11}{4} R + R} = \dfrac{11}{15} R$.

Finally this R_{p2} and two R are in series, $\quad R_{s3} = 2R + \dfrac{11}{15} R = \boxed{41R/15 = 2.73R}$.

99.   Use the results in Exercise 18.98,

The current through the first two R's (from left) is

$I_1 = I_2 = \dfrac{V}{R_{s3}} = \dfrac{12.0 \text{ V}}{2.73(10.0 \ \Omega)} = \boxed{0.440 \text{ A}}$.

The voltage across R_{p2} is $\quad V_{p2} = I_1 R_{p2} = (0.440 \text{ A}) \dfrac{11}{15} (10.0 \ \Omega) = 3.23 \text{ V}$.

So the current through the third R is $\quad I_3 = \dfrac{3.23 \text{ V}}{10.0 \ \Omega} = \boxed{0.323 \text{ A}}$.

The current through the next two R's is $\quad I_4 = I_5 = \dfrac{3.23 \text{ V}}{11(10.0 \ \Omega)/4} = \boxed{0.117 \text{ A}}$.

The voltage across R_{p1} is $\quad V_{p1} = I_4 R_{p1} = (0.117 \text{ A}) \dfrac{3}{4} (10.0 \ \Omega) = 0.878 \text{ V}$.

So $\quad I_6 = \dfrac{0.878 \text{ V}}{10.0 \ \Omega} = \boxed{0.0878 \text{ A}}, \quad I_7 = I_8 = I_9 = \dfrac{0.878 \text{ V}}{3(10.0 \ \Omega)} = \boxed{0.0293 \text{ A}}$.

100. $V_C = V_0 \left(1 - e^{-t/\tau}\right)$. At V_m, $\quad V_m = V_0 \left(1 - e^{-t_m/\tau}\right)$, $\quad \text{☞} \quad e^{-t_m/\tau} = 1 - \dfrac{V_m}{V_0}$.

So $\quad \dfrac{t_m}{\tau} = \ln \dfrac{V_0}{V_0 - V_m}$, i.e., $\quad t_m = RC \ln \dfrac{V_0}{V_0 - V_m}$. Similarly, $\quad t_b = RC \ln \dfrac{V_0}{V_0 - V_b}$.

Therefore $\quad T = T_b - T_m = RC \ln \dfrac{V_0(V_0 - V_m)}{(V_0 - V_b)V_0} = RC \ln \dfrac{V_0 - V_m}{V_0 - V_b}$. (because $\ln x - \ln y = \ln \dfrac{x}{y}$).

101. When there is no current in the ammeter, $\varepsilon_1 = IR_1$ and $\varepsilon_2 = IR_2$.

Dividing the two equations gives $\dfrac{\varepsilon_2}{\varepsilon} = \dfrac{R_2}{R_1}$, or $\varepsilon_2 = \dfrac{R_2}{R_1} = \varepsilon_1$.

102. (a) $P = \dfrac{V^2}{R}$, ☞ $R = \dfrac{V^2}{P} = \dfrac{(110\ \text{V})^2}{100\ \text{W}} = 121\ \Omega$.

So $I_1 = I_2 = \dfrac{V}{2R} = \dfrac{110\ \text{V}}{2(121\ \Omega)} = \boxed{0.45\ \text{A}}$. $P_1 = P_2 = (0.455\ \text{A})^2 (121\ \Omega) = \boxed{25\ \text{W}}$.

(b) $I_1 = I_2 = \dfrac{110\ \text{V}}{121\ \Omega} = \boxed{0.91\ \text{A}}$ and $P_1 = P_2 = \boxed{100\ \text{W}}$.

103. Top loop: $R_{p1} = \dfrac{(12\ \Omega)(6.0\ \Omega)}{12\ \Omega + 6.0\ \Omega} = 4.0\ \Omega$, $\qquad R_{s1} = 4.0\ \Omega + 3.0\ \Omega = 7.0\ \Omega$.

$R_{p2} = \dfrac{(7.0\ \Omega)(4.0\ \Omega)}{7.0\ \Omega + 4.0\ \Omega} = 2.55\ \Omega$.

$R_{s2} = 2.545\ \Omega + 7.0\ \Omega + 10\ \Omega + 5.0\ \Omega = 24.55\ \Omega$.

Bottom loop: $R_{p1} = \dfrac{(4.0\ \Omega)(4.0\ \Omega)}{4.0\ \Omega + 4.0\ \Omega} = 2.0\ \Omega$, $\qquad R_{s1} = 2.0\ \Omega + 2.0\ \Omega = 4.0\ \Omega$,

$R_{p2} = \dfrac{(4.0\ \Omega)(6.0\ \Omega)}{4.0\ \Omega + 6.0\ \Omega} = 2.4\ \Omega$.

Top and bottom combination, $R_p = \dfrac{(24.55\ \Omega)(2.4\ \text{W})}{24.55\ \Omega + 2.4\ \Omega} = 2.19\ \Omega$.

Finally, $R_s = 2.19\ \Omega + 6.0\ \Omega + 2.0\ \Omega = 10.2\ \Omega$.

$I = \dfrac{V}{R_s} = \dfrac{120\ \text{V}}{10.2\ \Omega} = \boxed{11.8\ \text{A}}$.

104. $P = \dfrac{V^2}{R}$, ☞ $R = \dfrac{V^2}{P} = \dfrac{(12\ \text{V})^2}{3.2\ \text{W}} = 45\ \Omega$.

Since $30\ \Omega < 45\ \Omega < 60\ \Omega$, they cannot be connected in series or parallel.

Also $45\ \Omega = 30\ \Omega + 15\ \Omega = 30\ \Omega + \dfrac{(30\ \Omega)(30\ \Omega)}{30\ \Omega + 30\ \Omega}$.

So the connection is $\boxed{\text{two in parallel and in series with the other resistor}}$.

105. (a) $\varepsilon = 3(1.5\ \text{V}) = 4.5\ \text{V}$. $I = \dfrac{\varepsilon}{R + r} = \dfrac{4.5\ \text{V}}{10\ \Omega + 3(0.02\ \Omega)} = 0.447\ \text{A}$.

So $V = IR = (0.447\ \text{A})(10\ \Omega) = \boxed{4.47\ \text{V}}$.

(b) As determined in (a), $I = \boxed{0.447\ \text{A}}$.

106. $I_g = \dfrac{V}{r + R_m}$, ☞ $R_m = \dfrac{V}{I_g} - r$.

So $R_1 = \dfrac{20\text{ V}}{200 \times 10^{-6}\text{ A}} - 50\ \Omega = 9.995 \times 10^4\ \Omega \approx \boxed{100\text{ k}\Omega}$,

$R_2 = \dfrac{100\text{ V}}{200 \times 10^{-6}\text{ A}} - 50\ \Omega = 4.9995 \times 10^5\ \Omega \approx \boxed{500\text{ k}\Omega}$,

$R_3 = \dfrac{200\text{ V}}{200 \times 10^{-6}\text{ A}} - 50\ \Omega = 9.9995 \times 10^5\ \Omega \approx \boxed{1.00\text{ M}\Omega}$.

107. $I_g = \dfrac{IR_s}{r + R_s}$, ☞ $R_s = \dfrac{I_g r}{I - I_g}$. So $R_{s1} = \dfrac{(100 \times 10^{-6}\text{ A})(100\ \Omega)}{1.0\text{ A} - 100 \times 10^{-6}\text{ A}} = 1.0 \times 10^{-2}\ \Omega = \boxed{10\text{ m}\Omega}$,

$R_{s2} = \dfrac{(100 \times 10^{-6}\text{ A})(100\ \Omega)}{5.0\text{ A} - 100 \times 10^{-6}\text{ A}} = \boxed{2.0\text{ m}\Omega}$, and $R_{s3} = \dfrac{(100 \times 10^{-6}\text{ A})(100\ \Omega)}{10\text{ A} - 100 \times 10^{-6}\text{ A}} = \boxed{1.0\text{ m}\Omega}$.

CHAPTER 19

1.   (e), because unlike poles attract.

2.   (b).

3.   (c).

4.   The magnet would attract the unmagnetized iron bar when a pole end is placed at the center of its long side. If the end of the unmagnetized bar were placed at the center of the long side of the magnet, it would not be attracted.

5.   Similarities: Two kinds of poles, north and south (charges, positive and negative); like poles (charges) repel and unlike poles (charges) attract.

        Differences: Poles come in pairs (single charge can exist).

6.   (b), according to the right-hand rule.

7.   No . Charge must be in motion to experience magnetic force.

8.   Into the page , according to the right-hand rule.

9.   They are either parallel or opposite . When $\theta = 0°$, there is no magnetic force because $F = qvB \sin \theta$.

10.   (a) The magnitude of the magnetic force on them is the same . The magnitude of the force depends on charge ($F = qvB \sin \theta$,) and proton and electron has the same magnitude of charge.

        (b) Electron has greater acceleration due to its smaller mass. Since $F = ma$, the smaller the mass, the greater the acceleration.

11.   Not necessarily , because there still could be a magnetic force. If the magnetic field and the velocity of the charged particle make an angle of either 0° or 180°, there is no magnetic force because $F = qvB \sin \theta$.

12.   (a) According to the right-hand rule: (1) negative charge , (2) no charge , (3) positive charge .

        (b) The radius of the circular orbit is proportional to the mass, so $m_3 > m_1$.

13.   (a) The bottom half would have a magnetic field directed into the page and the top half would have a magnetic field directed out of the page.

(b) They are the $\boxed{\text{same}}$ since centripetal force does not change the speed of the particle.

14.   (a) According to the right-hand force rule, the magnetic force is directed $\boxed{\text{into the page}}$.

(b) $F = qvB \sin \theta$, ☞ $B = \dfrac{F}{qB \sin \theta} = \dfrac{20 \text{ N}}{(0.25 \text{ C})(2.0 \times 10^2 \text{ m/s}) \sin 90°} = \boxed{0.40 \text{ T}}$.

15. $F = qvB \sin \theta$, ☞ $v = \dfrac{F}{qB \sin \theta} = \dfrac{10 \text{ N}}{(0.05 \text{ C})(0.080 \text{ T}) \sin 90°} = \boxed{2.5 \times 10^3 \text{ m/s}}$.

16.   If the charges are electrons (negative), an excess negative charge accumulates on the left side of the strip, and if positive, on the right side of the strip. The sign of the voltage drop across the strip would then indicate the type of charge.

17.   The magnetic field has to be to the left, looking in the direction of the beam, so the magnetic force points upward. $F = qvB \sin \theta = mg$,

so $B = \dfrac{mg}{qv \sin \theta} = \dfrac{(1.67 \times 10^{-27} \text{ kg})(9.80 \text{ m/s}^2)}{(1.6 \times 10^{-19} \text{ C})(5.0 \times 10^6 \text{ m/s}) \sin 90°} = \boxed{2.0 \times 10^{-14} \text{ T to the left}}$, looking in the direction of the beam, so the magnetic force points upward, opposite to gravity.

18.   (a) According to the right-hand force rule and the fact that electron carries negative charge, the magnetic field is directed in the $\boxed{-z}$ direction.

(b) From $F = qvB \sin \theta$,

$B = \dfrac{F}{qv \sin \theta} = \dfrac{5.0 \times 10^{-19} \text{ N}}{(1.6 \times 10^{-19} \text{ C})(3.0 \times 10^6 \text{ m/s}) \sin 90°} = \boxed{1.0 \times 10^{-6} \text{ T}}$.

19.   (a) $F = qvB \sin \theta = (1.6 \times 10^{-19} \text{ C})(2.0 \times 10^4 \text{ m/s})(1.2 \times 10^{-3} \text{ T}) \sin 90° = \boxed{3.8 \times 10^{-18} \text{ N}}$.

(b) $F = (1.6 \times 10^{-19} \text{ C})(2.0 \times 10^4 \text{ m/s})(1.2 \times 10^{-3} \text{ T}) \sin 45° = \boxed{2.7 \times 10^{-18} \text{ N}}$.

(c) $F = \boxed{0}$ since $\sin 0° = 0$.

20. $F = qvB \sin \theta = F_0 \sin \theta$, ☞ $\sin \theta = \frac{1}{2}$.

So $\theta = \boxed{30° \text{ or } 150°}$.

21. (a) $a = \dfrac{F}{m} = \dfrac{qvB \sin \theta}{m} = \dfrac{(1.6 \times 10^{-19}\,\text{C})(3.0 \times 10^{5}\,\text{m/s})(0.50\,\text{T}) \sin 37^{\circ}}{1.67 \times 10^{-27}\,\text{kg}} = \boxed{8.6 \times 10^{12}\,\text{m/s}^2}$.

The direction of initial acceleration is horizontal toward the right, looking in direction of velocity.

(b) Since $F = q v B \sin \theta$ independent of mass, the force on the electron has the

$\boxed{\text{same magnitude but in the opposite direction}}$, because the electron has negative charge.

22. (d).

23. The $\boxed{\text{magnetic force on the electron beam}}$, which "prints" pictures, causes the deflection of the electrons.

24. $v = \dfrac{V}{Bd} = \dfrac{E}{B} = \dfrac{8.0 \times 10^{3}\,\text{V/m}}{0.040\,\text{T}} = \boxed{2.0 \times 10^{5}\,\text{m/s}}$.

25. (a) $v = \dfrac{V}{Bd}$, ☞ $V = vBd = (8.0 \times 10^{4}\,\text{m/s})(1.5\,\text{T})(0.015\,\text{m}) = \boxed{1.8 \times 10^{3}\,\text{V}}$.

(b) It is the $\boxed{\text{same voltage}}$, 1.8×10^{3} V, because it is $\boxed{\text{independent of charge}}$ on the particle.

26. (a) $v = \dfrac{V}{Bd} = \dfrac{E}{B} = \dfrac{3000\,\text{N/C}}{0.030\,\text{T}} = \boxed{1.0 \times 10^{5}\,\text{m/s}}$.

(b) It is the $\boxed{\text{same speed}}$, 1.0×10^{5} m/s, because it is $\boxed{\text{independent of charge}}$ on the particle.

27. $K = \frac{1}{2}mv^2$, ☞ $v = \sqrt{\dfrac{2K}{m}} = \sqrt{\dfrac{2(10 \times 10^{3}\,\text{eV})(1.6 \times 10^{-19}\,\text{J/eV})}{2.25 \times 10^{-28}\,\text{kg}}} = 3.77 \times 10^{6}\,\text{m/s}$.

$v = \dfrac{E}{B}$, ☞ $B = \dfrac{E}{v} = \dfrac{2.0 \times 10^{3}\,\text{V/m}}{3.77 \times 10^{6}\,\text{m/s}} = \boxed{5.3 \times 10^{-4}\,\text{T}}$.

28. $v = \dfrac{V}{Bd} = \dfrac{E}{B} = \dfrac{1.0 \times 10^{3}\,\text{V/m}}{0.10\,\text{T}} = 1.0 \times 10^{4}\,\text{m/s}$. Here the magnetic force provides centripetal force for the

circular motion. Since $F = qvB \sin \theta = m\dfrac{v^2}{R}$,

$m = \dfrac{qBR \sin \theta}{v} = \dfrac{(1.6 \times 10^{-19}\,\text{C})(0.10\,\text{T})(0.012\,\text{m}) \sin 90^{\circ}}{1.0 \times 10^{4}\,\text{m/s}} = \boxed{1.9 \times 10^{-26}\,\text{kg}}$.

29. (a) $v = \dfrac{V}{Bd} = \dfrac{E}{B} = \dfrac{1.0 \times 10^{3}\,\text{V/m}}{0.100\,\text{T}} = 1.0 \times 10^{4}\,\text{m/s}$.

In circular motion magnetic force provides centripetal force. $F = qvB \sin \theta = m\dfrac{v^2}{R}$,

so $m = \dfrac{qBR \sin \theta}{v} = \dfrac{(2 \times 1.6 \times 10^{-19}\,\text{C})(0.10\,\text{T})(0.015\,\text{m}) \sin 90^{\circ}}{1.0 \times 10^{4}\,\text{m/s}} = \boxed{4.8 \times 10^{-26}\,\text{kg}}$.

(b) $K = \frac{1}{2}mv^2 = \frac{1}{2}(4.8 \times 10^{-26} \text{ kg})(1.0 \times 10^4 \text{ m/s})^2 = \boxed{2.4 \times 10^{-18} \text{ J}}$.

(c) $\boxed{\text{No}}$, the kinetic does not increase. The centripetal force (magnetic force) is perpendicular to velocity so the $\boxed{\text{work is equal to zero}}$.

30. $K = \frac{1}{2}mv^2$, ☞ $v = \sqrt{\dfrac{2K}{m}} = \sqrt{\dfrac{2(10 \times 10^3 \text{ eV})(1.6 \times 10^{-19} \text{ J/eV})}{1.67 \times 10^{-27} \text{ kg}}} = 1.38 \times 10^6 \text{ m/s}$.

In this circular motion, the magnetic force provides the centripetal force.

$F = qvB \sin\theta = m\dfrac{v^2}{R}$, ☞ $B = \dfrac{mv}{qR\sin\theta} = \dfrac{(1.67 \times 10^{-27} \text{ kg})(1.38 \times 10^6 \text{ m/s})}{(1.6 \times 10^{-19} \text{ C})(0.50 \text{ m})\sin 90°} = \boxed{2.9 \times 10^{-2} \text{ T}}$.

31. (d), according to the force right-hand rule.

32. $\boxed{\text{Attract}}$ for currents in the same direction and $\boxed{\text{repel}}$ for opposite currents.

33. $\boxed{\text{It shortens}}$ because the coils of the spring attract each other due to the magnetic fields created in the coils.

34. $\boxed{\text{Yes, with magnetic field perpendicular to plane of loop}}$.

35. $\boxed{\text{Yes}}$, the direction of the magnetic field can be determined. You can orient the current-carrying wire in a direction that is not east-west and then observe the magnetic force on the current-carrying wire. Then use the right-hand force rule to determine the direction of the magnetic field.

36. (d).

37. Pushing the button in both cases completes the circuit. The current in the wires activates the electromagnet, causing the clapper to be attracted and ring the bell. However, this breaks the armature contact and opens the circuit. Holding the button causes this to repeat, and the bell rings continuously. For the chimes, when the circuit is completed, the electromagnet attracts the core and compresses the spring. Inertia causes it to hit one tone bar, and the spring force then sends the core in the opposite direction to strike the other bar.

38. (a) The magnetic force is in the $\boxed{+y}$ direction according to the right-hand force rule, (upward as $+z$).

(b) $F = ILB \sin\theta = (5.0 \text{ A})(1.0 \text{ m})(0.30 \text{ T})\sin 90° = \boxed{1.5 \text{ N}}$.

39. $F = ILB \sin\theta = (20 \text{ A})(2.0 \text{ m})(0.050 \text{ T})\sin 37° = \boxed{1.2 \text{ N perpendicular to the plane of } \mathbf{B} \text{ and } I}$.

40. (a) To the right .   (b) Toward top of page .

(c) Into the page .   (d) To the left .

(e) Into or out of the page .

41. $F = ILB \sin \theta,$ ☞ $B = \dfrac{F}{IL \sin \theta} = \dfrac{1.0 \times 10^{-2}\ \text{N}}{(4.0\ \text{A})(0.50\ \text{m}) \sin 90°} = \boxed{5.0 \times 10^{-3}\ \text{T north to south}}.$

42. $F = ILB \sin \theta = (15\ \text{A})(0.75\ \text{m})(1.0 \times 10^{-4}\ \text{T}) \sin 30° = \boxed{5.6 \times 10^{-4}\ \text{N}}.$

43. (a) $F = ILB \sin \theta,$ ☞ $\dfrac{F}{L} = IB \sin \theta = IB \sin 0° = \boxed{0}.$

(b) $\dfrac{F}{L} = (10\ \text{A})(0.40\ \text{T}) \sin 90° = \boxed{4.0\ \text{N/m in} +z}.$

(c) $\dfrac{F}{L} = (10\ \text{A})(0.40\ \text{T}) \sin 90° = \boxed{4.0\ \text{N/m in} -y}.$

(d) $\dfrac{F}{L} = (10\ \text{A})(0.40\ \text{T}) \sin 90° = \boxed{4.0\ \text{N/m in} -z}.$

(e) $\dfrac{F}{L} = (10\ \text{A})(0.40\ \text{T}) \sin 90° = \boxed{4.0\ \text{N/m in} +y}.$

44. $F = ILB \sin \theta,$ ☞ $I = \dfrac{F}{LB \sin \theta} = \dfrac{0.050\ \text{N}}{(0.25\ \text{m})(0.30\ \text{T}) \sin 90°} = \boxed{0.67\ \text{A in} -z}.$

45. B_x has no contribution to force since $\sin \theta = 0°.$

$F_z = I_x LB_y \sin \theta,$ ☞ $\dfrac{F_z}{L} = I_x B_y \sin \theta = (10\ \text{A})(0.040\ \text{T}) \sin 90° = \boxed{0.40\ \text{N/m in} +z\ \text{direction}}.$

46. $\dfrac{F}{L} = \dfrac{\mu_0 I_1 I_2}{2\pi d} = \dfrac{(4\pi \times 10^{-7}\ \text{T·m/A})(15\ \text{A})^2}{2\pi(0.15\ \text{m})} = \boxed{3.0 \times 10^{-4}\ \text{N/m repulsive}}.$ It is repulsive because the

currents are opposite and so the fields in between the wires are in the same direction.

47. (a) The forces on the wires are attractive . Assume the currents are upward in both wires. The magnetic

field by the left wire on the right wire is directed into the page, according to the right-hand source rule.

Then the magnetic force on the right wire is to the left according to the right-hand force rule. Vice versa,

the force on the left wire is to the right so they attract.

(b) $\dfrac{F}{L} = \dfrac{\mu_0 I_1 I_2}{2\pi d} = \dfrac{(4\pi \times 10^{-7}\ \text{T·m/A})(2.0\ \text{A})(4.0\ \text{A})}{2\pi(0.24\ \text{m})} = \boxed{6.7 \times 10^{-6}\ \text{N/m}}.$

48. (a) The forces on the wires are $\boxed{\text{repulsive}}$. Assume the current in the left wire is up and the current in the right wire is down. The magnetic field by the left wire on the right wire is directed into the page, according to the right-hand source rule. Then the magnetic force on the right wire is to the right according to the right-hand force rule. Vice versa, the force on the left wire is to the left so they repel.

(b) $\dfrac{F}{L} = \dfrac{\mu_o I_1 I_2}{2\pi d} = \dfrac{(4\pi \times 10^{-7}\ \text{T·m/A})(3.0\ \text{A})^2}{2\pi(0.10\ \text{m})} = \boxed{1.8 \times 10^{-5}\ \text{N/m}}$.

49. $F = ILB \sin \theta = (1000\ \text{A})(15\ \text{m})(5.0 \times 10^{-5}\ \text{T}) \sin 90° = \boxed{0.75\ \text{N upward}}$.

50. $\dfrac{F}{L} = \dfrac{\mu_o I_1 I_2}{2\pi d} = \dfrac{(4\pi \times 10^{-7}\ \text{T·m/A})(8.0\ \text{A})(2.0\ \text{A})}{2\pi(0.12\ \text{m})} = \boxed{2.7 \times 10^{-5}\ \text{N/m toward wire 2}}$,

since the force is attractive.

51. $\dfrac{F}{L} = \dfrac{\mu_o I_1 I_2}{2\pi d} = \dfrac{(4\pi \times 10^{-7}\ \text{T·m/A})(2.0\ \text{A})(8.0\ \text{A})}{2\pi\ (0.12\ \text{m})} = \boxed{2.7 \times 10^{-5}\ \text{N/m toward wire 1}}$,

since the force is attractive.

52. (a) Use the result of Exercise 47(a). The top wire must attract the lower wire so it can stay in equilibrium. For the forces $\boxed{\text{to attract}}$, the $\boxed{\text{currents must be in the same direction}}$.

(b) Magnetic force cancels gravity. $F = mg$.

So $\dfrac{F}{L} = \dfrac{\mu_o I_1 I_2}{2\pi d} = \dfrac{mg}{L}$. Therefore for a length of 1 m, we have

$I = I_1 = I_2 = \sqrt{\dfrac{2\pi d m g}{\mu_o}} = \sqrt{\dfrac{2\pi(0.020\ \text{m})(1.5 \times 10^{-3}\ \text{kg})(9.80\ \text{m/s}^2)}{4\pi \times 10^{-7}\ \text{T·m/A}}} = \boxed{38\ \text{A}}$.

53. For the left segment, $F_L = ILB \sin \theta = (5.0\ \text{A})(0.50\ \text{m})(1.0\ \text{T}) \sin 90° = \boxed{2.5\ \text{N to the left}}$.

For the right segment, $F_R = (5.0\ \text{A})(0.50\ \text{m})(1.0\ \text{T}) \sin 90° = \boxed{2.5\ \text{N to the right}}$.

For the top segment, $F_L = (5.0\ \text{A})(3 \times 0.50\ \text{m})(1.0\ \text{T}) \sin 90° = \boxed{7.5\ \text{N to the top}}$.

54. (a) For the magnetic torque to be at maximum, $\boxed{\text{the plane of the coil should be parallel to } \mathbf{B}}$.

$\tau = IAB \sin \theta$ and the angle θ here is between the $\mathbf{B}$ filed and a direction perpendicular to the plane of the coil. When $\theta = 90°$, τ is maximum.

(b) $m = IA = (1.5\ \text{A})(0.20\ \text{m})(0.30\ \text{m}) = \boxed{9.0 \times 10^{-2}\ \text{A·m}^2}$.

$\tau = IAB \sin \theta = mB \sin \theta = (9.0 \times 10^{-4}\ \text{A·m}^2)(1.6\ \text{T}) = \boxed{0.14\ \text{m·N}}$.

55. The net force is $\boxed{\text{zero}}$ because the magnetic field generated by one wire is parallel to the current in the other wire.

$\boxed{\text{Yes}}$, there is a net torque on each wire.

56. $\theta = 90° - 30° = 60°$ (θ is the angle between the normal to the plane and the field).

$\tau = IAB \sin \theta = (0.25 \text{ A})(0.20 \text{ m}^2)(0.30 \text{ T}) \sin 60° = \boxed{0.013 \text{ m}\cdot\text{N}}$.

57. (a), according to the right-hand source rule.

58. (b), according to the right-hand source rule.

59. (b), according to the right-hand source rule.

60. The current direction is $\boxed{\text{counterclockwise}}$ according to the right-hand source rule.

61. The magnetic field strength is $\boxed{\text{halved}}$ as the field depends inversely on the distance, $B = \dfrac{\mu_0 I}{2\pi d}$.

62. $\boxed{\text{Not necessarily}}$. The magnetic field in a solenoid depends on the current in it and the turn per unit length, not just the number of turns. For example, if the 200 turns is over 0.20 m and the 100 turns is over 0.10 m, then they will have the same turns per unit length and then the same magnetic field.

63. $B = N\dfrac{\mu_0 I}{2r}$, ☞ $I = \dfrac{2rB}{N\mu_0} = \dfrac{2(0.15 \text{ m})(0.80 \times 10^{-3} \text{ T})}{(50)(4\pi \times 10^{-7} \text{ T}\cdot\text{m/A})} = \boxed{3.8 \text{ A}}$.

64. $B = \dfrac{\mu_0 I}{2\pi d} = \dfrac{(4\pi \times 10^{-7} \text{ T}\cdot\text{m/A})(2.5 \text{ A})}{2\pi(0.25 \text{ m})} = \boxed{2.0 \times 10^{-6} \text{ T}}$.

65. $B = \dfrac{\mu_0 I}{2\pi d}$, ☞ $d = \dfrac{\mu_0 I}{2\pi B} = \dfrac{(4\pi \times 10^{-7} \text{ T}\cdot\text{m/A})(5.0 \text{ A})}{2\pi(4.0 \times 10^{-6} \text{ T})} = \boxed{0.25 \text{ m}}$.

66. $n = \dfrac{100 \text{ turns}}{0.20 \text{ m}} = 500 \text{ turns/m}$.   Since $B = \mu_0 nI$,

$I = \dfrac{B}{\mu_0 n} = \dfrac{1.5 \times 10^{-3} \text{ T}}{(4\pi \times 10^{-7} \text{ T}\cdot\text{m/A})(500 \text{ /m})} = \boxed{2.4 \text{ A}}$.

67. (a) The directions of the fields by the two wires are opposite. $B = \dfrac{\mu_0 I}{2\pi d}$.

$$B_1 = \frac{(4\pi \times 10^{-7}\ \text{T·m/A})(8.0\ \text{A})}{2\pi(0.060\ \text{m})} = 2.67 \times 10^{-5}\ \text{T},$$

$$B_2 = \frac{(4\pi \times 10^{-7}\ \text{T·m/A})(2.0\ \text{A})}{2\pi(0.060\ \text{m})} = 6.67 \times 10^{-6}\ \text{T}.$$

So the net field is $B = B_1 - B_2 = 2.67 \times 10^{-5}\ \text{T} - 6.67 \times 10^{-6}\ \text{T} = \boxed{2.0 \times 10^{-5}\ \text{T}}$.

(b) Assume the net field is zero at x from wire 1.

$$B_1 = \frac{\mu_0(8.0\ \text{A})}{2\pi x} = \frac{\mu_0(2.0\ \text{A})}{2\pi(0.12\ \text{m} - x)}, \quad \text{or} \quad x = 4(0.12\ \text{m} - x).$$

Solve for $x = 9.6 \times 10^{-2}\ \text{m} = \boxed{9.6\ \text{cm from wire 1}}$.

68. (a) The fields by the two wires are equal in magnitude and opposite in direction. So the net field is $\boxed{0}$.

(b) The fields by the two wires are equal in magnitude and in the same direction. So the net field is

$$B = 2B_R = 2\frac{\mu_0 I}{2\pi d} = \frac{\mu_0 I}{\pi d} = \frac{(4\pi \times 10^{-7}\ \text{T·m/A})(4.0\ \text{A})}{\pi(0.25\ \text{m})}$$

$$= \boxed{6.4 \times 10^{-6}\ \text{T}}.$$

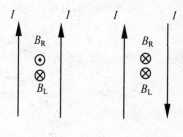

69. The magnitudes at both locations are the same.

Calculate for the location to the right of I_2. $B = \dfrac{\mu_0 I}{2\pi d}$.

$$B_1 = \frac{(4\pi \times 10^{-7}\ \text{T·m/A})(1.5\ \text{A})}{2\pi(0.35\ \text{m})} = 8.57 \times 10^{-7}\ \text{T},$$

$$B_2 = \frac{(4\pi \times 10^{-7}\ \text{T·m/A})(1.5\ \text{A})}{2\pi(0.15\ \text{m})} = 2.0 \times 10^{-6}\ \text{T}.$$

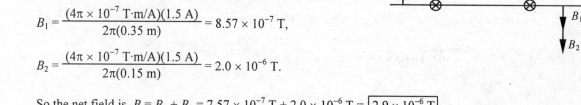

So the net field is $B = B_1 + B_2 = 7.57 \times 10^{-7}\ \text{T} + 2.0 \times 10^{-6}\ \text{T} = \boxed{2.9 \times 10^{-6}\ \text{T}}$.

70. $d = \sqrt{(0.12\ \text{m})^2 + (0.090\ \text{m})^2} = 0.15\ \text{m}, \quad \theta = \tan^{-1}\dfrac{0.12\ \text{m}}{0.090\ \text{m}} = 53.1°.$

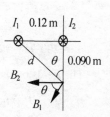

$$B_2 = \frac{\mu_0 I_2}{2\pi d_2} = \frac{(4\pi \times 10^{-7}\ \text{T·m/A})(2.0\ \text{A})}{2\pi(0.090\ \text{m})} = 4.44 \times 10^{-6}\ \text{T},$$

so $\mathbf{B}_2 = -4.44 \times 10^{-6}\ \text{T}\ \hat{\mathbf{x}},$

$$B_1 = \frac{(4\pi \times 10^{-7}\ \text{T·m/A})(8.0\ \text{A})}{2\pi(0.15\ \text{m})} = 1.07 \times 10^{-5}\ \text{T}.$$

$\mathbf{B}_1 = (1.07 \times 10^{-5}\ \text{T})(-\cos 53.1°\ \hat{\mathbf{x}} - \sin 53.1°\ \hat{\mathbf{y}}) = -6.42 \times 10^{-6}\ \text{T}\ \hat{\mathbf{x}} - 8.56 \times 10^{-6}\ \text{T}\ \hat{\mathbf{y}}.$

So the net field is $\mathbf{B} = \mathbf{B}_1 + \mathbf{B}_2 = -1.09 \times 10^{-5}\ \text{T}\ \hat{\mathbf{x}} - 8.56 \times 10^{-6}\ \text{T}\ \hat{\mathbf{y}}$,

or $B = \sqrt{(1.09 \times 10^{-5}\ \text{T})^2 + (8.56 \times 10^{-6}\ \text{T})^2} = \boxed{1.4 \times 10^{-5}\ \text{T}}.$

The angle between the field and a horizontal line to the left is

$\alpha = \tan^{-1} \dfrac{8.56 \times 10^{-6}\ \text{T}}{1.09 \times 10^{-5}\ \text{T}} = \boxed{38°\ \text{below a horizontal line to the left}}.$

71. The fields by the two wires are in the same direction.

$B_1 = \dfrac{\mu_0 I_1}{2\pi d_1} = \dfrac{(4\pi \times 10^{-7}\ \text{T·m/A})(8.0\ \text{A})}{2\pi(0.060\ \text{m})} = 2.67 \times 10^{-5}\ \text{T},$

$B_2 = \dfrac{(4\pi \times 10^{-7}\ \text{T·m/A})(2.0\ \text{A})}{2\pi(0.060\ \text{m})} = 6.67 \times 10^{-6}\ \text{T}.$

So the net field is $B = B_1 + B_2 = 2.67 \times 10^{-5}\ \text{T} + 6.67 \times 10^{-6}\ \text{T} = \boxed{3.3 \times 10^{-5}\ \text{T}}.$

72. The Earth's magnetic field at the equator is about $10^{-5}\ \text{T}$.

$B = \dfrac{\mu_0 I}{2r}, \quad \Rightarrow \quad I = \dfrac{2rB}{\mu_0} = \dfrac{2(0.10\ \text{m})(10^{-5}\ \text{T})}{4\pi \times 10^{-7}\ \text{T·m/A}} = \boxed{1.6\ \text{A}}.$

73. $B = N \dfrac{\mu_0 I}{2r} = \dfrac{4(4\pi \times 10^{-7}\ \text{T·m/A})(2.0\ \text{A})}{2(0.050\ \text{m})} = \boxed{1.0 \times 10^{-4}\ \text{T, away from the observer}}.$

74. (a) It is $\boxed{\text{toward}}$ the observer.

(b) $B = \dfrac{\mu_0 I}{2r} = \dfrac{(4\pi \times 10^{-7}\ \text{T·m/A})(1.8\ \text{A})}{0.12\ \text{m}} = \boxed{1.9 \times 10^{-5}\ \text{T}}.$

75. The currents are opposite, and so the fields produced by the two loops are also opposite.

So $B_1 = \dfrac{\mu_0 I_1}{2r_1} = \dfrac{\mu_0 I_2}{2r_2}, \quad \Rightarrow \quad r_2 = \dfrac{I_2}{I_1} r_1 = \dfrac{2.0\ \text{A}}{1.0\ \text{A}}(5.0\ \text{cm}) = \boxed{10\ \text{cm}}.$

76. $n = \dfrac{1000}{0.10\ \text{m}} = 10\,000\ /\text{m}.\quad B = \mu_0 nI,$

$I = \dfrac{B}{\mu_0 n} = \dfrac{4.0 \times 10^{-4}\ \text{T}}{(4\pi \times 10^{-7}\ \text{T·m/A})(10\,000\ /\text{m})} = \boxed{3.2 \times 10^{-2}\ \text{A}}.$

77. $n_1 = 200\ /\text{cm} = 200 \times 10^2\ /\text{m}$ and $n_2 = 180\ /\text{cm} = 180 \times 10^2\ /\text{m}.$

The fields by the two coils are opposite. So the net field is

$B = B_2 - B_1 = \mu_0 n_2 I_2 - \mu_0 n_1 I_1$

$= (4\pi \times 10^{-7}\ \text{T·m/A})[(180 \times 10^2\ /\text{m})(15\ \text{A}) - (200 \times 10^2\ /\text{m})(10\ \text{A})] = \boxed{8.8 \times 10^{-2}\ \text{T}}.$

78.   The two fields by the two wires are perpendicular to each other.

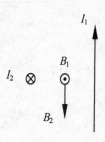

$$B_1 = \frac{\mu_0 I_1}{2\pi d_1} = \frac{(4\pi \times 10^{-7} \text{ T·m/A})(15 \text{ A})}{2\pi(0.10 \text{ m})} = 3.0 \times 10^{-5} \text{ T along the page out.}$$

$B_2 = B_1 = 3.0 \times 10^{-5}$ T into the page.

So the net field is

$$B = \sqrt{B_1^2 + B_2^2} = \sqrt{(3.0 \times 10^{-5} \text{ T})^2 + (3.0 \times 10^{-5} \text{ T})^2} = \boxed{4.2 \times 10^{-5} \text{ T}}.$$

79. $$d = \sqrt{(a/2)^2 + (a/2)^2} = \frac{a}{\sqrt{2}}.$$

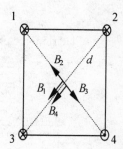

$$B_1 = B_2 = B_3 = B_4 = \frac{\mu_0 I}{2\pi d} = \frac{\mu_0 I}{2\pi(a/\sqrt{2})} = \frac{\mu_0 I}{\sqrt{2}\ \pi a}.$$

So the net field is $B = B_1 + B_4 = 2\dfrac{\mu_0 I}{\sqrt{2}\ \pi a} = \boxed{\dfrac{\sqrt{2}\ \mu_0 I}{\pi a}},$

$\boxed{\text{at } 45° \text{ toward the lower-left wire}}$ (wire 3).

80.   (a) Magnetic force provides centripetal force. $F = qvB \sin \theta = m\dfrac{v^2}{R}$,

so $R = \dfrac{mv}{qB \sin \theta} = \dfrac{mv}{qB}$ $(\sin 90° = 1).$

The frequency is $f = \dfrac{1}{T} = \dfrac{1}{2\pi R/v} = \dfrac{v}{2\pi R} = \boxed{\dfrac{qB}{2\pi m}}.$

(b) $T = \dfrac{1}{f} = \boxed{\dfrac{2\pi m}{qB}}$, independent of m and v.

(c) $R = \dfrac{(9.11 \times 10^{-31} \text{ kg})(10^5 \text{ m/s})}{(1.6 \times 10^{-19} \text{ C})(10^{-4} \text{ T})} = \boxed{5.7 \times 10^{-3} \text{ m}}.$

$f = \dfrac{(1.6 \times 10^{-19} \text{ C})(10^{-4} \text{ T})}{2\pi(9.11 \times 10^{-31} \text{ kg})} = \boxed{2.8 \times 10^6 \text{ Hz}}.$

81.   (b).

82.   (d).

83.   The direction of the magnetic field is $\boxed{\text{away from you}}$, according to the right-hand source rule (electron has negative charge).

84. It is [to increase the magnetic permeability and magnetic field], because the magnetic field is proportional to the magnetic permeability of the material.

85. You can destroy or reduce the magnetic field of a permanent magnet [by hitting or heating it].

86. (a) $B = \mu n I = K_m \mu_o n I = (2000)(4\pi \times 10^{-7} \text{ T·m/A})(100 \times 10^2 \text{ /m})(1.2 \text{ A}) = \boxed{30 \text{ T}}$.

(b) $B_o = \mu_o n I$, ☞ $\dfrac{B}{B_o} = K_m = 2.0 \times 10^3$. So $\boxed{B = (2.0 \times 10^3) B_o}$.

87. Electric force provides centripetal force. $F = \dfrac{kq_1 q_2}{r^2} = \dfrac{ke^2}{r^2} = m\dfrac{v^2}{r}$,

so $v = \sqrt{\dfrac{k}{mr}}\, e = \sqrt{\dfrac{9.0 \times 10^9 \text{ N·m}^2/\text{C}^2}{(9.11 \times 10^{-31} \text{ kg})(0.053 \times 10^{-9} \text{ m})}}\,(1.6 \times 10^{-19} \text{ C}) = 2.18 \times 10^6 \text{ m/s}$.

$I = \dfrac{q}{T} = \dfrac{e}{2\pi r/v} = \dfrac{ev}{2\pi r}$. Therefore

$B = \dfrac{\mu_o I}{2r} = \dfrac{\mu_o\, ev/(2\pi r)}{2r} = \dfrac{\mu_o\, ev}{4\pi r^2} = \dfrac{(4\pi \times 10^{-7} \text{ T·m/A})(1.6 \times 10^{-19} \text{ C})(2.18 \times 10^6 \text{ m/s})}{4\pi(0.053 \times 10^{-9} \text{ m})^2} = \boxed{12 \text{ T}}$.

88. (d).

89. (b).

90. (a) $\boxed{\text{Zero}}$.

(b) $\boxed{\text{Up}}$.

(c) $\boxed{\text{East}}$.

91. It is a [north magnetic pole] by definition since a South Pole of a compass is attracted to it.

92. $K = \tfrac{1}{2}mv^2$, ☞ $v = \sqrt{\dfrac{2K}{m}} = \sqrt{\dfrac{2(3.0 \times 10^3 \text{ eV})(1.6 \times 10^{-19} \text{ J/eV})}{1.67 \times 10^{-27} \text{ kg}}} = 7.58 \times 10^5 \text{ m/s}$.

$v = \dfrac{E}{B} = \dfrac{V}{Bd}$, ☞ $B = \dfrac{V}{vd} = \dfrac{250 \text{ V}}{(7.58 \times 10^5 \text{ m/s})(0.10 \text{ m})} = \boxed{3.3 \times 10^{-3} \text{ T}}$.

93. $B = \mu_o \dfrac{N_1}{\ell} I_1 + \mu_o \dfrac{N_2}{\ell} I_2 = \dfrac{4\pi \times 10^{-7} \text{ T·m/A}}{0.10 \text{ m}}\,[(3000)(5.0 \text{ A}) + (2000)(10 \text{ A})] = \boxed{0.44 \text{ T}}$.

94. (a) The direction is to ⟨west⟩ according to the right-hand force rule (electron carries negative charge).

(b) $F = qvB \sin\theta = (1.6 \times 10^{-19} \text{ C})(10^3 \text{ m/s})(5.0 \times 10^{-5} \text{ T}) \sin 90° = \boxed{8.0 \times 10^{-21} \text{ N}}$.

95. Magnetic force provides the centripetal force.

$F = qvB \sin\theta = m\dfrac{v^2}{R}$, ☞ $v = \dfrac{qBR \sin 90°}{m}$. So

$K = \frac{1}{2}mv^2 = \frac{1}{2}m\dfrac{q^2 B^2 R^2}{m^2} = \dfrac{q^2 B^2 R^2}{2m} = \dfrac{(1.6 \times 10^{-19} \text{ C})^2 (0.80 \text{ T})^2 (0.046 \text{ m})^2}{2(1.67 \times 10^{-27} \text{ kg})} = \boxed{1.0 \times 10^{-14} \text{ J}}$.

96. $\tau = NIAB \sin\theta = NIL^2 B \sin\theta$, where θ is the angle between the normal to the plane and the field.

$N = 1$ and $\theta = 90° - 50° = 40°$. So $L = \sqrt{\dfrac{\tau}{IB \sin\theta}} = \sqrt{\dfrac{0.15 \text{ m·N}}{(10 \text{ A})(0.500 \text{ T}) \sin 40°}} = \boxed{0.22 \text{ m}}$.

97. (a) $K = \frac{1}{2}mv^2$, ☞ $v = \sqrt{\dfrac{2K}{m}} = \sqrt{\dfrac{2(1.0 \times 10^3 \text{ eV})(1.6 \times 10^{-19} \text{ J/eV})}{1.67 \times 10^{-27} \text{ kg}}} = 4.38 \times 10^5 \text{ m/s}$.

Magnetic force provides the necessary centripetal force.

$F = qvB \sin\theta = m\dfrac{v^2}{R}$, ☞ $R = \dfrac{mv}{qB} = \dfrac{(1.67 \times 10^{-27} \text{ kg})(4.38 \times 10^5 \text{ m/s})}{(1.6 \times 10^{-19} \text{ C})(4.5 \times 10^{-3} \text{ T})} = \boxed{1.0 \text{ m}}$.

(b) $T = \dfrac{2\pi R}{v} = \dfrac{2\pi m}{qB} = \dfrac{2\pi(1.67 \times 10^{-27} \text{ kg})}{(1.6 \times 10^{-19} \text{ C})(4.5 \times 10^{-3} \text{ T})} = \boxed{1.5 \times 10^{-5} \text{ s}}$.

98. (a) The electric force on the electron is downward because the electric field is upward and electrons have negative charge. So the magnetic force on the electron must be upward to pass undeflected. According to the right-hand force rule, the magnetic field should be directed ⟨east⟩ (again due to the fact that electrons have negative charges).

(b) $v = \dfrac{V}{Bd} = \dfrac{E}{B}$, ☞ $B = \dfrac{E}{v} = \dfrac{100 \text{ V/m}}{2.0 \times 10^2 \text{ m/s}} = \boxed{0.50 \text{ T}}$.

99. $F = qvB \sin\theta = mg$, ☞ $v = \dfrac{mg}{qB \sin\theta} = \dfrac{(9.11 \times 10^{-31} \text{ kg})(9.80 \text{ m/s}^2)}{(1.6 \times 10^{-19} \text{ C})(0.010 \text{ T}) \sin 90°} = \boxed{5.6 \times 10^{-9} \text{ m/s}}$.

100. For maximum force, $F = qvB \sin\theta = qvB$,

so $B = \dfrac{F}{qv} = \dfrac{1.8 \times 10^{-6} \text{ N}}{(4.0 \times 10^{-8} \text{ C})(3.0 \times 10^2 \text{ m/s})} = \boxed{0.15 \text{ T}}$.

101. $\tau = NIAB \sin\theta = (1)(10 \text{ A})(0.20 \text{ m})(0.30 \text{ m})(0.050 \text{ T}) \sin 90° = \boxed{3.0 \times 10^{-2} \text{ m·N}}$,

where θ is the angle between the normal to the loop and the field.

CHAPTER 20

ELECTROMAGNETIC INDUCTION AND WAVES

1.	(d).

2.	(d).

3.	(d).

4.	(a) When the bar magnet enters the coil, the needle deflects to one side, and when the magnet leaves the coil, the needle reverses direction.

	(b) No , by Lenz's law, it is repelled, moving toward the loop, and attracted as it leaves the loop.

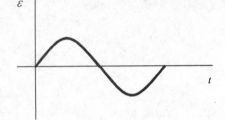

5.	The direction is counterclockwise (in head-on view) .

6.	According to Faraday's law, the factors affecting the magnitude of the induced emf in a solenoid are the number of turns and rate of magnetic flux change with time .

7.	No , it does not depend on the magnetic flux. It depends on the rate of the flux change with time .

8.	The one from the plastic tube will emerge first. When the one falls into the copper tube, a current will be induced by the changing magnetic flux in the copper tube. This current will generate a magnetic field opposite to the one of the magnet. The two fields will generate an attractive force and slow down the falling of the magnet. There is no such current in the plastic tube because it is an insulator.

9.	Sound waves cause the resistance of the button to change as described. This results in a change in the current, so the sound waves produce electrical pulses. These pulses travel through the phone lines and to a receiver. The receiver has a coil wrapped around a magnet, and the pulses create a varying magnetic field as they pass through the coil causing the diaphragm to vibrate and thus produce sound waves as the diaphragm vibrates in the air.

10. $\Phi = BA \cos \theta$, where θ is the angle between the field and the normal to the loop.

    (a) $\Phi = BA \cos 90° = \boxed{0}$.

    (b) $\Phi = (0.30 \text{ T})(0.015 \text{ m}^2) \cos (90° - 37°) = \boxed{2.7 \times 10^{-3} \text{ T·m}^2}$.

    (c) $\Phi = (0.30 \text{ T})(0.015 \text{ m}^2) \cos 0° = \boxed{4.5 \times 10^{-3} \text{ T·m}^2}$.

11.   (a) $\Phi = BA \cos \theta = BA \cos 90° = \boxed{0}$.

    (b) $\Phi = (0.15 \text{ T})(\pi)(0.20 \text{ m})^2 \cos 0° = \boxed{1.9 \times 10^{-2} \text{ T·m}^2}$.

    (c) $\Phi = (0.15 \text{ T})(\pi)(0.20 \text{ m})^2 \cos 40° = \boxed{1.4 \times 10^{-2} \text{ T·m}^2}$.

12. $\mathscr{E} = -N\dfrac{\Delta\Phi}{\Delta t} = -N\dfrac{A\Delta B}{\Delta t} = -(1)\dfrac{(0.020 \text{ m}^2)(0 - 0.30 \text{ T})}{0.0045 \text{ s}} = \boxed{1.3 \text{ V}}$.

13. The length of the third side of the right triangle is $\sqrt{(0.500 \text{ m})^2 - (0.400 \text{ m})^2} = 0.300$ m.

    $\Phi = BA \cos \theta = (0.550 \text{ T})(\tfrac{1}{2})(0.300 \text{ m})(0.400 \text{ m}) \cos 0° = \boxed{3.3 \times 10^{-2} \text{ T·m}^2}$.

14.   (a) $\Phi = NBA \cos \theta$, ☞ $A = \dfrac{\Phi}{NB \cos \theta} = \dfrac{0.50 \text{ T·m}^2}{(10)(0.25 \text{ T}) \cos 0°} = \boxed{0.20 \text{ m}^2}$.

    (b) $\theta = 90° - 60° = 30°$. $A = \dfrac{0.50 \text{ T·m}^2}{(10)(0.25 \text{ T}) \cos 30°} = \boxed{0.23 \text{ m}^2}$.

15. $\Phi = BA \cos \theta = (\mu_0 nI)A \cos 0° = (4\pi \times 10^{-7} \text{ T·m/A})(250 \text{ /m})(1.5 \text{ A})(\pi)(0.030 \text{ m})^2 = \boxed{1.3 \times 10^{-6} \text{ T·m}^2}$.

16. $\mathscr{E} = -N\dfrac{\Delta\Phi}{\Delta t} = -N\dfrac{A\Delta B}{\Delta t} = -(1)\dfrac{(0.40 \text{ m}^2)(0 - 0.20 \text{ T})}{10^{-3} \text{ s}} = \boxed{80 \text{ V}}$.

17. $\mathscr{E} = -N\dfrac{\Delta\Phi}{\Delta t} = -N\dfrac{A\Delta B}{\Delta t} = -(1)\dfrac{(0.40 \text{ m})^2(0 - 0.100 \text{ T})}{0.010 \text{ s}} = \boxed{1.6 \text{ V}}$.

18. $\mathscr{E} = -N\dfrac{\Delta\Phi}{\Delta t} = -N\dfrac{A\Delta B}{\Delta t} = -(60)\dfrac{5.0 \text{ Wb} - 35 \text{ Wb}}{0.10 \text{ s}} = 1.8 \times 10^4 \text{ V}$.

So $R = \dfrac{\mathscr{E}}{I} = \dfrac{1.8 \times 10^4 \text{ V}}{3.6 \times 10^{-3} \text{ A}} = \boxed{5.0 \text{ M}\Omega}$.

19. $\mathscr{E} = IR = (40 \text{ A})(2.5 \ \Omega) = 100 \text{ V}.$ Also $\mathscr{E} = -N\dfrac{\Delta\Phi}{\Delta t},$

so $\Delta t = -N\dfrac{\Delta\Phi}{\mathscr{E}} = -(1)\dfrac{-30 \text{ T·m}^2}{100 \text{ V}} = \boxed{0.30 \text{ s}}.$

20. $\mathscr{E} = -N\dfrac{\Delta\Phi}{\Delta t} = -N\dfrac{A\Delta B}{\Delta t},$ ☞ $\Delta B = -\dfrac{\mathscr{E}\Delta t}{NA} = -\dfrac{(9.0 \text{ V})(0.20 \text{ s})}{(50)(\pi)(0.10 \text{ m})^2} = -1.15 \text{ T}.$

So the final magnetic field is $1.5 \text{ T} + (-1.15 \text{ T}) = \boxed{0.35 \text{ T}}.$

21. (a) The direction is $\boxed{\text{counterclockwise}}$ according to Lenz's law.

(b) $\mathscr{E} = -N\dfrac{\Delta\Phi}{\Delta t} = -N\dfrac{B\Delta A}{\Delta t} = -(1)\dfrac{(0.15 \text{ T})(\pi)[(0.20 \text{ m})^2 - (0.10 \text{ m})^2]}{0.040 \text{ s}} = -\boxed{0.35 \text{ V}}.$

22. (a) $\mathscr{E} = -N\dfrac{\Delta\Phi}{\Delta t} = -N\dfrac{A\Delta B}{\Delta t} = -(1)\dfrac{(0.10 \text{ m}^2)(1.0 \text{ T} - 0)}{2.0 \times 10^{-3} \text{ s}} = -\boxed{50 \text{ V}}.$

(b) $\mathscr{E} = -(10)\dfrac{(0.10 \text{ m}^2)(0.6 \text{ T} - 1.0 \text{ T})}{5.0 \times 10^{-3} \text{ s} - 2.0 \times 10^{-3} \text{ s}} = +\boxed{13 \text{ V}}.$

(c) $\mathscr{E} = -(10)\dfrac{(0.10 \text{ m}^2)(0.6 \text{ T} - 0.6 \text{ T})}{9.0 \times 10^{-3} \text{ s} - 5.0 \times 10^{-3} \text{ s}} = \boxed{0}.$

(d) $\mathscr{E} = -(10)\dfrac{(0.10 \text{ m}^2)(0 \text{ T} - 0.6 \text{ T})}{14 \times 10^{-3} \text{ s} - 9.0 \times 10^{-3} \text{ s}} = +\boxed{12 \text{ V}}.$

23. (a) There will be no induced emf $\boxed{\text{at the equator}}$ because the metal rod is parallel to the magnetic field there.

(b) From Example 20.4, the magnitude of the induced emf is

$\mathscr{E} = BLv = (1.0 \times 10^{-5} \text{ T})(1.0 \text{ m})(5.0 \text{ m/s}) = 5.0 \times 10^{-5} \text{ V} = \boxed{50 \ \mu\text{V}}.$

24. $v = 320 \text{ km/h} = 88.9 \text{ m/s}.$ From Example 20.4, the magnitude of the induced emf is

$\mathscr{E} = BLv = (5.0 \times 10^{-5} \text{ T})(30 \text{ m})(88.9 \text{ m/s}) = \boxed{0.13 \text{ V}}.$

25. (a) From Example 20.4, the magnitude of the induced emf is

$\mathscr{E} = BLv = (0.30 \text{ T})(0.20 \text{ m})(10 \text{ m/s}) = \boxed{0.60 \text{ V}}.$

(b) But $I = \boxed{0}$ since the metal frame is connected to insulators.

26. (a) The – sign means that the final magnetic field direction is opposite that of the initial field.

(b) $\mathscr{E} = -N\dfrac{\Delta\Phi}{\Delta t} = -(1)\dfrac{-20\text{ Wb} - 40\text{ Wb}}{1.5 \times 10^{-3}\text{ s}} = 4.0 \times 10^4\text{ V}$.

27. When the area is parallel to the field, the flux is zero because $\theta = 90°$ ($\Phi = BA\cos\theta$).

So $\mathscr{E} = -N\dfrac{\Delta\Phi}{\Delta t} = -(10)\dfrac{(1.8\text{ T})(0.055\text{ m}^2)\cos 0° - 0}{0.25\text{ s}} = -4.0\text{ V}$.

28. (a) It is higher. The change in magnetic flux is greater if it is flipped by 180° than by 90° because $\cos 0° - \cos 180° = 2$ and $\cos 0° - \cos 90° = 1$. A greater change in magnetic flux will result in a higher emf if the time interval is the same.

(b) $\mathscr{E} = -N\dfrac{\Delta\Phi}{\Delta t} = -(10)\dfrac{(1.8\text{ T})(0.055\text{ m}^2)(\cos 0° - \cos 180°)}{0.25\text{ s}} = -8.0\text{ V}$.

29. For the lower incline, the angle between the normal to the incline and the field is

$\theta = \sin\dfrac{0.25\text{ m}}{0.30\text{ m}} = 56.4°$.

$\Phi = BA\cos\theta = (0.50\text{ T})(0.30\text{ m})(0.45\text{ m})\cos 56.4° = 0.037\text{ T·m}^2$.

For the upper incline, the angle between the normal to the incline and the field is

$\theta = \sin\dfrac{0.20\text{ m}}{0.25\text{ m}} = 53.1°$.

$\Phi = (0.50\text{ T})(0.45\text{ m})(0.25\text{ m})\cos 53.1° = 0.034\text{ T·m}^2$.

For back side, $A = (0.45\text{ m})\left(\sqrt{(0.25\text{ m})^2 - (0.20\text{ m})^2} + \sqrt{(0.30\text{ m})^2 - (0.25\text{ m})^2}\right) = 0.142\text{ m}^2$.

$\Phi = (0.50\text{ T})(0.142\text{ m}^2)\cos 0° = 0.071\text{ T·m}^2$. The flux through all other surfaces is zero.

30. (c). The maximum induced emf is directly proportional to the area of the loop.

31. (c).

32. (a) When the value of emf is minimum, the plane of the loop is perpendicular to the field. At this position the magnetic flux is maximum; thus, when it rotates to a slightly different position, the change in flux will be small.

(b) When the magnetic flux is a minimum, the plane of the loop is parallel to the field. At this position the flux is minimum; thus, when it rotates to a slightly different position, the change in flux will be big (any change from zero is a big change).

33. The magnet moving through the coils produces a current. As the magnet moves up and down in the coil it will induce a current in the coil that will light the bulb. However, the magnet produces the current (Faraday's law of induction) at the expense of its kinetic energy and potential energy. The magnet's motion will therefore damp out.

34. If the armature is jammed or turns very slowly, there will be no back emf and therefore a large current.

35. $\mathscr{E} = \mathscr{E}_o \sin 2\pi f t$, where $\mathscr{E}_o = NBA\omega$.

So the factors affecting the maximum emf are $N, B, A,$ and ω.

36. (a) After half a period the voltage will be maximum (magnitude, the voltage is actually negative) again.

$$t = \frac{T}{2} = \frac{1}{2f} = \frac{1}{2(60 \text{ Hz})} = \boxed{1/120 \text{ s}}.$$

(b) After one-quarter of a period the voltage will be zero.

$$t = \frac{T}{4} = \frac{1}{4(60 \text{ Hz})} = \boxed{1/240 \text{ s}}.$$

(c) After one period, the value returns. $t = \dfrac{1}{60 \text{ Hz}} = \boxed{1/60 \text{ s}}$.

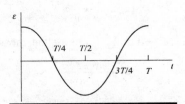

37. (a) $\mathscr{E}_o = NBA\omega = (1)(0.015 \text{ T})(0.10 \text{ m})^2 (2\pi)(60 \text{ Hz}) = \boxed{0.057 \text{ V}}$.

(b) $\mathscr{E}_o \propto N$, so $\mathscr{E}_o = \boxed{0.57 \text{ V}}$.

38. (a) $\mathscr{E} = \mathscr{E}_o \sin 2\pi f t = \mathscr{E}_o \sin 2\pi(60 \text{ Hz})t = \boxed{\mathscr{E}_o \sin 120\pi t}$.

(b) $\mathscr{E}_o = NBA\omega = 2\pi NBAf = 2\pi(10)(0.350 \text{ T})(50 \times 10^{-4} \text{ m}^2)(60 \text{ Hz}) = \boxed{6.6 \text{ V}}$.

39. (a) There are two possible voltages because the initial voltage direction was not specified, thus, there are two possible directions.

(b) From Exercise 20.38, $\mathscr{E} = \mathscr{E}_o \sin (120\pi t) = \pm(120 \text{ V}) \sin [(120\pi)(1/180 \text{ s})] = \boxed{\pm 104 \text{ V}}$.

40. $\mathscr{E}_o = NBA\omega = 2\pi NBAf$,

so $N = \dfrac{\mathscr{E}_o}{2\pi BAf} = \dfrac{400 \text{ V}}{2\pi(0.200 \text{ T})(\pi)(0.15 \text{ m})^2 (60 \text{ Hz})} = \boxed{75 \text{ loops}}$.

41.   (a) From Exercise 20.38, $\mathcal{E} = \mathcal{E}_0 \sin 120\pi t = (100 \text{ V}) \sin [(120\pi)(1/240 \text{ s})] = \boxed{100 \text{ V}}$.

        (b) When emf passes through zero in changing to a negative polarity, $t_1 = T/2 = 1/120$ s.

        $\mathcal{E} = (100 \text{ V}) \sin [(120\pi)(1/120 \text{ s} + 1/120 \text{ s})] = \boxed{0 \text{ V}}$.

42. $\mathcal{E}_0 = NBA\omega = 2\pi NBAf = 2\pi(20)(0.800 \text{ T})(\pi)(0.10 \text{ m})^2 (60 \text{ Hz}) = \boxed{1.9 \times 10^2 \text{ V}}$.

        This maximum value (positive or negative) is attained every half of a period.

        $t = \dfrac{T}{2} = \dfrac{1}{2f} = \dfrac{1}{2(60 \text{ Hz})} = \boxed{1/120 \text{ s}}$.

43. $\mathcal{E}_0 = NBA\omega = 2\pi NBAf$,   ☞ $f = \dfrac{\mathcal{E}_0}{2\pi NBA} = \dfrac{24 \text{ V}}{2\pi(100)(0.250 \text{ T})(0.080 \text{ m})(0.12 \text{ m})} = \boxed{16 \text{ Hz}}$.

44.   (a) Because $\mathcal{E}_0 = NBA\omega$, $\boxed{\text{it does not matter which one he doubles}}$.

        (b) $\mathcal{E}_0 = NBA\omega$. $\mathcal{E}_{0A} = (1)(0.020 \text{ T})(100 \times 10^{-4} \text{ m}^2)(2\pi)(60 \text{ Hz}) = 0.075 \text{ V}$.

                                $\mathcal{E}_{0B} = (1)(0.200 \text{ T})(75 \times 10^{-4} \text{ m}^2)(2\pi)(120 \text{ Hz}) = 1.1 \text{ V}$.

        So $\boxed{\text{student B's}}$ has the greater maximum emf.

45.   (a) The operating current is $\boxed{\text{lower than 44 A}}$ (110 V/2.50 Ω = 44 A) because of the back emf induced

        when the motor turns. The back emf lowers the effective voltage on the motor, thus, the current is lower

        than 44 A.

        (b) $\mathcal{E}_b = V - IR$,   ☞ $I = \dfrac{V - \mathcal{E}_b}{R} = \dfrac{110 \text{ V} - 100 \text{ V}}{2.50 \, \Omega} = \boxed{4.00 \text{ A}}$.

46.   (a) $\mathcal{E}_b = V - IR$,   ☞ $I = \dfrac{V - \mathcal{E}_b}{R} = \dfrac{12 \text{ V} - 10 \text{ V}}{0.40 \, \Omega} = \boxed{5.0 \text{ A}}$.

        (b) When initially starting up, there is no back emf,   so $I = \dfrac{12 \text{ V}}{0.40 \, \Omega} = \boxed{30 \text{ A}}$.

47.   (a) $\mathcal{E}_b = V - IR = 240 \text{ V} - (16 \text{ A})(1.5 \, \Omega) = \boxed{216 \text{ V}}$.

        (b) When initially starting up, there is no back emf,   so $I = \dfrac{240 \text{ V}}{1.5 \, \Omega} = \boxed{160 \text{ A}}$.

        (c) $R_{total} = \dfrac{240 \text{ V}}{25 \text{ A}} = 9.6 \, \Omega$,   so $R_s = 9.6 \, \Omega - 1.5 \, \Omega = \boxed{8.1 \, \Omega}$.

48.   (b).

49.   (c).

50. It should be transmitted at $\boxed{\text{high voltage, thus low current, to reduce joule heat}}$. Since power, $P = IV$, a higher voltage will result in a lower current, and joule heat is equal to I^2R, where R is the resistance of the transmission lines.

51. $\boxed{\text{Yes}}$, a step-up transformer can be used as a step-down transformer. You just need to $\boxed{\text{reverse the primary and secondary coils}}$, so there are more turns on the high voltage side.

52. $\boxed{\text{No}}$, a transformer cannot work using dc voltages. Since a dc voltage cannot change the current in the transformer, $\boxed{\text{dc voltage cannot generate varying magnetic field, so no voltage can be induced}}$.

53. First of all, the dc voltage has to be converted to a time-varying voltage. The points in older cars and electronic devices in newer cars achieved this. The coil functions as a step-up transformer to achieve high-voltage pulses. The distributor distributes the high-voltage pulses to different spark plugs to ignite the gas–air mixture.

54. (a) This is a $\boxed{\text{step–up}}$ because there are more turns in the secondary, $N_s > N_p$.

   (b) $\dfrac{I_p}{I_s} = \dfrac{V_s}{V_p} = \dfrac{N_s}{N_p} = \dfrac{450}{75} = \boxed{6{:}1}$.

   (c) $\dfrac{V_p}{V_s} = \dfrac{N_p}{N_s} = \dfrac{75}{450} = \boxed{1{:}6}$.

55. (a) $\dfrac{I_p}{I_s} = \dfrac{V_s}{V_p} = \dfrac{N_s}{N_p}$, ☞ $N_p = \dfrac{V_p}{V_s} N_s = \dfrac{8.0\ \text{V}}{2000\ \text{V}} (4000) = \boxed{16}$ turns.

   (b) $I_p = \dfrac{N_s}{N_p} I_s = \dfrac{4000}{16} (2.0\ \text{A}) = \boxed{5.0 \times 10^2\ \text{A}}$.

56. (a) $\dfrac{I_p}{I_s} = \dfrac{V_s}{V_p} = \dfrac{N_s}{N_p}$, ☞ $V_s = \dfrac{N_s}{N_p} V_p = \dfrac{180}{720} (120\ \text{V}) = \boxed{30\ \text{V}}$.

   (b) $I_s = \dfrac{N_p}{N_s} I_p = \dfrac{720}{180} (15\ \text{A}) = \boxed{60\ \text{A}}$.

57. $\dfrac{N_p}{N_s} = \dfrac{V_p}{V_s} = \dfrac{120\ \text{V}}{5.0\ \text{V}} = \boxed{24{:}1}$.

58. (a) $\dfrac{I_p}{I_s} = \dfrac{V_s}{V_p} = \dfrac{N_s}{N_p} = \dfrac{10\ \text{A}}{4.0\ \text{A}} = 2.5$.   So $N_s = 2.5\ (120\ \text{V}) = \boxed{3.0 \times 10^2\ \text{V}}$.

   (b) $N_p = \dfrac{4.0\ \text{A}}{10\ \text{A}} N_s = \dfrac{800}{2.5} = \boxed{3.2 \times 10^2}$ turns.

59. (a) $\dfrac{I_p}{I_s} = \dfrac{V_s}{V_p} = \dfrac{N_s}{N_p}$, ☞ $I_s = \dfrac{N_p}{N_s} I_p = \dfrac{840}{120}(2.50\text{ A}) = \boxed{17.5\text{ A}}$.

(b) $V_s = \dfrac{110}{840}(120\text{ V}) = \boxed{15.7\text{ V}}$.

60. Since $\dfrac{I_s}{I_p} = \dfrac{V_p}{V_s}$, the efficiency $= \dfrac{I_s V_s}{I_p V_p} = \dfrac{V_p}{V_s}\dfrac{V_s}{V_p} = 1 = 100\%$, which implies that it is under

$\boxed{\text{ideal conditions}}$ and there is no loss to the wires in the windings, etc.

61. (a) This transformer is $\boxed{\text{non-ideal}}$ because the power in the secondary is lower than that in the primary.

$P_s = V_s I_s = (9.0\text{ V})(0.300\text{ A}) = 2.7\text{ W} < 6.0\text{ W} = P_p$, so $\boxed{P_s < P_p}$.

(b) $\varepsilon = \dfrac{P_s}{P_p} = \dfrac{2.7\text{ W}}{6.0\text{ W}} = \boxed{45\%}$.

62. (a) $\dfrac{I_p}{I_s} = \dfrac{V_s}{V_p} = \dfrac{N_s}{N_p}$, ☞ $N_s = \dfrac{V_s}{V_p} N_p = \dfrac{20\text{ V}}{120\text{ V}}(300) = \boxed{50}$ turns.

(b) $I_p = \dfrac{50}{300}(0.50\text{ A}) = \boxed{8.3 \times 10^{-2}\text{ A}}$.

63. (a) $\dfrac{N_s}{N_p} = \dfrac{V_s}{V_p} = \dfrac{6.0\text{ V}}{120\text{ V}} = \boxed{1:20}$.

(b) $I_p = \dfrac{1}{20}(0.50\text{ A}) = \boxed{2.5 \times 10^{-2}\text{ A}}$.

64. $\dfrac{I_p}{I_s} = \dfrac{V_s}{V_p} = \dfrac{N_s}{N_p}$, ☞ $N_s = \dfrac{V_s}{V_p} N_p = \dfrac{10\,000\text{ V}}{440\text{ V}}(150) = \boxed{3.4 \times 10^3\text{ turns}}$.

65. (a) Without stepping up, $E_o = P_o t = I_o^2 Rt = (20\text{ A})^2(0.80\text{ }\Omega/\text{km})(80.0\text{ km})(5.00\text{ h}) = 128\text{ kWh}$.

With stepping up, $I = I_s = \dfrac{132}{3000}(20\text{ A}) = 0.88\text{ A}$.

$E = (0.88\text{ A})^2(0.80\text{ }\Omega/\text{km})(80.0\text{ km})(5.00\text{ h}) = 0.248\text{ kWh}$.

So the energy saved is $128\text{ kWh} - 0.248\text{ kWh} = \boxed{128\text{ kWh}}$.

(b) The savings is $(128\text{ kWh}/5.00\text{ h})(30 \times 24\text{ h})(\$0.10/\text{kWh}) = \boxed{\$1840}$.

66. $I_s = \dfrac{P_s}{V_s} = \dfrac{10 \times 10^6\text{ W}}{20\,000\text{ V}} = 500\text{ A}$. $\quad I_p = \dfrac{V_s}{V_p} I_s = \dfrac{20\,000\text{ V}}{100\,000\text{ V}}(500\text{ A}) = 100\text{ A}$.

So the currents in the primary and secondary are $\boxed{100\text{ A and } 500\text{ A}}$.

67. (a) At the area substation, $\frac{N_s}{N_p} = \frac{V_s}{V_p} = \frac{100\,000\text{ V}}{200\,000\text{ V}} = \boxed{1:2}$;

at the distributing station, $\frac{N_s}{N_p} = \frac{7200\text{ V}}{100\,000\text{ V}} = \boxed{1:14}$; at the utility pole, $\frac{N_s}{N_p} = \frac{240\text{ V}}{7200\text{ V}} = \boxed{1:30}$.

(b) At the area substation, $\frac{I_s}{I_p} = \frac{V_p}{V_s} = \frac{200\,000\text{ V}}{100\,000\text{ V}} = \boxed{2.0}$;

at the distributing station, $\frac{I_s}{I_p} = \frac{100\,000\text{ V}}{7200\text{ V}} = \boxed{14}$; at the utility pole, $\frac{I_s}{I_p} = \frac{7200\text{ V}}{240\text{ V}} = \boxed{30}$.

(c) Overall, $\frac{I_s}{I_p} = \frac{200\,000\text{ V}}{240\text{ V}} = \boxed{833}$.

68. (a) $P_o = I^2 R = (50\text{ A})^2 (1.2\ \Omega/\text{km})(25\text{ km}) = \boxed{75\text{ kW}}$.

(b) $P = \frac{P_o}{15} = \frac{75\,000\text{ W}}{15} = 5000\text{ W}$.

So $I = \sqrt{\frac{P}{R}} = \sqrt{\frac{5000\text{ W}}{(1.2\ \Omega/\text{km})(25\text{ km})}} = 12.9\text{ A}$.

Therefore $V_s = \frac{I_p}{I_s}\, V_p = \frac{50\text{ A}}{12.9\text{ A}}\,(20\,000\text{ V}) = \boxed{77\text{ kV}}$.

69. (a) $I_s = \frac{V_p}{V_s}\, I_p = \frac{440\text{ V}}{44\,000\text{ V}}\,(50\text{ A}) = 0.50\text{ A}$. $P_o = I^2 R = (0.50\text{ A})^2 (1.2\ \Omega/\text{km})(175\text{ km}) = \boxed{53\text{ W}}$.

(b) $\frac{N_p}{N_s} = \frac{V_p}{V_s} = \frac{44\,000\text{ V}}{220\text{ V}} = \boxed{200}$.

70. (b).

71. (d).

72. $\boxed{\text{No, dc current cannot generate varying magnetic fields}}$. It takes an alternating current to emit electromagnetic waves, and the current from a battery is dc.

73. Infrared (heat) radiation is absorbed by clouds (water molecules), but the sunburning ultraviolet is not.

74. The pressure is greater on a $\boxed{\text{shiny}}$ surface. This is similar to the change in momentum. For example, if an object of momentum p is reflected with the same momentum, the change in momentum is $\Delta p = p - (-p) = 2p$. If the object stops, then the change in momentum is $\Delta p = 0 - (-p) = p$. Due to reflection, the change in momentum of the radiation is greater (twice as large if the reflection is perfect). In other words,

$\boxed{\text{reflection causes the shiny surface to experience twice the pressure}}$

75. According to $c = \lambda f$, wavelength and frequency are inversely proportional to each other. Thus,

$\boxed{\text{radar frequencies are much higher because the wavelengths are much shorter}}$.

76. (a) $f = \dfrac{c}{\lambda} = \dfrac{3.00 \times 10^8 \text{ m/s}}{2.0 \text{ m}} = \boxed{1.5 \times 10^8 \text{ Hz}}$.

(b) $f = \dfrac{3.00 \times 10^8 \text{ m/s}}{25 \text{ m}} = \boxed{1.2 \times 10^7 \text{ Hz}}$.

(c) $f = \dfrac{3.00 \times 10^8 \text{ m/s}}{75 \text{ m}} = \boxed{4.0 \times 10^6 \text{ Hz}}$.

77. For AM: $\lambda_{\min} = \dfrac{c}{f_{\max}} = \dfrac{3.00 \times 10^8 \text{ m/s}}{1.7 \times 10^6 \text{ Hz}} = \boxed{1.8 \times 10^2 \text{ m}}$;

$\lambda_{\max} = \dfrac{3.00 \times 10^8 \text{ m/s}}{0.53 \times 10^6 \text{ Hz}} = \boxed{5.7 \times 10^2 \text{ m}}$.

For FM: $\lambda_{\min} = \dfrac{3.00 \times 10^8 \text{ m/s}}{108 \times 10^6 \text{ Hz}} = \boxed{2.8 \text{ m}}$;

$\lambda_{\max} = \dfrac{3.00 \times 10^8 \text{ m/s}}{88 \times 10^6 \text{ Hz}} = \boxed{3.4 \text{ m}}$.

For TV: $\lambda_{\min} = \dfrac{3.00 \times 10^8 \text{ m/s}}{890 \times 10^6 \text{ Hz}} = \boxed{0.34 \text{ m}}$,

$\lambda_{\max} = \dfrac{3.00 \times 10^8 \text{ m/s}}{54 \times 10^6 \text{ Hz}} = \boxed{5.6 \text{ m}}$.

78. The radar pulse travels twice the distance (to and from).

$d = \dfrac{ct}{2} = \dfrac{(3.00 \times 10^8 \text{ m/s})(0.24 \times 10^{-3} \text{ s})}{2} = 3.6 \times 10^4 \text{ m} = \boxed{36 \text{ km}}$.

79. The wave travels twice the distance in the time interval.

$t = 2\dfrac{d}{c} = \dfrac{2(240\,000 \text{ mi})(1609 \text{ m/mi})}{3.00 \times 10^8 \text{ m/s}} = \boxed{2.6 \text{ s}}$.

80. $f_o = \dfrac{c}{\lambda_o} = \dfrac{3.00 \times 10^8 \text{ m/s}}{600 \times 10^{-9} \text{ m}} = 5.0 \times 10^{14} \text{ Hz}$; $f_g = \dfrac{3.00 \times 10^8 \text{ m/s}}{510 \times 10^{-9} \text{ m}} = 5.88 \times 10^{14} \text{ Hz}$.

So $\Delta f = 5.88 \times 10^{14} \text{ Hz} - 5.0 \times 10^{14} \text{ Hz} = \boxed{8.8 \times 10^{13} \text{ Hz}}$.

81. For AM: $L = \dfrac{\lambda}{4} = \dfrac{c/f}{4} = \dfrac{c}{4f} = \dfrac{3.00 \times 10^8 \text{ m/s}}{4(0.53 \times 10^6 \text{ Hz} + 1.7 \times 10^6 \text{ Hz})/2} = \boxed{67 \text{ m}}$.

For FM: $L = \dfrac{3.00 \times 10^8 \text{ m/s}}{4(88 \times 10^6 \text{ Hz} + 108 \times 10^6 \text{ Hz})/2} = \boxed{0.77 \text{ m}}$.

82.   (a) According to $c = \lambda f$, wavelength and frequency are inversely proportional to each other. So the longer the distance between the cold spots, the longer the wavelength, $\boxed{\text{the lower the frequency}}$.

(b) $\lambda = 2(5.0 \text{ cm}) = 10 \text{ cm} = 0.10 \text{ m}.$ $f = \dfrac{c}{\lambda} = \dfrac{3.00 \times 10^8 \text{ m/s}}{0.10 \text{ m}} = \boxed{3.0 \times 10^9 \text{ Hz or } 3.0 \text{ GHz}}.$

83.   (a) At start-up, there is no back emf. So $I_o = \dfrac{V}{R} = \dfrac{120 \text{ V}}{4.0 \text{ }\Omega} = \boxed{30 \text{ A}}.$

(b) $\mathcal{E}_b = V - IR,$ ☞ $I = \dfrac{V - \mathcal{E}_b}{R} = \dfrac{120 \text{ V} - 110 \text{ V}}{4.0 \text{ }\Omega} = \boxed{2.5 \text{ A}}.$

84.   It is a step-down transformer, so the $\boxed{\text{primary}}$ has more turns.

$\dfrac{N_p}{N_s} = \dfrac{V_p}{V_s} = \dfrac{120 \text{ V}}{4.5 \text{ V}} = \boxed{27}.$

85. $\Phi = BA \cos \theta = B\pi r^2 \cos \theta,$ ☞ $r = \sqrt{\dfrac{\Phi}{\pi B \cos \theta}} = \sqrt{\dfrac{0.12 \text{ T·m}^2}{\pi (0.150 \text{ T}) \cos 45°}} = \boxed{0.60 \text{ m}}.$

86. $\dfrac{I_p}{I_s} = \dfrac{V_s}{V_p} = \dfrac{N_s}{N_p},$ ☞ $N_s = \dfrac{V_s}{V_p} N_p = \dfrac{240 \text{ V}}{1.5 \times 10^3 \text{ V}} (500) = \boxed{80 \text{ turns}}.$

87.   There are two zeros in each period. So the frequency of zero emf is $2f = 2(50 \text{ Hz}) = 100 \text{ Hz}.$

Therefore the period is $\dfrac{1}{100 \text{ Hz}} = 0.01 \text{ s}$, i.e., $\boxed{\text{once every } 0.01 \text{ s}}.$

88.   (a) $\mathcal{E}_b = V - IR,$ ☞ $R = \dfrac{V - \mathcal{E}_b}{I} = \dfrac{120 \text{ V} - 96 \text{ V}}{6.0 \text{ A}} = 4.0 \text{ }\Omega.$

At start-up, there is no back emf. So $I = \dfrac{V}{R} = \dfrac{120 \text{ V}}{4.0 \text{ }\Omega} = \boxed{30 \text{ A}}.$

(b) $R_{\text{total}} = \dfrac{120 \text{ V}}{15 \text{ A}} = 8.0 \text{ }\Omega,$ ☞ $R_s = 8.0 \text{ }\Omega - 4.0 \text{ }\Omega = \boxed{4.0 \text{ }\Omega}.$

89.   (a) The direction of the induced current is $\boxed{\text{up}}$, according to Lenz's law.

(b) $I = \dfrac{\mathcal{E}}{R} = \dfrac{BLv}{R} = \dfrac{(0.250 \text{ T})(0.50 \text{ m})(2.0 \text{ m/s})}{10 \text{ }\Omega} = 2.5 \times 10^{-2} = \boxed{25 \text{ mA}}.$

90.   (a) $\dfrac{I_p}{I_s} = \dfrac{V_s}{V_p} = \dfrac{N_s}{N_p},$ ☞ $V_s = \dfrac{N_s}{N_p} V_p = \dfrac{840}{120} (120 \text{ V}) = \boxed{840 \text{ V}}.$

(b) $I_s = \dfrac{N_p}{N_s} I_p = \dfrac{120}{840} (14 \text{ A}) = \boxed{2.0 \text{ A}}.$

91. $\Phi = BA \cos \theta = (0.75 \text{ T})(1.0 \text{ m})^2 \cos 0° = \boxed{0.75 \text{ T·m}^2}$.

92. (a) $\dfrac{I_p}{I_s} = \dfrac{V_s}{V_p} = \dfrac{N_s}{N_p}$, ☞ $I_s = \dfrac{N_p}{N_s} I_p = \dfrac{80}{360}(3.0 \text{ A}) = \boxed{0.67 \text{ A}}$.

(b) $V_s = \dfrac{360}{80}(12 \text{ V}) = \boxed{54 \text{ V}}$.

(c) $P_s = V_s I_s = (54 \text{ V})(0.667 \text{ A}) = \boxed{36 \text{ W}}$.

93. $P = \dfrac{\mathcal{E}^2}{R}$, ☞ $\mathcal{E} = \sqrt{PR} = \sqrt{(5.0 \text{ W})(0.20 \text{ Ω})} = 1.0 \text{ V}$.

$\mathcal{E} = -N\dfrac{\Delta\Phi}{\Delta t} = N\dfrac{A\Delta B}{\Delta t}$, ☞ $\dfrac{\Delta B}{\Delta t} = \dfrac{\mathcal{E}}{NA} = \dfrac{1.0 \text{ V}}{(1)(0.50 \text{ m})^2} = \boxed{4.0 \text{ T/s}}$.

94. There are two polarity changes in each period.

So the period is $f = \dfrac{1}{2(0.010 \text{ s})} = \boxed{50 \text{ Hz}}$.

95. $I_s = \dfrac{P_s}{V_s} = \dfrac{6.6 \times 10^3 \text{ W}}{220 \text{ V}} = 30 \text{ A}$; $I_p = \dfrac{V_s}{V_p} I_s = \dfrac{220 \text{ V}}{20\,000 \text{ V}}(30 \text{ A}) = 0.33 \text{ A}$.

So the currents are $\boxed{0.33 \text{ A and } 30 \text{ A}}$.

96. $f = \dfrac{c}{\lambda} = \dfrac{3.00 \times 10^8 \text{ m/s}}{3 \times 10^{-15} \text{ m}} = \boxed{1 \times 10^{23} \text{ Hz}}$.

97. (a) Since the frequency is 50 Hz, the rotation rate is $\boxed{50 \text{ rotations/s}}$.

(b) No, if they are ideal (lossless), the same turn ratios would work. However, in reality the 50-Hz delivery would have fewer losses because the eddy currents are less due to the fact that the magnetic flux in the transformer is changing less rapidly..

CHAPTER 21

1. (a).

2. The average current in an ac circuit is zero because the current has direction or it can be either positive or negative. However, $\boxed{\text{power depends on the current squared}}$ so it is non-directional. Therefore power does not average out to zero.

3. That means the $\boxed{\text{voltage and current reach maximum or minimum at the same time}}$.

4. According to Ohm's law, the $\boxed{\text{current is half}}$ of that in a 240-V source because the voltage is half. Since power is equal to voltage times current, the $\boxed{\text{power is 1/4}}$ of the designed power.

5. $\boxed{\text{No}}$, the circuit element cannot be a resistor. $\boxed{\text{Voltage and current should be in phase for a resistor}}$.

6. $(V_o)_{120} = \sqrt{2}\,(V_{rms})_{120} = \sqrt{2}\,(120\text{ V}) = \boxed{170\text{ V}}$, and $(V_o)_{240} = \sqrt{2}\,(V_{rms})_{240} = \sqrt{2}\,(240\text{ V}) = \boxed{339\text{ V}}$.

7. $I_o = \sqrt{2}\,I_{rms} = \sqrt{2}\,(5.0\text{ A}) = \boxed{7.1\text{ A}}$.

8. $V_{rms} = \dfrac{V_o}{\sqrt{2}} = \dfrac{156\text{ V}}{\sqrt{2}} = \boxed{110\text{ V}}$.

9. $\bar{P} = I_{rms}^2\,R,$ ☞ $I_{rms} = \sqrt{\dfrac{\bar{P}}{R}} = \sqrt{\dfrac{15\text{ W}}{10\text{ }\Omega}} = \boxed{1.2\text{ A}}$.

10. (a) $V_{rms} = I_{rms}R = (0.75\text{ A})(5.0\text{ }\Omega) = \boxed{3.8\text{ V}}$;

    $V_o = \sqrt{2}\,V_{rms} = \sqrt{2}\,(3.75\text{ V}) = \boxed{5.3\text{ V}}$.

    (b) $\bar{P} = I_{rms}V_{rms} = (0.75\text{ A})(3.75\text{ V}) = \boxed{2.8\text{ W}}$.

11. (a) $\bar{P} = I_{rms}V_{rms}$, $I_{rms} = \dfrac{\bar{P}}{V_{rms}} = \dfrac{1200\text{ W}}{120\text{ V}} = \boxed{10\text{ A}}$.

    (b) $I_o = \sqrt{2}\,I_{rms} = \sqrt{2}\,(10\text{ A}) = \boxed{14\text{ A}}$.

    (c) $R = \dfrac{V_{rms}}{I_{rms}} = \dfrac{120\text{ V}}{10\text{ A}} = \boxed{12\text{ }\Omega}$.

12. (a) The current in a resistor will be $\boxed{\text{in phase}}$ with the voltage.

(b) $I = \dfrac{V}{R} = \dfrac{(170\text{ V})\sin(120t)}{10\ \Omega} = \boxed{(17\text{ A})\sin(120t)}$.

13. (a) $\bar{P} = I_{rms}^2 R$, ☞ $I_{rms} = \sqrt{\dfrac{\bar{P}}{R}} = \sqrt{\dfrac{500\text{ W}}{25\ \Omega}} = \boxed{4.5\text{ A}}$;

$I_o = \sqrt{2}\,I_{rms} = \sqrt{2}\,(4.47\text{ A}) = \boxed{6.3\text{ A}}$.

(b) $V_{rms} = I_{rms}R = (4.47\text{ A})(25\ \Omega) = \boxed{112\text{ V}}$; $V_o = \sqrt{2}\,V_{rms} = \sqrt{2}\,(112\text{ V}) = \boxed{158\text{ V}}$.

14. (a) There are $\boxed{\text{two}}$ possible answers, because the voltage could be increasing or decreasing at the $t = 0$ moment. In other words, it could be either positive or negative since the direction is not specified.

(b) $T = \dfrac{1}{f} = \dfrac{1}{60\text{ Hz}} = 1/60$ s so $1/240$ s is ¼ the period. That is, the voltage at $1/240$ s is either at the maximum or the minimum (negative side). Therefore, $V_{1/240\text{ s}} = \boxed{\pm 85\text{ V}}$.

15. It takes $t = \dfrac{T}{4}$ for the voltage to go from zero to its maximum value. So $T = 4(4.2\text{ ms}) = 16.8\text{ ms}$.

Therefore $f = \dfrac{1}{T} = \dfrac{1}{16.8 \times 10^{-3}\text{ s}} = 59.5\text{ Hz}$.

Thus $V = V_o\sin 2\pi ft = \sqrt{2}\,V_{rms}\sin 2\pi ft = \sqrt{2}\,(120\text{ V})\sin[2\pi(59.5)t] = \boxed{(170\text{ V})\sin(119\pi t)}$.

16. $\bar{P} = \dfrac{V_{rms}^2}{R}$, ☞ $R = \dfrac{V_{rms}^2}{\bar{P}} = \dfrac{(120\text{ V})^2}{100\text{ W}} = \boxed{144\ \Omega}$.

$I_{rms} = \dfrac{V_{rms}}{R} = \dfrac{120\text{ V}}{144\ \Omega} = \boxed{0.833\text{ A}}$.

17. $I_{rms} = \dfrac{\bar{P}}{V_{rms}} = \dfrac{40\text{ W}}{120\text{ V}} = \boxed{0.33\text{ A}}$ and $I_o = \sqrt{2}\,I_{rms} = \sqrt{2}\,(0.333\text{ A}) = \boxed{0.47\text{ A}}$.

18. (a) $I_{rms} = \dfrac{\bar{P}}{V_{rms}} = \dfrac{50 \times 10^3\text{ W}}{240\text{ V}} = 208\text{ A}$, so $I_o = \sqrt{2}\,I_{rms} = \sqrt{2}\,(208\text{ A}) = \boxed{2.9 \times 10^2\text{ A}}$.

(b) $V_o = \sqrt{2}\,V_{rms} = \sqrt{2}\,(240\text{ V}) = \boxed{3.4 \times 10^2\text{ V}}$.

19. $I_{rms} = \dfrac{I_o}{\sqrt{2}} = \dfrac{8.0\text{ A}}{\sqrt{2}} = 5.66\text{ A}$; $V_{rms} = \dfrac{V_o}{\sqrt{2}} = \dfrac{60\text{ V}}{\sqrt{2}} = 42.4\text{ V}$.

So $\bar{P} = I_{rms}V_{rms} = (5.66\text{ A})(42.4\text{ V}) = \boxed{2.4 \times 10^2\text{ W}}$.

20. $\bar{P} = I_{rms}V_{rms} = \dfrac{I_o}{\sqrt{2}}\dfrac{V_o}{\sqrt{2}} = \dfrac{I_oV_o}{2} = \dfrac{(2.5\ A)(16\ V)}{2} = \boxed{20\ W}$.

21.   (a) Since $\quad I = I_o \sin 2\pi ft$, $\quad 2\pi ft = 380t$. $\quad$ So $\quad f = \dfrac{380}{2\pi} = \boxed{60\ Hz}$.

         (b) $I_{rms} = \dfrac{I_o}{\sqrt{2}} = \dfrac{2.0\ A}{\sqrt{2}} = \boxed{1.4\ A}$.

         (c) $\bar{P} = I_{rms}^2 R = (1.41\ A)^2 (60\ \Omega) = \boxed{1.2 \times 10^2\ W}$.

         (d) $V_o = I_o R = (2.0\ A)(60\ \Omega) = 120\ V$. $\quad$ So $\quad \boxed{V = (120\ V)\sin 380t}$.

         (e) $P = VI = (120\ V)(2.0\ A)\sin^2 380t$. $\quad$ So $\quad \boxed{P = (240\ W)\sin^2 380t}$.

         (f) $P = (240\ W)\dfrac{1 - \cos 2(380t)}{2} = 120\ W - (120\ W)\cos 2(380t)$.

         The average of a sine or cosine function is zero. So $\bar{P} = 120\ W$, the same as in (c).

22.   (b).

23.   (c).

24.   (b).

25.   For a capacitor, the *lower the frequency*, the longer the charging time in each cycle. If the frequency is very low (dc), then the charging time is very long, so it acts as an ac open circuit.
     For an inductor, the *lower the frequency*, the more slowly the current changes in the inductor The more slowly the current changes, the less back emf is induced in the inductor, resulting in less resistance to current

26.   In an ac circuit, a capacitor can oppose current. This is because as the capacitor charges, the voltage across its plates increases, opposing the current. Also, an inductor can oppose current because the induced emf opposes the change in flux and thus opposes the current in the circuit.

27.   One cycle is equal to 2π radians or $360°$. "The voltage across an inductor leads the current by $90°$" means the voltage leads the current by a quarter-cycle or reaches maximum a quarter-cycle ahead of the current. "The voltage across a capacitor lags the current by $90°$" means the voltage lags the current by a quarter-cycle or reaches maximum a quarter-cycle after the current.

28. $\boxed{No}$, an inductor cannot oppose dc current. $\boxed{Dc\ situations\ cannot\ create\ self\text{-}induced\ emf}$, so dc current is not opposed.

29. At $t = 0$, $I = 120$ A, or at maximum. The voltage is then $\boxed{\text{zero}}$, because $\boxed{\text{current leads voltage by } 90°}$ in a capacitor. That is, when current is maximum, voltage is 1/4 period behind, or at zero.

30. $X_C = \dfrac{1}{2\pi f C}$, ☞ $f = \dfrac{1}{2\pi C X_C} = \dfrac{1}{2\pi(25 \times 10^{-6} \text{ F})(25 \text{ } \Omega)} = \boxed{2.5 \times 10^2 \text{ Hz}}$.

31. $X_C = \dfrac{1}{2\pi f C} = \dfrac{1}{2\pi(60 \text{ Hz})(2.0 \times 10^{-6} \text{ F})} = \boxed{1.3 \times 10^3 \text{ } \Omega}$.

32. $X_C = \dfrac{1}{2\pi f C}$, ☞ $C = \dfrac{1}{2\pi f X_C} = \dfrac{1}{2\pi(60 \text{ Hz})(100 \text{ } \Omega)} = \boxed{2.65 \times 10^{-5} \text{ F}}$.

33. (a) $X_L = 2\pi f L = 2\pi(60 \text{ Hz})(0.050 \text{ H}) = \boxed{19 \text{ } \Omega}$.

    (b) $I_{rms} = \dfrac{V_{rms}}{X_L} = \dfrac{120 \text{ V}}{18.8 \text{ } \Omega} = \boxed{6.4 \text{ A}}$.

    (c) $\boxed{\text{Voltage leads current by } 90°}$ in an inductor.

34. $X_C = \dfrac{1}{2\pi f C} = \dfrac{1}{2\pi(60 \text{ Hz})(50 \times 10^{-6} \text{ F})} = 53.1 \text{ } \Omega$. So $I_{rms} = \dfrac{V_{rms}}{X_C} = \dfrac{120 \text{ V}}{53.1 \text{ } \Omega} = \boxed{2.3 \text{ A}}$.

35. Since $X_C = \dfrac{1}{2\pi f C}$ and $I_{rms} = \dfrac{V_{rms}}{X_C}$, $\dfrac{I_{rms2}}{I_{rms1}} = \dfrac{V/X_{C2}}{V/X_{C1}} = \dfrac{X_{C1}}{X_{C2}} = \dfrac{C_2}{C_1} = \dfrac{0.40 \text{ } \mu\text{F}}{0.25 \text{ } \mu\text{F}} = 1.6$.

    Therefore the percentage change is $\dfrac{I_{rms2} - I_{rms1}}{I_{rms1}} = \dfrac{I_{rms2}}{I_{rms1}} - 1 = 0.60$, i.e., $\boxed{\text{an increase of } 60\%}$.

36. $X_L = 2\pi f L$, ☞ $L = \dfrac{X_L}{2\pi f} = \dfrac{90 \text{ } \Omega}{2\pi(60 \text{ Hz})} = \boxed{0.24 \text{ H}}$.

37. $X_L = 2\pi f L$, ☞ $f = \dfrac{X_L}{2\pi L} = \dfrac{400 \text{ } \Omega}{2\pi(0.250 \text{ H})} = \boxed{255 \text{ Hz}}$.

38. (a) The capacitate reactance will be $\boxed{1/3}$ times the original reactance because X_C is inversely proportional to frequency, $X_C = \dfrac{1}{2\pi f C}$.

    (b) $\dfrac{(X_C)_2}{(X_C)_1} = \dfrac{f_1}{f_2} = \dfrac{120 \text{ Hz}}{60 \text{ Hz}} = 2$. So $(X_C)_2 = 2(X_C)_1 = 2(100 \text{ } \Omega) = \boxed{200 \text{ } \Omega}$.

39. (a) $X_L = 2\pi f L = 2\pi(60 \text{ Hz})(0.150 \text{ H}) = 56.5 \ \Omega.$ $V_{rms} = I_{rms}X_L = (1.6 \text{ A})(56.5 \ \Omega) = \boxed{90 \text{ V}}.$

(b) $\boxed{\text{Voltage leads current by } 90°}$.

40. $X_L = 2\pi f L = X_C = \dfrac{1}{2\pi f C},$ ☞ $L = \dfrac{1}{4\pi^2 f^2 C} = \dfrac{1}{4\pi^2 (60 \text{ Hz})^2 (10 \times 10^{-6} \text{ F})} = \boxed{0.70 \text{ H}}.$

41. $X_C = \dfrac{V_{rms}}{I_{rms}} = \dfrac{120 \text{ V}}{0.20 \text{ A}} = 600 \ \Omega.$

$X_C = \dfrac{1}{2\pi f C},$ ☞ $C = \dfrac{1}{2\pi X_C f} = \dfrac{1}{2\pi(600 \ \Omega)(60 \text{ Hz})} = 4.4 \times 10^{-6} \text{ F} = \boxed{4.4 \ \mu\text{F}}.$

42. (a) The inductive reactance will be 1/2 times the original reactance because X_L is proportional to frequency, $X_L = 2\pi f L.$ Then according to Ohm's law, the rms current will be $\boxed{2}$ times the original rms current. Therefore, the rms current is inversely proportional to the frequency.

(b) $\dfrac{(I_{rms})_2}{(I_{rms})_1} = \dfrac{f_1}{f_2} = \dfrac{40 \text{ Hz}}{120 \text{ Hz}} = 1/3.$ So $(I_{rms})_2 = (1/3)(I_{rms})_1 = (1/3)(9.0 \text{ A}) = \boxed{3.0 \text{ A}}.$

43. (d).

44. (a).

45. (d).

46. At resonance, $X_L = X_C,$ so $Z = \sqrt{R^2 + (X_L - X_C)^2} = \sqrt{R^2} = \boxed{R}$, i.e., $\boxed{\text{impedance is at minimum}}.$

47. $\boxed{\text{No}}$, there is no power delivered to capacitors or inductors in an ac circuit. For either a pure capacitive or inductive circuit, the phase angle $\phi = 90°$, and the power factor is $\cos \phi$ and $\cos 90° = 0.$

48. Resonance occurs when $X_L = X_C$ so $f_o = \dfrac{1}{2\pi\sqrt{LC}}.$ The factors that determine the resonant frequency of an RLC circuit are $\boxed{\text{capacitance and inductance}}.$ $\boxed{\text{No}}$, resistance is not a factor.

49. (a) $X_L = 2\pi f L = 2\pi(60 \text{ Hz})(0.45 \text{ H}) = \boxed{1.7 \times 10^2 \ \Omega}.$

(b) $Z = \sqrt{R^2 + (X_L - X_C)^2} = \sqrt{(100 \ \Omega)^2 + (170 \ \Omega - 0)^2} = \boxed{2.0 \times 10^2 \ \Omega}.$

50.   (a) $X_C = \dfrac{1}{2\pi f C} = \dfrac{1}{2\pi(60\ \text{Hz})(25 \times 10^{-6}\ \text{F})} = \boxed{1.1 \times 10^2\ \Omega}$.

$Z = \sqrt{R^2 + (X_L - X_C)^2} = \sqrt{(200\ \Omega)^2 + (0 - 106\ \Omega)^2} = 226\ \Omega = \boxed{2.3 \times 10^2\ \Omega}$.

(b) $I_{rms} = \dfrac{V_{rms}}{Z} = \dfrac{120\ \text{V}}{226\ \Omega} = \boxed{0.53\ \text{A}}$.

51.   (a) $X_L = 2\pi f L = 2\pi(60\ \text{Hz})(0.100\ \text{H}) = \boxed{38\ \Omega}$.

$Z = \sqrt{R^2 + (X_L - X_C)^2} = \sqrt{(100\ \Omega)^2 + (38\ \Omega - 0)^2} = 107\ \Omega = \boxed{1.1 \times 10^2\ \Omega}$.

(b) $I_{rms} = \dfrac{V_{rms}}{Z} = \dfrac{120\ \text{V}}{107\ \Omega} = \boxed{1.1\ \text{A}}$.

52.   (a) $X_C = \dfrac{1}{2\pi f C} = \dfrac{1}{2\pi(60\ \text{Hz})(6.0 \times 10^{-6}\ \text{F})} = 442\ \Omega = \boxed{4.4 \times 10^2\ \Omega}$.

(b) $Z = \sqrt{R^2 + (X_L - X_C)^2} = \sqrt{(250\ \Omega)^2 + (0 - 442\ \Omega)^2} = 508\ \Omega = \boxed{5.1 \times 10^2\ \Omega}$.

53.   (a) The phase angle will be $\boxed{\text{negative}}$, because this is a capacitive circuit.

$\phi = \tan^{-1} \dfrac{X_L - X_C}{R}$, with $X_L = 0$, ϕ is negative.

(b) $\phi = \tan^{-1} \dfrac{0 - 50\ \Omega}{100\ \Omega} = \boxed{-27°}$.

54.   (a) At resonance, $f_o = \dfrac{1}{2\pi\sqrt{LC}} = \dfrac{1}{2\pi\sqrt{(0.30\ \text{H})(8.0 \times 10^{-6}\ \text{F})}} = \boxed{1.0 \times 10^2\ \text{Hz}}$.

(b) At resonance, $Z = R = \boxed{25\ \Omega}$.

55.   (a) This circuit is $\boxed{\text{in resonance}}$, because $\boxed{X_L = X_C,\ \text{so}\ Z = R}$.

(b) If the frequency f is doubled, R remains the same, X_L doubles to 80 Ω because $X_L = 2\pi f L$, and X_C halves

to 20 Ω, since $X_C = \dfrac{1}{2\pi f C}$. So $Z = \sqrt{R^2 + (X_L - X_C)^2} = \sqrt{(40\ \Omega)^2 + (80\ \Omega - 20\ \Omega)^2} = \boxed{72\ \Omega}$.

56.   (a) You can change $\boxed{\text{resistance}}$ without upsetting the condition of resonance. At resonance, $X_L = X_C$. So as

long as that condition is maintained, the condition satisfies.

(b) $X_C = \dfrac{1}{2\pi f C} = \dfrac{1}{2\pi(60\ \text{Hz})(3.5 \times 10^{-6}\ \text{F})} = 758\ \Omega$.

At resonance, $X_L = X_C = 2\pi f L$. So $L = \dfrac{758\ \Omega}{2\pi(60\ \text{Hz})} = \boxed{2.0\ \text{H for any resistance}}$.

57. $Z = \sqrt{R^2 + (X_L - X_C)^2} = \sqrt{(500\ \Omega)^2 + (188\ \Omega - 758\ \Omega)^2} = 758\ \Omega.$

$\tan\phi = \dfrac{X_L - X_C}{R} = \dfrac{188\ \Omega - 758\ \Omega}{500\ \Omega} = -1.14,$ ☞ $\phi = -48.7°.$

So $\bar{P} = \dfrac{V_{rms}^2}{Z}\cos\phi = \dfrac{(240\ \text{V})^2}{758\ \Omega}\cos(-48.7°) = \boxed{50\ \text{W}}.$

58.   At resonance, $f_o = \dfrac{1}{2\pi\sqrt{LC}} = \dfrac{1}{2\pi\sqrt{(0.100\ \text{H})(5.00\times10^{-6}\ \text{F})}} = \boxed{225\ \text{Hz}}.$

59. $f_o = \dfrac{1}{2\pi\sqrt{LC}},$ so $C = \dfrac{1}{4\pi^2 f_o^2 L} = \dfrac{1}{4\pi^2(980\times10^3\ \text{Hz})^2(0.50\times10^{-3}\ \text{H})} = \boxed{5.3\times10^{-11}\ \text{F}}.$

60. f_o must range from 530 kHz to 1710 kHz.

$C_1 = \dfrac{1}{4\pi^2(530\times10^3\ \text{Hz})^2(0.50\times10^{-3}\ \text{H})} = 1.8\times10^{-10}\ \text{F}.$

$C_2 = \dfrac{1}{4\pi^2(1710\times10^3\ \text{Hz})^2(0.50\times10^{-3}\ \text{H})} = 1.7\times10^{-11}\ \text{F}.$

So the range is from $\boxed{1.7\times10^{-11}\ \text{F to } 1.8\times10^{-10}\ \text{F}}.$

61. $X_L = 2\pi fL = 2\pi(60\ \text{Hz})(0.250\ \text{H}) = 94.2\ \Omega,$ $X_C = \dfrac{1}{2\pi fC} = \dfrac{1}{2\pi(60\ \text{Hz})(40\times10^{-6}\ \text{F})} = 66.3\ \Omega.$

ab: $Z = \sqrt{R^2 + (X_L - X_C)^2} = X_L = 94.2\ \Omega,$ $I_{rms} = \dfrac{V_{rms}}{Z} = \dfrac{120\ \text{V}}{94.2\ \Omega} = \boxed{1.3\ \text{A}}.$

ac: $Z = \sqrt{(30\ \Omega)^2 + (94.2\ \Omega)^2} = 98.9\ \Omega,$ $I_{rms} = \dfrac{120\ \text{V}}{98.9\ \Omega} = \boxed{1.2\ \text{A}}.$

bc: $Z = R = 30\ \Omega,$ $I_{rms} = \dfrac{120\ \text{V}}{30\ \Omega} = \boxed{4.0\ \text{A}}.$

cd: $Z = X_C = 66.3\ \Omega,$ $I_{rms} = \dfrac{120\ \text{V}}{66.3\ \Omega} = \boxed{1.8\ \text{A}}.$

bd: $Z = \sqrt{(30\ \Omega)^2 + (66.3\ \Omega)^2} = 72.8\ \Omega,$ $I_{rms} = \dfrac{120\ \text{V}}{72.8\ \Omega} = \boxed{1.6\ \text{A}}.$

ad: $Z = \sqrt{(30\ \Omega)^2 + (94.2\ \Omega - 66.3\ \Omega)^2} = 41.0\ \Omega,$ $I_{rms} = \dfrac{120\ \text{V}}{41.0\ \Omega} = \boxed{2.9\ \text{A}}.$

62.   (a) The phase angle of this circuit is $\boxed{\text{positive}}$, as this is an inductive circuit.

$\phi = \tan^{-1}\dfrac{X_L - X_C}{R},$ with $X_C = 0,$ ϕ is positive.

(b) $X_L = 2\pi fL = 2\pi(60\ \text{Hz})(0.15\ \text{H}) = 56.5\ \Omega.$ $\tan\phi = \dfrac{56.5\ \Omega - 0}{30\ \Omega} = 1.88,$ ☞ $\phi = \boxed{62°}.$

(c) $Z = \sqrt{R^2 + (X_L - X_C)^2} = \sqrt{(30\ \Omega)^2 + (56.5\ \Omega)^2} = 64.0\ \Omega.$

So $\quad I_{rms} = \dfrac{V_{rms}}{Z} = \dfrac{120\ V}{64.0\ \Omega} = \boxed{1.9\ A}.$

(d) $P = I_{rms}\, V_{rms} \cos\phi = (1.88\ A)((120\ V) \cos 62.0° = \boxed{1.1 \times 10^2\ W}.$

63. $\quad \overline{P} = I_{rms}\, V_{rms} \cos\phi, \quad ☞ \quad I_{rms} = \dfrac{\overline{P}}{V_{rms} \cos\phi} = \dfrac{1200\ W}{(120\ V)(0.75)} = \boxed{13\ A}.$

64. (a) $Z = \sqrt{R^2 + (X_L - X_C)^2} = \sqrt{(10\ \Omega)^2 + (120\ \Omega - 120\ \Omega)^2} = 10\ \Omega.$

$I_{rms} = \dfrac{V_{rms}}{Z} = \dfrac{220\ V}{10\ \Omega} = 22\ A. \quad$ So $\quad (V_{rms})_R = I_{rms} R = (22\ A)(10\ \Omega) = \boxed{220\ V}.$

(b) $(V_{rms})_L = I_{rms} X_L = (22\ A)(120\ \Omega) = \boxed{2.64 \times 10^3\ V}.$

(c) $(V_{rms})_C = I_{rms} X_C = (22\ A)(120\ \Omega) = \boxed{2.64 \times 10^3\ V}.$

65. $f_0 = \dfrac{1}{2\pi\sqrt{LC}} = \dfrac{1}{2\pi\sqrt{(0.250\ H)(0.80 \times 10^{-6}\ F)}} = 356\ Hz.$

$X_L = 2\pi f L = 2\pi(356\ Hz)(0.250\ H) = 559\ \Omega,$

$X_C = \dfrac{1}{2\pi f C} = \dfrac{1}{2\pi(356\ Hz)(0.80 \times 10^{-6}\ F)} = 559\ \Omega.$

$Z = R = 25\ \Omega, \quad I_{rms} = \dfrac{V_{rms}}{Z} = \dfrac{12\ V}{25\ \Omega} = 0.48\ A.$

So $(V_{rms})_R = I_{rms} R = (0.48\ A)(25\ \Omega) = \boxed{12\ V}, \ (V_{rms})_L = I_{rms} X_L = (0.48\ A)(559\ \Omega) = \boxed{2.7 \times 10^2\ V},$

and $(V_{rms})_C = I_{rms} X_C = (0.48\ A)(559\ \Omega) = \boxed{2.7 \times 10^2\ V}.$

66. In Exercises 64 and 65, $(V_{rms})_R$, $(V_{rms})_C$, and $(V_{rms})_L$ are all rms voltages. Due to phase differences, these rms voltages are *not* reached at the same time. Instantaneously, however, $V_R + V_C + V_L$ is still equal to the source voltage.

67. (a) The impedance is $\boxed{\text{equal to } 25\ \Omega}$. At resonance, $X_L = X_C$, so $Z = R$.

(b) $X_L = 2\pi f L = 2\pi(60\ Hz)(0.450\ H) = 170\ \Omega, \ X_C = \dfrac{1}{2\pi f C} = \dfrac{1}{2\pi(60\ Hz)(5.00 \times 10^{-6}\ F)} = 531\ \Omega.$

$Z = \sqrt{R^2 + (X_L - X_C)^2} = \sqrt{(25.0\ \Omega)^2 + (170\ \Omega - 531\ \Omega)^2} = \boxed{362\ \Omega}.$

68. (a) $\tan\phi = \dfrac{X_L - X_C}{R} = \dfrac{500\ \Omega - 300\ \Omega}{400\ \Omega} = 0.50, \quad ☞ \quad \phi = 26.6°.$

So the power factor is $\cos\phi = \cos(26.6°) = \boxed{0.894}.$

(b) $X_C = \dfrac{1}{2\pi f C}$, ☞ $C = \dfrac{1}{2\pi f X_C} = \dfrac{1}{2\pi(60 \text{ Hz})(300 \text{ }\Omega)} = 8.84 \times 10^{-6} \text{ F}$.

For the power factor to be 1, $\phi = 0°$ or $X_L = X_C$.

$$C_{\text{total}} = \dfrac{1}{2\pi(60 \text{ Hz})(300 \text{ }\Omega)} = 5.31 \times 10^{-6} \text{ F} < 8.84 \times 10^{-6} \text{ F}.$$

So a series capacitor is needed. $\dfrac{1}{C_{\text{total}}} = \dfrac{1}{C} + \dfrac{1}{C'}$,

so $C' = \dfrac{C\,C_{\text{total}}}{C - C_{\text{total}}} = \dfrac{(8.84 \times 10^{-6} \text{ F})(5.31 \times 10^{-6} \text{ F})}{8.84 \times 10^{-6} \text{ F} - 5.31 \times 10^{-6} \text{ F}} = 1.33 \times 10^{-5} \text{ F} = \boxed{13.3 \text{ }\mu\text{F; series}}$.

69. In resonance, $\bar{P}_o = \dfrac{V_{\text{rms}}^2}{R} = \dfrac{(120 \text{ V})^2}{50 \text{ }\Omega} = 288 \text{ W}$.

Not in resonance, $X_L = 2\pi f L = 2\pi(60 \text{ Hz})(0.15 \text{ H}) = 56.5 \text{ }\Omega$,

$$X_C = \dfrac{1}{2\pi f C} = \dfrac{1}{2\pi(60 \text{ Hz})(20 \times 10^{-6} \text{ F})} = 133 \text{ }\Omega.$$

$$Z = \sqrt{R^2 + (X_L - X_C)^2} = \sqrt{(50 \text{ }\Omega)^2 + (56.5 \text{ }\Omega - 133 \text{ }\Omega)^2} = 91.4 \text{ }\Omega.$$

$$I_{\text{rms}} = \dfrac{V_{\text{rms}}}{Z} = \dfrac{120 \text{ V}}{91.4 \text{ }\Omega} = 1.31 \text{ A}.$$

Only the resistor dissipates power. So $\bar{P} = I_{\text{rms}}^2 R = (1.31 \text{ A})^2 (50 \text{ }\Omega) = 86.2 \text{ W}$.

Therefore the percentage is $\dfrac{\bar{P}}{\bar{P}_o} = \dfrac{86.2 \text{ W}}{288 \text{ W}} = \boxed{30\%}$.

70. (a) $V_o = \sqrt{2}\,V_{\text{rms}} = \sqrt{2}\,(120 \text{ V}) = \boxed{170 \text{ V}}$.

(b) $\bar{P} = I_{\text{rms}} V_{\text{rms}}$, ☞ $I_{\text{rms}} = \dfrac{\bar{P}}{V_{\text{rms}}} = \dfrac{60 \text{ W}}{120 \text{ V}} = 0.50 \text{ A}$.

So $I_o = \sqrt{2}\,I_{\text{rms}} = \sqrt{2}\,(0.50 \text{ A}) = \boxed{0.707 \text{ A}}$.

71. $I_o = \sqrt{2}\,I_{\text{rms}} = \sqrt{2}\,(0.25 \text{ A}) = \boxed{0.35 \text{ A}}$.

72. (a) $X_L = 2\pi f L = 2\pi(60 \text{ Hz})(0.40 \text{ H}) = 151 \text{ }\Omega$. So $I_{\text{rms}} = \dfrac{V_{\text{rms}}}{X_L} = \dfrac{120 \text{ V}}{151 \text{ }\Omega} = \boxed{0.80 \text{ A}}$.

(b) The $\boxed{\text{voltage leads the current by } 90°}$.

73. Since $f_o = \dfrac{1}{2\pi\sqrt{LC}}$,

$$C = \dfrac{1}{4\pi^2 f_o^2 L} = \dfrac{1}{4\pi^2(98.9 \times 10^6 \text{ Hz})^2(1.50 \times 10^{-6} \text{ H})} = \boxed{1.7 \times 10^{-12} \text{ F}}.$$

74.   (a) $X_L = 2\pi f L = 2\pi(60 \text{ Hz})(0.100 \text{ H}) = \boxed{38 \text{ } \Omega}$.

(b) $Z = \sqrt{R^2 + (X_L - X_C)^2} = \sqrt{(50 \text{ } \Omega)^2 + (37.7 \text{ } \Omega)^2} = \boxed{63 \text{ } \Omega}$.

(c) $I_{rms} = \dfrac{V_{rms}}{Z} = \dfrac{110 \text{ V}}{62.6 \text{ } \Omega} = \boxed{1.8 \text{ A}}$.

(d) Only the resistor dissipates power. So the power dissipated in the coil is $\boxed{\text{zero}}$.

75. $\tan \phi = \dfrac{X_L - X_C}{R} = \dfrac{38 \text{ } \Omega}{50 \text{ } \Omega} = 0.76$,   ☞ $\phi = \boxed{37°}$.

76.   (a) $X_C = \dfrac{1}{2\pi f C} = \dfrac{1}{2\pi(60 \text{ Hz})(1.0 \times 10^{-6} \text{ F})} = \boxed{2.7 \times 10^3 \text{ } \Omega}$.

(b) $I_{rms} = \dfrac{V_{rms}}{X_C} = \dfrac{120 \text{ V}}{2650 \text{ } \Omega} = \boxed{4.5 \times 10^{-2} \text{ A}}$.

(c) The current leads the voltage by 90° and so the phase angle is $\boxed{-90°}$.

77.   From $X_C = \dfrac{1}{2\pi f C}$ and $X_L = 2\pi f L$, we can see that the capacitor opposes current more strongly at lower frequencies and the inductor opposes current more strongly at high frequencies. In Fig. 21.18a, the inductor in series with R_L filters out the high frequency current, so only the low frequency current reaches R_L. In Fig. 21.18b, the capacitor in series with R_L filters out the low frequency current, so only the high frequency current reaches R_L.

78.   (a) The phase angle is $\boxed{\text{zero, as } X_L = X_C}$, according to $\phi = \tan^{-1} \dfrac{X_L - X_C}{R}$.

(b) $f_o = \dfrac{1}{2\pi\sqrt{LC}}$,   ☞ $C = \dfrac{1}{4\pi^2 f_o^2 L} = \dfrac{1}{4\pi^2 (60 \text{ Hz})(0.750 \text{ H})} = \boxed{9.4 \text{ } \mu\text{F}}$.

CHAPTER 22

REFLECTION AND REFRACTION OF LIGHT

1. (c).

2. (c).

3. (d).

4. (d).

5. Water surface has waves, only certain segments of the surface are oriented so as to reflect the Sun's image toward us at any instant. It is like reflections from a series of little mirrors oriented in different directions. The reflecting facets change almost randomly from moment to moment as the water surface undulates.

6. The angle of reflection will $\boxed{\text{never}}$ be smaller than the angle of incidence. The angle of reflection is always equal to the angle of incidence, according to the law of reflection.

7. $\boxed{\text{No}}$. If it is reflecting 100%, then you cannot see its surface but the reflections of other objects. Typical mirrors reflect less than 95% of the light so we can still see its surface.

8. This is $\boxed{\text{irregular or diffuse}}$ reflection because the page surface is microscopically rough.

9. After rain, water fills the unevenness of the road. The reflection off the road is specular, so images of buildings, trees, and so on are formed. When the road is dry, the unevenness of the road causes diffuse reflection, so there are no images of buildings, trees, etc.

10. Since $\theta_i = \theta_r$, the angle between the beams is $35° + 35° = \boxed{70°}$.

11. $\theta_i = \theta_r = 32°$ from the normal. So the angle between the surface and the beam is $90° - \theta_r = \boxed{58°}$.

12. (a) Since $\theta_i = \theta_r$ and $\alpha + \theta_i = 90°$, $\theta_r = \theta_i = \boxed{90° - \alpha}$.

    (b) $\theta_r = \theta_i = 90° - 43° = \boxed{47°}$

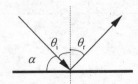

13. See the diagram for the solution of Exercise 12. $\theta_i = 90° - 55° = 35°$.

So $\theta_r = \theta_i = \boxed{35°}$.

14. (a) If the angle of incidence is β, the angle of reflection is also β. So the angle formed by the left mirror and the reflecting light off the left mirror is $90° - \beta$.

Then the angle between the right mirror and the light incident on the right mirror is $180° - [(90° - \beta) + \alpha] = 90° + \beta - \alpha$. Therefore the angle of incidence on the right mirror is

$90° - [90° + \beta - \alpha] = \alpha - \beta$.

Thus the angle of reflection off the right mirror is also $\boxed{\alpha - \beta}$.

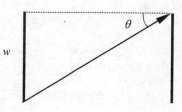

(b) For $\alpha = 60°$ and $\beta = 40°$, the angle of reflection off the right mirror is $\alpha - \beta = 60° - 40° = \boxed{20°}$.

15. (a) From the diagram, we can see that $\tan \theta = w/d$, so the angle of incidence will be $\boxed{\tan^{-1} w/d}$.

(b) $\theta = \tan^{-1} \dfrac{25 \text{ cm}}{50 \text{ cm}} = \tan^{-1} 0.50 = \boxed{27°}$.

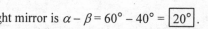

16. $\tan \theta_i = \dfrac{2.5 \text{ m}}{3.0 \text{ m}} = 0.833$,

so $\theta_i = \theta_r = \tan^{-1} 0.833 = \boxed{40°}$.

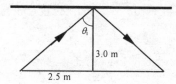

17. $A = a^2$, ☞ $a = \sqrt{A} = \sqrt{900 \text{ cm}^2} = 30 \text{ cm} = 0.30 \text{ m}$.

Use similar triangles. $\dfrac{d + 0.45 \text{ m} + 0.45 \text{ m}}{8.50 \text{ m}} = \dfrac{0.45 \text{ m}}{0.30 \text{ m}}$, ☞ $d = \boxed{12 \text{ m}}$.

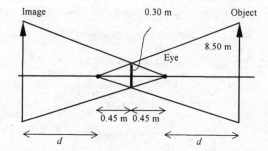

18. According to the law of reflection,

$\beta = 180° - [\alpha + (90° - \theta_{i_1})] = 90° - \alpha + \theta_{i_1}$.

So   the angle of reflection from the second mirror is

$\theta_{r_2} = 90° - \beta = \alpha - \theta_{i_1}$.

(a) $\theta_{r_2} = 70° - 35° = \boxed{35°}$.

(b) $\theta_{r_2} = 115° - 60° = \boxed{55°}$.

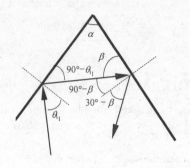

19. If $\alpha = \boxed{90°}$, $\theta_{i_1} + \theta_{r_2} = 90°$ and the two normals are perpendicular to each other. So the reflected ray is parallel to the incident ray for $\boxed{\text{any } \theta_{i_1}}$.

20. (b), because $n_1 \sin\theta_1 = n_2 \sin\theta_2$. When $n_1 > n_2$, $\theta_1 < \theta_2$, so refracted ray is bent away from the normal.

21. (d).

22. It is because $\boxed{\text{light speed depends on medium}}$. For example, light speed is different in air from in water. Because of the speed difference, light changes direction when entering a different medium at an angle of incidence that is not zero.

23. $\boxed{\text{Yes}}$, wavelength changes. $\boxed{\text{No}}$, frequency does not change. $\boxed{\text{Yes}}$, speed changes since $v = \lambda f$.

24. $\boxed{\text{Ice is less dense than water}}$. In general, the lower the mass density, the lower the index of refraction.

25. (b).

26. Total internal reflection occurs when $\boxed{n_1 > n_2 \text{ and } \theta_i > \theta_c}$.

27. This severed look is because the angle of refraction is different for air-glass interface than for water-glass interface. The top portion refracts from air to glass, and the bottom portion refracts from water to glass. This is different from what's on Fig.22.12b. In that figure, we see the top portion in air directly and the bottom portion in water through refraction from water to air. The angle of refraction made the pencil appear to be bent.

28.   Initially, light has to travel along a straight line to reach our eyes, and the top of the container blocks the light from the bottom of the coin. When water is added, the light coming out of water is bent into the air with a larger angle of refraction, so it reaches our eyes.

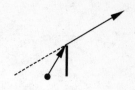

29.   The laser has a better chance to hit the fish. The fish appears to the hunter at a location different from its true location due to refraction. The laser beam obeys the same law of refraction and retraces the light the hunter sees to the fish. The arrow goes into the water in a near-straight line path.

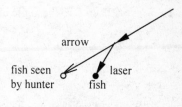

30.   No . Total internal reflection can occur only if light is traveling from glass to air (from high index to low index) AND the angle of incidence is greater than the critical angle.

31.   It is useful due to some of its unique properties. An fiber optic is very flexible, small in size, and can be inserted in almost everywhere, compared to the old mechanical-based devices with mirrors and lenses.

32. $n = \dfrac{c}{v} = \dfrac{3.00 \times 10^8 \text{ m/s}}{2.13 \times 10^8 \text{ m/s}} = \boxed{1.41}$.

33. $n = \dfrac{c}{v}$, ☞ $v = \dfrac{c}{n}$. So $\dfrac{v_Z}{v_D} = \dfrac{n_D}{n_Z} = \dfrac{2.42}{1.92} = 1.26$.

So the percentage difference is $\dfrac{v_Z - v_D}{v_D} = 1 - \dfrac{v_Z}{v_D} = 0.26 = \boxed{26\% \text{ greater in zircon}}$.

34.   (a) According to Snell's law, the angle of refraction will be $\boxed{\text{less than}}$ the angle of incidence because water has a higher index of refraction.

(b) $n_1 \sin \theta_1 = n_2 \sin \theta_2$, ☞ $\sin \theta_2 = \dfrac{n_1 \sin \theta_1}{n_2} = \dfrac{(1)\sin 60°}{1.33} = 0.651$. So $\theta_2 = \boxed{41°}$.

35. $n_1 \sin \theta_1 = n_2 \sin \theta_2$, ☞ $\sin \theta_1 = \dfrac{n_2 \sin \theta_2}{n_1} = \dfrac{(1.33)\sin 20°}{1} = 0.455$. So $\theta_1 = \boxed{27°}$.

36. $n_1 \sin \theta_1 = n_2 \sin \theta_2$, ☞ $n_2 = \dfrac{n_1 \sin \theta_1}{\sin \theta_2} = \dfrac{(1)\sin 50°}{\sin 35°} = \boxed{1.34}$.

37.   (a) Light should be directed from $\boxed{\text{diamond to air}}$, because diamond has a higher index of refraction.

(b) $\theta_c = \sin^{-1} \dfrac{n_2}{n_1} = \sin^{-1} \dfrac{1}{2.42} = \boxed{24°}$.

38. $\theta_c = \sin^{-1} \dfrac{n_2}{n_1},$ ☞ $n_1 = \dfrac{n_2}{\sin \theta_c} = \dfrac{1}{\sin 41.8°} = \boxed{1.50}.$

39. $n_1 \sin \theta_1 = n_2 \sin \theta_2,$ ☞ $\sin \theta_1 = \dfrac{n_2 \sin \theta_2}{n_1} = \dfrac{(1.46) \sin 30°}{1} = 0.73.$ So $\theta_1 = 47°.$

Therefore the angle of reflection is also $\boxed{47°}$, according to the law of reflection.

40. $n_1 \sin \theta_1 = n_2 \sin \theta_2,$ ☞ $\sin \theta_2 = \dfrac{n_1 \sin \theta_1}{n_2} = \dfrac{(1) \sin 55°}{1.49} = 0.550.$ So $\theta_2 = 33°.$

Therefore the angle relative to the surface is $90° - \theta_2 = \boxed{57°}.$

41. The frequency does not change and is still $\boxed{6.5 \times 10^{14} \text{ Hz}}$.

$\lambda = \dfrac{v}{f} = \dfrac{c}{fn} = \dfrac{3.00 \times 10^8 \text{ m/s}}{(6.5 \times 10^{14} \text{ Hz})(1.66)} = \boxed{2.8 \times 10^{-7} \text{ m}}.$

42. $\dfrac{v_B}{v_A} = \dfrac{c/n_B}{c/n_A} = \dfrac{n_A}{n_B} = \dfrac{4/3}{5/4} = \boxed{\dfrac{16}{15}}.$

43. $f_A = f_B.$ $\quad \dfrac{\lambda_B}{\lambda_A} = \dfrac{v_B/f}{v_A/f} = \dfrac{v_B}{v_A} = \boxed{\dfrac{16}{15}}.$

44. $\lambda_m = \dfrac{\lambda}{n} = \dfrac{193 \text{ nm}}{1.376} = \boxed{140 \text{ nm}},$ $\quad f = f_m = \dfrac{c}{\lambda} = \dfrac{3.00 \times 10^8 \text{ m/s}}{193 \times 10^{-9} \text{ m}} = \boxed{1.55 \times 10^{15} \text{ Hz}}.$

45. (a) This is caused by $\boxed{\text{refraction}}$ of light in the water-air interface. The angle of refraction in air is greater

than the angle of incidence in water so the object immersed in water appears closer to the surface.

(b) From the figure, the distance a is common to both d and d', and using trigonometry

$\tan \theta_1 = \dfrac{a}{d'}$ and $\tan \theta_2 = \dfrac{a}{d}.$

Combining these two equations to form a ratio: $\quad \dfrac{d'}{d} = \dfrac{\tan \theta_2}{\tan \theta_1}$ or $d' = \dfrac{\tan \theta_2}{\tan \theta_1} d.$

If $\theta < 15°$, $\tan \theta \approx \sin \theta.$ So $\dfrac{d'}{d} = \dfrac{\tan \theta_2}{\tan \theta_1} \approx \dfrac{\sin \theta_2}{\sin \theta_1} = \dfrac{1}{n}$ (Snell's law).

Therefore $d' \approx \dfrac{d}{n}.$

46.   The first refraction is at the air-glass interface and the second refraction is at the glass-water interface.

$$n_1 \sin \theta_1 = n_2 \sin \theta_2, \quad \text{☞} \quad \sin \theta_2 = \frac{n_1 \sin \theta_1}{n_2} = \frac{(1) \sin 40°}{1.50} = 0.429. \quad \text{So} \quad \theta_2 = 25.4°.$$

The critical angle at the glass-water interface is $\theta_c = \sin^{-1} \frac{n_3}{n_2} = \sin^{-1} \frac{1.33}{1.50} = \sin^{-1} 0.887 = 62.5°.$

Therefore the angle of incidence at the glass-water interface is smaller than the critical angle. Thus there is no total internal reflection and $\boxed{\text{yes}}$, the fish is illuminated.

47.   (a) This arrangement depends on $\boxed{\text{the indices of refraction of both}}$ media, because $\theta_c \geq \sin^{-1} \frac{n_2}{n_1}$.

(b) Air: $\theta_c \geq \sin^{-1} \frac{n_2}{n_1}, \quad \text{☞} \quad n_1 \geq \frac{n_2}{\sin \theta_c} = \frac{1}{\sin 45°} = \boxed{1.41}.$

Water: $n_1 \geq \frac{n_2}{\sin \theta_c} = \frac{1.33}{\sin 45°} = \boxed{1.88}.$

48.   (a) $\theta_c = \sin^{-1} \frac{n_2}{n_1} = \sin^{-1} \frac{1}{1.85} = \sin^{-1} 0.541 = 32° < 45°.$ So $\boxed{\text{yes}}$, there is total internal reflection.

(b) $\theta_c = \sin^{-1} \frac{1.33}{1.85} = \sin^{-1} 0.719 = 46° > 45°.$ So $\boxed{\text{no}}$, there is no total internal reflection.

49.   (a) Repeat the calculation in Example 22.4. $\sin \theta_2 = \frac{\sin 40°}{1.65} = 0.390, \quad \text{☞} \quad \theta_2 = 22.9°.$

(b) The length of the ray inside the plate is $r = \frac{y}{\cos \theta_2}.$

So the perpendicular distance between the two rays is

$$d = r \sin (\theta_1 - \theta_2) = \frac{y}{\cos \theta_2} \sin (\theta_1 - \theta_2) = \frac{10.0 \text{ cm}}{\cos 22.9°} \sin (40° - 22.9°) = \boxed{3.2 \text{ cm}}.$$

50.   Use the result of Exercise 45b. $d' = \frac{d}{n} = \frac{3.2 \text{ m}}{1.33} = \boxed{2.4 \text{ m}}.$

51.   Use the result of Exercise 45b. $d' = \frac{d}{n}, \quad \text{☞} \quad \frac{d'}{d} = \frac{1}{n} = \frac{1}{1.33} = 0.75 = \boxed{75\%}.$

52.   The setting is at zero altitude or 90° from the normal above water, so the angle incidence in the water should be equal to the critical angle of

$$\theta_c = \sin^{-1} \frac{n_2}{n_1} = \sin^{-1} \frac{1}{1.33} = \sin^{-1} 0.752 = 48.8°.$$

Then the angle to the surface is $90° - 48.8° = \boxed{41.2°}.$

53. $\theta_c = \sin^{-1} \dfrac{n_2}{n_1} = \sin^{-1} \dfrac{1}{1.33} = 49°$. So the 50° angle will be totally reflected and the 40° angle will refract

     through. Therefore $\boxed{\text{seen for 40° and not for 50°}}$.

54.   (a) $\boxed{\text{No}}$, 45° is not the actual altitude of the Sun due to refraction. The altitude is measured from the

     horizon, and so the angle from the normal is (90° − altitude). The actual altitude should be smaller than 45°

     as it is equal to $90° - \theta_1$. Since $\theta_1 > 45° = \theta_2$ because $n_1 < n_2$.

     (b) $n_1 \sin \theta_1 = n_2 \sin \theta_2$,   ☞ $\sin \theta_1 = \dfrac{n_2 \sin \theta_2}{n_1} = \dfrac{(1.33) \sin (90° - 45°)}{1} = 0.940$.

     So $\theta_1 = 70°$.   Therefore the actual altitude is $90° - 70° = \boxed{20°}$.

55. $\theta_2 = \tan^{-1} \dfrac{0.90 \text{ m}}{1.50 \text{ m}} = \tan^{-1} 0.60 = 31.0°$. $n_1 \sin \theta_1 = n_2 \sin \theta_2$,

     so $\sin \theta_1 = \sin \theta = \dfrac{n_2 \sin \theta_2}{n_1} = \dfrac{(1.33) \sin 31.0°}{1} = 0.685$.

     Therefore $\theta = \boxed{43°}$.

56.   We can measure the angles of incidence and refraction from the photography and calculate the index of

     refraction of the fluid from the law of refraction. $\theta_1 \approx 65°$ and $\theta_2 \approx 43°$.

     $n_1 \sin \theta_1 = n_2 \sin \theta_2$,   ☞ $n_2 = \dfrac{n_1 \sin \theta_1}{\sin \theta_2} \approx \dfrac{(1) \sin 65°}{\sin 43°} = \boxed{1.3}$.

57.   (a) $\theta_c = \sin^{-1} \dfrac{n_2}{n_1} = \sin^{-1} \dfrac{1}{1.60} = \boxed{38.7°} < 45°$. So the answer is $\boxed{\text{no}}$, the beam is not transmitted but

     internally reflected.

     (b) $\theta_c = \sin^{-1} \dfrac{n_2}{n_1} = \sin^{-1} \dfrac{1.20}{1.60} = 48.6° > 45°$. So the beam is not internally reflected and is $\boxed{\text{transmitted}}$.

58.   Use the result of Exercise 45b. $d' = \dfrac{d}{n} = \dfrac{2.5 \text{ cm}}{1.52} = \boxed{1.6 \text{ cm}}$.

59. $\theta_2 = \tan^{-1} \dfrac{0.50 \text{ m}}{0.75 \text{ m}} = \tan^{-1} 0.667 = 33.7°$. $n_1 \sin \theta_1 = n_2 \sin \theta_2$,

     so $\sin \theta_1 = \dfrac{n_2 \sin \theta_2}{n_1} = \dfrac{(1.33) \sin 33.7°}{1} = 0.738$.

     Therefore $\theta_1 = 47.5°$.

     Thus $d = (1.8 \text{ m}) \tan \theta_1 = (1.8 \text{ m}) \tan 47.5° = \boxed{2.0 \text{ m}}$.

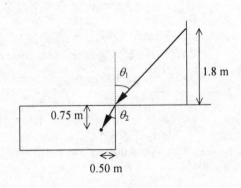

60.   To see the whole newspaper print, the minimum angle of refraction is 45°.

The maximum $n_1 \sin\theta_1$ is (1) sin 90° = 1.

$n_2 \sin\theta_2 = 1.66 \sin 45° = 1.17 > 1$.

So $\boxed{\text{no}}$, it is impossible.

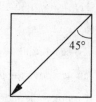

61.   (a) For refraction at the prism-prism interface,   (1.60) sin 45° = (1.40) sin θ_2,

so $\theta_2 = \sin^{-1} 0.808 = 53.9°$.

For the prism-air interface,

$\theta_3 = 180° - [135° + (90° - \theta_2)] = \theta_2 - 45° = 53.9° - 45° = 8.9°$.

So   (1.40) sin 8.9° = (1) sin θ.

Therefore $\theta = \sin^{-1} 0.217 = \boxed{12.5°}$.

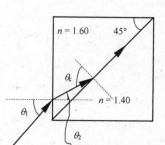

(b) $\theta_c = \sin^{-1} \dfrac{n_2}{n_1} = \sin^{-1} \dfrac{1.40}{1.60} = 61.0°$.

This is the angle required at the interface.

For the air-prism interface,

$\theta_2 = 180° - [135° + (90° - \theta_c)] = \theta_c - 45° = 61.0° - 45° = 16.0°$.

So   (1) sin θ_1 = (1.60) sin 16°.

Therefore $\theta_1 = \sin^{-1} 0.441 = \boxed{26.2°}$.

62.   (d).

63.   (b).

64.   It is due to the $\boxed{\text{different speeds of different frequencies in the material}}$. This, in turn, causes the different indices of refraction, therefore the different angles of refraction.

65.   In a square block, $n_1 \sin\theta_1 = n_2 \sin\theta_2 = n_3 \sin\theta_3$, where 1 is air, 2 is glass, and 3 is air again. The angle of refraction on the second refraction is the same as the angle of incidence on the first refraction ($\theta_1 = \theta_3$), so all colors or frequencies that were separated from the first refraction will have the same angle of refraction on exiting the block. See Example 22.4 in the textbook for more details. So the second refraction almost neutralizes the first refraction's dispersion. In a prism, there are $\boxed{\text{two refractions and two dispersions}}$ because both refractions cause the refracted light to bend downward, therefore doubling the effect or dispersion.

66. $\boxed{\text{No}}$, the light will be further dispersed by the second prism.

67. To see a rainbow, the light has to be behind you. Actually, you won't see a primary rainbow if the Sun's angle above the horizon is greater than 42°. Therefore you cannot look up to find a rainbow, thus you cannot walk under a rainbow.

68. $\boxed{\text{Color B}}$ has a longer wavelength. For normal dispersion, shorter wavelength bends more than longer wavelength after refracting through a prism.

69. (a) $\boxed{\text{The angle of incidence is approximately zero}}$, so there is no dispersion because the angle of refraction for all colors is also zero.

    (b) $\boxed{\text{No}}$ as explained in (a). $\boxed{\text{No}}$, the speeds are different.

70. (a) $\boxed{\text{Blue}}$ will experience more refraction because its index of refraction differs more than for red, compared with the index of refraction of air. According to Snell's law, blue will have a smaller angle of refraction or deviates more from the angle of incidence.

    (b) $n_1 \sin \theta_1 = n_R \sin \theta_R = n_B \sin \theta_B$, ☞ $\sin \theta_R = \dfrac{n_1 \sin \theta_1}{n_R} = \dfrac{(1) \sin 37°}{1.515} = 0.3972$.

    So $\theta_R = 23.406°$. $\sin \theta_B = \dfrac{(1) \sin 37°}{1.523} = 0.3952$.

    Therefore $\theta_B = 23.275°$.

    Hence $\Delta\theta = \theta_R - \theta_B = 23.406° - 23.275° = \boxed{0.131°}$.

71. $\theta_{cR} = \sin^{-1} \dfrac{1}{n_R} = \sin^{-1} \dfrac{1}{1.515} = 41.30°$, and $\theta_{cB} = \sin^{-1} \dfrac{1}{1.523} = 41.04°$.

    So $\boxed{\text{red is transmitted and blue is internally reflected}}$.

72. $n_1 \sin \theta_1 = n_R \sin \theta_R = n_B \sin \theta_B$, ☞ $\sin \theta_R = \dfrac{n_1 \sin \theta_1}{n_R} = \dfrac{(1) \sin 30°}{1.4925} = 0.33501$.

    So $\theta_R = 19.573°$.

    $\Delta\theta = \theta_R - \theta_B$, ☞ $\theta_B = \theta_R - \Delta\theta = 19.573° - (0.00131 \text{ rad}) \times \dfrac{180°}{\pi \text{ rad}} = 19.498°$.

    Therefore $n_B = \dfrac{(1) \sin 30°}{\sin 18.498°} = \boxed{1.4980}$.

73.   (a) For the first air-prism interface,   (1) sin 80.0° = (1.400) sin θ_2,

So $\theta_2 = \sin^{-1} 0.7034.$ Therefore $\theta_2 = 44.70°.$

For the second prism-air interface,

$\theta_3 = 180° - (120° + \theta_2) = 60° - \theta_2 = 60° - 44.70° = 15.30°.$

(1.400) sin 15.30° = (1) sin θ, so $\theta = \sin^{-1} 0.3693 = 21.68° = \boxed{21.7°}.$

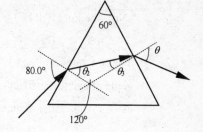

(b) For blue light, $\theta_2 = \sin^{-1} \dfrac{\sin 80.0°}{1.403} = 44.58°.$ $\theta_3 = 60° - 44.58° = 15.42°.$

So $\theta = \sin^{-1}[(1.403) \sin 15.42°] = 21.90°.$ Therefore $\Delta\theta = 21.90° - 21.68° = \boxed{0.22°}.$

(c) For blue light, $\theta_2 = \sin^{-1} \dfrac{\sin 80.0°}{1.405} = 44.50°.$ $\theta_3 = 60° - 44.50° = 15.50°.$

So $\theta = \sin^{-1}[(1.405) \sin 15.50°] = 22.05°.$

Therefore $\Delta\theta = 22.05° - 21.68° = \boxed{0.37°}.$

74. $n_1 \sin \theta_1 = n_2 \sin \theta_2,$ so $\sin \theta_2 = \dfrac{n_1 \sin \theta_1}{n_2} = \dfrac{(1) \sin 50°}{1.33} = 0.576.$

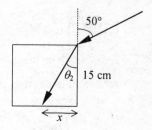

Therefore $\theta_2 = 35.2°.$

Thus $x = (15 \text{ cm}) \tan \theta_2 = (15 \text{ cm}) \tan 35.2° = \boxed{11 \text{ cm}}.$

75.   (a) $\theta_c = \sin^{-1} \dfrac{n_2}{n_1} = \sin^{-1} \dfrac{1.7}{2.0} = \boxed{58°}.$

(b) There must be a total internal reflection at the n_2-air interface.

$\theta_{c2} = \sin^{-1} \dfrac{1}{n_2} = \sin^{-1} \dfrac{1}{1.7} = 36.0°,$ so $\theta_2 = \theta_{c2}.$

$n_1 \sin \theta_1 = n_2 \sin \theta_2,$ ☞ $\sin \theta_1 = \dfrac{n_2 \sin \theta_2}{n_1} = \dfrac{(1.7) \sin 36.0°}{2.0} = 0.50.$

Therefore $\theta_1 = \boxed{30°}.$

76.   The angle of incidence is $90° - 50° = 40°.$ So the angle of reflection is also $\boxed{40°}.$

77. $n_1 \sin \theta_1 = n_2 \sin \theta_2,$ ☞ $n_2 = \dfrac{n_1 \sin \theta_1}{\sin \theta_2} = \dfrac{(1.33) \sin 45°}{\sin 35°} = \boxed{1.64}.$

78. (a) $n_1 \sin \theta_1 = n_2 \sin \theta_2$, ☞ $\sin \theta_2 = \dfrac{n_1 \sin \theta_1}{n_2} = \dfrac{(1) \sin 40°}{1.52} = 0.423$. So $\theta_2 = \boxed{25°}$.

(b) $v = \dfrac{c}{n} = \dfrac{3.00 \times 10^8 \text{ m/s}}{1.52} = \boxed{1.97 \times 10^8 \text{ m/s}}$.

(c) $\lambda_m = \dfrac{\lambda}{n} = \dfrac{550 \text{ nm}}{1.52} = \boxed{362 \text{ nm}}$.

79. $n_1 \sin \theta_1 = n_2 \sin \theta_2$, ☞ $\sin \theta_2 = \dfrac{n_1 \sin \theta_1}{n_2} = 0$. So $\theta_2 = 0$, not refracted.

So there is $\boxed{\text{no change in direction}}$.

80. Since water has an index of refraction of 1.33, closer to that of the glass, the spectrum emerging from the prism will be $\boxed{\text{less separated}}$. This can be seen with Snell's law. An extreme case would be for the index of refraction of the glass to be the same as that of the surrounding. In this case, the whole prism surrounding is optically indistinguishable so there will be no refraction; therefore the spectrum will $\boxed{\text{disappear}}$.

81. (a) $n_A \sin \theta_A = n_B \sin \theta_B$, ☞ $\sin \theta_B = \dfrac{n_A \sin \theta_A}{n_B} = \dfrac{n_A}{n_B} \sin \theta_A = (1.5) \sin 30° = 0.75$.

So $\theta_B = \sin^{-1} 0.75 = \boxed{49°}$.

(b) $n = \dfrac{c}{v}$, ☞ $v = \dfrac{c}{n}$. So $\dfrac{v_B}{v_A} = \dfrac{n_A}{n_B} = \boxed{1.5}$.

(c) Frequency does not change, so $\dfrac{f_B}{f_A} = \boxed{1}$.

(d) $\theta_c = \sin^{-1} \dfrac{n_B}{n_A} = \sin^{-1} 1/1.5 = \sin^{-1} 0.667 = \boxed{42°}$.

CHAPTER 23

From the spherical-mirror equation or the thin-lens equation, $\frac{1}{d_o} + \frac{1}{d_i} = \frac{1}{f}$, we have

$$\frac{1}{d_i} = \frac{1}{f} - \frac{1}{d_o} = \frac{d_o - f}{d_o f} \quad . \quad \text{Or} \quad d_i = \frac{d_o f}{d_o - f}. \text{ This is used in the solutions of many exercises.}$$

1.   (b).

2.   (c).

3.   (a) Reflections from the window are seen clearly against a dark background. During the day, light passes both ways through the pane, and although some is reflected, it is difficult to see the reflection due to the light coming through. At night, there is little light coming through the pane, so the reflections are seen much more clearly.

(b) The two images are due to reflections on both sides of the pane of glass, producing two similar images.

(c) This works on a combination of half-silvering and bright light on one side and dark on the other. For example, at night people inside the house cannot see things outside because there is little light coming through the window from the outside, and they see their own reflections.

4.   During the day, the reflection is mainly from the silvered back surface. During the night, when the switch is flipped, the reflection comes from the front side. And so there is a reduction of intensity and glare because the front side reflects only about 5% of the light, which is more than enough to see due to the dark background.

5.   (a) The left-right reversal is an apparent one. It is caused by the front-back reversal. Right and left are directional senses like clockwise and counterclockwise, rather than fixed directions referenced to a coordinate system.

(b) No. If you rotate your body 90°, it is still a left-right reversal.

6.   The magnification is $\boxed{+1}$. The "+" sign signifies that the orientations of the object and the image are the same. "1" means the object and the image have the same size.

7.   When viewed by a driver through a rear view mirror, the right-left reversal property of the image formed by a plane mirror will make it read "AMBULANCE."

8.   No , virtual images cannot be seen on a screen because no rays physically intersect at the image .

9.   It is infinite, because it cannot focus light to a point .

10.   (a) Image distance equals object distance. The distance from object to image is 2.0 m $+ 2.0$ m $=$ 4.0 m .

      (b) Upright, virtual, and same size .

11.   (a) Image distance equals object distance ($d_i = d_o$).

      So the distance from object to image is 40 cm $+ 40$ cm $=$ 0.80 m .

      (b) The image has the same height as the object. So it is 5.0 cm .

      (c) The image is unmagnified and upright. So the magnification is +1.0 .

12.   Image distance equals object distance. The distance from object to image is 2.5 m $+ 2.5$ m $=$ 5.0 m .

13.   (a) Image distance equals object distance and so it is 1.5 m behind the mirror .

      (b) The image also moves at 0.5 m/s toward the dog, and so the relative velocity of the dog to the image is

      0.5 m/s $+ 0.5$ m/s $=$ 1.0 m/s .

14.   The image formed by the wall mirror is 0.90 m $+ 0.90$ m $= 1.80$ m behind the woman or

      1.80 m $+ 0.30$ m $= 2.10$ m behind the hand mirror. The image formed by the hand mirror is then 2.10 m in

      front of the hand mirror or 2.10 m $+ 0.30$ m $=$ 2.4 m in front of the woman.

15.   (a) You see multiple images caused by reflections off two mirrors.

      (b) The first image by the north mirror is 3.0 m behind the *north* mirror .

      This image is 3.0 m $+ 3.0$ m $+ 5.0$ m $= 11$ m from the south mirror. So the second image by the south

      mirror is 11 m behind the *south* mirror .

      The first image by the south mirror is 5.0 m behind the *south* mirror .

      This image is 5.0 m $+ 5.0$ m $+ 3.0$ m $= 13$ m from the north mirror. So the second image by the north

      mirror is 13 m behind the *north* mirror .

16.   (a) The mirror needs to be half as tall as the object as explained in Example 23.7. So it is $\boxed{0.85 \text{ m}}$ tall.

(b) It is independent of object distance, and it is still $\boxed{0.85 \text{ m}}$.

17.   The two triangles (with d_o and d_i as base, respectively) are similar to each other because all three angles of one triangle are the same as those of the other triangle due to the law of reflection. Furthermore, the two triangles share the same height, the common vertical side. Therefore the two triangles are identical. Hence $d_o = d_i$.

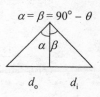

18.   The image I_3 is a degenerated image (i.e., two images). One is the image of I_1 by the top mirror and the other is the image of I_2 by the side mirror on top of each other. This happens when the mirrors are at 90° to each other. In Fig 23.24b, the mirrors are not at 90° to each other. So the degeneracy is lifted, and the two images are not on top of each other.

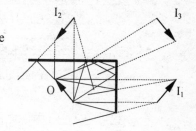

19.   (d).

20.   (a).

21.   (a) The plane mirror gives a large view of the area immediately around that side of the truck. The small convex mirror gives a wide-angle perspective of the road in back of both sides of the truck (but the image is smaller).

(b) These are convex mirrors that give a better field of view, but also images are smaller than objects (so the image distances are smaller than object distances) and hence appear closer than they actually are.

(c) Yes, it can be considered as a converging mirror, because it collects a large amount of radio waves and focuses them onto a small area.

22.   (a) A spoon can behave as either a concave or a convex mirror depending on which side you use for reflection. If you use the concave side, you normally see an inverted image. If you use the convex side, you always see an upright image.

(b) $\boxed{\text{Yes}}$, if you are very close (inside the center of curvature) to the spoon on the concave side, you can see an upright image.

23.	(a) The image is smaller than the object, and it is possible to "see your full body in 10 cm" in a diverging mirror.

(b) As the ball swings toward the mirror and approaches the focal point, the image enlarges. An enlarged image appears to be closer to our eyes, and so it appears to move toward the observer, therefore, it produces the effect of appearing to "jump" out of the mirror as the ball swings through the focal point.

24.	The image of a distant object (at infinity) is formed on a screen in the focal plane. The distance from the vertex of the mirror to the plane is the focal length.

25.	No, convex mirror produces only reduced images (smaller than objects).

26.	It should be concave because it can form an image larger than the object. A convex mirror always form images smaller than the objects.

27.	$f = \dfrac{R}{2} = \dfrac{10 \text{ cm}}{2} = \boxed{5.0 \text{ cm}}$.

28.	$d_o = 20$ cm, $f = \dfrac{R}{2} = \dfrac{30 \text{ cm}}{2} = 15$ cm.	$d_i = \dfrac{d_o f}{d_o - f} = \dfrac{(20 \text{ cm})(15 \text{ cm})}{20 \text{ cm} - 15 \text{ cm}} = \boxed{60 \text{ cm}}$.

$M = -\dfrac{d_i}{d_o} = -\dfrac{60 \text{ cm}}{20 \text{ cm}} = -3.0$.	So	$h_i = M h_o = -3.0 \, (3.0 \text{ cm}) = -9.0$ cm.	It is $\boxed{9.0 \text{ cm}}$ tall.

29.	$d_i = \dfrac{(10 \text{ cm})(15 \text{ cm})}{10 \text{ cm} - 15 \text{ cm}} = \boxed{-30 \text{ cm}}$.	$M = -\dfrac{-30 \text{ cm}}{10 \text{ cm}} = +3.0$.

So	$h_i = +3.0 \, (1.5 \text{ cm}) = \boxed{9.0 \text{ cm; virtual, upright, and magnified}}$.

30.	(a) It is seen from the ray diagram below, that the image is $\boxed{\text{virtual, upright, and reduced}}$.

(b) $d_o = 30$ cm, $f = -60$ cm (convex mirror).	$d_i = \dfrac{d_o f}{d_o - f} = \dfrac{(30 \text{ cm})(-60 \text{ cm})}{30 \text{ cm} - (-60 \text{ cm})} = \boxed{-20 \text{ cm}}$.

$M = -\dfrac{d_i}{d_o} = -\dfrac{-20 \text{ cm}}{30 \text{ cm}} = 2/3$.	So	$\boxed{h_i = (2/3) h_o}$.

31. (a) $d_o = 5.0$ cm, $d_i = -10$ cm (virtual image).

$$\frac{1}{f} = \frac{1}{d_o} + \frac{1}{d_i} = \frac{1}{5.0 \text{ cm}} + \frac{1}{-10 \text{ cm}} = \frac{1}{10 \text{ cm}},$$

so $f = \boxed{10 \text{ cm}}$,   and $R = 2f = \boxed{20 \text{ cm}}$.

(b) $M = -\dfrac{d_i}{d_o} = -\dfrac{-10 \text{ cm}}{5.0 \text{ cm}} = +2$ So $h_i = Mh_o = +2 \,(1.5 \text{ cm}) = \boxed{3.0 \text{ cm}}$.

32. (a) $d_o = 40$ cm $d_o = 30$ cm

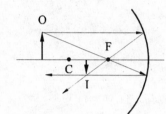   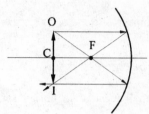

$d_o = 15$ cm $d_o = 5.0$

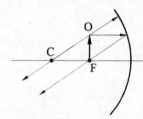   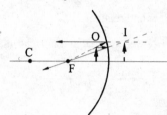

(b) $f = \dfrac{R}{2} = \dfrac{30 \text{ cm}}{2} = 15$ cm.

$d_o = 40$ cm: $d_i = \dfrac{d_o f}{d_o - f} = \dfrac{(40 \text{ cm})(15 \text{ cm})}{40 \text{ cm} - 15 \text{ cm}} = \boxed{24 \text{ cm}}$.

$M = -\dfrac{d_i}{d_o} = -\dfrac{24 \text{ cm}}{40 \text{ cm}} = -0.60.$ $h_i = Mh_o = -0.60 \,(3.0 \text{ cm}) = -1.8 \text{ cm} = \boxed{1.8 \text{ cm, real and inverted}}$.

$d_o = 30$ cm: $d_i = \dfrac{(30 \text{ cm})(15 \text{ cm})}{30 \text{ cm} - 15 \text{ cm}} = \boxed{30 \text{ cm}}$.

$M = -\dfrac{30 \text{ cm}}{30 \text{ cm}} = -1.0.$ $h_i = -1.0 \,(3.0 \text{ cm}) = -3.0 \text{ cm} = \boxed{3.0 \text{ cm, real and inverted}}$.

$d_o = 15$ cm: $d_i = \dfrac{(15 \text{ cm})(15 \text{ cm})}{15 \text{ cm} - 15 \text{ cm}} = \boxed{\infty}$.   The characteristics of the image are not defined.

$d_o = 5.0$ cm: $d_i = \dfrac{(5.0 \text{ cm})(15 \text{ cm})}{5.0 \text{ cm} - 15 \text{ cm}} = \boxed{-7.5 \text{ cm}}$.

$M = -\dfrac{-7.5 \text{ cm}}{5.0 \text{ cm}} = +1.5.$ $h_i = +1.5 \,(3.0 \text{ cm}) = \boxed{4.5 \text{ cm, virtual and upright}}$.

33. $\dfrac{1}{d_o} + \dfrac{1}{d_i} = \dfrac{1}{f}$, ☞ $\dfrac{1}{2f} + \dfrac{1}{d_i} = \dfrac{1}{f}$. so $\dfrac{1}{d_i} = \dfrac{1}{f} - \dfrac{1}{2f} = \dfrac{1}{2f}$, or $d_i = 2f$.

$M = -\dfrac{d_i}{d_o} = -\dfrac{2f}{2f} = -1$.

Therefore, the image is inverted (– magnification), and the same size as the object ($|M| = 1$).

34. Since $d_o < f$, $d_i = \dfrac{d_o f}{d_o - f} < 0$. Also $M = -\dfrac{d_i}{d_o} = -\dfrac{f}{d_o - f} = \dfrac{f}{f - d_o} > +1$.

So the image is virtual (negative d_i), upright (positive M), and magnified ($|M| > 1$).

35. f is negative for a convex mirror. So $d_i = \dfrac{d_o f}{d_o - f} = \dfrac{d_o(-|f|)}{d_o + |f|} < 0$.

Also $M = -\dfrac{d_i}{d_o} = -\dfrac{d_o(-|f|)}{d_o(d_o + |f|)} = \dfrac{|f|}{d_o + |f|} < +1$.

Therefore the image is virtual (negative d_i), upright (positive M), and reduced ($|M| < 1$).

36. (a) The mirror is $\boxed{\text{convex, because the erect image is smaller than the object}}$. Only a convex mirror can

form an image that is erect and reduced.

(b) $d_o = 18$ cm, $M = +\frac{1}{2}$ (it is a virtual and upright image). $d_i = -Md_o = -\frac{1}{2}(18 \text{ cm}) = -9.0$ cm.

$\dfrac{1}{f} = \dfrac{1}{d_o} + \dfrac{1}{d_i} = \dfrac{1}{18 \text{ cm}} + \dfrac{1}{-9.0 \text{ cm}} = -\dfrac{1}{18 \text{ cm}}$, ☞ $f = \boxed{-18 \text{ cm}}$.

37. $d_o = 20$ cm, $M = +1.5$ (upright image). $d_i = -Md_o = -1.5(20 \text{ cm}) = -30$ cm.

$\dfrac{1}{f} = \dfrac{1}{d_o} + \dfrac{1}{d_i} = \dfrac{1}{20 \text{ cm}} + \dfrac{1}{-30 \text{ cm}} = \dfrac{1}{60 \text{ cm}}$, ☞ $f = 60$ cm.

So $R = 2f = \boxed{120 \text{ cm}}$.

38. (a) $d_o = 50$ cm, $M = +3.0$. Since M is positive, the image is $\boxed{\text{virtual and upright}}$.

(b) $d_i = -Md_o = -3.0(50 \text{ cm}) = -150$ cm.

$\dfrac{1}{f} = \dfrac{1}{d_o} + \dfrac{1}{d_i} = \dfrac{1}{50 \text{ cm}} + \dfrac{1}{-150 \text{ cm}} = \dfrac{2}{150 \text{ cm}}$, so $f = 75$ cm.

Therefore $R = 2f = \boxed{150 \text{ cm}}$.

39. $f = \dfrac{R}{2} = \dfrac{-4.5 \text{ cm}}{2} = -2.25$ cm (convex surface), $M = +\frac{1}{2}$ (virtual image). $d_i = -Md_o = -\dfrac{d_o}{2}$.

So $\dfrac{1}{f} = \dfrac{1}{d_o} + \dfrac{1}{d_i} = \dfrac{1}{d_o} - \dfrac{1}{d_o/2} = -\dfrac{1}{d_o}$, ☞ $d_o = -f = \boxed{2.3 \text{ cm}}$.

40. (a) The mirror is $\boxed{\text{converging, because the image is magnified}}$. Only converging mirror can form a magnified image.

(b) $M = +4.0$ (upright image). $d_i = -Md_o = -4.0d_o$.

So $\dfrac{1}{f} = \dfrac{1}{d_o} + \dfrac{1}{d_i} = \dfrac{1}{d_o} + \dfrac{1}{-4.0d_o} = \dfrac{3}{4.0d_o}$.

Therefore it is a $\boxed{\text{concave}}$ mirror with $f = \boxed{\frac{4}{3}d_o}$.

41. (a) See diagram below.

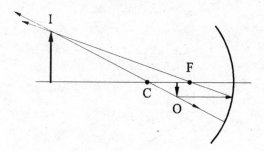

(b) $f = \dfrac{R}{2} = \dfrac{30\text{ cm}}{2} = 15$ cm, $\quad d_o = 20$ cm. $\quad d_i = \dfrac{d_o f}{d_o - f} = \dfrac{(20\text{ cm})(15\text{ cm})}{20\text{ cm} - 15\text{ cm}} = \boxed{60\text{ cm}}$.

$M = -\dfrac{d_i}{d_o} = -\dfrac{60\text{ cm}}{20\text{ cm}} = \boxed{-3.0,\text{ real and inverted}}$.

42. (a) The mirror is $\boxed{\text{concave, because the image is magnified}}$. Only concave mirror can form a magnified image.

(b) $d_o = 12$ cm, $\quad M = \dfrac{9.0\text{ cm}}{3.0\text{ cm}} = +3.0$. $\quad d_i = -Md_o = -3.0\ (12\text{ cm}) = -36$ cm.

So $\dfrac{1}{f} = \dfrac{1}{d_o} + \dfrac{1}{d_i} = \dfrac{1}{12\text{ cm}} + \dfrac{1}{-36\text{ cm}} = \dfrac{1}{18\text{ cm}}$, ☞ $f = 18$ cm.

So $R = 2f = \boxed{36\text{ cm}}$.

43. $d_o = 2.5$ m, $\quad M = +2.0$. $\quad d_i = -Md_o = -2.0\ (2.5\text{ m}) = -5.0$ m.

So $\dfrac{1}{f} = \dfrac{1}{d_o} + \dfrac{1}{d_i} = \dfrac{1}{2.5\text{ m}} + \dfrac{1}{-5.0\text{ m}} = \dfrac{1}{5.0\text{ cm}}$, ☞ $f = 5.0$ m

Therefore $R = 2f = \boxed{10\text{ m}}$.

44. (a) $d_i = \dfrac{d_o f}{d_o - f} = \dfrac{f}{1 - f/d_o}$.

$|M| = \dfrac{d_i}{d_o} = \dfrac{f}{d_o - f}$.

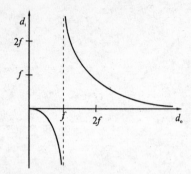

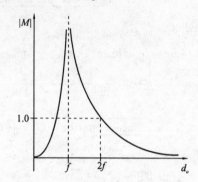

(b) $d_i = \dfrac{d_o (-f)}{d_o + f} = \dfrac{-f}{1 + f/d_o}$.

$|M| = \dfrac{d_i}{d_o} = \dfrac{-f}{d_o + f}$.

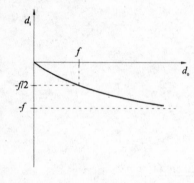

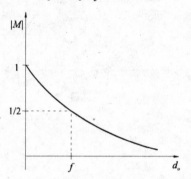

45. $d_o = 30$ cm, $f = 20$ cm. $d_i = \dfrac{d_o f}{d_o - f} = \dfrac{(30 \text{ cm})(20 \text{ cm})}{30 \text{ cm} - 20 \text{ cm}} = \boxed{60 \text{ cm}}$.

$M = -\dfrac{d_i}{d_o} = -\dfrac{60 \text{ cm}}{30 \text{ cm}} = -2.0$. So the image is $\boxed{\text{real, inverted, and magnified}}$.

46. $d_i = \dfrac{d_o f}{d_o - f}$. For concave, $M = -\dfrac{d_i}{d_o} = \dfrac{f}{f - d_o} = +1.8$, ☞ $f = \dfrac{9}{4} d_o$.

For convex, we replace f with $-|f| = -f$.

So $M = \dfrac{f}{f + d_o} = \dfrac{9/4 \, d_o}{9/4 \, d_o + d_o} = \dfrac{9}{13} = \boxed{0.69}$.

47. $f = \dfrac{R}{2} = \dfrac{20 \text{ cm}}{2} = 10$ cm, $M = \pm 2.0$, the + is for a virtual image and the − is for a real image.

$d_i = -M d_o = \mp 2.0 d_o$. $\dfrac{1}{f} = \dfrac{1}{d_o} + \dfrac{1}{d_i}$, so $\dfrac{1}{10 \text{ cm}} = \dfrac{1}{d_o} + \dfrac{1}{\mp 2.0 d_o}$,

or $\dfrac{2 \mp 1}{2 d_o} = \dfrac{1}{10 \text{ cm}}$.

Solving, $d_o = \dfrac{10 \text{ cm}}{2} (2 \mp 1) = \boxed{5.0 \text{ cm or } 15 \text{ cm}}$.

48. (a) $d_o = 100$ m, $f = -0.400$ m.

$$d_i = \frac{d_o f}{d_o - f} = \frac{(100 \text{ m})(-0.400 \text{ m})}{100 \text{ m} - (-0.400 \text{ m})} = -0.398 \text{ m} = \boxed{-39.8 \text{ cm}}.$$

$$M = -\frac{d_i}{d_o} = -\frac{-0.398 \text{ m}}{100 \text{ m}} = +0.00398. \quad \text{So} \quad h_i = M h_o = +0.00398 \, (2.0 \text{ m}) = \boxed{0.80 \text{ cm}}.$$

(b) $d_i = \frac{(10.0 \text{ m})(-0.400 \text{ m})}{10.0 \text{ m} - (-0.400 \text{ m})} = -0.385 \text{ m} = \boxed{-38.5 \text{ cm}}.$

$$M = -\frac{-0.385 \text{ m}}{10.0 \text{ m}} = +0.0385. \quad \text{So} \quad h_i = +0.0385 \, (2.0 \text{ m}) = \boxed{7.7 \text{ cm}}.$$

49. $\boxed{\text{Yes}}$, it is possible. One is a real image and the other is a virtual image.

$$f = \frac{R}{2} = \frac{40 \text{ cm}}{2} = 20 \text{ cm}, \quad M = \pm 3.0, \text{ the } + \text{ is for a virtual image and the } - \text{ is for a real image.}$$

$$d_i = -M d_o = \mp 3.0 d_o. \quad \frac{1}{f} = \frac{1}{d_o} + \frac{1}{d_i}, \quad \text{so} \quad \frac{1}{20 \text{ cm}} = \frac{1}{d_o} + \frac{1}{\mp 3.0 d_o},$$

or $\frac{3 \mp 1}{3 d_o} = \frac{1}{20 \text{ cm}}.$ Solving, $d_o = \frac{20 \text{ cm}}{3} (3 \mp 1) = \boxed{13 \text{ cm or } 27 \text{ cm}}.$

50. (d).

51. (c).

52. (b).

53. When the fish is inside the focal point, the image is upright, virtual, and magnified.

54. $\boxed{\text{Yes}}$. If the object is inside the focal point ($\boxed{d_o < f}$), the image of a real object is virtual, upright, and magnified.

55. You can $\boxed{\text{locate the image of a distant object}}$. The distance from the converging lens to the image is the focal length. $\boxed{\text{No}}$, the same method won't work for a diverging lens because a diverging lens does not form real images of real objects.

56. The object distance should be between the focal length and twice the focal length, i.e., $\boxed{2f > d_o > f}$. In this region, the image is real, inverted, and magnified.

57. $d_i = \dfrac{d_o f}{d_o - f} = \dfrac{(50.0\ \text{cm})(10.0\ \text{cm})}{50.0\ \text{cm} - (10.0\ \text{cm})} = \boxed{12.5\ \text{cm}}$. $M = -\dfrac{d_i}{d_o} = -\dfrac{12.5\ \text{cm}}{50.0\ \text{cm}} = \boxed{-0.25}$.

58. $\dfrac{1}{f} = \dfrac{1}{d_o} + \dfrac{1}{d_i} = \dfrac{1}{30\ \text{cm}} + \dfrac{1}{15\ \text{cm}} = \dfrac{1}{10\ \text{cm}}$, ☞ $f = \boxed{10\ \text{cm}}$.

59. $f = 20\ \text{cm}$, $d_i = 200\ \text{cm}$. $d_o = \dfrac{d_i f}{d_i - f} = \dfrac{(200\ \text{cm})(20\ \text{cm})}{200\ \text{cm} - 20\ \text{cm}} = \boxed{22\ \text{cm}}$.

60. (a) It is seen from the ray diagram below that the image is $\boxed{\text{virtual, upright, magnified}}$.

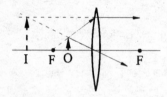

(b) $d_i = \dfrac{d_o f}{d_o - f} = \dfrac{(15\ \text{cm})(22\ \text{cm})}{15\ \text{cm} - 22\ \text{cm}} = \boxed{-47\ \text{cm}}$.

$M = -\dfrac{d_i}{d_o} = -\dfrac{-47.1\ \text{cm}}{15\ \text{cm}} = \boxed{+3.1}$.

61. (a) $f = -18.0\ \text{cm}$, $d_o = 10\ \text{cm}$.

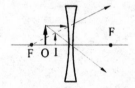

$d_i = \dfrac{d_o f}{d_o - f} = \dfrac{(10\ \text{cm})(-18.0\ \text{cm})}{10\ \text{cm} - (-18.0\ \text{cm})} = \boxed{-6.4\ \text{cm}}$.

$M = -\dfrac{d_i}{d_o} = -\dfrac{-6.43\ \text{cm}}{10\ \text{cm}} = \boxed{+0.64,\ \text{virtual and upright}}$.

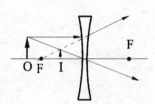

(b) $d_i = \dfrac{(25\ \text{cm})(-18.0\ \text{cm})}{25\ \text{cm} - (-18.0\ \text{cm})} = \boxed{-10.5\ \text{cm}}$.

$M = -\dfrac{-10.5\ \text{cm}}{25\ \text{cm}} = \boxed{+0.42,\ \text{virtual and upright}}$.

62. For a diverging lens, the focal length is negative.

$d_i = \dfrac{d_o f}{d_o - f} = \dfrac{-d_o |f|}{d_o + |f|} < 0$, so the image is always virtual.

$M = -\dfrac{d_i}{d_o} = -\dfrac{-|f|}{d_o + |f|} = \dfrac{|f|}{d_o + |f|} < 1$, since $d_o + |f| > |f|$.

Therefore $0 < M < 1$, i.e., the image is upright and reduced.

63. (a) $f = 12$ cm, $M = -2.0$ (real). $d_i = -Md_o = 2.0d_o$.

$$\frac{1}{f} = \frac{1}{d_o} + \frac{1}{d_i} = \frac{1}{d_o} + \frac{1}{2.0d_o} = \frac{3}{2d_o}, \quad \text{☞} \quad d_o = \frac{3}{2}f = \frac{3}{2}(12 \text{ cm}) = \boxed{18 \text{ cm}}.$$

(b) $M = +2.0$ (virtual). $d_i = -Md_o = -2.0d_o$.

$$\frac{1}{f} = \frac{1}{d_o} + \frac{1}{-2.0d_o} = \frac{1}{2d_o}, \quad \text{☞} \quad d_o = \frac{1}{2}f = \frac{1}{2}(12 \text{ cm}) = \boxed{6.0 \text{ cm}}.$$

64. (a) $\frac{1}{f} = \frac{1}{d_o} + \frac{1}{d_i} = \frac{1}{6.0 \text{ cm}} + \frac{1}{400 \text{ cm}} = 0.169 \text{ m}^{-1}, \quad \text{☞} \quad f = \boxed{5.9 \text{ cm}}.$

(b) $M = -\frac{d_i}{d_o} = -\frac{400 \text{ cm}}{6.0 \text{ cm}} = -66.7$. $h_i = Mh_o = -66.7(1.0 \text{ cm}) = -66.7 \text{ cm} = \boxed{67 \text{ cm, inverted}}.$

65. $d_o = 4.0$ m, $M = \frac{h_i}{h_o} = \frac{-35 \text{ mm}}{1.7 \times 10^3 \text{ mm}} = -0.0206$ (inverted).

$d_i = -Md_o = 0.0206(4.0 \text{ m}) = 0.0824$ m.

$$\frac{1}{f} = \frac{1}{d_o} + \frac{1}{d_i} = \frac{1}{4.0 \text{ m}} + \frac{1}{0.0824 \text{ m}} = 12.4 \text{ m}^{-1}, \quad \text{☞} \quad f = 0.081 \text{ m} = \boxed{8.1 \text{ cm}}.$$

66. $d_o = 10$ cm, $M = +\frac{1}{5}$ (image by concave lens is always virtual). $d_i = -Md_o = -\frac{1}{5}d_o$.

$$\frac{1}{f} = \frac{1}{d_o} + \frac{1}{d_i} = \frac{1}{d_o} + \frac{1}{-\frac{1}{5}d_o} = \frac{-4}{d_o}, \quad \text{☞} \quad f = -\frac{d_o}{4} = -\frac{10 \text{ cm}}{4} = \boxed{-2.5 \text{ cm}}.$$

67. $d_i = \frac{d_o f}{d_o - f}, \quad \text{☞} \quad d = d_o + d_i = d_o + \frac{d_o f}{d_o - f} = \frac{d_o(d_o - f)}{d_o - f} + \frac{d_o f}{d_o - f} = \frac{d_o^2}{d_o - f}.$

The quantity $\frac{d_o^2}{d_o - f}$ reaches its minimum when $d_o = 2f$ (try it), that is, the minimum distance between the object and the image for sharp image to form is $d_{min} = 4f$.

$f = 10$ cm, $d = d_o + d_i = 40$ cm. So $d = 4f$, which is the minimum distance for a sharp image to form.

Therefore $d_o = d_i = \boxed{20 \text{ cm}}$, and $M = -\frac{d_i}{d_o} = \boxed{-1}$.

68. (a) From similar triangles, $\frac{d_i - f}{f} = -\frac{y_i}{y_o}$, where the negative is introduced because the image is inverted.

Also $-\frac{y_i}{y_o} = \frac{d_i}{d_o}$. So $\frac{d_i - f}{f} = \frac{d_i}{d_o}$, or $d_o d_i - d_o f = d_i f$, that is, $d_i f + d_o f = d_o d_i$.

Dividing by $d_o d_i f$ on both sides gives $\frac{1}{d_o} + \frac{1}{d_i} = \frac{1}{f}$.

(b) $M = \frac{y_i}{y_o} = -\frac{d_i}{d_o}$ from the similar triangles in (a).

69.   (a) From the result of Exercise 23.67, the minimum distance between the object and the image is $4f$ for a

sharp image to form. At this minimum distance, $d_o = d_i = 2f$. So $M = -\dfrac{d_i}{d_o} = -1$ (i.e., a real image).

Therefore the minimum distance for a real image to form is also $\boxed{4f}$.

(b) For a biconvex lens, a virtual image forms when $0 < d_o < f$. When d_o approaches, $d_i = \dfrac{d_o f}{d_o - f}$ also

approaches 0. So the distance between the object and the image approaches $\boxed{0}$.

70. $d_o = 3.0$ cm, $M = +3.5$ (virtual image). $d_i = -Md_o = -3.5\,(3.0\ \text{cm}) = -10.5$ cm.

$$\frac{1}{f} = \frac{1}{d_o} + \frac{1}{d_i} = \frac{1}{3.0\ \text{cm}} + \frac{1}{-10.5\ \text{cm}} = 0.238\ \text{cm}^{-1}, \quad \textrm{☞} \quad f = \boxed{4.2\ \text{cm}}.$$

71.   (a) $d_o = 30$ cm, $f = -45$ cm. $d_i = \dfrac{d_o f}{d_o - f} = \dfrac{(30\ \text{cm})(-45\ \text{cm})}{30\ \text{cm} - (-45\ \text{cm})} = \boxed{-18\ \text{cm}}.$

(b) $d_i = \dfrac{(30\ \text{cm})(57\ \text{cm})}{30\ \text{cm} - 57\ \text{cm}} = \boxed{-63\ \text{cm}}.$

72.   For the lens, $d_{i1} = \dfrac{d_{o1} f_1}{d_{o1} - f_1} = \dfrac{(0.40\ \text{m})(0.15\ \text{m})}{0.40\ \text{m} - 0.15\ \text{m}} = 0.24$ m.

$M_1 = -\dfrac{d_{i1}}{d_{o1}} = -\dfrac{0.24\ \text{m}}{0.40\ \text{m}} = -0.60.$ The image by the lens is the object for the mirror.

For the mirror, $d_{o2} = 0.50\ \text{m} - d_{i1} = 0.50\ \text{m} - 0.24\ \text{m} = 0.26$ m.

$d_{i2} = \dfrac{(0.26\ \text{m})(0.13\ \text{m})}{0.26\ \text{m} - 0.13\ \text{m}} = \boxed{0.26\ \text{m in front of the concave mirror}}.$

$M_2 = -\dfrac{0.26\ \text{m}}{0.26\ \text{m}} = -1.$ So $M_{\text{total}} = M_1 M_2 = (-0.60)(-1.0) = \boxed{0.60,\ \text{real and upright}}.$

73.   (a) $d_o = 1.5$ m, $f = 0.045$ m. $d_i = \dfrac{d_o f}{d_o - f} = \dfrac{(1.5\ \text{m})(0.045\ \text{m})}{1.5\ \text{m} - 0.045\ \text{m}} = 0.046\ \text{m} = \boxed{4.6\ \text{cm}}.$

(b) $M = -\dfrac{d_i}{d_o} = -\dfrac{0.046\ \text{m}}{1.5\ \text{m}} = -0.0309.$ So $h_i = Mh_o = -0.0309\,(26\ \text{cm}) = \boxed{0.80\ \text{cm, inverted}}.$

74.   For the objective, $d_{i1} = \dfrac{d_{o1} f_o}{d_{o1} - f_o} = \dfrac{(0.30\ \text{cm})(0.28\ \text{cm})}{0.30\ \text{cm} - 0.28\ \text{cm}} = 4.2$ cm.

The image by the objective is the object for the eyepiece.

For the eyepiece, $d_{o2} = 7.0\ \text{cm} - d_{i1} = 7.0\ \text{cm} - 4.2\ \text{cm} = 2.8$ cm.

$d_{i2} = \dfrac{d_{o2} f_e}{d_{o2} - f_e} = \dfrac{(2.8\ \text{cm})(3.3\ \text{cm})}{2.8\ \text{cm} - 3.3\ \text{cm}} = -18$ cm.

So the image is $\boxed{18\ \text{cm to the left of the eyepiece; virtual image}}.$

75. For L_1, $d_{i1} = \dfrac{d_{o1} f_o}{d_{o1} - f_o} = \dfrac{(50 \text{ cm})(30 \text{ cm})}{50 \text{ cm} - 30 \text{ cm}} = 75 \text{ cm}$.

$M_1 = -\dfrac{d_{i1}}{d_{o1}} = -\dfrac{75 \text{ cm}}{50 \text{ cm}} = -1.5$.

The image by L_1 is the object for L_2.

For L_2, $d_{o2} = d - d_{i1} = 60 \text{ cm} - 75 \text{ cm} = -15 \text{ cm}$, where d is the distance between the lenses. A negative object means that the "object" is on the image side.

$d_{i2} = \dfrac{d_{o2} f_2}{d_{o2} - f_2} = \dfrac{(-15 \text{ cm})(20 \text{ cm})}{-15 \text{ cm} - 20 \text{ cm}} = \boxed{8.6 \text{ cm}}$. $M_2 = -\dfrac{d_{i2}}{d_{o2}} = -\dfrac{8.57 \text{ cm}}{-15 \text{ cm}} = 0.57$.

So $M_{\text{total}} = M_1 M_2 = (-1.5)(0.57) = -0.86 = \boxed{0.86; \text{ real and inverted}}$.

76. According to the definition of lateral magnification,

$M_1 = -\dfrac{h_{i1}}{h_{o1}}$, $M_2 = -\dfrac{h_{i2}}{h_{o2}}$, and $M = \dfrac{h_{i2}}{h_{o1}}$.

Since $h_{o2} = h_{i1}$ (the image formed by the first lens is the object for the second lens),

$M_1 M_2 = \dfrac{h_{i1}}{h_{o1}} \dfrac{h_{i2}}{h_{o2}} = \dfrac{h_{i2}}{h_{o1}} = M_{\text{total}}$.

77. For f_1, $\dfrac{1}{d_{o1}} + \dfrac{1}{d_{i1}} = \dfrac{1}{f_1}$.   Eq. (1)

The image by f_1 is the object for f_2.

For f_2, $d_{o2} = d - d_{i1} = 0 - d_{i1}$, where $d = 0$ is the distance between the lenses.

So $\dfrac{1}{d_{o2}} + \dfrac{1}{d_{i2}} = -\dfrac{1}{d_{i1}} + \dfrac{1}{d_{i2}} = \dfrac{1}{f_2}$.   Eq. (2)

Eq. (1) + Eq. (2) gives $\dfrac{1}{d_{o1}} + \dfrac{1}{d_{i2}} = \dfrac{1}{f_1} + \dfrac{1}{f_2} = \dfrac{1}{f}$,

where $d_{o1} = d_o$ and $d_{i2} = d_i$ are the object and image distance for the lens system.

Therefore $\dfrac{1}{f} = \dfrac{1}{f_1} + \dfrac{1}{f_2}$.

78. (b).

79. For a rectangular glass block, $R_1 = R_2 = \infty$. So $\dfrac{1}{f} = (n-1)\left(\dfrac{1}{R_1} - \dfrac{1}{R_2}\right) = 0$.

Therefore $f = \boxed{\infty}$, i.e., it has no focusing power.

80. (a) $\dfrac{1}{f} = (n-1)\left(\dfrac{1}{R_1} - \dfrac{1}{R_2}\right)$ assumes $n_{air} = 1$. If the index of refraction of the surrounding is not air, the lens

maker's equation needs to be modified as $\dfrac{1}{f} = (n/n_m - 1)\left(\dfrac{1}{R_1} - \dfrac{1}{R_2}\right)$, where n_m is the index of refraction

of the surroundings. So the answer is $\boxed{\text{yes}}$, there is a change in the focal length. When n_2 changes from 1

to 1.33 (index of refraction of water), the focal length will $\boxed{\text{increase}}$ in water because $1/f$ is smaller.

(b) In this case, $n_1 < n_2$ so $(n_1/n_2 - 1) < 0$ (i.e., the focal length changes sign).

Therefore a $\boxed{\text{diverging lens becomes converging lens and vice versa}}$.

81. $\boxed{\text{No}}$. The general lens maker's equation is $\dfrac{1}{f} = (n/n_m - 1)\left(\dfrac{1}{R_1} - \dfrac{1}{R_2}\right)$, where n_m is the index of refraction

of the surrounding. If $n_m > n$, f is negative.

82. Our eyes are "designed" or used to to see things clearly when our surroundings are air. When you are

underwater, the index of refraction of the surroundings (water now) changes. From Exercise 23.80(a), the

focal length of the eyes changes so everything is blurry. When you wear goggles, the surroundings of the

eyes are again air, so you can see things clearly.

83. $P = \dfrac{1}{f}$, ☞ $f = \dfrac{1}{P} = \dfrac{1}{-2.0\,\text{D}} = \boxed{-0.50\,\text{m}}$.

84. $P = \dfrac{1}{f} = (n-1)\left(\dfrac{1}{R_1} - \dfrac{1}{R_2}\right)$, ☞ $\left(\dfrac{1}{R_1} - \dfrac{1}{R_2}\right) = \dfrac{P}{n-1} = \dfrac{1.5\,\text{D}}{1.6-1} = 2.5\,\text{D}$.

So $\dfrac{1}{R_2} = \dfrac{1}{R_1} - 2.5\,\text{D} = \dfrac{1}{0.20\,\text{m}} - 2.5\,\text{D} = 2.5\,\text{D}$.

Therefore $R_2 = \dfrac{1}{2.5\,\text{D}} = 0.40\,\text{m} = \boxed{40\,\text{cm}}$.

85. $P = \dfrac{1}{f} = (n-1)\left(\dfrac{1}{R_1} - \dfrac{1}{R_2}\right) = (1.35 - 1)\left(\dfrac{1}{\infty} - \dfrac{1}{0.50\,\text{m}}\right) = \boxed{-0.70\,\text{D}}$.

86. (a) The focal length will $\boxed{\text{increase}}$. The general lens maker's equation is $\dfrac{1}{f} = (n/n_m - 1)\left(\dfrac{1}{R_1} - \dfrac{1}{R_2}\right)$,

where n_m is the index of refraction of the surrounding. If air is replaced by water, n_m increases from 1 to

1.33, so $1/f$ decreases and the focal length increases.

(b) Air:
$$\frac{1}{f} = (n/n_m - 1)\left(\frac{1}{R_1} - \frac{1}{R_2}\right) = (1.6/1 - 1)\left(\frac{1}{0.30 \text{ m}} - \frac{1}{-0.40 \text{ m}}\right) = 3.5 \text{ D},$$

so $f = 0.29 \text{ m} = \boxed{29 \text{ cm}}$.

Water:
$$\frac{1}{f} = (n/n_m - 1)\left(\frac{1}{R_1} - \frac{1}{R_2}\right) = (1.6/1.33 - 1)\left(\frac{1}{0.30 \text{ m}} - \frac{1}{-0.40 \text{ m}}\right) = 1.184 \text{ D},$$

so $f = 0.84 \text{ m} = \boxed{84 \text{ cm}}$.

87. Since the Moon is so far away, its image will be at the focal plane, and so $d_i = f = 60$ mm.

$$M = -\frac{d_i}{d_o} = -\frac{60 \times 10^{-3} \text{ m}}{3.8 \times 10^8 \text{ m}} = -1.58 \times 10^{-10}.$$

So $h_i = Mh_o = -1.58 \times 10^{-10} (3.5 \times 10^6 \text{ m}) = -5.5 \times 10^{-4} \text{ m} = \boxed{0.55 \text{ mm}}$, inverted.

88. (a) It must be a $\boxed{\text{convex}}$ mirror since a concave mirror can only form magnified virtual images.

(b) $M = +0.50$ (virtual), $d_o = 7.0$ cm. $d_i = -Md_o = -0.50 (7.0 \text{ cm}) = -3.5$ cm.

$$\frac{1}{f} = \frac{1}{d_o} + \frac{1}{d_i} = \frac{1}{7.0 \text{ cm}} + \frac{1}{-3.5 \text{ cm}} = -\frac{1}{7.0 \text{ cm}}, \quad \text{☞} \quad f = -7.0 \text{ cm}.$$

So $R = 2|f| = \boxed{14 \text{ cm}}$.

89. $f = \dfrac{R}{2} = \dfrac{50 \text{ cm}}{2} = 25 \text{ cm}, \quad d_o = 75$ cm.

$$d_i = \frac{d_o f}{d_o - f} = \frac{(75 \text{ cm})(25 \text{ cm})}{75 \text{ cm} - 25 \text{ cm}} = \boxed{37.5 \text{ cm}}.$$

$$M = -\frac{d_i}{d_o} = -\frac{37.5 \text{ cm}}{75 \text{ cm}} = -0.50.$$

So $h_i = Mh_o = -0.50 (6.0 \text{ cm}) = -3.0 \text{ cm} = \boxed{3.0 \text{ cm, real and inverted}}$.

90. (a) The mirror is $\boxed{\text{concave}}$ because only concave mirror can form magnified images.

(b) $d_o = 10.0$ cm, $M = +4.00$.

Since $M = -\dfrac{d_i}{d_o}$, $d_i = -Md_o = -(4.00)(10.0 \text{ cm}) = -40.0$ cm.

$$\frac{1}{f} = \frac{1}{d_o} + \frac{1}{d_i} = \frac{1}{10.0 \text{ cm}} + \frac{1}{-40.0 \text{ cm}} = \frac{3}{40.0 \text{ cm}}.$$

So $f = \dfrac{40.0 \text{ cm}}{3} = \boxed{13.3 \text{ cm}}$.

91.　The image formed by the converging lens is at the mirror. This image is the object for the diverging lens. If the mirror is at the focal point of the diverging lens, the rays refracted after the diverging lens will be parallel to the axis. These rays will be reflected back parallel to the axis by the mirror and will form another image at the mirror. This second image is now the object for the converging lens. By reversing the rays, a sharp image is formed on the screen located where the original object is. Therefore the distance from the diverging lens to the mirror is the focal length of the diverging lens.

92.　The two shaded triangles are similar to each other.　So　$|M| = \dfrac{h_i}{h_o} = \dfrac{d_i}{d_o}$.

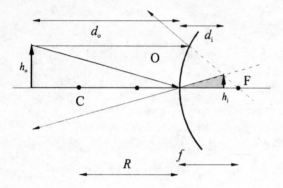

93.　$d_o = 20$ cm,　　$M = -2.5$ (real, inverted).

$d_i = -Md_o = 2.5(20 \text{ cm}) = 50$ cm.

$$\frac{1}{f} = \frac{1}{d_o} + \frac{1}{d_i} = \frac{1}{20 \text{ cm}} + \frac{1}{50 \text{ cm}} = \frac{7}{100 \text{ cm}} .$$

So　$f = \dfrac{100 \text{ cm}}{7} = \boxed{14 \text{ cm}}$.

94.　Since the mirror and lens equations are the same and the definition of the lateral magnification are also the same mathematically, the graphs are exactly the same as those in Exercise 23.44.

95.　$f_1 = f_2 = \dfrac{1}{P} = \dfrac{1}{10 \text{ D}} = 0.10$ m $= 10$ cm.

For the first lens,　　$d_{i1} = \dfrac{d_{o1}f_1}{d_{o1} - f_1} = \dfrac{(60 \text{ cm})(10 \text{ cm})}{60 \text{ cm} - 10 \text{ cm}} = 12$ cm,

$$M_1 = -\frac{d_{i1}}{d_{o1}} = -\frac{12 \text{ cm}}{60 \text{ cm}} = -0.20.$$

The image by the first lens is the object for the second lens.

For the second lens,　　$d_{o2} = d - d_{i1} = 20 \text{ cm} - 12 \text{ cm} = 8.0$ cm,

where d is the distance between the two lenses.

$$d_{i2} = \frac{d_{o2} f_2}{d_{o2} - f_2} = \frac{(8.0 \text{ cm})(10 \text{ cm})}{8.0 \text{ cm} - 10 \text{ cm}} = -40 \text{ cm, i.e., 40 cm on the object side from lens 2.}$$

Therefore the position of the image relative to lens 1 is

$20 \text{ cm} - 40 \text{ cm} = -20 \text{ cm} = \boxed{20 \text{ cm on object side of first lens}}$.

$$M_2 = -\frac{d_{i2}}{d_{o2}} = -\frac{-40 \text{ cm}}{8.0 \text{ cm}} = +5.0.$$

So $\quad M_{\text{total}} = M_1 M_2 = (-0.20)(5.0) = \boxed{-1.0, \text{ virtual and inverted}}$.

96. For the first lens, $\quad d_{o1} = 15 \text{ cm}, \quad f_1 = 10 \text{ cm}. \quad d_{i1} = \frac{d_{o1} f_1}{d_{o1} - f_1} = \frac{(15 \text{ cm})(10 \text{ cm})}{15 \text{ cm} - 10 \text{ cm}} = 30 \text{ cm}.$

$M_1 = -\frac{d_{i1}}{d_{o1}} = -\frac{30 \text{ cm}}{15 \text{ cm}} = -2.0.$ The image of the first lens is the object for the second lens.

For the second lens, $\quad d_{o2} = d - d_{i1} = 60 \text{ cm} - 30 \text{ cm} = 30 \text{ cm}$, where d is the distance between the lenses.

$d_{i2} = \frac{d_{o2} f_2}{d_{o2} - f_2} = \frac{(30 \text{ cm})(20 \text{ cm})}{30 \text{ cm} - 20 \text{ cm}} = \boxed{60 \text{ cm to right of second lens}}$.

$M_2 = -\frac{d_{i2}}{d_{o2}} = -\frac{60 \text{ cm}}{30 \text{ cm}} = -2.0. \quad M_{\text{total}} = M_1 M_2 = (-2.0)(-2.0) = \boxed{4.0, \text{ real and upright}}$.

97. (a) The lens should be $\boxed{\text{convex}}$ because only convex lens can form magnified images.

(b) $d_o = 5.00 \text{ cm}, \quad M = +5.00.$ Since $M = -\frac{d_i}{d_o}, \quad d_i = -Md_o = -(5.00)(5.00 \text{ cm}) = -25.0 \text{ cm}.$

$$\frac{1}{f} = \frac{1}{d_o} + \frac{1}{d_i} = \frac{1}{5.00 \text{ cm}} + \frac{1}{-25.0 \text{ cm}} = \frac{4}{25.0 \text{ cm}}.$$

So $\quad f = \frac{25.0 \text{ cm}}{4} = \boxed{6.25 \text{ cm}}$.

98. (a) Since the index of refraction of the lens is greater than that of air, the angle of refraction is smaller than the angle of incidence at the air–lens interface and greater than the angle of incidence at the lens–air interface. So both refractions bend the incident light toward the axis.

(a)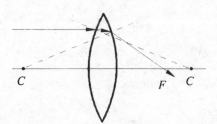

(b)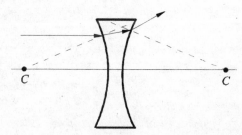

(b) For the same reason, the rays bend away from the axis due to the opposite curvatures of the surfaces

99. The general lens maker's equation is $\dfrac{1}{f} = (n/n_m - 1)\left(\dfrac{1}{R_1} - \dfrac{1}{R_2}\right)$, where n_m is the index of refraction of the surroundings.

$$\frac{f_{\text{water}}}{f_{\text{air}}} = \frac{(n/n_{\text{air}} - 1)}{(n/n_{\text{water}} - 1)} = \frac{1.62/1 - 1}{1.62/1.33 - 1} = 2.84.$$

So $f_{\text{water}} = 2.84\,(30\text{ cm}) = \boxed{85\text{ cm}}$.

100. $d_o = 30$ cm, $d_i = 20$ cm (real because on a screen).

$$\frac{1}{f} = \frac{1}{d_o} + \frac{1}{d_i} = \frac{1}{30\text{ cm}} + \frac{1}{20\text{ cm}} = \frac{5}{60\text{ cm}}, \quad \text{so} \quad f = \frac{60\text{ cm}}{5} = 12\text{ cm}.$$

Therefore $R = 2f = \boxed{24\text{ cm}}$.

101. (a) See the ray diagram below.

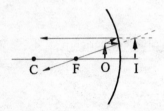

(b) $d_o = 20$ cm, $M = +1.5$ (virtual). $d_i = -Md_o = -1.5\,(20\text{ cm}) = -30$ cm.

$$\frac{1}{f} = \frac{1}{d_o} + \frac{1}{d_i} = \frac{1}{20\text{ cm}} + \frac{1}{-30\text{ cm}} = \frac{1}{60\text{ cm}}, \quad ☞ \quad f = \boxed{60\text{ cm}}.$$

CHAPTER 24

PHYSICAL OPTICS: THE WAVE NATURE OF LIGHT

The results from the small angle approximation ($\sin \theta \approx$ than $\theta = y/L$) is used in many interference and diffraction exercises: $y_n \approx \dfrac{nL\lambda}{d}$, $\Delta y = \dfrac{L\lambda}{d}$, $y_m = \dfrac{mL\lambda}{w}$, and $\Delta y = \dfrac{L\lambda}{w}$.

1. (b), because $\sin \theta_n = \dfrac{n\lambda}{d} \propto \dfrac{1}{d}$.

2. (a). Constructive interference occurs when $\Delta L = n\lambda$, $n = 0, 1, 2, \dots$.

3. Since $\sin \theta_n = \dfrac{n\lambda}{d} \propto \lambda$, $\boxed{\text{blue}}$ is closer to the central maximum.

4. There will be $\boxed{\text{no interference fringes, just uniform light intensity}}$, if the light is not coherent.

5. The path-length difference will change because of the airplane. This change in path-length difference results in a change in the condition of interference, i.e., constructive is no longer constructive, etc. Therefore, the pictures flutter.

6. $\boxed{\text{No, flashlights are not coherent}}$.

7. Since $\Delta y = \dfrac{L\lambda}{d} \propto \lambda$, $\boxed{\text{the spacing between the maxima would increase}}$ if wavelength increases.

8. $\boxed{\text{No}}$, this is not a violation of the conservation of energy. $\boxed{\text{There are dark fringes}}$, and the energy is simply redistributed (energy is moved from the dark fringes to the bright fringes). The total energy is still conserved.

9. We approximate $\tan \theta$ with $\sin \theta$. So the percentage difference is
    $$\frac{\tan \theta - \sin \theta}{\tan \theta} = \frac{\tan 15° - \sin 15°}{\tan 15°} = 0.034 = \boxed{3.4\%}.$$

10. $0.75 \text{ m} = 0.50 \text{ m} + 0.25 \text{ m} = 1.5(0.50 \text{ m}) = 1.5\lambda$. So the waves will interfere $\boxed{\text{destructively}}$.

    $1.0 \text{ m} = 0.50 \text{ m} + 0.50 \text{ m} = 2(0.50 \text{ m}) = 2\lambda$. So the waves will interfere $\boxed{\text{constructively}}$.

11.   (a) $\Delta L = r_2 - r_1 = \sqrt{(15.0\text{ m} - 4.0\text{ m})^2 + (20.0\text{ m} - 3.0\text{ m})^2}$

$$-\sqrt{(15.0\text{ m} - 2.0\text{ m})^2 + (20.0\text{ m} - 5.0\text{ m})^2} = 0.40\text{ m} = \frac{(1)\lambda}{2}.$$

So $\lambda = 2(0.40\text{ m}) = \boxed{0.80\text{ m}}$.

(b) $\Delta\theta = \dfrac{2\pi\Delta L}{\lambda} = \dfrac{2\pi}{\lambda}(0.40\text{ m}) = \dfrac{\pi}{4}$,   ☞ $\lambda = 8(0.40\text{ m}) = \boxed{3.2\text{ m}}$.

12.   (a) $d\sin\theta = \dfrac{m\lambda}{2}$, where $\sin\theta \approx \tan\theta = \dfrac{y_m}{L}$,   ☞ $\boxed{y_m = \dfrac{m\lambda L}{2d} \quad (m = 1, 3, 5, \ldots)}$.

$$\Delta y = y_{m+2} - y_m = \frac{(m+2)\lambda L}{2d} - \frac{m\lambda L}{2d} = \boxed{\frac{\lambda L}{d}}.$$

(b) The third dark fringe corresponds to $m = 5$.   So $\Delta L = \dfrac{m\lambda}{2} = \dfrac{5\lambda}{2} = \boxed{2.5\lambda}$.

13. $d\sin\theta = n\lambda$,   ☞ $\sin\theta_2 = \dfrac{n\lambda}{d} = \dfrac{(2)(550 \times 10^{-9}\text{ m})}{50 \times 10^{-6}\text{ m}} = 0.022$.

So $\theta_2 = \sin^{-1} 0.022 = \boxed{1.3°}$.

14.   (a) Since $\Delta y = \dfrac{L\lambda}{d} \propto \lambda$, the distance between the bright fringes will $\boxed{\text{increase}}$ if wavelength increases.

(b) $y_n \approx \dfrac{nL\lambda}{d}$, the distance is equal to $\Delta y = y_3 - y_0 = \dfrac{3L\lambda}{d} = \dfrac{3(1.5\text{ m})(680 \times 10^{-9}\text{ m})}{0.25 \times 10^{-3}\text{ m}} = \boxed{1.2\text{ cm}}$.

15.   (a) $y_n \approx \dfrac{nL\lambda}{d}$,   ☞ $\lambda = \dfrac{y_n d}{nL} = \dfrac{(0.0660\text{ m})(0.0250 \times 10^{-3}\text{ m})}{(3)(1.25\text{ m})} = 4.40 \times 10^{-7}\text{ m} = \boxed{440\text{ nm}}$.

(b) $y_2 = \dfrac{(2)(1.25\text{ m})(4.40 \times 10^{-7}\text{ m})}{0.0250 \times 10^{-3}\text{ m}} = \boxed{4.40\text{ cm}}$.

16.   From $\Delta y = \dfrac{L\lambda}{d}$,

$$\lambda = \frac{d\Delta y}{L} = \frac{(0.20 \times 10^{-3}\text{ m})(0.45 \times 10^{-2}\text{ m})}{1.5\text{ m}} = 6.00 \times 10^{-7}\text{ m} = \boxed{600\text{ nm (orange-yellow color)}}.$$

17.   (a) Since $\Delta y = \dfrac{L\lambda}{d} \propto \dfrac{1}{d}$, the distance between the bright fringes would $\boxed{\text{decrease}}$ if distance between

the slits were increased.

(b) $\Delta y = \dfrac{L\lambda}{d} = \dfrac{(3.00\text{ m})(640 \times 10^{-9}\text{ m})}{1.0 \times 10^{-3}\text{ m}} = \boxed{1.9\text{ mm}}$.

18. (a) Since $\theta_0 = 0$, the angular separation is equal to the angular position of the second-order bright fringe.

$$d\sin\theta = n\lambda, \quad \Rightarrow \quad \sin\theta = \frac{n\lambda}{d} = \frac{(2)(550\times10^{-9}\text{ m})}{1.75\times10^{-4}\text{ m}} = 6.29\times10^{-3}.$$

So $\theta_2 = \sin^{-1} 6.29\times10^{-3} = 0.36°$. $\Delta\theta = \theta_2 - \theta_0 = 0.36° - 0 = \boxed{0.36°}$.

(b) $y_2 \approx L\tan\theta_2 = (2.00\text{ m})\tan 0.36° = \boxed{1.26\text{ cm}}$.

19. (a) From $d\sin\theta = n\lambda$,

$$\lambda = \frac{d\sin\theta}{n} = \frac{(0.0350\times10^{-3}\text{ m})\sin(0.0230\text{ rad})}{2} = 4.02\times10^{-7}\text{ m} = \boxed{402\text{ nm, violet}}.$$

(b) $y_2 = L\tan\theta_2 = (1.50\text{ m})\tan(0.0230\text{ rad}) = \boxed{3.45\text{ cm}}$.

20. (a) If it is in water, $\lambda' = \dfrac{\lambda}{n} = \dfrac{\lambda}{1.33}$.

Since $\Delta y = \dfrac{L\lambda}{d} \propto \lambda$, the spacing of the interference fringes will $\boxed{\text{decrease}}$ if wavelength decreases.

(b) $\Delta y' = \dfrac{\Delta y}{1.33} = \dfrac{1.2\text{ cm}}{1.33} = \boxed{9.0\text{ mm}}$.

21. $y_n = \dfrac{n\lambda L}{d}, \quad \Rightarrow \quad \dfrac{(3)(600\text{ nm})L}{d} = \dfrac{(4)\lambda_2 L}{d}.$ So $\lambda_2 = \dfrac{3}{4}(600\text{ nm}) = \boxed{450\text{ nm}}$.

22. (a) because only the reflection at n_0—n_1 interface has 180° phase shift.

23. (a) because both reflections have 180° phase shifts.

24. The path-length difference in the film would be different (rather than directly down and back in terms of t alone), and the angular dependence and Snell's law would have to be used to determine the conditions for interference.

25. The wavelengths that are not visible in the reflected light are $\boxed{\text{all wavelengths except bluish purple}}$.

26. $\boxed{\text{No}}$, because there are regions where waves interfere constructively. The total energy is still conserved.

27. It is always dark because of $\boxed{\text{destructive interference due to the 180° phase shift}}$. If there had not been the 180° phase shift, zero thickness would have corresponded to constructive interference.

28. The index of refraction of kerosene must be [less than] that of water. If the thinnest part (thickness equal to zero) is bright, there is constructive interference. So neither beam should have 180° phase shift or both beams should have 180° phase shift. Had the index of refraction of kerosene been greater than that of water, the beam reflected at the air-kerosene would have an 180° phase shift, but the beam reflected at the kerosene-water would not have the phase shift.

29. (a) $\lambda_n = \dfrac{\lambda}{n} = \dfrac{550 \text{ nm}}{1.5} = 367$ nm. $t = 1.1 \times 10^{-5}$ m $= 30(367 \times 10^{-9}$ m$) = \boxed{30\lambda}$.

(b) The path length difference $\Delta L = 2t = 2(30\lambda) = 60\lambda$. However, the first reflection has an 180° phase shift. So they will interfere $\boxed{\text{destructively}}$.

30. $t_{min} = \dfrac{\lambda}{4n_1} = \dfrac{700 \text{ nm}}{4(1.40)} = \boxed{1.25 \text{ nm}}$.

31. $t_{min} = \dfrac{\lambda}{4n_1}$,   ☞ $\Delta t = \dfrac{1}{4n_1} \Delta\lambda = \dfrac{1}{4(1.38)}(300 \text{ nm}) = \boxed{54 \text{ nm}}$.

32. (a) $\boxed{\text{Yes}}$, the thickness are different for $n_{solar} > n_{film}$ or $n_{solar} < n_{film}$, because of the 180° phase shift.

(b) $t_{min} = \dfrac{\lambda}{4n_1} = \dfrac{550 \text{ nm}}{4(1.22)} = \boxed{113 \text{ nm}}$.

33. The first reflection has 180° phase shift. So the condition for destructive interference becomes

$\Delta L = 2t = \lambda_n$, where $\lambda_n = \dfrac{\lambda}{n}$.   So $t = \dfrac{\lambda}{2n}$.

Therefore $t_1 = \dfrac{480 \text{ nm}}{2(1.50)} = \boxed{160 \text{ nm}}$ and $t_2 = \dfrac{600 \text{ nm}}{2(1.50)} = \boxed{200 \text{ nm}}$.

34. $t_{min} = \dfrac{\lambda}{4n_1} = \dfrac{c/f}{4n_1} = \dfrac{c}{4fn_1} = \dfrac{3.00 \times 10^8 \text{ m/s}}{4(3.75 \times 10^{14} \text{ Hz})(1.20)} = 1.67 \times 10^{-7}$ m $= \boxed{167 \text{ nm}}$.

35. (a) The two rays for interference are the reflections from the bottom surface of the top plate and the top surface from the bottom plate. The reflection from the top surface of the bottom plate has 180° phase shifts, so the condition for constructive interference for reflection is $\Delta L = 2t = \dfrac{\lambda}{2}$,

so $t = \dfrac{\lambda}{4} = \dfrac{632.8 \text{ nm}}{4} = \boxed{158.2 \text{ nm}}$.

(b) Constructive for transmission is the same as destructive for reflection.

So $\Delta L = 2t = \lambda$,   ☞ $t = \dfrac{\lambda}{2} = \dfrac{632.8 \text{ nm}}{2} = \boxed{316.4 \text{ nm}}$.

36.   (a) The two rays for interference are the reflections from the bottom surface of the top plate and the top surface from the bottom plate. As the distance between the top and bottom plates increases, so does the path length difference. The path-length difference will alternate between $n\lambda$ and $(n + \frac{1}{2})\lambda$, where n is an integer. Therefore, the interference pattern consists of $\boxed{\text{equally spaced bright and dark fringes}}$.

(a) The reflection from the top surface of the bottom plate has $180°$ phase shifts (half-wave), so the condition for constructive interference for reflection is $\Delta L = 2t + \dfrac{\lambda}{2} = m\lambda$, $m = 1, 2, 3, \ldots$.

So $\boxed{2t = (m - \frac{1}{2})\lambda,\ m = 1, 2, 3, \ldots}$.

37.   From Exercise 24.36(b), $2t = (m - \frac{1}{2})\lambda$. $d = t = \dfrac{(6 - \frac{1}{2})(550 \times 10^{-9}\ \text{m})}{2} = \boxed{1.51 \times 10^{-6}\ \text{m}}$.

38.   (b).

39.   (a). As the number of lines per unit length increases, the spacing between adjacent slits, d, decreases, so the spacing between bright fringes increases. This is because $d \sin \theta = n\lambda$ or $\sin \theta \propto 1/d$.

40. $w \sin \theta = m\lambda$. If $w = \lambda$, then $\sin \theta = m$. The maximum value for $\sin \theta$ is 1.

So the answer for $m = 2$ is $\boxed{\text{no}}$, it cannot be seen.

For the $m = 1$ dark fringe, the answer is $\boxed{\text{yes (barely, seen at } \theta = 90°)}$.

41.   If the slit length is comparable to the width, $\boxed{\text{a second diffraction pattern in addition to the first}}$ will also be observed. $\boxed{\text{The second diffraction pattern is perpendicular to the first}}$.

42.   The width of the central maximum is $2\Delta y = 2y_1 = \dfrac{2L\lambda}{w}$. If the wavelength increases, the width of the central maximum $\boxed{\text{increases, because it is directly proportional to wavelength}}$.

43.   According to $\underline{d} \sin \theta = n\lambda$, the advantage is a $\boxed{\text{more spread-out diffraction pattern, because } d \text{ is small}}$.

44.   (a) The width of the central maximum is $2\Delta y = 2y_1 = \dfrac{2L\lambda}{w} = \dfrac{2(1.0\ \text{m})(480 \times 10^{-9}\ \text{m})}{0.20 \times 10^{-3}\ \text{m}} = \boxed{4.8\ \text{mm}}$.

(b) The width of the side maxima is half the width of the central maximum.

$\Delta y_3 = \Delta y_4 = \dfrac{L\lambda}{w} = \boxed{2.4\ \text{mm}}$.

45. (a) The width of the central maximum is

$$2\Delta y = 2y_1 = \frac{2L\lambda}{w} = \frac{2(1.0\text{ m})(680 \times 10^{-9}\text{ m})}{0.025 \times 10^{-3}\text{ m}} = \boxed{5.4\text{ cm}}.$$

(b) The width of the side maxima is half the width of the central maximum. $\Delta y = \boxed{2.7\text{ cm}}$.

46. $d \sin \theta = n\lambda$, ☞ $\sin \theta = \dfrac{n\lambda}{d} = \dfrac{2(550 \times 10^{-9}\text{ m})}{1.25 \times 10^{-6}\text{ m}} = 0.880.$

So $\theta = \sin^{-1} 0.880 = \boxed{61.6°}$.

47. (a) $d \sin \theta = m\lambda$, ☞ $\lambda = \dfrac{d \sin \theta}{m} = (0.025\text{ m}) \sin 10° = 4.3 \times 10^{-3}\text{ m} = \boxed{4.3\text{ mm}}$.

(b) $f = \dfrac{c}{\lambda} = \dfrac{3.00 \times 10^8\text{ m/s}}{4.34 \times 10^{-3}\text{ m}} = 6.9 \times 10^{10}\text{ Hz}$, i.e., $\boxed{\text{microwave}}$.

48. (a) The width of the central maximum is $2\Delta y = 2y_1 = \dfrac{2L\lambda}{w} \propto 1/w$. So the width of the central maximum will $\boxed{\text{decrease}}$ if the width of the slit in increased.

(b) $w \sin \theta = m\lambda$, ☞ $\theta = \sin^{-1} \dfrac{m\lambda}{w} = \sin^{-1} \dfrac{(2)(680 \times 10^{-9}\text{ m})}{0.50 \times 10^{-3}\text{ m}} = \boxed{0.16° = 2.7 \times 10^{-3}\text{ rad}}$.

$\Delta y = L \tan \theta = (1.80\text{ m}) \tan 0.156° = \boxed{4.9\text{ mm}}$.

49. The width of the central maximum is

$$2\Delta y = 2y_1 = \frac{2L\lambda}{w} = \frac{2(1.80\text{ m})(680 \times 10^{-9}\text{ m})}{0.50 \times 10^{-3}\text{ m}} = \boxed{4.9\text{ mm}}.$$

50. $\lambda = \dfrac{c}{f} = \dfrac{3.00 \times 10^8\text{ m/s}}{5.0 \times 10^{17}\text{ Hz}} = 6.0 \times 10^{-10}\text{ m}.$

$2d \sin \theta = n\lambda$, ☞ $d = \dfrac{n\lambda}{2 \sin \theta} = \dfrac{(1)(6.0 \times 10^{-10}\text{ m})}{2 \sin 25°} = \boxed{7.1 \times 10^{-10}\text{ m}}$.

51. $d = \dfrac{1}{7500\text{ lines/cm}} = 1.33 \times 10^{-4}\text{ cm} = 1.33 \times 10^{-6}\text{ m}.$ $d \sin \theta = n\lambda$, ☞ $\theta = \sin^{-1} \dfrac{n\lambda}{d}.$

For blue, $\theta_{1b} = \sin^{-1} \dfrac{420 \times 10^{-9}\text{ m}}{1.33 \times 10^{-6}\text{ m}} = \boxed{18.4°}$. $\theta_{2b} = \sin^{-1} \dfrac{(2)(420 \times 10^{-9}\text{ m})}{1.33 \times 10^{-6}\text{ m}} = \boxed{39.2°}$.

For red, $\theta_{1r} = \sin^{-1} \dfrac{680 \times 10^{-9}\text{ m}}{1.33 \times 10^{-6}\text{ m}} = \boxed{30.7°}$. $\theta_{2r} = \sin^{-1} \dfrac{(2)(680 \times 10^{-9}\text{ m})}{1.33 \times 10^{-6}\text{ m}} = \sin^{-1} 1.02.$

Since $\sin 90° = 1$, it is $\boxed{\text{not possible}}$ to locate it.

52. (a) From $d \sin \theta = n\lambda$, we can see that the order number is $n = \dfrac{d \sin \theta}{\lambda}$. The maximum value for $\sin \theta$ is 1,

so the maximum number of bright fringes that can be observed (n_{max}) depends on $\boxed{d \text{ and } \lambda}$.

(b) $d = \dfrac{1}{10\,000 \text{ lines/cm}} = 1.0 \times 10^{-4}$ cm $= 1.0 \times 10^{-6}$ m.

$d \sin \theta = n\lambda$, ☞ $n_{max} = \dfrac{d \sin 90°}{\lambda} = \dfrac{d}{\lambda} = \dfrac{1.0 \times 10^{-6} \text{ m}}{560 \times 10^{-9} \text{ m}} = 1.8$.

So there are $\boxed{3}$ orders of maxima corresponding to $\boxed{n = 0,\ 1 \text{ (two of them)}}$.

53. (a) $d \sin \theta = n\lambda$, ☞ $d = \dfrac{n\lambda}{\sin \theta} = \dfrac{(2)(700 \times 10^{-9} \text{ m})}{\sin 20°} = 4.09 \times 10^{-6}$ m $= 4.09 \times 10^{-4}$ cm.

So the number of lines per cm is $\dfrac{1}{4.09 \times 10^{-4} \text{ cm}} = \boxed{2.44 \times 10^3 \text{ lines/cm}}$.

(b) In order to see the whole spectrum, we must see red because it has the longest wavelength.

$n_{max} = \dfrac{d \sin 90°}{\lambda} = \dfrac{d}{\lambda} = \dfrac{4.09 \times 10^{-6} \text{ m}}{700 \times 10^{-9} \text{ m}} = 5.8$.

There are $\boxed{11}$ orders of maxima for $n = 0, 1, 2, 3, 4,$ or 5 (one for $n = 0$ and two for $n = 1, 2, 3, 4,$ and 5).

54. $d = \dfrac{1}{4000 \text{ lines/cm}} = 2.5 \times 10^{-4}$ cm $= 2.5 \times 10^{-6}$ m. $d \sin \theta = n\lambda$, ☞ $\theta = \sin^{-1} \dfrac{n\lambda}{d}$.

If they do overlap, it will be the first-order red to the second-order blue.

For blue, $\theta_{2b} = \sin^{-1} \dfrac{(2)(400 \times 10^{-9} \text{ m})}{2.5 \times 10^{-6} \text{ m}} = 18.7°$.

For red, $\theta_{1r} = \sin^{-1} \dfrac{700 \times 10^{-9} \text{ m}}{2.5 \times 10^{-6} \text{ m}} = 16.3°$.

So $\theta_{2b} > \theta_{1r}$; $\boxed{\text{no}}$, they do not overlap.

55. (a) $\boxed{\text{Blue}}$ will be closer to the central maximum, because it has a shorter wavelength. From $d \sin \theta = n\lambda$,

we can see that the shorter the wavelength, the smaller the $\sin \theta$ or θ.

(b) $d = \dfrac{1}{8000 \text{ lines/cm}} = 1.25 \times 10^{-4}$ cm $= 1.25 \times 10^{-6}$ m. $d \sin \theta = n\lambda$, ☞ $\theta = \sin^{-1} \dfrac{n\lambda}{d}$.

For blue, $\theta_{1b} = \sin^{-1} \dfrac{400 \times 10^{-9} \text{ m}}{1.25 \times 10^{-6} \text{ m}} = 18.7°$.

For red, $\theta_{1r} = \sin^{-1} \dfrac{700 \times 10^{-9} \text{ m}}{1.25 \times 10^{-6} \text{ m}} = 34.1°$.

So $\Delta \theta = \theta_{1r} - \theta_{1b} = \boxed{15.4°}$.

56. $d = \dfrac{1}{8000 \text{ cm}} = 1.25 \times 10^{-4} \text{ cm} = 1.25 \times 10^{-6} \text{ m}.$

$d \sin \theta = n\lambda, \quad \text{☞} \quad n_{max} = \dfrac{d \sin 90°}{\lambda} = \dfrac{d}{\lambda} = \dfrac{1.25 \times 10^{-6} \text{ m}}{632.8 \times 10^{-9} \text{ m}} = 1.98.$

So $n_{max} = 1.$ $\theta = \sin^{-1} \dfrac{n\lambda}{d} = \sin^{-1} \dfrac{(1)(632.8 \times 10^{-9} \text{ m})}{1.25 \times 10^{-6} \text{ m}} = 30.4°.$

Therefore $\boxed{\text{two, at } \pm 30.4°}$ for $n = 1.$

57. $d \sin \theta = n\lambda, \quad \text{☞} \quad \theta = \sin^{-1} \dfrac{n\lambda}{d}.$

For violet, $\qquad \qquad \qquad \theta_{3v} = \sin^{-1} \dfrac{(3)(400 \text{ nm})}{d} = \sin^{-1} \dfrac{1200 \text{ nm}}{d}.$

For yellow-orange, $\qquad \qquad \theta_{2y} = \sin^{-1} \dfrac{(2)(600 \text{ nm})}{d} = \sin^{-1} \dfrac{1200 \text{ nm}}{d}.$

So $\quad \theta_{3v} = \theta_{2y},$ i.e., they overlap.

58. (a) $\boxed{\text{Yes}}$, this is possible because of diffraction. The boy on the right could be at a diffraction minimum so he cannot hear the whistle.

(b) $\lambda = \dfrac{v}{f} = \dfrac{335 \text{ m/s}}{1000 \text{ Hz}} = 0.335 \text{ m}.$ $w \sin \theta = m\lambda, \quad \text{☞} \quad \theta = \sin^{-1} \dfrac{m\lambda}{w}.$

$\theta_1 = \sin^{-1} \dfrac{0.335 \text{ m}}{1.0 \text{ m}} = 19.6°.$ So there is a minimum at 19.6°, and therefore the boys cannot hear.

59. (d).

60. (a).

61. Looking through the lens of one pair while rotating the lens of the other pair in front of the first pair. If the intensity changes as the lenses are rotated, both pairs are polarized. If the intensity does not change, either both are not polarized or one of the two pairs is not polarized.

62. We see the rainbow by the scattering of light from the water droplets. The light is partially polarized in the horizontal direction, so the axis of the analyzer should be in the horizontal direction. We can never block out the polarized light completely because it is only partially polarized.

63. When the axes are perpendicular, it darkens, and when the axes are parallel it lightens.

(a) $\boxed{\text{Twice}}$. (b) $\boxed{\text{Four times}}$.

(c) $\boxed{\text{None}}$. (d) $\boxed{\text{Six times}}$.

---

64. When the material is in air, the polarizing or Brewster angle θ_p satisfies $\boxed{n = \tan \theta_p}$. We can calculate n by measuring θ_p.

65. $\boxed{\text{No}}$, it cannot be polarized because a $\boxed{\text{sound wave is a longitudinal wave}}$. Only transverse waves can be polarized.

66. In selective absorption, $\boxed{\text{one of the two electric field components is absorbed}}$.

67. $\boxed{\text{The numbers appear and disappear as the sunglasses are rotated}}$ because the light from the numbers on a calculator is polarized.

68. Since $n_1 = 1$ (air), $\tan \theta_p = \dfrac{n_2}{n_1} = n_2$. So $\theta_p = \tan^{-1} n_2 = \tan^{-1} 1.4$ to $\tan^{-1} 1.7 = \boxed{54° \text{ to } 60°}$.

69. Since $n_1 = 1$ (air), $\tan \theta_p = \dfrac{n_2}{n_1} = n_2$. $n_2 = \tan \theta_p = \tan 58° = \boxed{1.6}$.

70. $I = I_o \cos^2 \theta$.

For $\theta = 30°$, $\quad I = I_o \cos^2 30° = 0.75 I_o$.

For $\theta = 45°$, $\quad I = I_o \cos^2 45° = 0.50 I_o$.

So $\boxed{30°}$ will allow more light to be transmitted.

71. (a) Since only one of the two electric field components in unpolarized light of intensity I_o can pass a polarizer, the light intensity transmitted through the polarizer is $\boxed{0.50 I_o}$.

(b) $\cos^2 30° = 0.75$. So the intensity pass through the analyzer is $0.75 \, (050) I_o = \boxed{0.375 I_o}$.

72. In air, $\tan \theta_p = n$, ☞ $\theta_p = \tan^{-1} n$. So $\theta_1 = \theta_p = \tan^{-1} n = \tan^{-1} 1.62 = 58.3°$.

$n_1 \sin \theta_1 = n_2 \sin \theta_2$, ☞ $\sin \theta_2 = \dfrac{n_1 \sin \theta_1}{n_2} = \dfrac{(1) \sin 58.3°}{1.62} = 0.525$. So $\theta_2 = \boxed{31.7°}$.

73. In air, $\sin \theta_C = 1/n$. $n = \dfrac{1}{\sin \theta_C} = \dfrac{1}{\sin 45°} = 1.41$.

Also in air, $\tan \theta_p = n$, ☞ $\theta_p = \tan^{-1} n = \tan^{-1} 1.41 = \boxed{55°}$.

74.   (a) $\boxed{\text{Yes}}$. That the polarization is maximum in the reflected light does not means that the light intensity is maximum in the reflected light. There will still be transmitted light, which is also polarized, but the polarization direction is perpendicular to that of the reflected light.

(b) Since $n_1 = 1$ (air), $\tan \theta_p = \dfrac{n_2}{n_1} = n_2$.   So $\theta_p = \tan^{-1} n_2$.

Therefore $\theta_1 = \theta_p = \tan^{-1} n_2 = \tan^{-1} 1.22 = 50.7°$.

$n_1 \sin \theta_1 = n_2 \sin \theta_2$,   ☞ $\sin \theta_2 = \dfrac{n_1 \sin \theta_1}{n_2} = \dfrac{(1) \sin 50.7°}{1.22} = 0.634$.   So $\theta_2 = \boxed{39.3°}$.

75.   Since $n_1 = 1$ (air), $\tan \theta_p = \dfrac{n_2}{n_1} = n_2$.   So $\theta_p = \tan^{-1} n_2 = \tan^{-1} 1.55 = \boxed{57.2°}$.

Since the glass is vertical, this is the Sun's altitude angle.

76.   In water, $\theta_p = \tan^{-1} \dfrac{n_2}{n_1} = \tan^{-1} \dfrac{1.60}{1.33} = \boxed{50.3°}$.

77.   In water, $\theta_p = \tan^{-1} \dfrac{n_2}{n_1}$.

The angle of incidence at the water–glass interface must be $\theta_p = \tan^{-1} \dfrac{1.52}{1.33} = 48.8°$.

For the air–water interface, $n_1 \sin \theta_1 = n_2 \sin \theta_2$,   ☞ $\sin \theta_1 = \dfrac{n_2 \sin \theta_2}{n_1} = (1.33) \sin 48.8° > 1$.

So the answer is $\boxed{\text{no}}$.

78.   (a) since the scattering is inversely proportional to wavelength.

79.   Blue scatters more efficiently than red. In the morning and evening, the blue component of the light from the Sun is scattered more in the denser atmosphere near the Earth, so we see red when we look in the direction of the rising or setting Sun. During the day, we mainly see the blue component from overhead scattering.

80.   (a) This is caused by the $\boxed{\text{variable air molecule density}}$.

(b) There is no air on the surface of the Moon, and so an astronaut would see a $\boxed{\text{black}}$ sky.

81.   Since $n_1 = 1$ (air), $\tan \theta_p = \dfrac{n_2}{n_1} = n_2$.   So $n_2 = \tan \theta_p = \tan (1.05 \text{ rad}) = \boxed{1.74}$.

82. $\Delta y = \dfrac{\lambda L}{w}$,   ☞ $\dfrac{\Delta y}{\Delta y_0} = \dfrac{\lambda}{\lambda_0} \dfrac{L}{L_0} \dfrac{w_0}{w} = \dfrac{450 \text{ nm}}{600 \text{ nm}} \dfrac{2}{3} \dfrac{1}{2} = 0.25$.   So $\boxed{\Delta y = 0.25 \Delta y_0}$.

83.   Since $n_1 = 1$ (air), $\tan \theta_p = \dfrac{n_2}{n_1} = n_2$.   So $\theta_p = \tan^{-1} n_2 = \tan^{-1} 1.5 = \boxed{56°}$.

84. $d = \dfrac{1}{1000 \text{ lines/cm}} = 1.00 \times 10^{-3}$ cm $= 1.00 \times 10^{-5}$ m.

    $d \sin \theta = n\lambda$,   ☞ $\lambda = \dfrac{d \sin \theta}{n} = (1.00 \times 10^{-5} \text{ m}) \sin 2.6° = 4.54 \times 10^{-7}$ m $= \boxed{454 \text{ nm}}$.

85.   (a) From the result of Exercise 24.36(b), for bright fringes, $2t = (m - \frac{1}{2})\lambda, \ m = 1, 2, 3, \ldots$.

    So $2 \Delta t = (m + 1 - \frac{1}{2})\lambda - (m - \frac{1}{2})\lambda = \lambda$,   ☞ $\Delta t = \dfrac{\lambda}{2}$.

    (b) Replacing λ by $\lambda_n = \dfrac{\lambda}{n}$. So the result is $\Delta t = \boxed{\dfrac{\lambda}{2n}}$.

86. $d \sin \theta = n\lambda$,   ☞ $d = \dfrac{n\lambda}{\sin \theta} = \dfrac{(2)(700 \times 10^{-9} \text{ m})}{\sin 10°} = 8.06 \times 10^{-6}$ m $= 8.06 \times 10^{-4}$ cm.

    So the number of lines per cm is $\dfrac{1}{8.06 \times 10^{-4} \text{ cm}} = \boxed{1.2 \times 10^3 \text{ lines/cm}}$.

87.   This angle is the angle for the first bright fringe. From $d \sin \theta = n\lambda$

    $\sin \theta = \dfrac{n\lambda}{d} = \dfrac{(1)(480 \times 10^{-9} \text{ m})}{0.075 \times 10^{-3} \text{ m}} = 6.4 \times 10^{-3}$. So $\theta = \sin (6.4 \times 10^{-3}) = \boxed{0.37°}$

88. $y_3 - y_1 = 2\Delta y = \dfrac{2\lambda L}{d} = \dfrac{2(500 \times 10^{-9} \text{ m})(1.0 \text{ m})}{40 \times 10^{-6} \text{ m}} = \boxed{2.5 \text{ cm}}$.

89. $t_{min} = \dfrac{\lambda}{4n_1}$,   ☞ $\lambda = 4n_1 t_{min} = 4(1.4)(1.0 \times 10^{-7} \text{ m}) = 5.60 \times 10^{-7}$ m $= \boxed{560 \text{ nm}}$.

90. $d = \dfrac{1}{9000 \text{ lines/cm}} = 1.11 \times 10^{-4}$ cm $= 1.11 \times 10^{-6}$ m. $d \sin \theta = n\lambda$, ☞ $n_{max} = \dfrac{d \sin 90°}{\lambda} = \dfrac{d}{\lambda}$.

    For red, $n_{max} = \dfrac{1.11 \times 10^{-6} \text{ m}}{700 \times 10^{-9} \text{ m}} = 1.6$.   So $n_{max} = \boxed{1 \text{ for red}}$.

    For violet, $n_{max} = \dfrac{1.11 \times 10^{-6} \text{ m}}{400 \times 10^{-9} \text{ m}} = 2.8$.   So $n_{max} = \boxed{2 \text{ for violet}}$.

91. $d \sin \theta = n\lambda$,   ☞ $\lambda = \dfrac{d \sin \theta}{n} = \dfrac{(0.350 \times 10^{-3} \text{ m}) \sin 0.160°}{2} = 4.89 \times 10^{-7}$ m $= \boxed{489 \text{ nm}}$.

92. $t_{min} = \dfrac{\lambda}{4n_1} = \dfrac{450 \text{ nm}}{4(1.35)} = \boxed{83.3 \text{ nm}}$.

CHAPTER 25

1.   (b).

2.   (d).

3.   The eye focuses by changing the shape of its lens to change the focal length according to the lens-maker's equation. The focal length is adjusted to form a sharp image. The image distance is fairly constant and so is the distance from the lens to the retina. From the thin lens equation, the eye must have long focal length for looking at distant objects and so the radius is large; the eye must have short focal length for looking at close objects and so the radius is small.

4.   It is $\boxed{\text{inverted}}$. The object distance is greater than twice the focal length ($d_o > 2f$), so the image is real, inverted, and reduced.

5.   The pre-flash occurs before the aperture is open and the film exposed. The bright light causes the iris to reduce down (giving a small pupil) so that when the second flash comes momentarily, you don't have a wide opening through which you get the red-eye reflection from the retina.

6.   Iris, crystalline lens, and retina correspond to the $\boxed{\text{aperture, lens, and film, respectively}}$, of the camera.

7.   (a) The eye is $\boxed{\text{nearsighted}}$ because the far point is not at infinity.

        (b) The eye is $\boxed{\text{farsighted}}$ because the near point is not 25 cm.

        (c) $\boxed{\text{For (a), diverging; for (b), converging}}$.

8. $\boxed{\text{Yes}}$. The image is $\boxed{\text{smaller for nearsightedness and larger for farsigntedness}}$. See Fig. 25.3 and 25.4a.

9.   (a) $P = \dfrac{1}{f} = \dfrac{1}{0.20 \text{ m}} = \boxed{+5.0 \text{ D}}$.

        (b) $P = \dfrac{1}{-0.50 \text{ m}} = \boxed{-2.0 \text{ D}}$.

10. (a) $\boxed{\text{Diverging}}$ contact lens should be prescribed because the person is nearsighted.

(b) The lens is to form an image of an object at infinity at the far point (90 cm).

$d_o = \infty$, $d_i = -90$ cm (image is on the object side).

$$P = \frac{1}{f} = \frac{1}{d_o} + \frac{1}{d_i} = \frac{1}{\infty} + \frac{1}{-0.90 \text{ m}} = \frac{1}{-0.90 \text{ m}} = \boxed{-1.1 \text{ D}}.$$

11. (a) $\boxed{\text{Converging}}$ contact lens should be prescribed because the person is farsighted.

(b) The lens is to form an image of an object at 25 cm at the near point (50 cm).

$d_o = 25$ cm $= 0.25$ m, $\quad d_i = -50$ cm $= -0.50$ m (image on the object side).

$$P = \frac{1}{f} = \frac{1}{d_o} + \frac{1}{d_i} = \frac{1}{0.25 \text{ m}} + \frac{1}{-0.50 \text{ m}} = \frac{1}{0.50 \text{ m}} = \boxed{+2.0 \text{ D}}.$$

12. (a) She is $\boxed{\text{nearsighted}}$ because she cannot clearly see distant objects.

(b) The $\boxed{\text{diverging}}$ lens is to form an image of an object at infinity at the far point (12.5 m).

$d_o = \infty$, $\quad d_i = -12.5$ m (virtual image on object side).

$$P = \frac{1}{f} = \frac{1}{d_o} + \frac{1}{d_i} = \frac{1}{\infty} + \frac{1}{-12.5 \text{ m}} = \boxed{-0.080 \text{ D}}.$$

13. The $\boxed{\text{diverging}}$ lens is to form an image of an object at infinity at the far point (200 cm).

$d_o = \infty$, $\quad d_i = -200$ cm $= -2.00$ m (image on object side).

$$P = \frac{1}{f} = \frac{1}{d_o} + \frac{1}{d_i} = \frac{1}{\infty} + \frac{1}{-2.00 \text{ m}} = \boxed{-0.50 \text{ D}}.$$

14. (a) $\boxed{\text{converging}}$ lens will allow her to read the text at the normal near point.

(b) The lens is to form an image of an object at 25 cm at the near point (0.80 m).

$d_o = 25$ cm, $\quad d_i = -0.80$ m $= -80$ cm (image on object side).

$$\frac{1}{f} = \frac{1}{d_o} + \frac{1}{d_i} = \frac{1}{25 \text{ cm}} + \frac{1}{-80 \text{ cm}} = 0.0275 \text{ cm}^{-1}, \quad \text{☞} \quad f = \boxed{36 \text{ cm}}.$$

15. (a) The patient has to $\boxed{\text{take them out}}$ to see distant objects. This is because the positive contact lens will alter the person's far point.

(b) The lens is to form an image of an object at 25 cm at the near point (100 cm).

$d_o = 25$ cm $= 0.25$ m, $\quad d_i = -100$ cm $= -1.0$ m (virtual image on object side).

$$P = \frac{1}{f} = \frac{1}{d_o} + \frac{1}{d_i} = \frac{1}{0.25 \text{ cm}} + \frac{1}{-1.0 \text{ m}} = \boxed{+3.0 \text{ D}}.$$

16. The lens is to form an image, of an object at 25 cm, at the near point (0.95 m).

$d_o = 25$ cm $= 0.25$ m, $d_i = -0.95$ m (image on object side).

$$P = \frac{1}{f} = \frac{1}{d_o} + \frac{1}{d_i} = \frac{1}{0.25 \text{ m}} + \frac{1}{-0.95 \text{ m}} = \boxed{+2.9 \text{ D}}.$$

17. (a) $\boxed{\text{Converging}}$ lens because he is farsighted.

(b) The contact lens is to form an image of an object at 25 cm at the near point (1.5 m).

$d_o = 25$ cm $= 0.25$ m, $d_i = -1.5$ m (image on object side).

$$P = \frac{1}{f} = \frac{1}{d_o} + \frac{1}{d_i} = \frac{1}{0.25 \text{ m}} + \frac{1}{-1.5 \text{ m}} = \boxed{+3.3 \text{ D}}.$$

18. (a) The lens is to form an image of an object at infinity at the far point (150 m).

$d_o = \infty$, $d_i = -150$ cm $= -1.50$ m (image on object side).

$$P = \frac{1}{f} = \frac{1}{d_o} + \frac{1}{d_i} = \frac{1}{\infty} + \frac{1}{-1.50 \text{ m}} = \boxed{-0.67 \text{ D}}.$$

(b) $\dfrac{1}{d_i} = \dfrac{1}{f} - \dfrac{1}{d_o} = -0.667 \text{ D} - \dfrac{1}{0.25 \text{ m}} = -4.67 \text{ D}$,

so $d_i = -0.21$ m < -0.25 m.

Therefore the answer is $\boxed{\text{yes}}$ and the near point is $\boxed{21 \text{ cm}}$.

(c) $\boxed{\text{30–40 years old}}$ from Table 25.1.

19. First find his new near point. $d_o = 33$ cm $= 0.33$ m, $P = \dfrac{1}{f} = +2.0$ D.

$$\frac{1}{d_i} = \frac{1}{f} - \frac{1}{d_o} = +2.0 \text{ D} - \frac{1}{0.33 \text{ m}} = -1.0 \text{ D}, \text{ so } d_i = -1.0 \text{ m}.$$

Therefore the near point is 1.0 m.

To bring this near point to 25 cm, the power of the new lenses must be

$$P' = \frac{1}{f'} = \frac{1}{0.25 \text{ m}} + \frac{1}{-1.0 \text{ m}} = \boxed{+3.0 \text{ D}}.$$

20. Top: $d_o = \infty$, $d_i = -500$ cm $= -5.0$ m (virtual image on object side).

$$P = \frac{1}{f} = \frac{1}{d_o} + \frac{1}{d_i} = \frac{1}{\infty} + \frac{1}{-5.0 \text{ m}} = \boxed{-0.20 \text{ D}}.$$

Bottom: $d_o = 25$ cm $= 0.25$ m, $d_i = -70$ cm $= -0.70$ m (virtual image on object side).

$$P = \frac{1}{0.25 \text{ m}} + \frac{1}{-0.70 \text{ m}} = \boxed{+2.6 \text{ D}}.$$

21.   First calculate the power of the lens from the far points. $d_o = \infty$, $d_i = -4.0$ m (image on object side).

$$P = \frac{1}{f} = \frac{1}{d_o} + \frac{1}{d_i} = \frac{1}{\infty} + \frac{1}{-4.0 \text{ m}} = -0.25 \text{ D}.$$

For the near points, $d_i = -0.20$ m.

$$\frac{1}{d_o} = P - \frac{1}{d_o} = -0.25 \text{ D} - \frac{1}{-0.20 \text{ m}} = 4.75 \text{ m}^{-1}, \quad \text{☞} \quad d_o = 0.21 \text{ m} = \boxed{21 \text{ cm}}.$$

22.   (a) $d_o = \infty$, $d_i = -(750 \text{ cm} - 2.0 \text{ cm}) = -748 \text{ cm} = -7.48$ m (image on object side).

$$P = \frac{1}{f} = \frac{1}{d_o} + \frac{1}{d_i} = \frac{1}{\infty} + \frac{1}{-7.48 \text{ m}} = \boxed{-0.13 \text{ D}}.$$

(b) If contact lens is used, $d_i = -7.5$ m. $P = \frac{1}{\infty} + \frac{1}{-7.5 \text{ m}} = \boxed{-0.13 \text{ D}}$

23.   Nearsightedness, $d_o = \infty$, $d_i = -(220 \text{ cm} - 3.0 \text{ cm}) = -2.17$ m (image on object side).

$$P = \frac{1}{f} = \frac{1}{d_o} + \frac{1}{d_i} = \frac{1}{\infty} + \frac{1}{-2.17 \text{ m}} = -0.46 \text{ D}.$$

Right farsightedness: $d_o = 25 \text{ cm} - 3.0 \text{ cm} = 0.22$ m, $d_i = -0.320$ m (image on object side).

$$P_r = \frac{1}{0.22 \text{ m}} + \frac{1}{-0.320 \text{ m}} = 1.42 \text{ D}.$$

Left farsightedness: $d_o = 25 \text{ cm} - 3.0 \text{ cm} = 0.22$ m, $d_i = -0.420$ m (image on object side).

$$P_r = \frac{1}{0.22 \text{ m}} + \frac{1}{-0.420 \text{ m}} = 2.16 \text{ D}.$$

So the prescription is $\boxed{\text{right: } +1.42 \text{ D}, -0.46 \text{ D; left: } +2.16 \text{ D}, -0.46 \text{ D}}$.

24.   (d).

25.   (d).

26.   A short focal length lens has a very small radius according to the lens-maker's equation in Chapter 24. The aberration (geometrical optics or small angle approximation is no longer valid if the object is large compared with the size of the lens) will be bigger and bigger as the focal length gets smaller and smaller. This limits the magnification to about 3× to 4×.

27.   The object should be $\boxed{\text{inside}}$ the focal length. When the object is inside the focal length, the image is virtual, upright, and magnified.

28. $\theta_1 \approx \dfrac{y}{L} = \dfrac{1.0 \text{ m}}{500 \text{ m}} = \boxed{2.0 \times 10^{-3} \text{ rad}}$.

$\theta_2 = \dfrac{1.0 \text{ m}}{1025 \text{ m}} = \boxed{9.8 \times 10^{-4} \text{ rad}}$.

29. (a) $d_i = \dfrac{d_o f}{d_o - f} = \dfrac{(10 \text{ cm})(18 \text{ cm})}{10 \text{ cm} - 18 \text{ cm}} = -22.5 \text{ cm}.$ $M = -\dfrac{d_i}{d_o} = -\dfrac{-22.5 \text{ cm}}{10 \text{ cm}} = \boxed{2.3\times}$.

(b) $m = \dfrac{\theta}{\theta_o} = \dfrac{y_o/10 \text{ cm}}{y_o/25 \text{ cm}} = \boxed{2.5\times}$.

30. $m = 1 + \dfrac{25 \text{ cm}}{f} = 1 + \dfrac{25 \text{ cm}}{12 \text{ cm}} = \boxed{3.1\times}$.

31. (a) $m = 1 + \dfrac{25 \text{ cm}}{f} = 1 + \dfrac{25 \text{ cm}}{15 \text{ cm}} = \boxed{2.7\times}$.

(b) $m = \dfrac{25 \text{ cm}}{f} = \dfrac{25 \text{ cm}}{15 \text{ cm}} = \boxed{1.7\times}$.

32. (a) $f = 8.0 \text{ cm}, \quad d_i = -25 \text{ cm (virtual)}. \quad d_o = \dfrac{d_i f}{d_i - f} = \dfrac{(-25 \text{ cm})(8.0 \text{ cm})}{-25 \text{ cm} - 8.0 \text{ cm}} = \boxed{6.1 \text{ cm}}$.

(b) $m = 1 + \dfrac{25 \text{ cm}}{f} = 1 + \dfrac{25 \text{ cm}}{8.0 \text{ cm}} = \boxed{4.1\times}$.

33. $f = \dfrac{1}{P} = \dfrac{1}{3.5 \text{ D}} = 0.286 \text{ m} = 28.6 \text{ cm}.$ So $m = 1 + \dfrac{25 \text{ cm}}{f} = 1 + \dfrac{25 \text{ cm}}{28.6 \text{ cm}} = \boxed{1.9\times}$.

34. (a) Yes, $\boxed{\text{there is a limit}}$. The image has to be at the near point of the eye (25 cm). That sets a limit on the object distance according to the thin-lens equation.

(b) $f = \dfrac{1}{P} = \dfrac{1}{10 \text{ D}} = 0.10 \text{ m} = 10 \text{ cm}, \quad d_i = -25 \text{ cm}.$

$d_o = \dfrac{d_i f}{d_i - f} = \dfrac{(-25 \text{ cm})(10 \text{ cm})}{-25 \text{ cm} - 10 \text{ cm}} = \boxed{7.1 \text{ cm}}$.

(b) $m = 1 + \dfrac{25 \text{ cm}}{f} = 1 + \dfrac{25 \text{ cm}}{10 \text{ cm}} = \boxed{3.5\times}$.

35. (a) $f = \dfrac{1}{P} = \dfrac{1}{3.0 \text{ D}} = 0.333 \text{ m} = 33.3 \text{ cm}.$

$m = 1 + \dfrac{25 \text{ cm}}{f} = 1 + \dfrac{25 \text{ cm}}{33.3 \text{ cm}} = \boxed{1.8\times}$.

(b) $m = 1 + \dfrac{10 \text{ cm}}{33.3 \text{ cm}} = \boxed{1.3\times}$.

36. $M_{\text{total}} = -\dfrac{(25 \text{ cm})L}{f_o f_e}$, ☞ $P_o = \dfrac{1}{f_o} = -\dfrac{M_{\text{total}} f_e}{(0.25 \text{ m})L} = -\dfrac{(-360)(0.0080 \text{ cm})}{(0.25 \text{ cm})(0.15 \text{ cm})} = \boxed{+77 \text{ D}}$.

37.   (a) $\boxed{\text{The one with the short focal length}}$ should be used as the objective.

        (b) $M_{\text{total}} = -\dfrac{(25 \text{ cm})L}{f_o f_e} = -\dfrac{(25 \text{ cm})(15 \text{ cm})}{(0.35 \text{ cm})(3.0 \text{ cm})} = -357\times \approx \boxed{-360\times}$.

38. $M_{\text{total}} = -\dfrac{(25 \text{ cm})L}{f_o f_e} = -\dfrac{(25 \text{ cm})(18 \text{ cm})}{(0.45 \text{ cm})(3.0 \text{ cm})} = -333\times \approx \boxed{-330\times}$.

39.   (a) $M_{\text{total}} = -\dfrac{(25 \text{ cm})L}{f_o f_e} = -\dfrac{(25 \text{ cm})(22 \text{ cm})}{(0.50 \text{ cm})(3.25 \text{ cm})} = -338\times \approx \boxed{-340\times}$.

        (b) $m = 1 + \dfrac{25 \text{ cm}}{f_e} = 1 + \dfrac{25 \text{ cm}}{3.25 \text{ cm}} = 8.7\times$.   So the percentage is $\dfrac{340\times}{8.7 \times} = 39 = \boxed{3900\%}$.

40. $M_{\text{total}} = -\dfrac{(25 \text{ cm})L}{f_o f_e}$, ☞ $f_e = -\dfrac{(25 \text{ cm})L}{f_o M_{\text{total}}} = -\dfrac{(25 \text{ cm})(20 \text{ cm})}{(0.75 \text{ cm})(-150)} = \boxed{4.4 \text{ cm}}$.

41. $d_i = \dfrac{d_o f}{d_o - f}$, $M_o = -\dfrac{d_i}{d_o} = \dfrac{f}{f - d_o} = \dfrac{1}{1 - d_o/f} = \dfrac{1}{1 - d_o D} = \dfrac{1}{1 - (5.0 \times 10^{-3} \text{ m})(250 \text{ D})} = -4.0\times$.

        $M_{\text{total}} = M_o m_e$, ☞ $m_e = \dfrac{M_{\text{total}}}{M_o} = \dfrac{-100\times}{-4.0\times} = \boxed{25\times}$.

42.   From thin lens equation: $d_o = \dfrac{d_i f}{d_i - f}$, ☞ $\dfrac{d_i}{d_o} = \dfrac{d_i - f}{f} = \dfrac{-(D - d) - f}{f}$.

        By small angle approximation: $m = \dfrac{\theta_i}{\theta_o} = \dfrac{y_i/D}{y_o/25 \text{ cm}} = \dfrac{y_i}{y_o} \dfrac{25 \text{ cm}}{D}$.

        By similar triangles: $\dfrac{y_i}{y_o} = \dfrac{-d_i}{d_o}$, the negative sign is introduced because d_i is negative (virtual image).

        So $m = \dfrac{(D - d) + f}{f} \dfrac{25 \text{ cm}}{D} = \dfrac{25}{f}\left(1 - \dfrac{d}{D}\right) + \dfrac{25}{D}$.

43. $d_i = \dfrac{d_o f}{d_o - f} = \dfrac{(5.0 \text{ cm})(10 \text{ cm})}{5.0 \text{ cm} - 10 \text{ cm}} = -10 \text{ cm}$.   So $D = 4.0 \text{ cm} + 10 \text{ cm} = 14 \text{ cm}$.

        From Exercise 25.42, $m = \dfrac{25}{f}\left(1 - \dfrac{d}{D}\right) + \dfrac{25}{D} = \dfrac{25 \text{ cm}}{10 \text{ cm}}\left(1 - \dfrac{4.0 \text{ cm}}{14 \text{ cm}}\right) + \dfrac{25 \text{ cm}}{14 \text{ cm}} = \boxed{3.6\times}$.

44.	(a) For greater magnification, the focal length of the objective should be as short as possible, and the magnification of the eye piece should be as great as possible. So the answers are:

$\boxed{\text{greatest: } 1.6 \text{ mm/10×; least: } 16 \text{ mm/5×}}$.

(b) $d_o = \dfrac{d_i f_o}{d_i - f_o}$, ☞ $M_o = -\dfrac{d_i}{d_o} = -\dfrac{d_i - f_o}{f_o}$. So $M_1 = -\dfrac{150 \text{ mm} - 16 \text{ mm}}{16 \text{ mm}} = -8.38\times$,

$M_2 = -\dfrac{150 \text{ mm} - 4.0 \text{ mm}}{4.0 \text{ mm}} = -36.5\times$, and $M_3 = -\dfrac{150 \text{ mm} - 1.6 \text{ mm}}{1.6 \text{ mm}} = -92.8\times$.

Therefore $M_{max} = (-92.8\times)(10\times) = \boxed{-930\times}$ and $M_{min} = (-8.38\times)(5.0\times) = \boxed{-42\times}$.

45.	(b).

46.	(d).

47.	$\boxed{\text{No}}$, the whole star can still be seen. The obstruction will reduce the intensity or brightness of the image.

48.	This is because $\boxed{\text{reflection is frequency independent}}$. All frequency reflects with the same angle of reflection. In refraction, however, the angle of refraction depends on the frequency due to dispersion.

49.	$\boxed{\text{The one with the longer focal length}}$ should be used as the objective for a telescope. The magnification of the telescope is proportional to the focal length of the objective ($m = -f_o/f_e$).

50.	$m = -\dfrac{f_o}{f_e} = -\dfrac{50 \text{ cm}}{2.5 \text{ cm}} = \boxed{-20\times}$.

51.	(a) $m = -\dfrac{f_o}{f_e} = -\dfrac{60 \text{ cm}}{15 \text{ cm}} = \boxed{-4.0\times}$.

(b) $L = f_o + f_e = 60 \text{ cm} + 15 \text{ cm} = \boxed{75 \text{ cm}}$.

52.	$L = f_o + f_e$, ☞ $f_o = L - f_e = 1.5 \text{ m} - 10 \times 10^{-3} \text{ m} \approx 1.49 \text{ m}$.

$m = -\dfrac{f_o}{f_e} = -\dfrac{1.49 \text{ m}}{10 \times 10^{-3} \text{ m}} = -149\times \approx \boxed{-150\times}$.

53.	(a) $m = -\dfrac{f_o}{f_e} = -\dfrac{87.5 \text{ cm}}{0.800 \text{ cm}} = -109\times \approx \boxed{-110\times}$.

(b) $L = f_o + f_e = 87.5 \text{ cm} + 0.800 \text{ cm} = \boxed{88.3 \text{ cm}}$.

54. (a) The erecting lens will [increase the physical length of the telescope]. Its purpose is to reverse the orientation of the image formed by the objective so the final image is erect.

(b) With the erecting lens, the image is erect so the magnification is positive.

$$m = \frac{f_o}{f_e} = \frac{40 \text{ cm}}{15 \text{ cm}} = \boxed{2.7\times}.$$

(c) $L = f_o + f_e + 4f_i = 40 \text{ cm} + 15 \text{ cm} + 4(20 \text{ cm}) = \boxed{135 \text{ cm}}$.

55. (a) For greater magnification, the focal length of the objective should be as long as possible, and the focal length of the eyepiece should be as short as possible because $m = -\frac{f_o}{f_e}$. So the answers are:

maximum magnification: [60.0 cm and 0.80 cm]; minimum magnification: [40.0 cm and 0.90 cm].

(b) $m_1 = -\frac{f_{o1}}{f_{e1}} = \frac{60.0 \text{ cm}}{0.80 \text{ cm}} = -\boxed{75\times}$, $\quad m_2 = -\frac{40.0 \text{ cm}}{0.90 \text{ cm}} = -\boxed{44\times}$.

56. $m = -\frac{f_o}{f_e} = -50\times$, ☞ $f_o = 50f_e$. Eq. (1)

$L = f_o + f_e = 1.02 \text{ m}.$ Eq. (2)

Solving, $f_o = \boxed{1.00 \text{ m}}$ and $f_e = \boxed{2.0 \text{ cm}}$.

57. $\theta_i \approx \tan \theta_i = \frac{y_i}{f_e}$ and $\theta_o = \frac{y_i}{f_o}$. So $m = \frac{\theta_i}{\theta_o} = \frac{y_i/f_e}{y_i/f_o} = \frac{f_o}{f_e}$.

58. (c).

59. (a) since $\theta_{min} = \frac{1.22\lambda}{D}$.

60. (d).

61. [Smaller] minimum angle of resolution corresponds to higher resolution because smaller details can be resolved at smaller angle of resolution.

62. The other advantage of using a large mirror is [higher resolution, due to large aperture]. The minimum angle of resolution is inversely proportional to the aperture, $\theta_{min} = \frac{1.22\lambda}{D}$. The smaller than angle, the greater the resolution because smaller details can be observed.

63. The central maximum of one pattern falls on the first minimum of the other. The angular position of the first minimum is determined by $w \sin \theta \approx w\theta = m\lambda = (1)\lambda$.

So $\theta_{min} = \dfrac{\lambda}{w} = \dfrac{680 \times 10^{-9} \text{ m}}{0.55 \times 10^{-3} \text{ m}} = \boxed{1.2 \times 10^{-3} \text{ rad}}$.

64. From Exercise 25.63, $\lambda = \theta_{min} w = (0.0055 \text{ rad})(0.10 \times 10^{-3} \text{ m}) = 5.5 \times 10^{-7} \text{ m} = \boxed{550 \text{ nm}}$.

65. $\theta_{min} = \dfrac{1.22\lambda}{D} = \dfrac{1.22(550 \times 10^{-9} \text{ m})}{8.2 \text{ m}} = \boxed{8.18 \times 10^{-8} \text{ rad}}$.

66. $\theta_{min} = \dfrac{1.22\lambda}{D} = \dfrac{1.22(550 \times 10^{-9} \text{ m})}{(200 \text{ in})(0.0254 \text{ m/in})} = \boxed{1.32 \times 10^{-7} \text{ rad}}$.

$\dfrac{(\theta_{min})_{\text{Hale}}}{(\theta_{min})_{\text{European Southern Observatory}}} = \dfrac{1.32 \times 10^{-7} \text{ rad}}{8.18 \times 10^{-8} \text{ rad}} = 1.6$.

So the $\boxed{\theta_{min} \text{ by Hale is 1.6 times greater}}$.

67. (a) The eye obtain the maximum resolution (smallest minimum angle of resolution) for objects of $\boxed{\text{blue}}$ color. This is because the minimum angle of resolution is proportional to wavelength, $\theta_{min} = \dfrac{1.22\lambda}{D}$, and blue has the shorter wavelength.

(b) $\theta_{min} = \dfrac{1.22\lambda}{D} = \dfrac{1.22(550 \times 10^{-9} \text{ m})}{7.0 \times 10^{-3} \text{ m}} = \boxed{9.6 \times 10^{-5} \text{ rad}}$.

68. Use the result from Exercise 25.67(b).

$\theta = \dfrac{d}{L} = \dfrac{3.0 \times 10^{6} \text{ km}}{3.1 \times 10^{8} \text{ km}} = 9.7 \times 10^{-3} \text{ rad} > 9.6 \times 10^{-5} \text{ rad}$.

So in theory, the answer is $\boxed{\text{yes}}$, it is possible.

69. Use the result from Exercise 25.67(b).

$\theta_{min} = 9.6 \times 10^{-5} \text{ rad} = \dfrac{d}{L} = \dfrac{1.7 \text{ m}}{L}$, ☞ $L = 1.8 \times 10^{4} \text{ m} = \boxed{18 \text{ km}}$

70. (a) Violet light has the highest resolution. The angular separation of the stars must be larger than the minimum angle of resolution.

$\theta_{min} = \dfrac{1.22\lambda}{D} = \dfrac{1.22(400 \times 10^{-9} \text{ m})}{0.300 \text{ m}} = \boxed{1.63 \times 10^{-6} \text{ rad}}$.

(b) The lateral distance is $d = \theta L = (1.63 \times 10^{-6} \text{ rad})(6.00 \times 10^{23} \text{ m}) = \boxed{9.76 \times 10^{17} \text{ m}}$.

71.   (a) For best magnification, the high f_o/f_e ratio is desired. For best resolution, the large objective diameter should be used. So the answers are: $\boxed{(1)\ B,\ (2)\ A}$.

(b) $m_A = -\dfrac{f_{oA}}{f_{eA}} = -\dfrac{90.0\text{ cm}}{0.84\text{ cm}} = -107\times,\qquad m_B = -\dfrac{85.0\text{ cm}}{0.77\text{ cm}} = \boxed{-110\times}$.

$(\theta_{min})_A = \dfrac{1.22\lambda}{D_A} = \dfrac{1.22(550\times 10^{-9}\text{ m})}{0.75\text{ m}} = \boxed{8.9\times 10^{-7}\text{ rad}}$.

$(\theta_{min})_B = \dfrac{1.22(550\times 10^{-9}\text{ m})}{0.60\text{ m}} = 1.1\times 10^{-6}\text{ rad}$.

72.   (a) $\theta_{min} = \dfrac{1.22\lambda}{D} = \dfrac{1.22(570\times 10^{-9}\text{ m})}{0.0250\text{ m}} = \boxed{2.78\times 10^{-5}\text{ rad}}$.

(b) $s = f\,\theta_{min} = (30.0\text{ mm})(2.78\times 10^{-5}\text{ rad}) = \boxed{8.34\times 10^{-4}\text{ mm}}$.

73.   (a) $\theta_{min} = \dfrac{1.22\lambda}{D} = \dfrac{1.22(546.1\times 10^{-9}\text{ m})}{0.0120\text{ m}} = \boxed{5.55\times 10^{-5}\text{ rad}}$.

(b) $\boxed{\text{Blue}}$, shortest λ, smallest θ_{min}, highest resolution.

(c) $\theta'_{min} = \dfrac{1.22\,\lambda'}{D} = \dfrac{1.22\lambda}{nD}$.   So the percentage is $\dfrac{\Delta\theta}{\theta_{min}} = \dfrac{1 - 1/n}{1} = 1 - \dfrac{1}{1.50} = \boxed{33.3\%}$.

74.   (d).

75.   (d).

76.   With red light, red and white appear red; blue appears black.
With green light, only white appears green; both red and blue appear black.
With blue light, red appears black; white and blue appear blue.

77.   Since white is obtained by adding colors, it cannot be obtained by the subtractive method. That method subtracts colors, and the one we see is the one that is not absorbed.
Black objects do not absorb all wavelengths of light. We see the objects because we perceive the extremely faint light as black. (Think of twilight vision.)

78.   The liquid is dark or colored because it absorbs all light except that color. The amount of light absorbed by an object always depends on how much material is absorbing the light. Foam has very low material density and it can only absorb very little light or almost all light is reflected; therefore, the foam is generally white.

79.   White light enters the blue filter, which allows the green, blue, and violet to pass through; when it passes through the yellow filter, only the $\boxed{\text{green}}$ emerges.

80. The lens is to form an image of an object at infinity at the far point (130 cm).

$d_o = \infty$, $d_i = -130$ cm $= -1.3$ m (image on object side).

$$P = \frac{1}{f} = \frac{1}{d_o} + \frac{1}{d_i} = \frac{1}{\infty} + \frac{1}{-1.3 \text{ m}} = \boxed{-0.77 \text{ D}}.$$

81. $$\theta_{min} = \frac{1.22\lambda}{D} = \frac{1.22(4.0 \text{ m})}{300 \text{ m}} = \boxed{1.6 \times 10^{-2} \text{ rad}}.$$

82. $$L = f_o + f_e + 4f_i, \quad \text{☞} \quad f_i = \frac{L - f_o - f_e}{4} = \frac{80 \text{ cm} - 45 \text{ cm} - 15 \text{ cm}}{4} = \boxed{5.0 \text{ cm}}.$$

83. The far point is at the image location with glasses. $d_o = \infty$, $P = \frac{1}{f} = -0.15$ D.

$$\frac{1}{d_o} + \frac{1}{d_i} = \frac{1}{f} = P, \quad \text{so} \quad d_i = f = \frac{1}{P} = \frac{1}{-0.15 \text{ D}} = -6.7 \text{ m}.$$

Therefore the far point is $\boxed{6.7 \text{ m}}$.

84. $$m = \frac{25 \text{ cm}}{f} = \frac{25 \text{ cm}}{15 \text{ cm}} = \boxed{1.7\times}.$$

85. According to the Raleigh criteria, the minimum angle of resolution is

$$\theta_{min} = \frac{\lambda}{w} = \frac{550 \times 10^{-9} \text{ m}}{0.050 \times 10^{-3} \text{ m}} = \boxed{1.1 \times 10^{-2} \text{ rad}}.$$

86. $$M_{total} = -\frac{(25 \text{ cm})L}{f_o f_e} = -\frac{L}{f_o}\frac{25 \text{ cm}}{f_e} = -\frac{L}{f_o} m_e = -\frac{(15.0 \text{ cm})}{0.400 \text{ cm}}(10.0) = \boxed{-375\times}.$$

87. $$m = \frac{25 \text{ cm}}{f} = 1 + \frac{25 \text{ cm}}{12 \text{ cm}} = \boxed{2.1\times}.$$

88. $$m = -\frac{f_o}{f_e} = -\frac{50 \text{ cm}}{1.5 \text{ cm}} = -33.3\times. \quad \theta_o = \frac{0.10 \text{ m}}{50 \text{ m}} = 2.0 \times 10^{-3} \text{ rad}.$$

So $\theta = |m|\theta_o = (33.3)(2.0 \times 10^{-3} \text{ rad}) = 0.0666 \text{ rad} = \boxed{3.8°}.$

89. The near point is at the image location with glasses.

$$d_o = 25 \text{ cm} = 0.25 \text{ m}, \quad f = \frac{1}{P} = \frac{1}{2.8 \text{ D}} = 0.357 \text{ m}.$$

$$d_i = \frac{d_o f}{d_o - f} = \frac{(0.25 \text{ m})(0.357 \text{ m})}{0.25 \text{ m} - 0.357 \text{ m}} = -0.834 \text{ m}. \quad \text{So the near point is } \boxed{83 \text{ cm}}.$$

90. $m = 1 + \dfrac{25\ \text{cm}}{f}$, ☞ $f = \dfrac{25\ \text{cm}}{m-1} = \dfrac{25\ \text{cm}}{3-1} = \boxed{13\ \text{cm}}$.

91. $M_{\text{total}} = -\dfrac{(25\ \text{cm})L}{f_o f_e} = -\dfrac{(25\ \text{cm})(15\ \text{cm})}{(0.75\ \text{cm})(1.0\ \text{cm})} = \boxed{-500\times}$.

92. (a) Since the amount of light depends on the area of the aperture $A = 4\pi D^2$, the amount of light is inversely proportional to the square of the f-stop. $\dfrac{A_2}{A_1} = \dfrac{(\text{f–stop})_1}{(\text{f–stop})_2}$.

So (1) $\dfrac{A_{3.2}}{A_8} = \dfrac{8^2}{(3.2)^2} = \boxed{6.3}$ (2) $\dfrac{A_{16}}{A_8} = \dfrac{8^2}{16^2} = \boxed{0.25}$.

(b) The amount of light is also proportional to the exposure time.

So $A_8 t_8 = A_{5.6} t_{5.6}$, ☞ $t_{5.6} = \dfrac{A_8}{A_{5.6}} t_8 = \dfrac{5.6^2}{8^2}\left(\dfrac{1}{60}\ \text{s}\right) = \boxed{\dfrac{1}{120}\ \text{s}}$.

93. Assume the diameter of a typical iris is 1.0 cm and use 550 nm as the wavelength.

The resolution is $\theta_{\min} = \dfrac{1.22\lambda}{D} = \dfrac{1.22(550 \times 10^{-9}\ \text{m})}{0.010\ \text{m}} = 6.7 \times 10^{-5}\ \text{rad}$.

The resolving power on the Earth is then $s = d\theta_{\min} = (150 \times 10^3\ \text{m})(6.7 \times 10^{-5}\ \text{rad}) = 10\ \text{m} \approx 33\ \text{ft}$.

So, in theory, she is able to identify $\boxed{\text{objects as large as typical houses}}$.

CHAPTER 26

1.   (d).

2.   (a).

3.   (a).

4.   (c).

5.   The centripetal acceleration due to the rotation of the Earth is very small for most purposes, so we can ignore it; therefore, we can treat the Earth as an inertial frame of reference.

6.   Take eastward as positive.

(a) $v_{BA} = v_B - v_A = -65$ km/h $- 85$ km/h $= -150$ km/h $= \boxed{150 \text{ km/h westward}}$.

(b) $v_{BA} = 65$ km/h $- 85$ km/h $= -20$ km/h $= \boxed{20 \text{ km/h westward}}$.

7.   (a) The speed of sound relative to you is $v = 345$ m/s $+ 10.0$ m/s $= 355$ m/s.

So $t = \dfrac{d}{v} = \dfrac{1.20 \times 10^3 \text{ m}}{355 \text{ m/s}} = \boxed{3.38 \text{ s}}$.

(b) The speed of sound relative to you is $v = 345$ m/s $+ (-10.0$ m/s$) = 335$ m/s.

So $t = \dfrac{1.20 \times 10^3 \text{ m}}{335 \text{ m/s}} = \boxed{3.58 \text{ s}}$.

8.   (a) The velocity relative to ground is 200 km/h $+ (-35$ km/h$) = \boxed{165 \text{ km/h}}$.

(b) The velocity relative to ground is 200 km $+ 25$ km/h $= \boxed{225 \text{ km/h}}$.

9.   Maximum speed occurs when the boat and water are moving in the same direction. The velocity of the boat relative to the ground is 50 m/s $+ 5$ m/s $= \boxed{55 \text{ m/s}}$.

Minimum speed occurs when the boat and water are moving in opposite directions. The velocity of the boat relative to the ground is 50 m/s $+ (-5$ m/s$) = \boxed{45 \text{ m/s}}$.

10. (a) The time it takes is $\boxed{\text{longer}}$. Although it takes less time on the trip in the direction of the current, it takes more time on the trip in the direction opposite the current. The extra time in the opposite direction more than offsets the lesser time in the direction of the current.

(b) When there is no current, the time is $t_1 = \dfrac{1000 \text{ m}}{20 \text{ m/s}} + \dfrac{1000 \text{ m}}{20 \text{ m/s}} = \boxed{100 \text{ s}}$.

In the direction of current: the relative velocity is 20 m/s + 5.0 m/s = 25 m/s.

In the direction opposite the current: the relative velocity is 20 m/s – 5.0 m/s = 15 m/s.

So the time is $t_2 = \dfrac{1000 \text{ m}}{25 \text{ m/s}} + \dfrac{1000 \text{ m}}{15 \text{ m/s}} = \boxed{107 \text{ s}}$.

11. The time between adjacent gaps is $t = \dfrac{\theta}{\omega} = \dfrac{2\pi/N}{2\pi f} = \dfrac{1}{Nf}$.

So the speed of light is $c = \dfrac{2L}{t} = \dfrac{2L}{1/(Nf)} = 2fNL$.

12. (a).

13. (c).

14. $\boxed{c}$, since the speed of light is a constant.

15. $\boxed{\text{No}}$, it is not possible. Any inertial observer cannot measure an object with mass to travel at a speed equal to or greater than the speed of light, c.

16. (a) 300 m/s. An inertial frame O' moving at this velocity will determine the proper time of the two events.

(b) The time interval between these two events observed by another inertial frame is $\Delta t = \dfrac{\Delta t_o}{\sqrt{1 - v^2/c^2}}$, where Δt_o is the proper time. Δt can never be negative, and so the firing of the gun will always precede the hitting of the target.

17. (a) An inertial frame O' moving from A to B could see the two flashes simultaneously.
(b) From A to B.

18. (c), her friend does appear the same height because the height is perpendicular to their relative velocity.

19. $\boxed{\text{No}}$, this is not possible. From the boy's view, the barn is moving at the same speed, so it would appear to contract and be even shorter than 4.0 m.

20.　　$\boxed{\text{Yes}}$. You will find yourself younger after a high-speed space trip (close to c) due to time dilation. Your clock runs slower when you are moving at high speed.

21.　　Stationary　　　　　　　　　　　　　　　　　　　At very high speed $(0.5c)$

22.　　(a) $\boxed{\text{You}}$ are measuring the proper time because you and your clock are in the same frame of reference (no relative motion).

(b) $\boxed{\text{Your professor}}$ measures the proper length of the spacecraft because your professor and the spacecraft are in the same frame of reference (no relative motion).

23.　　The proper time is 10 min.　　$\Delta t = \dfrac{\Delta t_0}{\sqrt{1 - v^2/c^2}} = \dfrac{10 \text{ min}}{\sqrt{1 - 0.90^2}} = \boxed{23 \text{ min}}$

24.　　(a) According to your professor, your pulse rate is $\boxed{\text{less than 80 beats/min}}$. Due to time dilation, the time it takes for the heart to beat will increase, which will decrease the pulse rate.

(b) The proper time for one beat is $\dfrac{1}{80 \text{ beats/min}} = \dfrac{1}{80}$ min/beat.

So　　$\Delta t = \dfrac{\Delta t_0}{\sqrt{1 - v^2/c^2}} = \dfrac{1/80 \text{ min/beat}}{\sqrt{1 - 0.85^2}} = \dfrac{1}{42}$ min/beat.

Therefore, the number of beats per min is $\boxed{42 \text{ beats/min}}$.

25.　　The proper length is 15.0 m.　　$L = L_0 \sqrt{1 - v^2/c^2} = (15.0 \text{ m}) \sqrt{1 - (1/3)^2} = \boxed{14.1 \text{ m}}$.

26.　　(a) The length of the field will, according to the astronaut, be $\boxed{\text{shorter than 100 m}}$ due to length contraction.

(b) The proper length is 100 m.　　$L = L_0 \sqrt{1 - v^2/c^2} = (100 \text{ m}) \sqrt{1 - 0.75^2} = \boxed{66 \text{ m}}$.

(c) $\boxed{100 \text{ m}}$ is the proper length.

27.　　$\Delta t = \dfrac{\Delta t_0}{\sqrt{1 - v^2/c^2}}$,　　☞　　$v = \sqrt{1 - \Delta t_0^2/\Delta t^2}\, c = \sqrt{1 - 2.20^2/34.8^2}\, c = \boxed{0.998c}$.

28.   The one on the Earth will be 25 years + 39 years = $\boxed{64 \text{ years}}$ old.

For the one on the spaceship, we find the proper time because the 39 years is measured according to Earth time.

$$\Delta t = \frac{\Delta t_0}{\sqrt{1 - v^2/c^2}}, \qquad \Delta t_0 = \Delta t \sqrt{1 - v^2/c^2} = (39 \text{ years}) \sqrt{1 - 0.95^2} = 12.2 \text{ years}.$$

So the one on the spaceship is 25 years + 12.2 years = $\boxed{37 \text{ years}}$ old.

29.   (a) Compared with a clock on the spaceship, an Earth-based clock will measure $\boxed{\text{a longer time}}$ due to time dilation.

(b) The time on the spaceship is the proper time.

The time observed on Earth is $\Delta t = \dfrac{4.30 \text{ light-years}}{0.60c} = 7.17 \text{ years} = \boxed{7.2 \text{ years}}$.

$$\Delta t = \frac{\Delta t_0}{\sqrt{1 - v^2/c^2}}, \qquad \Delta t_0 = \Delta t \sqrt{1 - v^2/c^2} = (7.17 \text{ y}) \sqrt{1 - 0.60^2} = \boxed{5.7 \text{ years}}.$$

30.   The diameter is still 8.35 m because it is perpendicular to the relative velocity. The proper length is 35.0 m.

$$L = L_0 \sqrt{1 - v^2/c^2} = (35.0 \text{ m}) \sqrt{1 - 2.44^2/3.00^2} = 20.4 \text{ m}.$$

So the dimensions are $\boxed{\text{length of 20.4 m and diameter 8.35 m}}$.

31.   The proper length is 7.0 m. $L = L_0 \sqrt{1 - v^2/c^2} = (7.0 \text{ m}) \sqrt{1 - 0.65^2} = \boxed{5.3 \text{ m}}$.

We $\boxed{\text{assume relative velocity is parallel to length of pole}}$

32.   (a) The altitude is still 15.0 m because it is perpendicular to the relative velocity. The proper length of the base is 40.0 m. So the base is $L = L_0 \sqrt{1 - v^2/c^2} = (40.0 \text{ m}) \sqrt{1 - 0.90^2} = 17.44 \text{ m}.$

Therefore, the area is $A = \frac{1}{2}(17.44 \text{ m})(15.0 \text{ m}) = \boxed{131 \text{ m}^2}$.

(b) The angle between the hypotenuse and the base is $\theta = \tan^{-1}\left(\dfrac{15.0}{17.44}\right) = \boxed{40.7°}$.

33.   The proper length is the length of the meterstick, which is 1.0 m. $\dfrac{v}{c} = \dfrac{0.50 \text{ m}}{1.0 \text{ m}} = 0.50$.

$$L = L_0 \sqrt{1 - v^2/c^2}, \qquad v = c\sqrt{1 - L^2/L_0^2} = c\sqrt{1 - 0.50^2} = \boxed{0.87c}.$$

34. The time observed by an Earth-bound observer is $t = \dfrac{1.00 \text{ light-year}}{0.700c} = 1.429$ years.

The proper time is the one according to the pilot of the spaceship.

$\Delta t = \dfrac{\Delta t_0}{\sqrt{1 - v^2/c^2}}$, ☞ $\Delta t_0 = \Delta t \sqrt{1 - v^2/c^2} = (1.429 \text{ years}) \sqrt{1 - 0.700^2} = \boxed{1.02 \text{ years}}$

35. $\dfrac{v}{c} = \dfrac{(100 \text{ km/h})(1000 \text{ m/km})(1 \text{ h}/3600 \text{ s})}{3.00 \times 10^8 \text{ m/s}} = 9.26 \times 10^{-8} \ll 1$.

So $L = L_0 \sqrt{1 - v^2/c^2} \approx L_0 (1 - \tfrac{1}{2}v^2/c^2)$.

Therefore $\Delta L = L_0 - L = (5.00 \text{ m}) \left[\tfrac{1}{2}(9.26 \times 10^{-8})^2 \right] = \boxed{2.14 \times 10^{-14} \text{ m}}$.

36. (a) $\boxed{\text{The only thing that matters is that they are moving relative to one another}}$ because velocity is relative.

(b) The length of the meterstick is the proper length, and $\dfrac{v}{c} = \dfrac{1.0 \text{ yd}}{1.0 \text{ m}} = \dfrac{3(0.3048) \text{ m}}{1.0 \text{ m}} = 0.9144$.

$L = L_0 \sqrt{1 - v^2/c^2}$, ☞ $v = c\sqrt{1 - L^2/L_0^2} = c\sqrt{1 - 0.9144^2} = \boxed{0.40c}$.

37. The time observed by an Earth-bound observer is $\Delta t = \dfrac{9.0 \text{ light-years}}{v} = \dfrac{9.0 \text{ years}}{v/c}$.

The proper time is the ship time (12 years).

$\Delta t = \dfrac{\Delta t_0}{\sqrt{1 - v^2/c^2}}$, ☞ $\Delta t_0 = 12 \text{ years} = \Delta t \sqrt{1 - v^2/c^2} = \dfrac{9.0 \text{ years}}{v/c} \sqrt{1 - v^2/c^2}$.

Simplifying, $12^2 (v/c)^2 = 9^2 \left[1 - (v/c)^2\right]$ or $225 (v/c)^2 = 81$.

Solving, $v/c = 0.60$ or $v = \boxed{0.60c}$.

38. (d).

39. (b).

40. $\boxed{\text{No}}$, there are no such limits on momentum and energy as $p = \gamma mv$ and $E = \gamma mc^2$. γ and m can be anything from 0 to ∞.

41. $\boxed{\text{No}}$. To get to the speed of light means the object must have an infinite amount of energy, since when $v = c$, $\gamma = \infty$, and $E = \infty$. Since it takes an infinite amount of work to do this, no force can accomplish it.

42. $\boxed{\text{No}}$, this is not wrong. Due to the rest energy equation, $E_o = mc^2$, mass and rest energy are related by a constant (c^2), so it is convenient to just use the rest energy as a measure of the mass.

43. $\boxed{\text{Yes}}$, because the kinetic energy is much less than the rest-energy of the electron (2 keV << 511 keV).

$\boxed{\text{No}}$, because the kinetic energy is considerably greater than the rest-energy of the electron (2 MeV>> 0.511 MeV).

44. $E_o = mc^2 = (9.11 \times 10^{-31}\text{ kg})(3.00 \times 10^8\text{ m/s})^2 = 8.20 \times 10^{-14}\text{ J} \approx 0.511\text{ MeV}$.

$E = \gamma E_o = \dfrac{1}{\sqrt{1 - v^2/c^2}}\, E_o = \dfrac{1}{\sqrt{1 - 0.600^2}}\,(0.511\text{ MeV}) = \boxed{0.639\text{ MeV}}$.

45. (a) $E_o = mc^2 = (9.11 \times 10^{-31}\text{ kg})(3.00 \times 10^8\text{ m/s})^2 = 8.20 \times 10^{-14}\text{ J} \approx 0.511\text{ MeV}$.

$E = K + E_o = 2.5\text{ MeV} + 0.511\text{ MeV} = 3.011\text{ MeV}$.

$E = \gamma E_o = \dfrac{1}{\sqrt{1 - v^2/c^2}}\, E_o$,

so $\quad v = c\sqrt{1 - E_o^2/E^2} = c\sqrt{1 - (0.511)^2/(3.011)^2} = \boxed{0.985c}$.

(b) $K = q\Delta V = e(2.50\text{ MV}) = \boxed{2.50\text{ MeV}}$.

(c) $p = \gamma mv = \dfrac{mv}{\sqrt{1 - v^2/c^2}} = \dfrac{(9.11 \times 10^{-31}\text{ kg})(0.985)(3.00 \times 10^8\text{ m/s})}{\sqrt{1 - 0.985^2}} = \boxed{1.56 \times 10^{-21}\text{ kg·m/s}}$.

46. (a) $E = \gamma E_o = \dfrac{E_o}{\sqrt{1 - v^2/c^2}}$, $\quad\Rightarrow\quad v = c\sqrt{1 - E_o^2/E^2} = c\sqrt{1 - 1/(1.01)^2} = \boxed{0.14c}$.

(b) $v = c\sqrt{1 - 1/(1.99)^2} = \boxed{0.86c}$.

47. The energy required is $(250\,000)(1.5 \times 10^4\text{ kWh})(1000\text{ W/kW})(3600\text{ s/h}) = 1.35 \times 10^{16}\text{ J}$.

$E_o = mc^2$, $\quad\Rightarrow\quad m = \dfrac{E_o}{c^2} = \dfrac{1.35 \times 10^{16}\text{ J}}{(3.00 \times 10^8\text{ m/s})^2} = \boxed{0.15\text{ kg}}$.

48. The energy required is $(3.0 \times 10^{12}\text{ kWh})(1000\text{ W/kW})(3600\text{ s/h}) = 1.08 \times 10^{19}\text{ J}$.

$E_o = mc^2$, $\quad\Rightarrow\quad m = \dfrac{E_o}{c^2} = \dfrac{1.08 \times 10^{19}\text{ J}}{(3.00 \times 10^8\text{ m/s})^2} = 120\text{ kg}$.

With an efficiency of 25%, the amount of mass needed is $\dfrac{120\text{ kg}}{0.25} = \boxed{4.8 \times 10^2\text{ kg}}$.

49. From the work–energy theorem:

$$W = \Delta K = K - K_o = K = E_o(\gamma - 1) = mc^2 \left[\frac{1}{\sqrt{1 - (v/c)^2}} - 1 \right]$$

$$= (3.0 \times 10^6 \text{ kg})(3.00 \times 10^8 \text{ m/s})^2 \left[\frac{1}{\sqrt{1 - (v/c)^2}} - 1 \right]$$

$$= \boxed{1.6 \times 10^{24} \text{ J or } 150\,000 \text{ times more}} \text{ than } 1.08 \times 10^{19} \text{ J} = 3 \text{ trillion kWh.}$$

50. $E_o = mc^2 = (9.11 \times 10^{-31} \text{ kg})(3.00 \times 10^8 \text{ m/s})^2 = 8.20 \times 10^{-14} \text{ J} \approx 0.511 \text{ MeV.}$

$$E = \gamma E_o = \frac{E_o}{\sqrt{1 - v^2/c^2}}, \quad \text{☞} \quad v = c\sqrt{1 - E_o^2/E^2} = c\sqrt{1 - (0.511)^2/(2.8)^2} = 0.983c.$$

$$\text{So} \quad p = \frac{mv}{\sqrt{1 - v^2/c^2}} = \frac{(9.11 \times 10^{-31} \text{ kg})(0.983)(3.00 \times 10^8 \text{ m/s})}{\sqrt{1 - 0.983^2}} = \boxed{1.5 \times 10^{-21} \text{ kg·m/s}}.$$

51. $E_o = mc^2 = (9.11 \times 10^{-31} \text{ kg})(3.00 \times 10^8 \text{ m/s})^2 = 8.20 \times 10^{-14} \text{ J} \approx 0.511 \text{ MeV.}$

$$K = E - E_o = E_o(\gamma - 1) = E_o \left[\frac{1}{\sqrt{1 - (v/c)^2}} - 1 \right] = (0.511 \times 10^3 \text{ MeV}) \left[\frac{1}{\sqrt{1 - 0.50^2}} - 1 \right] = \boxed{79 \text{ keV}}.$$

52. (a) $E = K + E_o = 0.60E + E_o, \quad \text{☞} \quad 0.40E = E_o.$

Also $E = \dfrac{E_o}{\sqrt{1 - v^2/c^2}}, \quad \text{☞} \quad v = c\sqrt{1 - E_o^2/E^2} = c\sqrt{1 - 0.40^2} = 0.917c \approx \boxed{0.92c}.$

(b) $p = \dfrac{mv}{\sqrt{1 - v^2/c^2}} = \dfrac{(9.11 \times 10^{-31} \text{ kg})(0.917)(3.00 \times 10^8 \text{ m/s})}{\sqrt{1 - 0.917^2}} = \boxed{6.3 \times 10^{-22} \text{ kg·m/s}}.$

53. (a)   (b)

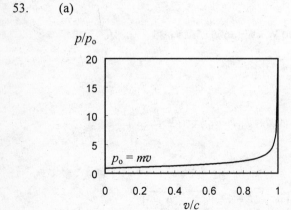

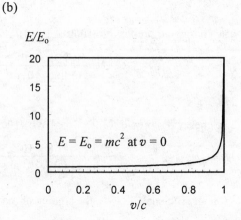

54. (a) $E_o = mc^2 = (1.67 \times 10^{-27}\text{ kg})(3.00 \times 10^8\text{ m/s})^2 = 1.502 \times 10^{-10}\text{ J} = 939\text{ MeV}$.

So $E = \dfrac{E_o}{\sqrt{1 - v^2/c^2}} = \dfrac{939\text{ MeV}}{\sqrt{1 - 0.35^2}} = \boxed{1.0 \times 10^3\text{ MeV}}$.

(b) $K = E - E_o = 1002\text{ MeV} - 939\text{ MeV} = \boxed{63\text{ MeV}}$.

(c) $p = \dfrac{mv}{\sqrt{1 - v^2/c^2}} = \dfrac{(1.67 \times 10^{-27}\text{ kg})(0.35)(3.00 \times 10^8\text{ m/s})}{\sqrt{1 - 0.35^2}} = \boxed{1.9 \times 10^{-19}\text{ kg·m/s}}$.

55. (a) $E = \dfrac{E_o}{\sqrt{1 - v^2/c^2}}$, ☞ $v = c\sqrt{1 - E_o^2/E^2} = c\sqrt{1 - 1/2.5^2} = \boxed{0.92c}$.

(b) $E_o = mc^2 = (1.67 \times 10^{-27}\text{ kg})(3.00 \times 10^8\text{ m/s})^2 = 1.502 \times 10^{-10}\text{ J} = 939\text{ MeV}$.

$K = E - E_o = (2.5 - 1)E_o = 1.5E_o = 1.5(939\text{ MeV}) = \boxed{1.4 \times 10^3\text{ MeV}}$.

56. (a) The Sun's mass will $\boxed{\text{decrease}}$ because some of it is converting to energy.

(b) $E_o = mc^2 = (1.989 \times 10^{30}\text{ kg})(3.00 \times 10^8\text{ m/s})^2 = 1.790 \times 10^{47}\text{ J}$.

$P = \dfrac{E_o}{t}$, ☞ $t = \dfrac{E_o}{P} = \dfrac{1.790 \times 10^{47}\text{ J}}{3.827 \times 10^{26}\text{ W}} = 4.678 \times 10^{20}\text{ s} = \boxed{1.483 \times 10^{13}\text{ years}}$.

57. $E_o = mc^2 = (5.00 \times 10^{-3}\text{ kg})(3.00 \times 10^8\text{ m/s})^2 = 4.50 \times 10^{14}\text{ J}$.

$P = \dfrac{E_o}{t}$, ☞ $t = \dfrac{E_o}{P} = \dfrac{4.5 \times 10^{14}\text{ J}}{100\text{ W}} = 4.5 \times 10^{12}\text{ s} = \boxed{1.43 \times 10^5\text{ years}}$.

58. (a) Water will have $\boxed{\text{more}}$ mass than ice because energy is needed to convert ice to water, and that energy becomes part of the internal energy of the water.

(b) The energy required to convert ice to water is $\Delta E = mL_f = (1.0\text{ kg})(3.33 \times 10^5\text{ J/kg}) = 3.33\text{ J}$.

$E_o = mc^2$, ☞ $\Delta E_o = \Delta mc^2$. So $\Delta m = \dfrac{E}{c^2} = \dfrac{3.33 \times 10^5\text{ J}}{(3.00 \times 10^8\text{ m/s})^2} = \boxed{3.7 \times 10^{-12}\text{ kg}}$.

$\boxed{\text{No}}$, this is not detectable as it is extremely small.

59. (a) $E_o = mc^2 = (9.11 \times 10^{-31}\text{ kg})(3.00 \times 10^8\text{ m/s})^2 = 8.20 \times 10^{-14}\text{ J} \approx 0.511\text{ MeV}$.

$K = E - E_o = E_o(\gamma - 1) = E_o\left[\dfrac{1}{\sqrt{1 - (v/c)^2}} - 1\right] = (0.511\text{ MeV})\left[\dfrac{1}{\sqrt{1 - 0.950^2}} - 1\right] = \boxed{1.13\text{ MeV}}$.

(b) $E = K + E_o = 1.13\text{ MeV} + 0.511\text{ MeV} = \boxed{1.64\text{ MeV}}$.

60.   (a) The total mass of the two particles after the collision is expected to be $\boxed{\text{equal to } 2m}$. In an elastic collision like that described, the total kinetic energy is conserved. Since the total energy is conserved, the total rest energy is also conserved. That is, the total rest mass will remain the same.

(b) Since total energy and momentum are both conserved, we calculate the total initial energy and momentum.

$$E_{\text{total}} = \gamma_1 E_{o1} + \gamma_2 E_{o2} = \frac{E_{o1}}{\sqrt{1 - v^2/c^2}} + E_{o2}.$$

Since $E_{o1} = E_{o2} = mc^2$, $E_{\text{total}} = \left[1 + \frac{1}{\sqrt{1 - (v/c)^2}} \right] mc^2.$

$$P_{\text{total}} = \gamma_1 mv_1 + \gamma_2 mv_2 = \frac{mv}{\sqrt{1 - v^2/c^2}} + 0 = \frac{mv}{\sqrt{1 - v^2/c^2}}.$$

61. $E^2 = \gamma^2 m^2 c^4 = \gamma^2 m^2 c^2 (c^2 + v^2 - v^2) = \gamma^2 m^2 v^2 c^2 + \gamma^2 m^2 c^4 \left(1 - \frac{v^2}{c^2} \right)$

$$= p^2 c^2 + \frac{m^2 c^4}{\left(\sqrt{1 - v^2/c^2} \right)^2} \left(1 - \frac{v^2}{c^2} \right) = p^2 c^2 + (mc^2)^2.$$

62.   (a) The minimum energy is the rest energy, which for a proton is

$E_o = mc^2 = (1.67 \times 10^{-27} \text{ kg})(3.00 \times 10^8 \text{ m/s})^2 = 1.502 \times 10^{-10} \text{ J} = \boxed{939 \text{ MeV} > 600 \text{ MeV}}$.

(b) $E = K + E_o = 600 \text{ MeV} + 939 \text{ MeV} = 1539 \text{ MeV}.$

$E = \frac{E_o}{\sqrt{1 - v^2/c^2}}, \quad \text{☞} \quad v = c\sqrt{1 - E_o^2/E^2} = c\sqrt{1 - (939)^2/(1539)^2} = \boxed{0.792c}.$

(c) $p = \frac{mv}{\sqrt{1 - v^2/c^2}} = \frac{(1.67 \times 10^{-27} \text{ kg})(0.792)(3.00 \times 10^8 \text{ m/s})}{\sqrt{1 - 0.792^2}} = \boxed{6.50 \times 10^{-19} \text{ kg·m/s}}.$

63.   (a).

64.   (d).

65.   (c), because the Schwarzschild radius defines the event horizon.

66. $\boxed{\text{It would be elongated or "stretched"}}$ by the gravity gradient (difference) of the black hole.

67.   (a) The event horizon for Jupiter would be $\boxed{\text{larger}}$ because it has more mass and the radius of the event

horizon is directly proportion to the mass, $R = \dfrac{2GM}{c^2}$.

    (b) $R_E = \dfrac{2GM_E}{c^2} = \dfrac{2(6.67 \times 10^{11} \text{ N·m}^2/\text{kg}^2)(6.0 \times 10^{24} \text{ kg})}{(3.00 \times 10^8 \text{ m/s})^2} = 8.9 \times 10^{-3} \text{ m} = \boxed{8.9 \text{ mm}}$.

    $R_J = \dfrac{2GM_J}{c^2} = \dfrac{2G(318M_E)}{c^2} = 318R_E = \boxed{2.8 \text{ m}}$.

68. $\rho = \dfrac{m}{V} = \dfrac{2.0 \times 10^{30} \text{ kg}}{4\pi(3.0 \times 10^3)^3/3} = \boxed{1.8 \times 10^{19} \text{ kg/m}^3}$.

69. $R = \dfrac{2GM}{c^2}$,   ☞ $M = \dfrac{Rc^2}{2G} = \dfrac{(5.00 \times 10^3 \text{ m})(3.00 \times 10^8 \text{ m/s})^2}{2(6.67 \times 10^{-11} \text{ N·m}^2/\text{kg}^2)} = \boxed{3.37 \times 10^{30} \text{ kg}}$.

    (b) $\rho = \dfrac{M}{V} = \dfrac{3.37 \times 10^{30} \text{ kg}}{4\pi(5.0 \times 10^3)^3/3} = \boxed{6.44 \times 10^{18} \text{ kg/m}^3}$.

70. $\boxed{\text{Drop the cup with the pole vertical}}$. By the principle of equivalence, the weight of the ball is effectively

zero in the falling reference frame. The ball is then subject only to the tension force of the stretched rubber

band and is pulled inside the cup.

71. $v = 7.5 \times 10^7 \text{ m/s} = 0.25c.$ $u = \dfrac{v + u'}{1 + vu'/c^2} = \dfrac{0.25c + 0.20c}{1 + (0.25)(0.20)} = \boxed{0.43c}$.

72. $u = \dfrac{v + u'}{1 + vu'/c^2} = \dfrac{0.40c + (-0.15c)}{1 + (0.40)(-0.15)} = \boxed{0.27c, \text{ same direction as spacecraft}}$.

73.   Use the rocket as the moving reference frame.

    $u = \dfrac{v + u'}{1 + vu'/c^2} = \dfrac{0.100c + (-0.250c)}{1 + (0.100)(-0.250)} = \boxed{-0.154 \ c \text{ (toward Earth)}}$.

74.   (a) The speed of one ship relative to the other is $\boxed{\text{less than } c}$ because c is the upper limit for all speeds.

    (b) $u = \dfrac{v + u'}{1 + vu'/c^2} = \dfrac{0.60c + 0.60c}{1 + (0.60c)(0.60c)/c^2} = \boxed{0.88c}$.

75.   Take the direction to the right as positive and use $u = \dfrac{v + u'}{1 + vu'/c^2}$, so $v = \dfrac{u - u'}{1 - uu'/c^2}$.

    (a) $v = \dfrac{u - u'}{1 - uu'/c^2} = \dfrac{-0.800c - 0.900c}{1 - (-0.800)(0.900)} = -0.988c = \boxed{0.988c \text{ to the left}}$.

    (b) $v = \dfrac{0.900c - (-0.800c)}{1 - (0.900)(-0.800)} = +0.988c = \boxed{0.988c \text{ to the right}}$.

76. $E_0 = mc^2 = (1.67 \times 10^{-27} \text{ kg})(3.00 \times 10^8 \text{ m/s})^2 = 1.503 \times 10^{-10} \text{ J} = \boxed{939 \text{ MeV}}$.

77. $\Delta t = \dfrac{\Delta t_0}{\sqrt{1 - v^2/c^2}}, \quad \text{☞} \quad \Delta t_0 = \sqrt{1 - v^2/c^2}\ \Delta t.$

So the time difference is $\Delta t - \Delta t_0 = \left(1 - \sqrt{1 - v^2/c^2}\right)t = \left(1 - \sqrt{1 - 0.60^2}\right)(24 \text{ h}) = \boxed{4.8 \text{ h}}$.

78. $v = 9.5 \times 10^7 \text{ m/s} = 0.317c$.

$E_0 = mc^2 = (9.11 \times 10^{-31} \text{ kg})(3.00 \times 10^8 \text{ m/s})^2 = 8.20 \times 10^{-14} \text{ J} \approx 0.511 \text{ MeV}$.

$E = \dfrac{E_0}{\sqrt{1 - v^2/c^2}} = \dfrac{0.511 \text{ MeV}}{\sqrt{1 - 0.317^2}} = \boxed{0.54 \text{ MeV}}$.

79. $L = L_0 \sqrt{1 - v^2/c^2} = (50 \text{ m})\sqrt{1 - 0.65^2} = 38 \text{ m}$. The height and width are the same.

So the dimensions are $\boxed{\text{length 38 m; height 2.5 m; width 2.0 m}}$.

80. $E_0 = mc^2 = (1.0 \text{ kg})(3.00 \times 10^8 \text{ m/s})^2 = 9.0 \times 10^{16} \text{ J} = (9.0 \times 10^{16} \text{ W·s})(1 \text{ kW}/1000 \text{ W})(3600 \text{ s/h})$

$= \boxed{2.5 \times 10^{10} \text{ kWh}}$.

81. The proper time is 30 min. $\Delta t = \dfrac{\Delta t_0}{\sqrt{1 - v^2/c^2}} = \dfrac{30 \text{ min}}{\sqrt{1 - 0.80^2}} = \boxed{50 \text{ min}}$.

82. The rest energy of an electron or a positron is

$E_0 = mc^2 = (9.11 \times 10^{-31} \text{ kg})(3.00 \times 10^8 \text{ m/s})^2 = 8.20 \times 10^{-14} \text{ J} \approx 0.511 \text{ MeV}$.

The total energy of the radiation is $0.511 \text{ MeV} + 0.511 \text{ MeV} = \boxed{1.02 \text{ MeV}}$.

83. The proper length is 150 m.

$L = L_0 \sqrt{1 - v^2/c^2}, \quad \text{☞} \quad v = c\sqrt{1 - L^2/L_0^2} = c\sqrt{1 - (110)^2/(150)^2} = \boxed{0.68c}$.

84. $E_0 = Pt = \dfrac{1.2 \times 10^9 \text{ W}}{0.33}(18 \text{ month})(30 \text{ day/month})(86400 \text{ s/day}) = 1.70 \times 10^{17} \text{ J}$.

$E_0 = mc^2, \quad \text{☞} \quad m = \dfrac{E_0}{c^2} = \dfrac{1.70 \times 10^{17} \text{ J}}{(3.00 \times 10^8 \text{ m/s})^2} = \boxed{1.9 \text{ kg}}$.

CHAPTER 27

1.   (d).

2.   (c).

3.   No , it actually emits 2^4 or 16 times the total radiation since the radiation rate depends on T^4.

4.   The red ones have the lower temperatures because red has a longer wavelength, and the wavelength of the most intense radiation is inversely proportional to temperature ($\lambda_{max} T = 2.9 \times 10^{-3}$ m·K).

5.   (a) $\lambda_{max} T = 2.9 \times 10^{-3}$ m·K,   ☞ $T = \dfrac{2.9 \times 10^{-3}\ \text{m·K}}{\lambda_{max}} = \dfrac{2.9 \times 10^{-3}\ \text{m·K}}{c} f \propto f.$

   (b) $T = \dfrac{2.9 \times 10^{-3}\ \text{m·K}}{\lambda_{max}} \propto \dfrac{1}{\lambda_{max}}.$

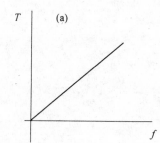

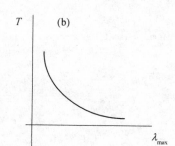

6. $\lambda_{max} T = 2.9 \times 10^{-3}$ m·K,   ☞ $T = \dfrac{2.9 \times 10^{-3}\ \text{m·K}}{\lambda_{max}} = \dfrac{2.9 \times 10^{-3}\ \text{m·K}}{700 \times 10^{-9}\ \text{m}} = \boxed{4.1 \times 10^3\ \text{K}}.$

7. $\lambda_{max} T = 2.9 \times 10^{-3}$ m·K,   ☞ $\lambda_{max} = \dfrac{2.9 \times 10^{-3}\ \text{m·K}}{T} = \dfrac{2.9 \times 10^{-3}\ \text{m·K}}{273\ \text{K}} = \boxed{1.06 \times 10^{-5}\ \text{m}}.$

   $f = \dfrac{c}{\lambda_{max}} = \dfrac{3.00 \times 10^8\ \text{m/s}}{1.06 \times 10^{-5}\ \text{m}} = \boxed{2.83 \times 10^{13}\ \text{Hz}}.$

8.   (a) If you have a fever, the wavelength of the radiation component of maximum intensity emitted by your body will decrease . Since $\lambda_{max} T = 2.9 \times 10^{-3}$ m·K, a higher T corresponds to a shorter λ_{max}.

   (b) $\lambda_{max} T = 2.9 \times 10^{-3}$ m·K,   ☞ $\lambda_{max} = \dfrac{2.9 \times 10^{-3}\ \text{m·K}}{T} = \dfrac{2.9 \times 10^{-3}\ \text{m·K}}{(273 + 32)\ \text{K}} = \boxed{9.5 \times 10^{-6}\ \text{m; infrared}}.$

9. $\lambda_{max} T = 2.9 \times 10^{-3}$ m·K, $\mathcal{F}$ $\lambda_{max} = \dfrac{2.9 \times 10^{-3} \text{ m·K}}{T} = \dfrac{2.9 \times 10^{-3} \text{ m·K}}{(273 + 27) \text{ K}} = 9.67 \times 10^{-6}$ m.

So $f = \dfrac{c}{\lambda_{max}} = \dfrac{3.00 \times 10^{8} \text{ m/s}}{9.67 \times 10^{-6} \text{ m}} = \boxed{3.1 \times 10^{13} \text{ Hz}}$.

10.   (a) The frequency of the most intense spectral component will $\boxed{\text{increase but not double}}$ if the temperature
is increased from 200°C to 400°C. The temperature used should be in kelvin, and 200°C = 473 K and
400°C = 673 K. 673 K is higher than 473 K but not double.

(b) $\lambda_{max} T = 2.9 \times 10^{-3}$ m·K, $\mathcal{F}$ $\lambda_{max} = \dfrac{2.9 \times 10^{-3} \text{ m·K}}{T}$.

$\Delta f = f_2 - f_1 = \dfrac{c}{\lambda_1} - \dfrac{c}{\lambda_2} = \dfrac{c\,T_2}{2.9 \times 10^{-3} \text{ m·K}} - \dfrac{c\,T_1}{2.9 \times 10^{-3} \text{ m·K}} = \dfrac{c}{2.9 \times 10^{-3} \text{ m·K}}\,\Delta T$

$= \dfrac{3.00 \times 10^{8} \text{ m/s}}{2.9 \times 10^{-3} \text{ m·K}} (200 \text{ K}) = \boxed{2.1 \times 10^{13} \text{ Hz}}$.

11. $\lambda_{max} T = 2.9 \times 10^{-3}$ m·K, $\mathcal{F}$ $\lambda_{max} = \dfrac{2.9 \times 10^{-3} \text{ m·K}}{T} = \dfrac{2.9 \times 10^{-3} \text{ m·K}}{373 \text{ K}} = 7.77 \times 10^{-6}$ m.

So $f = \dfrac{c}{\lambda_{max}} = \dfrac{3.00 \times 10^{8} \text{ m/s}}{7.77 \times 10^{-6} \text{ m}} = 3.86 \times 10^{13}$ Hz.

Therefore $E = hf = (6.63 \times 10^{-34} \text{ J·s})(3.86 \times 10^{13} \text{ Hz}) = \boxed{2.56 \times 10^{-20} \text{ J}}$.

12. $\lambda_{max} T = 2.9 \times 10^{-3}$ m·K, $\mathcal{F}$ $\lambda_{max} = \dfrac{2.9 \times 10^{-3} \text{ m·K}}{T} = \dfrac{2.9 \times 10^{-3} \text{ m·K}}{1000 \text{ K}} = 2.9 \times 10^{-6}$ m.

So $f = \dfrac{c}{\lambda_{max}} = \dfrac{3.00 \times 10^{8} \text{ m/s}}{2.9 \times 10^{-6} \text{ m}} = 1.03 \times 10^{14}$ Hz.

Therefore $E = hf = (6.63 \times 10^{-34} \text{ J·s})(1.03 \times 10^{14} \text{ Hz}) = 6.83 \times 10^{-20}$ J/quantum.
The number of quanta per square meter per second is

$n = \dfrac{I}{E} = \dfrac{2.0 \text{ W/m}^2}{6.83 \times 10^{-20} \text{ J/quantum}} = \boxed{2.9 \times 10^{19} \text{ quanta/(s·m}^2\text{)}}$.

13.   (b).

14.   (d).

15.   The energy packets of radio photons arrive in such quantity and so quickly that when they are converted to
sound, our ear cannot distinguish between discrete arrivals. It is somewhat analogeous to a movie, where
the picture is actually single frames passing in front of us at a rapid speed, but we see it as a smooth and
continuous moving picture. Likewise, although the radio signals are single frames, we hear the radio signals
continuously.

16. The X–ray photon has much more energy than the red-light photon ($E = hf$).

17. The energy of radiation is proportional to its intensity, according to the wave theory, and its frequency, according to the particle theory. It takes a certain amount of energy to eject a photoelectron. Since only the frequency, not the intensity, matters in this case, it favors the particle theory.

18. No, the election of photoelectrons is instantaneous as long as the frequency of the light is above the cut-off frequency. The ejection of the photoelectrons is independent of the intensity of the light. However, the number of photoelectrons depends on the intensity of light.

19. No, the number of photoelectrons ejected depends on the intensity of light. Frequency only determines if there is any election of photoelectron.

20. $E = hf = (6.63 \times 10^{-34} \text{ J·s})(5.0 \times 10^{14} \text{ Hz}) = \boxed{3.3 \times 10^{-19} \text{ J}}$.

21. $E = hf$, ☞ $f = \dfrac{E}{h} = \dfrac{3.3 \times 10^{-15} \text{ J}}{6.63 \times 10^{-34} \text{ J·s}} = 4.98 \times 10^{18} \text{ Hz}$.

    So $\lambda = \dfrac{c}{f} = \dfrac{3.00 \times 10^8 \text{ m/s}}{4.98 \times 10^{19} \text{ Hz}} = \boxed{6.0 \times 10^{-11} \text{ m; X ray}}$.

22. (a) A quantum of violet light has $\boxed{\text{more}}$ energy because the energy is proportional to frequency, $E = hf$, and frequency is inversely proportional to wavelength. So the shorter the wavelength, the higher the frequency and the higher the energy.

    (b) $E = hf$, ☞ $\dfrac{E_v}{E_r} = \dfrac{f_v}{f_r} = \dfrac{\lambda_r}{\lambda_v} = \dfrac{700 \text{ nm}}{400 \text{ nm}} = \boxed{1.75}$.

23. (a) $E = hf = \dfrac{hc}{\lambda} = \dfrac{1.24 \times 10^3 \text{ eV·nm}}{150 \text{ nm}} = 8.27 \text{ eV} = \boxed{1.32 \times 10^{-18} \text{ J}}$.

    (b) As in (a), $E = \boxed{8.27 \text{ eV}}$.

24. (a) Because $\phi_0 = hf_0 = \dfrac{hc}{\lambda_0}$, the threshold wavelength for metal A is $\boxed{\text{shorter}}$. The greater the work function, the higher the threshold (cut-off) frequency and the shorter the threshold wavelength.

    (b) $\phi_0 = hf_0 = \dfrac{hc}{\lambda_0}$, ☞ $\dfrac{\lambda_{oA}}{\lambda_{oB}} = \dfrac{\phi_{oB}}{\phi_{oA}} = \dfrac{1}{2}$. So $\lambda_{oA} = \dfrac{1}{2}\lambda_{oB} = \dfrac{1}{2}(620 \text{ nm}) = \boxed{310 \text{ nm}}$.

25. The kinetic energy is still $\boxed{3.0 \text{ eV}}$ since it is independent of the intensity.

26. In one minute, $E = Pt = 0.025(100 \text{ W})(60 \text{ s}) = 150 \text{ J}$.

$$E_o = hf = \frac{hc}{\lambda} = \frac{(6.63 \times 10^{-34} \text{ J·s})(3.00 \times 10^8 \text{ m/s})}{550 \times 10^{-9} \text{ m}} = 3.616 \times 10^{-19} \text{ J/quantum.}$$

So $n = \dfrac{E}{E_o} = \dfrac{150 \text{ J}}{3.616 \times 10^{-19} \text{ J/quantum}} = \boxed{4.15 \times 10^{20} \text{ quanta}}$.

27. (a) Since $eV_o = hf + \phi_o$, the slope of the graph is equal to Planck's constant.

$$h = \frac{[(3-1) \text{ eV}](1.6 \times 10^{-19} \text{ J/eV})}{(115 - 67) \times 10^{13} \text{ Hz}} = \boxed{6.7 \times 10^{-34} \text{ J·s}}.$$

(b) $\phi_o = hf_o = (6.63 \times 10^{-34} \text{ J·s})(43.9 \times 10^{13} \text{ Hz}) = \boxed{2.9 \times 10^{-19} \text{ J}}$.

28. $hf = eV_o + \phi_o = 2.50 \text{ eV} + 2.40 \text{ eV} = 4.90 \text{ eV} = 7.84 \times 10^{-19} \text{ J}$.

So $f = \dfrac{7.84 \times 10^{-19} \text{ J}}{6.63 \times 10^{-34} \text{ J·s}} = 1.183 \times 10^{15} \text{ Hz}$.

Therefore $\lambda = \dfrac{c}{f} = \dfrac{3.00 \times 10^8 \text{ m/s}}{1.183 \times 10^{15} \text{ Hz}} = 2.54 \times 10^{-7} \text{ m} = \boxed{254 \text{ nm}}$.

29. $hf_o = \phi_o$, ☞ $f_o = \dfrac{\phi_o}{h} = \dfrac{(2.8 \text{ eV})(1.6 \times 10^{-19} \text{ J/eV})}{6.63 \times 10^{-34} \text{ J·s}} = \boxed{6.8 \times 10^{14} \text{ Hz}}$.

30. (a) $K_{max} = \frac{1}{2}mv^2_{max} = hf - \phi_o = h(f - f_o) = hc\left(\dfrac{1}{\lambda} - \dfrac{1}{\lambda_o}\right)$, ☞ $v_{max} = \sqrt{\dfrac{2hc}{m}\left(\dfrac{1}{\lambda} - \dfrac{1}{\lambda_o}\right)}$.

$$v_{max} = \sqrt{\frac{2(6.63 \times 10^{-34} \text{ J·s})(3.00 \times 10^8 \text{ m/s})}{9.11 \times 10^{-31} \text{ kg}}\left(\frac{1}{400 \times 10^{-9} \text{ m}} - \frac{1}{500 \times 10^{-9} \text{ m}}\right)}$$

$$= \boxed{4.7 \times 10^5 \text{ m/s}}.$$

(b) Since $\lambda = \lambda_o$, $v_{max} = \boxed{0}$.

(c) Since $\lambda > \lambda_o$ $(f < f_o)$, there is $\boxed{\text{no emission}}$ of electrons.

31. $\phi_o = hf_o = \dfrac{hc}{\lambda_o} = \dfrac{1240 \text{ eV·nm}}{500 \text{ nm}} = \boxed{2.48 \text{ eV}}$.

32. (a) $eV_o = K_{max} = hf - \phi_o = \dfrac{hc}{\lambda} - \phi_o = \dfrac{1.24 \times 10^3 \text{ eV·nm}}{300 \text{ nm}} - 3.5 \text{ eV} = 0.63 \text{ eV}$.

So $V_o = \boxed{0.63 \text{ V}}$.

(b) $f_o = \dfrac{\phi_o}{h} = \dfrac{(3.5 \text{ eV})(1.6 \times 10^{-19} \text{ J/eV})}{6.63 \times 10^{-34} \text{ J·s}} = \boxed{8.4 \times 10^{14} \text{ Hz}}$.

33.   (a) There will be $\boxed{\text{no photoelectrons}}$. The energy difference between blue and red light is about

$$\frac{(6.63 \times 10^{-34}\ \text{J·s})(3.00 \times 10^8\ \text{m/s})}{420 \times 10^{-9}\ \text{m}} - \frac{(6.63 \times 10^{-34}\ \text{J·s})(3.00 \times 10^8\ \text{m/s})}{700 \times 10^{-9}\ \text{m}} = 2 \times 10^{-19}\ \text{J}.$$

This difference is more than the kinetic energy of 1.00×10^{-19} J. So red light will not have enough energy to eject photoelectrons.

(b) $K_{\max} = hf - \phi_0 = \dfrac{hc}{\lambda} - \phi_0$,

so $\phi_0 = \dfrac{hc}{\lambda} - K_{\max} = \dfrac{(6.63 \times 10^{-34}\ \text{J·s})(3.00 \times 10^8\ \text{m/s})}{420 \times 10^{-9}\ \text{m}} - 1.0 \times 10^{-19}\ \text{J} = 3.74 \times 10^{-19}\ \text{J}.$

$hf = \dfrac{hc}{\lambda} = \dfrac{(6.63 \times 10^{-34}\ \text{J·s})(3.00 \times 10^8\ \text{m/s})}{700 \times 10^{-9}\ \text{m}} = 2.84 \times 10^{-19}\ \text{J} < \phi_0.$

34.   (a) $K_{\max} = hf - \phi_0 = \dfrac{hc}{\lambda} - \phi_0 = \dfrac{1.24 \times 10^3\ \text{eV·nm}}{160\ \text{nm}} - 4.82\ \text{eV} = \boxed{2.93\ \text{eV}}.$

(b) $f_0 = \dfrac{\phi_0}{h} = \dfrac{(4.82\ \text{eV})(1.60 \times 10^{-19}\ \text{J/eV})}{6.63 \times 10^{-34}\ \text{J·s}} = \boxed{1.16 \times 10^{15}\ \text{Hz}}.$

35.   (a) $K_{\max} = hf - \phi_0$. The photoelectrons from $\boxed{\text{sodium}}$ will have a greater speed since it has a smaller ϕ_0 .

(b) $\lambda_0 = \dfrac{c}{f_0} = \dfrac{c}{\phi_0/h} = \dfrac{hc}{\phi_0}.$

So $\lambda_{\text{silver}} < \dfrac{1240\ \text{eV·nm}}{4.73\ \text{eV}} = \boxed{262\ \text{nm}},$

and $\lambda_{\text{sodium}} < \dfrac{1240\ \text{eV·nm}}{2.46\ \text{eV}} = \boxed{504\ \text{nm}}.$

36. $K_{\max} = hf - \phi_0 = \dfrac{hc}{\lambda} - \phi_0.$

For red, $K_{\text{red}} = \dfrac{hc}{700\ \text{nm}} - \phi_0\ ;$

for blue, $K_{\text{blue}} = \dfrac{hc}{400\ \text{nm}} - \phi_0.$

Dividing the two equations yields $2 = \dfrac{K_{\text{blue}}}{K_{\text{red}}} = \dfrac{\dfrac{hc}{400\ \text{nm}} - \phi_0}{\dfrac{hc}{700\ \text{nm}} - \phi_0}.$

So $\phi_0 = hc\left(\dfrac{2}{700\ \text{nm}} - \dfrac{1}{400\ \text{nm}}\right) = (1.24 \times 10^3\ \text{eV·nm})\left(\dfrac{2}{700\ \text{nm}} - \dfrac{1}{400\ \text{nm}}\right) = \boxed{0.44\ \text{eV}}.$

37. Since $K_{max} = hf - \phi_0$, the slope is equal to Planck's constant.

The slope of the line is about $\dfrac{(2.6 \text{ eV} - 0.60) \text{ eV}}{(9.9 - 5.0) \times 10^{14} \text{ Hz}} = 4.1 \times 10^{-15} \text{ eV/Hz} = 4.1 \times 10^{-15} \text{ eV·s}$.

$h \approx (4.1 \times 10^{-15} \text{ eV·s})(1.6 \times 10^{-19} \text{ J/eV}) = \boxed{6.6 \times 10^{-34} \text{ J·s}}$.

From the graph, $f_0 \approx 3.7 \times 10^{14}$ Hz.

So $\phi_0 = hf_0 = (6.63 \times 10^{-34} \text{ J·s})(3.7 \times 10^{14} \text{ Hz}) = 2.45 \times 10^{-19} \text{ J} = \boxed{1.5 \text{ eV}}$.

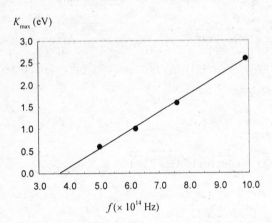

38. (d).

39. (d).

40. The maximum wavelength shift for Compton scattering from a molecule is $\boxed{\text{smaller}}$ compared with that from a free electron because the Compton wavelength is inversely proportional to the mass of the scattering particle and $\Delta\lambda_{max} = 2\lambda_C = 2\,\dfrac{h}{mc} \propto \dfrac{1}{m}$.

41. For each scattering the wavelength shift is approximately equal to $\Delta\lambda = \lambda_c = 0.00243$ nm.

The wavelength change from X ray to visible light is in the order of 550 nm − 0.01 nm = 550 nm.

So after approximately $\dfrac{550 \text{ nm}}{0.00243 \text{ nm}} = \boxed{200\,000}$ scatterings, X ray becomes visible light.

42. From energy conservation, the scattered $\boxed{\text{photon lost some energy in scattering}}$ because the free electron receives part of the incident energy. Since the energy of a photon is proportional to the frequency of the light or inversely proportional to wavelength, the scattered photon always has a longer wavelength.

43. $\Delta\lambda = \lambda_C (1 - \cos\theta)$, ☞ $\Delta\lambda_{max} = (0.00243 \text{ nm})(1 - \cos 180°) = (0.00243 \text{ nm})(2) = \boxed{4.86 \times 10^{-3} \text{ nm}}$.

44. $\Delta\lambda = \lambda_C(1 - \cos\theta) = (0.00243 \text{ nm})(1 - \cos 30°) = \boxed{3.26 \times 10^{-4} \text{ nm}}$.

45. $\Delta\lambda = \lambda_C(1 - \cos\theta) = (2.43 \times 10^{-12} \text{ m})(1 - \cos 45°) = 7.12 \times 10^{-13} \text{ m}$.

So $\lambda = \lambda_o + \Delta\lambda = 2.80 \times 10^{-10} \text{ m} + 7.12 \times 10^{-13} \text{ m} = 2.81 \times 10^{-10} \text{ m} = \boxed{0.281 \text{ nm}}$.

46. $\Delta\lambda = \lambda_C(1 - \cos\theta) = (2.43 \times 10^{-12} \text{ m})(1 - \cos 53°) = 9.68 \times 10^{-13} \text{ m}$.

So $\lambda = \lambda_o + \Delta\lambda = 0.0045 \times 10^{-9} \text{ m} + 9.68 \times 10^{-13} \text{ m} = 5.47 \times 10^{-12} \text{ m} = \boxed{0.0055 \text{ nm}}$.

47. (a) The scattered photon could have an energy of $\boxed{\text{less than 5.0 keV but not zero}}$. According to the conservation of energy and momentum, the free electron will carry some kinetic energy, and the scattered photon will also be moving away after the scattering.

(b) $E = \dfrac{hc}{\lambda} = \dfrac{1.24 \times 10^3 \text{ eV·nm}}{0.25 \text{ nm}} = 4.96 \times 10^3 \text{ eV} = 4.96 \text{ keV}$.

According to energy conservation, the electron has energy of 5.0 keV – 4.96 keV = $\boxed{40 \text{ eV}}$.

48. $\Delta\lambda = \lambda_C(1 - \cos\theta)$, ☞ $\cos\theta = 1 - \dfrac{\Delta\lambda}{\lambda_C} = 1 - \dfrac{0.000326 \text{ nm}}{0.00243 \text{ nm}} = 0.866$.

So $\theta = \boxed{30.0°}$.

49. $\Delta\lambda = \lambda_C(1 - \cos\theta)$, ☞ $\cos\theta = 1 - \dfrac{\Delta\lambda}{\lambda_C} = 1 - \dfrac{1.25 \times 10^{-4} \text{ nm}}{0.00243 \text{ nm}} = 0.9486$.

So $\theta = \boxed{18.5°}$.

50. (a) The Compton wavelength for a proton is $\boxed{\text{shorter}}$ because it depends inversely on mass, $\lambda_C = \dfrac{h}{mc}$, compared with the Compton wavelength for an electron.

(b) $\lambda_C = \dfrac{h}{m_p c^2} = \dfrac{6.63 \times 10^{-34} \text{ J·s}}{(1.67 \times 10^{-27} \text{ kg})(3.00 \times 10^8 \text{ m/s})} = \boxed{1.32 \times 10^{-15} \text{ m}}$.

(c) The maximum wavelength shift is equal to $2\lambda_C$ when $\theta = 180°$, from $\Delta\lambda = \lambda_C(1 - \cos\theta)$.

$\dfrac{(\Delta\lambda_e)_{max}}{(\Delta\lambda_p)_{max}} = \dfrac{2\lambda_{Ce}}{2\lambda_{Cp}} = \dfrac{2.43 \times 10^{-12} \text{ m}}{1.32 \times 10^{-15} \text{ m}} = \boxed{1.84 \times 10^3}$.

51. (d).

52. (a).

53. The theory applies only to atoms with a single electron because it does not include electron-electron interactions.

54. No , it does not take more energy to ionize the electron that is in an excited state than in the ground state. Actually, it takes less energy since the excited state has more energy than the ground state.

55. According to momentum conservation, the atom must recoil, so it carries some kinetic energy away; therefore, the energy of the photon is smaller than expected. Thus, the wavelength of the photon is longer.

56. If n doubles, the radius of the electron orbit quadruples as $r_n = 0.0529n^2$ nm.

57. Since $E_n = \dfrac{-13.6 \text{ eV}}{n^2}$, the energy increases (becoming less negative) by a factor of 4 , if n doubles. Since E_n is a negative number, increasing it means it has a smaller number, but is actually large (less negative).

58. (a) $\Delta E = (-13.6 \text{ eV}) \left(\dfrac{1}{n_f^2} - \dfrac{1}{n_i^2} \right) = (-13.6 \text{ eV}) \left(\dfrac{1}{2^2} - \dfrac{1}{1^2} \right) = \boxed{10.2 \text{ eV}}$.

(b) $\Delta E = (-13.6 \text{ eV}) \left(\dfrac{1}{3^2} - \dfrac{1}{2^2} \right) = \boxed{1.89 \text{ eV}}$.

59. (a) $\lambda = \dfrac{1.24 \times 10^3}{\Delta E \text{ (in eV)}} \text{ nm} = \dfrac{1.24 \times 10^3}{10.2} = 122 \text{ nm, i.e., } \boxed{\text{ultraviolet}}$.

(b) $\lambda = \dfrac{1.24 \times 10^3}{1.89} \text{ nm} = 656 \text{ nm, i.e., } \boxed{\text{visible (red)}}$.

60. (a) $\Delta E = (-13.6 \text{ eV}) \left(\dfrac{1}{n_f^2} - \dfrac{1}{n_i^2} \right) = (-13.6 \text{ eV}) \left(\dfrac{1}{\infty} - \dfrac{1}{2^2} \right) = \boxed{3.40 \text{ eV}}$.

(b) $\Delta E = (-13.6 \text{ eV}) \left(\dfrac{1}{\infty} - \dfrac{1}{3^2} \right) = \boxed{1.51 \text{ eV}}$.

61. (a) $\Delta E = (-13.6 \text{ eV}) \left(\dfrac{1}{n_f^2} - \dfrac{1}{n_i^2} \right) = (-13.6 \text{ eV}) \left(\dfrac{1}{5^2} - \dfrac{1}{2^2} \right) = 2.856 \text{ eV}$.

$f = \dfrac{\Delta E}{h} = \dfrac{(2.856 \text{ eV})(1.60 \times 10^{-19} \text{ J/eV})}{6.63 \times 10^{-34} \text{ J·s}} = \boxed{6.89 \times 10^{14} \text{ Hz}}$.

(b) $\Delta E = (-13.6 \text{ eV}) \left(\dfrac{1}{\infty} - \dfrac{1}{2^2} \right) = 3.40 \text{ eV}$.

$f = \dfrac{(3.40 \text{ eV})(1.60 \times 10^{-19} \text{ J/eV})}{6.63 \times 10^{-34} \text{ J·s}} = \boxed{8.21 \times 10^{14} \text{ Hz}}$.

62.   (a) $r_n = 0.0529n^2$ nm.

$r_3 = (0.0529)(2)^2$ nm = $\boxed{0.212 \text{ nm}}$.

(b) $r_6 = 0.0529(4)^2 = \boxed{0.846 \text{ nm}}$.

(c) $r_{10} = 0.0529(5)^2$ nm = $\boxed{1.32 \text{ nm}}$.

63. $r_n = 0.053n^2$ nm. ☞ $n = \sqrt{\dfrac{r_n}{0.053}} = \sqrt{\dfrac{0.5 \times 10^3 \text{ nm}}{0.053}}$ $\boxed{\approx 100}$.

64. $\dfrac{1}{\lambda} = \dfrac{1}{c/f} = \dfrac{f}{c} = \dfrac{\Delta E/h}{c} = \dfrac{\Delta E}{hc} = \dfrac{(-13.6 \text{ eV})\left(\dfrac{1}{n_f^2} - \dfrac{1}{n_i^2}\right)}{hc} = \dfrac{13.6 \text{ eV}}{hc}\left(\dfrac{1}{n_i^2} - \dfrac{1}{n_f^2}\right)$.

So $R = \dfrac{13.6 \text{ eV}}{hc} = \dfrac{(13.6 \text{ eV})(1.60 \times 10^{-19} \text{ C})}{(6.626 \times 10^{-34} \text{ J·s})(3.00 \times 10^8 \text{ m/s})} = \boxed{1.095 \times 10^{-2} \text{ nm}^{-1}}$.

65.   (a) $E_n = \dfrac{-13.6 \text{ eV}}{n^2}$. $E_3 = \dfrac{-13.6 \text{ eV}}{3^2} = \boxed{-1.51 \text{ eV}}$.

(b) $E_6 = \dfrac{-13.6 \text{ eV}}{6^2} = \boxed{-0.378 \text{ eV}}$.

(c) $E_{10} = \dfrac{-13.6 \text{ eV}}{10^2} = \boxed{-0.136 \text{ eV}}$.

66.   (a) $\Delta E = (-13.6 \text{ eV})\left(\dfrac{1}{n_f^2} - \dfrac{1}{n_i^2}\right) = (-13.6 \text{ eV})\left(\dfrac{1}{\infty} - \dfrac{1}{3^2}\right) = \boxed{1.51 \text{ eV}}$.

(b) $\Delta E = (-13.6 \text{ eV})\left(\dfrac{1}{\infty} - \dfrac{1}{5^2}\right) = \boxed{0.544 \text{ eV}}$.

(c) $\Delta E = (-13.6 \text{ eV})\left(\dfrac{1}{\infty} - \dfrac{1}{10^2}\right) = \boxed{0.136 \text{ eV}}$.

67.   (a) The kinetic energy of the emitted electron will $\boxed{\text{increase but not double}}$ if the energy of the photon is doubled. This is because part of the energy is used to overcome the ionization energy which does not double. Actually the energy of the emitted electron will more than double because the portion of energy left for the electron (after ionization energy) will be more than double.

(b) $E = hf = (6.63 \times 10^{-34} \text{ J·s})(7.00 \times 10^{15} \text{ Hz}) = 4.64 \times 10^{-18} \text{ J} = 29.0 \text{ eV}$.

The kinetic energy of the emitted electron would be $K = 29.0 \text{ eV} - 13.6 \text{ eV} = \boxed{15.4 \text{ eV}}$.

68. (a) $\Delta E = (-13.6 \text{ eV}) \left(\dfrac{1}{n_f^2} - \dfrac{1}{n_i^2} \right)$.

$\Delta E_{52} = (13.6 \text{ eV}) \left(\dfrac{1}{2^2} - \dfrac{1}{5^2} \right) = 2.856 \text{ eV}$.

$\lambda_{52} = \dfrac{1.24 \times 10^3}{\Delta E \text{ (in eV)}} \text{ nm} = \dfrac{1.24 \times 10^3}{2.856} \text{ nm} = \boxed{434 \text{ nm}}$.

$\Delta E_{21} = (13.6 \text{ eV}) \left(\dfrac{1}{1^2} - \dfrac{1}{2^2} \right) = 10.2 \text{ eV}$.

$\lambda_{21} = \dfrac{1.24 \times 10^3}{10.2} \text{ nm} = \boxed{122 \text{ nm}}$.

(b) $\boxed{\text{Yes, 5 to 2 is in the visible region}}$ (violet).

69. (a) The photon of greatest energy emitted is of the transition from $\boxed{n = 2 \text{ to } n = 1}$. The energy is inversely proportional to n^2. As n increases, the energy decreases dramatically. So the large energy difference occurs at small n numbers.

(b) $\Delta E = (-13.6 \text{ eV}) \left(\dfrac{1}{n_f^2} - \dfrac{1}{n_i^2} \right)$. $\Delta E_{53} = (13.6 \text{ eV}) \left(\dfrac{1}{3^2} - \dfrac{1}{5^2} \right) = 0.967 \text{ eV}$.

$\Delta E_{62} = (13.6 \text{ eV}) \left(\dfrac{1}{2^2} - \dfrac{1}{6^2} \right) = 2.97 \text{ eV}$. $\Delta E_{21} = (13.6 \text{ eV}) \left(\dfrac{1}{1^2} - \dfrac{1}{2^2} \right) = 10.2 \text{ eV}$.

70. The longest wavelength corresponds to the transition from $n = 2$ to 1.

$\Delta E = (-13.6 \text{ eV}) \left(\dfrac{1}{n_f^2} - \dfrac{1}{n_i^2} \right) = (13.6 \text{ eV}) \left(\dfrac{1}{1^2} - \dfrac{1}{2^2} \right) = 10.2 \text{ eV}$.

$\lambda = \dfrac{1.24 \times 10^3}{\Delta E \text{ (in eV)}} \text{ nm} = \dfrac{1.24 \times 10^3}{10.2} \text{ nm} = \boxed{122 \text{ nm; ultraviolet}}$.

71. (a) In a hydrogen-like ion, the energy is modified to $E = -\dfrac{(13.6 \text{ eV})Z^2}{n^2}$, where Z is the atomic number (number of protons). For He^+, $Z = 2$.

The binding energy is $\Delta E = E_\infty - E_1 = 0 - E_1 = \dfrac{(13.6 \text{ eV})(2)^2}{1^2} = \boxed{54.4 \text{ eV}}$.

(b) For Li^{2+}, $Z = 3$. So the binding energy is $-E_1 = \dfrac{(13.6 \text{ eV})(3)^2}{1^2} = \boxed{122 \text{ eV}}$.

72.   (a) $E = hf = \dfrac{hc}{\lambda} = \dfrac{1.24 \times 10^3}{\lambda \text{ (in nm)}} \text{ eV} = \dfrac{1.24 \times 10^3}{486 \text{ nm}} \text{ eV} = \boxed{2.55 \text{ eV}}$.

     (b) $\Delta E = (-13.6 \text{ eV}) \left(\dfrac{1}{n_f^2} - \dfrac{1}{n_i^2} \right) = 2.55 \text{ eV}$.

     Using trial and error we find $\boxed{n_i = 2 \text{ and } n_f = 4}$. This is the only transition that will have an energy

     difference of 2.55 eV.

73. $v = \dfrac{nh}{2\pi mr} = \dfrac{(6.63 \times 10^{-34} \text{ J} \cdot \text{s})n}{2\pi(9.11 \times 10^{-31} \text{ kg})(0.0529 \times 10^{-9} \text{ m})n^2} = \boxed{(2.2 \times 10^6 \text{ m/s})/n \text{ m/s}}$.

74.   The kinetic energy is $K = \dfrac{ke^2}{2r}$ and the potential energy is $U = -\dfrac{ke^2}{r}$.

     Thus, the total energy is

     $E = U + K = \dfrac{ke^2}{2r} - \dfrac{ke^2}{r} = -\dfrac{ke^2}{2r} = -\dfrac{(9.0 \times 10^9 \text{ N} \cdot \text{m}^2/\text{C}^2)(1.6 \times 10^{-19} \text{ C})^2}{2(0.0529 \times 10^{-9} \text{ m})}$

     $= -2.18 \times 10^{-18} \text{ J} = -13.6 \text{ eV}$.

75.   (a) $U = -\dfrac{ke^2}{r} = \boxed{-27.2 \text{ eV}}$ and $K = \dfrac{ke^2}{2r} = \boxed{+13.6 \text{ eV}}$.

     (b) $\boxed{|U| = 2K}$, potential energy is twice as large in magnitude.

76.   (b).

77.   Through stimulated emission, the photon from a laser is caused by electron transitions between two discrete energy levels and so there are only a few colors (frequencies). A light bulb emits thermal radiation at many different frequencies.

78.   The photon emitted by a electron in an excited state "stimulates" the emission of another photon by a different electron in the same excited state. So the emission of one photon results in two photons and four, eight, sixteen, etc. However, it takes energy to pump the electrons from a lower-energy level to a higher-energy level in the first place, so the pump is ultimately providing the amplification.

79.   Spontaneous emission is really a random emission. Electrons jump from a higher-energy orbit to a lower-energy orbit, and a photon is released in the process.

     Stimulated emission is kind of an induced or controlled emission. The electron in the higher-energy orbit can jump to a lower-energy orbit when a photon of energy equal the difference of the energy between the two orbits is introduced. In this respect, the process is not random but is totally controllable. Once there are enough electrons in the higher-energy orbit, the photons are introduced, and all the electrons will eventually jump to the lower-energy orbit. For each introduced photon, two photons of the same frequency are produced (the other one is from the emission of the electron transition).

80.   Each second $E = Pt = (750 \times 10^3 \text{ W})(1.0 \text{ s}) = 750 \times 10^3 \text{ J}.$

$E = nhf,$ ☞ $n = \dfrac{E}{hf} = \dfrac{750 \times 10^3 \text{ J}}{(6.63 \times 10^{-34} \text{ J·s})(98.9 \times 10^6 \text{ Hz})} = \boxed{1.14 \times 10^{31} \text{ photons}}.$

81. $E^2 = p^2 c^2 + (mc^2)^2 = p^2 c^2,$ ☞ $p = \dfrac{E}{c} = \dfrac{hf}{c} = \dfrac{h}{c/f} = \dfrac{h}{\lambda}.$

82. $K_{max} = eV_o = \tfrac{1}{2} mv^2 = \tfrac{1}{2}(9.11 \times 10^{-31} \text{ kg})(3.5 \times 10^5 \text{ m/s})^2 = 5.58 \times 10^{-20} \text{ J} = 0.349 \text{ eV}.$

$hf = eV_o + \phi_o,$ ☞ $\phi_o = hf - eV_o = \dfrac{hc}{\lambda} - eV_o = \dfrac{1.24 \times 10^3 \text{ eV·nm}}{340 \text{ nm}} - 0.349 \text{ eV} = \boxed{3.3 \text{ eV}}.$

83.   (a) $\Delta E = (-13.6 \text{ eV}) \left(\dfrac{1}{n_f^2} - \dfrac{1}{n_i^2} \right).$ $\Delta E_{13} = (-13.6 \text{ eV}) \left(\dfrac{1}{3^2} - \dfrac{1}{1^2} \right) = \boxed{12.1 \text{ eV}}.$

(b) $\Delta E_{15} = (-13.6 \text{ eV}) \left(\dfrac{1}{5^2} - \dfrac{1}{1^2} \right) = \boxed{13.1 \text{ eV}}.$

84. $E_o = hf = \dfrac{hc}{\lambda} = \dfrac{(6.63 \times 10^{-34} \text{ J·s})(3.00 \times 10^8 \text{ m/s})}{700 \times 10^{-9} \text{ m}} = 2.94 \times 10^{-19} \text{ J}.$

So $n = \dfrac{E}{E_o} = \dfrac{1.0 \text{ J}}{2.94 \times 10^{-19} \text{ J/quantum}} = \boxed{3.5 \times 10^{18} \text{ quanta}}.$

85. $\Delta\lambda = \lambda_C (1 - \cos\theta),$ ☞ $\cos\theta = 1 - \dfrac{\Delta\lambda}{\lambda_o} = 1 - 0.25 = 0.75.$ So $\theta = \boxed{41°}.$

86.   (a) $\boxed{\text{Four}}$ transitions result in the emission of light in the visible region.

(b) The energy of a typical photon in the visible region is about

$E_{min} = hf = \dfrac{hc}{\lambda} = \dfrac{1.24 \times 10^3 \text{ eV·nm}}{700 \text{ nm}} = 1.77 \text{ eV (red)},$

and $E_{max} = \dfrac{1.24 \times 10^3 \text{ eV·nm}}{400 \text{ nm}} = 3.1 \text{ eV (violet)}.$

Since $\Delta E = (-13.6 \text{ eV}) \left(\dfrac{1}{n_f^2} - \dfrac{1}{n_i^2} \right)$, the electron has to be in the $n = 2$ state, because $\Delta E_{32} = 1.89$ eV,

$\Delta E_{42} = 2.55$ eV, $\Delta E_{52} = 2.86$ eV, $\Delta E_{62} = 3.02$ eV.

The electron cannot be in the $n = 1$ state as $\Delta E_{21} = 10.2$ eV.

The electron cannot be in the $n = 3$ state either as $\Delta E_{43} = 0.66$ eV.

The wavelength are:

$$\lambda_{62} = \frac{1.24 \times 10^3 \text{ eV·nm}}{3.02 \text{ eV}} = \boxed{410 \text{ nm}}, \qquad \lambda_{52} = \frac{1.24 \times 10^3 \text{ eV·nm}}{2.86 \text{ eV}} = \boxed{434 \text{ nm}},$$

$$\lambda_{42} = \frac{1.24 \times 10^3 \text{ eV·nm}}{2.55 \text{ eV}} = \boxed{486 \text{ nm}}, \qquad \lambda_{32} = \frac{1.24 \times 10^3 \text{ eV·nm}}{1.89 \text{ eV}} = \boxed{656 \text{ nm}}.$$

CHAPTER 28

1. (c).

2. (d).

3. The wavelength associated with a moving car is too short compared to everyday dimensions so we do not observe the wave.

4. The ⟦baseball as its momentum is smaller⟧ due to its smaller mass. The de Broglie wavelength is inversely proportional to the mass, $\lambda = \dfrac{h}{mv}$.

5. The wavelength will be ⟦shorter as higher potential difference causes a higher momentum⟧. The de Broglie wavelength is inversely proportional to the momentum, $\lambda = \dfrac{h}{p}$.

6. $\lambda = \dfrac{h}{mv} = \dfrac{6.63 \times 10^{-34} \text{ J·s}}{(1000 \text{ kg})(25 \text{ m/s})} = \boxed{2.7 \times 10^{-38} \text{ m}}$.

7. (a) The electron will have ⟦a longer⟧ de Broglie wavelength due to its smaller mass. The de Broglie wavelength is inversely proportional to the mass, $\lambda = \dfrac{h}{mv}$.

    (b) $\lambda_{\text{electron}} = \dfrac{h}{mv} = \dfrac{6.63 \times 10^{-34} \text{ J·s}}{(9.11 \times 10^{-31} \text{ kg})(100 \text{ m/s})} = \boxed{7.28 \times 10^{-6} \text{ m}}$.

    $\lambda_{\text{proton}} = \dfrac{6.63 \times 10^{-34} \text{ J·s}}{(1.67 \times 10^{-27} \text{ kg})(100 \text{ m/s})} = \boxed{3.97 \times 10^{-9} \text{ m}}$.

8. $\lambda = \dfrac{h}{mv} = \dfrac{6.63 \times 10^{-34} \text{ J·s}}{(70 \text{ kg})(2.0 \text{ m/s})} = \boxed{4.7 \times 10^{-36} \text{ m}}$.

9. $K = \frac{1}{2}mv^2 = eV$, ☞ $v \propto \dfrac{1}{\sqrt{m}}$, so $\lambda = \dfrac{h}{mv} \propto \dfrac{1}{\sqrt{m}}$.

    Therefore $\dfrac{\lambda_e}{\lambda_p} = \sqrt{\dfrac{m_p}{m_e}} = \sqrt{\dfrac{1.67 \times 10^{-27} \text{ kg}}{9.11 \times 10^{-31} \text{ kg}}} = \boxed{43}$.

384 Chapter 28   Quantum Mechanics

10. (a) If the potential difference increases to nine times its original value, the new de Broglie wavelength will

be $\boxed{1/3}$ times that of the original. According to Eq. 28.3, $\lambda = \sqrt{\dfrac{1.50}{V}}$ nm, we can see that the de

Broglie wavelength is inversely proportional to the square root of potential difference.

(b) From Eq. 28.3: $\lambda = \sqrt{\dfrac{1.50}{V}}$ nm, so $\lambda \propto \dfrac{1}{\sqrt{V}}$.

Therefore $\dfrac{\lambda_2}{\lambda_1} = \sqrt{\dfrac{V_1}{V_2}} = \sqrt{\dfrac{250 \text{ kV}}{600 \text{ kV}}} = \boxed{0.645}$.

11. From Eq. 28.3: $\lambda = \sqrt{\dfrac{1.50}{V}}$ nm, ☞ $V = \dfrac{1.50}{\lambda^2} = \dfrac{1.50}{(0.010)^2} = \boxed{1.5 \times 10^4 \text{ V}}$.

12. From Eq. 28.3: $\lambda = \sqrt{\dfrac{1.50}{V}}$ nm, so $\lambda \propto \dfrac{1}{\sqrt{V}}$.

Therefore $\dfrac{\lambda_2}{\lambda_1} = \sqrt{\dfrac{V_1}{V_2}} = \sqrt{\dfrac{V_1}{2\,V_1}} = \dfrac{1}{\sqrt{2}} \approx \boxed{0.71}$.

13. (a) Its de Broglie wavelength will $\boxed{\text{decrease}}$ due to the potential difference. The proton will gain speed

from the potential difference and the de Broglie wavelength is inversely proportional to speed, $\lambda = \dfrac{h}{mv}$.

(b) The initial kinetic energy of the proton is

$K_0 = \frac{1}{2}mv_0^2 = \frac{1}{2}(1.67 \times 10^{-27} \text{ kg})(4.5 \times 10^4 \text{ m/s})^2 = 1.69 \times 10^{-18} \text{ J} = 10.6 \text{ eV}$.

Since the initial speed of the proton is 4.5×10^4 m/s, it had taken 10.6 V to accelerate the proton from rest
to this speed.

So $V_1 = 10.6$ V and $V_2 = 10.6$ V + 37 V = 47.6 V.

From Eq. 28.3: $\lambda = \sqrt{\dfrac{1.50}{V}}$ nm, so $\lambda \propto \dfrac{1}{\sqrt{V}}$.

Therefore, the percentage difference is

$\dfrac{\lambda_2 - \lambda_1}{\lambda_1} = \dfrac{\lambda_2}{\lambda_1} - 1 = \sqrt{\dfrac{V_1}{V_2}} - 1 = \sqrt{\dfrac{10.6 \text{ V}}{37.6 \text{ V}}} - 1 = -0.53 = \boxed{-53\% \text{ (a decrease)}}$.

14. $d \sin \theta = m\lambda$, ☞ $\lambda = \dfrac{d \sin \theta}{m} = \dfrac{(0.15 \times 10^{-9} \text{ m}) \sin 25°}{1} = 6.34 \times 10^{-11} \text{ m} = 0.0634 \text{ nm}$.

From Eq. 28.3: $\lambda = \sqrt{\dfrac{1.50}{V}}$ nm, ☞ $V = \dfrac{1.50}{\lambda^2} = \dfrac{1.50}{(0.0634)^2} = 3.7 \times 10^2 \text{ V}$.

Therefore, it is $= \boxed{3.7 \times 10^2 \text{ eV}}$.

15. The Earth revolves the Sun once a year, so $v = \dfrac{d}{t} = \dfrac{2\pi(1.5 \times 10^{11} \text{ m})}{365 \times 86\,400 \text{ s}} = 2.99 \times 10^4$ m/s.

$\lambda = \dfrac{h}{mv} = \dfrac{6.63 \times 10^{-34} \text{ J·s}}{(5.98 \times 10^{24} \text{ kg})(2.99 \times 10^4 \text{ m/s})} = \boxed{3.7 \times 10^{-63} \text{ m}}$.

16. (a) $\lambda = \dfrac{h}{mv} = \dfrac{6.63 \times 10^{-34} \text{ J·s}}{(9.11 \times 10^{-31} \text{ kg})(2.19 \times 10^6 \text{ m/s})} = \boxed{3.32 \times 10^{-10} \text{ m}}$.

(b) $2\pi r_1 = 2\pi(0.529 \times 10^{-10} \text{ m}) = \lambda$. So they are the $\boxed{\text{same}}$, since it is a standing wave.

17. From Eq. 28.3: $\lambda = \sqrt{\dfrac{1.50}{V}}$ nm, ☞ $V = \dfrac{1.50}{\lambda^2} = \sqrt{\dfrac{1.50}{(0.25)^2}} = \boxed{24 \text{ V}}$.

18. (c).

19. (b).

20. (a) The following standing waves can be set up in the well:

$L = \dfrac{n\lambda}{2}$, $n = 1, 2, 3, \ldots$ or $\lambda = \dfrac{2L}{n}$.

Also the wave function must be zero at $x = 0$ and $x = L$.

So $\psi_n = A \sin \dfrac{2\pi}{\lambda} x = A \sin \dfrac{n\pi x}{L}$ for $n = 1, 2, 3, \ldots$

(b) $K_n = \dfrac{p^2}{2m} = \dfrac{(h/\lambda)^2}{2m} = \dfrac{h^2}{2m\lambda^2} = \dfrac{h^2}{2m(2L/n)^2} = n^2 \dfrac{h^2}{8mL^2}$.

21. (a) Wave functions.   Probability density.

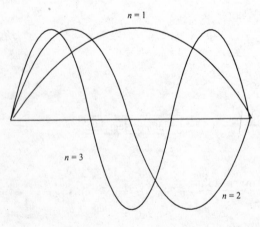

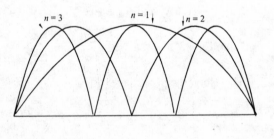

(b) The probability density is the highest at the center or $\boxed{x = L/2}$ so it is most likely to find the particle at that place.

22.   (b).

23.   (c).

24.   (a).

25.   The principle quantum number, n, gives information of the total energy and the orbit radius of an orbit in a hydrogen atom.

26.   When quantum numbers are large (> 1000), the transitions between energy levels are effectively continuous, and in agreement with classical predictions.

27.   The periodical table groups elements according to the values of quantum numbers n and l. Within a group, the elements have the same or very similar electronic configurations for the outmost electrons.

28.   (a) $2n^2 = 2(2)^2 = \boxed{8}$ and $2(3)^2 = \boxed{18}$.

(b) For $n = 2$:

(2, 1, 1, +1/2);   (2, 1, 1, –1/2);   (2, 1, 0, +1/2);   (2, 1, 0, –1/2);

(2, 1, –1, +1/2);   (2, 1, –1, –1/2);   (2, 0, 0, +1);   (2, 0, 0, –1/2).

For $n = 3$:

(3, 2, 2, +1/2);   (3, 2, 2, –1/2);   (3, 2, 1, +1/2);   (3, 2, 1, –1/2);

(3, 2, 0, +1/2);   (3, 2, 0, –1/2);   (3, 2, –1, +1/2);   (3, 2, –1, –1/2);

(3, 2, –2, +1/2);   (3, 2, –2, –1/2);   (3, 1, 1, +1);   (3, 1, 1, –1/2);

(3, 1, –1, +1/2);   (3, 1, –1, –1/2);   (3, 1, 0, +1/2);   (3, 1, 0, –1/2);

(3, 0, 0, +1/2);   (3, 0, 0, –1/2).

29.   (a) $2(2\ell + 1) = 2(0 + 1) = \boxed{2}$.

(b) $2[(2(3) + 1] = \boxed{14}$.

30.   (a) $\boxed{\ell = 2}$ has more sets of quantum numbers.

(b) For $n = 2$, there are $2n^2 = 2(2)^2 = 8$ sets of quantum numbers;

for $\ell = 2$, there are $2(2\ell + 1) = 2[2(2) + 1] = 10$ sets of quantum numbers.

31.   (a) Since m_ℓ could be 0, ±1, . . ., ±ℓ, the minimum ℓ is $\boxed{2}$.

(b) Since $\ell = 0, 1, . . ., n - 1$, the minimum n is $\boxed{3}$.

32.

N has 7 electrons

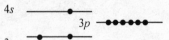
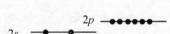

K has 19 electrons

33. (a) 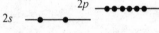 (b)

Na has 11 electrons

Ar has 18 electrons

34. (a) $\boxed{\text{Be}}$. (b) $\boxed{\text{N}}$.

(c) $\boxed{\text{Ne}}$. (d) $\boxed{\text{S}}$.

35. (a) $\boxed{1s^2\,2s^2\,2p^1}$. (b) $\boxed{1s^2\,2s^2\,2p^6\,3s^2\,3p^6\,4s^2}$.

(c) $\boxed{1s^2\,2s^2\,2p^6\,3s^2\,3p^6\,3d^{10}\,4s^2}$. (d) $\boxed{1s^2\,2s^2\,2p^6\,3s^2\,3p^6\,3d^{10}\,4s^2\,4p^6\,4d^{10}\,5s^2\,5p^2}$.

36. (a) If there were no electron spin, the $1s$ state would contain a maximum of $\boxed{\text{one}}$ electron because one set

of a unique quantum number set can only have one electron.

(b) The s state can have one electron, and the p state can have 3 electrons.

$1s^1$ is $\boxed{\text{hydrogen}}$ and $1s^1\,2s^1\,2p^3$ is $\boxed{\text{boron}}$.

37. $\boxed{\text{It would have a } 1s^3}$ and would be the first closed shell inert gas. With three spin orientations, s states can

contain three electrons without violating the Pauli exclusion principle.

38. (b).

39.   (b).

40.   Due to the uncertainty principle, the product of the uncertainty in position and the uncertainty in momentum (or mass times the uncertainty in velocity) cannot be zero. So there will always be uncertainly in both position and velocity.

41.   According to the uncertainty principle, the product of uncertainty in position and the uncertainty in momentum is in the order of Plank's constant. A bowling ball's diameter and mass are so large that the uncertainty in them (determined by the extremely small value of Planck's constant) is undetectable. However for an electron, with its very small mass, this is not true.

42. $(\Delta p)(\Delta x) \geq \dfrac{h}{2\pi}$,   ☞ $\Delta p \geq \dfrac{h}{2\pi(\Delta x)} = \dfrac{6.63 \times 10^{-34} \text{ J·s}}{2\pi(0.02 \text{ m})} = \boxed{5.3 \times 10^{-33} \text{ kg·m/s}}$.

43.   (a) The uncertainty in position for the proton and the electron are $\boxed{\text{the same}}$ since both have the same uncertainty in momentum.

       (b) $(\Delta p)(\Delta x) \geq \dfrac{h}{2\pi}$,   ☞ $\Delta x \geq \dfrac{h}{2\pi(\Delta p)} = \dfrac{6.63 \times 10^{-34} \text{ J·s}}{2\pi(2 \times 0.00025 \times 10^{-30} \text{ kg·m/s})} = \boxed{0.21 \text{ m}}$ for both.

44.   Since $(\Delta p)(\Delta x) \geq \dfrac{h}{2\pi}$ and $p = mv$,

       $\Delta v = \dfrac{\Delta p}{m} \geq \dfrac{h}{2\pi(\Delta x)m} = \dfrac{6.63 \times 10^{-34} \text{ J·s}}{2\pi[(0.10 - 0.050) \times 10^{-9} \text{ m}](9.11 \times 10^{-31} \text{ kg})} = \boxed{2.3 \times 10^{6} \text{ m/s}}$.

45.   Since $(\Delta p)(\Delta x) \geq \dfrac{h}{2\pi}$ and $p = mv$,

       $\Delta v \geq \dfrac{\Delta p}{m} \geq \dfrac{h}{2\pi(\Delta x)m} = \dfrac{6.63 \times 10^{-34} \text{ J·s}}{2\pi(2 \times 0.0005 \times 10^{-2} \text{ m})(0.50 \text{ kg})} = \boxed{2.1 \times 10^{-29} \text{ m/s}}$.

46. $K_{+} = 1.03(2.00 \text{ keV}) = 2.06 \text{ keV} = 3.30 \times 10^{-16} \text{ J}$; $K_{-} = 0.97(2.00 \text{ keV}) = 1.94 \text{ keV} = 3.10 \times 10^{-16} \text{ J}$.

       So $p_{+} = \sqrt{2mK} = \sqrt{2(9.11 \times 10^{-31} \text{ kg})(3.30 \times 10^{-16} \text{ J})} = 2.45 \times 10^{-23} \text{ kg·m/s}$;

       and $p_{-} = \sqrt{2(9.11 \times 10^{-31} \text{ kg})(3.10 \times 10^{-16} \text{ J})} = 2.38 \times 10^{-23} \text{ kg·m/s}$.

       Therefore $\Delta p = p_{+} - p_{-} = 7.00 \times 10^{-25} \text{ kg·m/s}$.

       Hence $(\Delta p)(\Delta x) \geq \dfrac{h}{2\pi}$,   ☞ $\Delta x \geq \dfrac{h}{2\pi(\Delta p)} = \dfrac{6.63 \times 10^{-34} \text{ J·s}}{2\pi(7.00 \times 10^{-25} \text{ kg·m/s})} = \boxed{1.5 \times 10^{-10} \text{ m}}$.

47. $(\Delta E)(\Delta t) \geq \dfrac{h}{2\pi}$,   ☞ $\Delta E \geq \dfrac{h}{2\pi(\Delta t)} = \dfrac{6.63 \times 10^{-34} \text{ J·s}}{2\pi(10^{-7} \text{ s})} = \boxed{1.1 \times 10^{-27} \text{ J}}$.

48. $(\Delta E)(\Delta t) \geq \dfrac{h}{2\pi}$, ☞ $\Delta t \geq \dfrac{h}{2\pi(\Delta E)} = \dfrac{6.63 \times 10^{-34} \text{ J·s}}{2\pi(2 \times 0.0003 \text{ eV})(1.6 \times 10^{-19} \text{ J/eV})} = \boxed{1.1 \times 10^{-12} \text{ s}}$.

49. (a) The answer is $\boxed{\text{smaller}}$. According to the uncertainty principle, $\Delta E \Delta t \geq \dfrac{h}{2\pi}$, the greater the lifetime,

Δt, the smaller the energy difference, therefore the smaller the width of spectral line.

(b) $(\Delta E)(\Delta t) \geq \dfrac{h}{2\pi}$, ☞ $\Delta E \geq \dfrac{h}{2\pi(\Delta t)}$. So $\dfrac{\Delta E_1}{\Delta E_2} = \dfrac{\Delta t_2}{\Delta t_1} = \dfrac{10^{-8} \text{ s}}{10^{-12} \text{ s}} = \boxed{10^4}$.

50. (d).

51. (a).

52. When matter and antimatter meet, they will annihilate each other, and energy will be converted from mass into electromagnetic energy.

53. (a) The rest energy of the electron-positron pair is 2×0.511 MeV = 1.022 MeV.

So the energy of the photon is greater than the rest mass of the pair. Therefore, the answer is $\boxed{\text{yes}}$.

(b) $E = hf$, ☞ $f = \dfrac{E}{h} = \dfrac{(1.04 \text{ MeV})(10^6 \text{ eV/MeV})(1.6 \times 10^{-19} \text{ J/eV})}{6.63 \times 10^{-34} \text{ J·s}} = \boxed{2.5 \times 10^{20} \text{ Hz}}$.

54. The rest energy of the electron pair is 2×0.511 MeV = 1.022 MeV.

From the conservation of energy and momentum, each photon will move in opposite direction with the

energy. So each will carry half the total energy or $\boxed{0.511 \text{ MeV}}$.

55. $E = hf \geq 2m_p c^2 = 2(1.67 \times 10^{-27} \text{ kg})(3.00 \times 10^8 \text{ m/s})^2 = 3.01 \times 10^{-10} \text{ J} = \boxed{1.9 \text{ GeV}}$.

56. (a) The pair production of a muon and an antimuon requires a photon of $\boxed{\text{more}}$ energy because the muons have more rest mass, so more energy is required.

(b) $E = hf \geq 2m_\mu c^2 = 207(2m_e c^2) = 207(1.022 \text{ MeV}) = \boxed{212 \text{ MeV}}$.

57. $d \sin \theta = m \lambda$, ☞ $\lambda = \dfrac{d \sin \theta}{m} = \dfrac{(0.190 \times 10^{-9} \text{ m}) \sin 45°}{1} = 1.34 \times 10^{-10} \text{ m} = 0.144 \text{ nm}$.

From Eq. 28.3: $\lambda = \sqrt{\dfrac{1.50}{V}}$ nm, ☞ $V = \dfrac{1.50}{\lambda^2} = \dfrac{1.50}{(0.134)^2} = \boxed{84 \text{ V}}$.

58. $(\Delta p)(\Delta x) \geq \dfrac{h}{2\pi}$, ☞ $\Delta x \geq \dfrac{h}{2\pi(\Delta p)} = \dfrac{h}{2\pi m(\Delta v)} = \dfrac{6.63 \times 10^{-34} \text{ J·s}}{2\pi(9.11 \times 10^{-31} \text{ kg})(0.00500 \text{ m/s})} = \boxed{2.32 \text{ cm}}$.

59. (a) $p = \dfrac{h}{\lambda} = \dfrac{hf}{c} = \dfrac{E}{c} = \dfrac{(7.5 \times 10^6 \text{ eV})(1.6 \times 10^{-19} \text{ J/eV})}{3.00 \times 10^8 \text{ m/s}} = \boxed{4.0 \times 10^{-21} \text{ kg·m/s}}$.

(b) $\lambda = \dfrac{h}{p} = \dfrac{6.63 \times 10^{-34} \text{ J·s}}{4.0 \times 10^{-21} \text{ kg·m/s}} = \boxed{1.7 \times 10^{-13} \text{ m}}$.

60. $K_+ = 1.03(5.00 \text{ keV}) = 5.15 \text{ keV} = 8.24 \times 10^{-16} \text{ J}$;

$K_- = 0.97(5.00 \text{ keV}) = 4.85 \text{ keV} = 7.76 \times 10^{-16} \text{ J}$.

So $p_+ = \sqrt{2mK} = \sqrt{2(9.11 \times 10^{-31} \text{ kg})(8.24 \times 10^{-16} \text{ J})} = 3.87 \times 10^{-23} \text{ kg·m/s}$;

and $p_- = \sqrt{2(9.11 \times 10^{-31} \text{ kg})(7.76 \times 10^{-16} \text{ J})} = 3.76 \times 10^{-23} \text{ kg·m/s}$.

Therefore $\Delta p = p_+ - p_- = 1.10 \times 10^{-24} \text{ kg·m/s}$.

Hence $(\Delta p)(\Delta x) \geq \dfrac{h}{2\pi}$, ☞ $\Delta x \geq \dfrac{h}{2\pi(\Delta p)} = \dfrac{6.63 \times 10^{-34} \text{ J·s}}{2\pi(1.10 \times 10^{-24} \text{ kg·m/s})} = \boxed{9.59 \times 10^{-11} \text{ m}}$.

61. The following standing waves can be set up in the well: $2L = \dfrac{n\lambda}{2}$, $n = 1, 2, 3, \ldots$,

or $\lambda = \dfrac{4L}{n}$. Also, the wave function must be zero at $x = \pm L$.

So $\psi_n = A \cos \dfrac{2\pi}{\lambda} x = A \cos \dfrac{n\pi x}{2L}$, $n = 1, 3, 5, \ldots$,

and $\psi_n = A \dfrac{2\pi}{\lambda} = A \sin \dfrac{n\pi x}{2L}$ for $n = 2, 4, 6, \ldots$.

62. $K_n = \dfrac{p^2}{2m} = \dfrac{(h/\lambda)^2}{2m} = \dfrac{h^2}{2m\lambda^2} = \dfrac{h^2}{2m(4L/n)^2} = n^2 \dfrac{h^2}{32mL^2}$, which is four times smaller than those in Exercise

28.20 because the well is twice as wide. K_n is proportional to $1/L^2$.

63. For ground state, $n = 1$, so the cosine wave function is considered.

The $\cos \theta$ function has a maximum at $\theta = 0$. So the particle is most likely to be found at $\boxed{x = 0}$.

The probability at $x = 0$ is $|\psi_n|^2 = A^2 \cos^2 0 = A^2$.

64. (a) $\lambda = \dfrac{h}{mv} = \dfrac{6.63 \times 10^{-34} \text{ J·s}}{(0.150 \text{ kg})(20 \text{ m/s})} = \boxed{2.21 \times 10^{-34} \text{ m}}$.

(b) 90 km/h = 25 m/s. $\lambda = \dfrac{6.63 \times 10^{-34} \text{ J·s}}{(1200 \text{ kg})(25 \text{ m/s})} = \boxed{2.21 \times 10^{-38} \text{ m}}$.

CHAPTER 29

The result of Exercise 29.39 is used in some exercises.

1.   (c).

2.   (d).

3.   (d).

4.   The nuclear force is an $\boxed{\text{attractive}}$ force. It acts between nucleons ($\boxed{\text{protons or neutrons}}$). It is a $\boxed{\text{short-range force}}$.

5.   The isotopes of an element have the $\boxed{\text{same number of protons}}$ but $\boxed{\text{different number of neutrons}}$.

6.   Based on the notation, $_{Z}^{A}X$, the number of protons is equal to the atomic number, Z, the number of neutrons is equal to the difference between the mass number and the atomic number, i.e., $N = A - Z$, and the number of electrons in a neutral atom is the same as the number of protons.

     (a) There are $\boxed{20\ p}$, $43 - 20 = \boxed{23\ n}$, and $\boxed{20\ e}$.

     (b) There are $\boxed{29\ p}$, $43 - 20 = \boxed{29\ n}$, and $\boxed{29\ e}$.

7.   (a) $\boxed{^{1}\text{H},\ ^{2}\text{D},\ ^{3}\text{T}}$.

     (b) $\boxed{\text{H}_2\text{O, D}_2\text{O, T}_2\text{O, HDO, HTO, DTO}}$.

     (c) $\boxed{\text{T}_2\text{O, HTO, DTO}}$.

8.   The mass number is $8 + 8 = 16$, $8 + 9 = 17$, and $8 + 10 = 18$, respectively.

     They are $\boxed{_{8}^{16}\text{O},\ _{8}^{17}\text{O},\ _{8}^{18}\text{O}}$.

9.   For argon, the number of neutrons is $N = A - Z = 40 - 18 = 22$.

     So for potassium, $A = Z + N = 19 + 22 = 41$, i.e., $\boxed{_{19}^{41}\text{K}}$.

10.   (a) For ^{24}Mg: $\boxed{12\ p}$, $24 - 12 = \boxed{12\ n}$, and $\boxed{12\ e}$.

   For ^{25}Mg: $\boxed{12\ p}$, $25 - 12 = \boxed{13\ n}$, and $\boxed{12\ e}$.

   (b) For ^{24}Mg: $\boxed{12\ p}$, $24 - 12 = \boxed{12\ n}$, and $\boxed{14\ e}$.

   For ^{25}Mg: $\boxed{12\ p}$, $25 - 12 = \boxed{13\ n}$, and $\boxed{14\ e}$.

   (c) For ^{24}Mg: $\boxed{12\ p}$, $24 - 12 = \boxed{12\ n}$, and $\boxed{11\ e}$.

   For ^{25}Mg: $\boxed{12\ p}$, $25 - 12 = \boxed{13\ n}$, and $\boxed{11\ e}$.

11.   There are 92 protons and 92 electrons in each U atom. The number of neutrons is $238 - 92 = 146$. So the answer is $\boxed{92\ p,\ 146\ n,\ and\ 92\ e}$.

12.   (a) Isotope of an element has the same $\boxed{\text{atomic number}}$.

   (b) Isotopes have the same Z but different A. For example, $\boxed{{}^{A+1}_{Z}X,\ {}^{A-1}_{Z}X}$.

13.   (a) $R_{He} = (1.2 \times 10^{-15}\ m)(4)^{1/3} = \boxed{1.9 \times 10^{-15}\ m}$; $R_{Ne} = (1.2 \times 10^{-15}\ m)(20)^{1/3} = \boxed{3.3 \times 10^{-15}\ m}$;

   $R_{Ar} = (1.2 \times 10^{-15}\ m)(40)^{1/3} = \boxed{4.1 \times 10^{-15}\ m}$; $R_{Kr} = (1.2 \times 10^{-15}\ m)(84)^{1/3} = \boxed{5.3 \times 10^{-15}\ m}$;

   $R_{Xe} = (1.2 \times 10^{-15}\ m)(132)^{1/3} = \boxed{6.1 \times 10^{-15}\ m}$; $R_{Rn} = (1.2 \times 10^{-15}\ m)(222)^{1/3} = \boxed{7.3 \times 10^{-15}\ m}$.

   (b) They are roughly from 10 000 to 50 000 times smaller than an atom.

14.   (d).

15. $\boxed{\text{No}}$, this is not a violation. In a negative beta decay for example, a proton, which is a nucleon, is created to make up for the loss of a neutron.

16.   Charge: α is positive; β is negative; γ is neutral.
   Mass: α is massive; β is less massive; γ is massless.

17.   (a) Because tritium, $^{3}_{1}$H, has one extra neutron compared to the stable deuterium ($^{2}_{1}$H), we expect $\boxed{\beta^{-}}$ decay.

   (b) For β^{-} decay: $^{3}_{1}H \rightarrow ^{3}_{2}He + ^{\ 0}_{-1}e$.

   The daughter nucleus is $\boxed{\text{helium-3; yes, it's stable}}$.

18. (a) $\boxed{^{60}_{27}\text{Co} \rightarrow \,^{60}_{28}\text{Ni} + \,^{0}_{-1}\text{e}}$.

(b) $\boxed{^{226}_{88}\text{Ra} \rightarrow \,^{222}_{86}\text{Rn} + \,^{4}_{2}\text{He}}$.

19. (a) $\boxed{^{237}_{93}\text{Np} \rightarrow \,^{233}_{91}\text{Pa} + \,^{4}_{2}\text{He}}$.

(b) $\boxed{^{32}_{15}\text{P} \rightarrow \,^{32}_{16}\text{S} + \,^{0}_{-1}\text{e}}$.

(c) $\boxed{^{56}_{27}\text{Co} \rightarrow \,^{56}_{26}\text{Fe} + \,^{0}_{+1}\text{e}}$.

(d) $\boxed{^{56}_{27}\text{Co} + \,^{0}_{-1}\text{e} \rightarrow \,^{56}_{26}\text{Fe}}$.

(e) $\boxed{^{42}_{19}\text{K}^{*} \rightarrow \,^{42}_{19}\text{K} + \gamma}$.

20. (a) In an α decay, the proton number decreases by two. So the decay product has $\boxed{\text{two}}$ fewer protons.

(b) α–decay: $\boxed{^{214}_{84}\text{Po} \rightarrow \,^{210}_{82}\text{Pb} + \,^{4}_{2}\text{He}}$.

21. α–β: $^{209}_{82}\text{Pb} + \,^{0}_{-1}\text{e} \leftarrow \,^{209}_{81}\text{Tl}$; $^{209}_{81}\text{Tl} + \,^{4}_{2}\text{He} \leftarrow \boxed{^{213}_{83}\text{Bi}}$.

β–α: $^{209}_{82}\text{Pb} + \,^{4}_{2}\text{He} \leftarrow \,^{213}_{84}\text{Po}$; $^{213}_{84}\text{Po} + \,^{0}_{-1}\text{e} \leftarrow \boxed{^{213}_{83}\text{Bi}}$.

22. (a) $\boxed{^{4}_{2}\text{He}}$.

(b) $\boxed{4(^{1}_{0}\text{n})}$.

(c) $\boxed{\gamma}$.

(d) $\boxed{^{29}_{12}\text{Mg}}$.

23. (a) $\boxed{^{4}_{2}\text{He}}$.

(b) $\boxed{^{0}_{-1}\text{e}}$.

(c) $\boxed{^{102}_{39}\text{Y}}$.

(d) $\boxed{^{23}_{11}\text{Na}^{*}}$.

(e) $\boxed{^{0}_{-1}\text{e}}$.

24. α–series: $\boxed{^{227}_{89}\text{Ac} \rightarrow ^{223}_{87}\text{Fr} + ^{4}_{2}\text{He}}$; $\boxed{^{223}_{87}\text{Fr} \rightarrow ^{223}_{88}\text{Ra} + ^{0}_{-1}\text{e}}$;

$\boxed{^{223}_{88}\text{Ra} \rightarrow ^{219}_{86}\text{Rn} + ^{4}_{2}\text{He}}$; $\boxed{^{219}_{86}\text{Rn} \rightarrow ^{215}_{84}\text{Po} + ^{4}_{2}\text{He}}$.

β–series: $\boxed{^{227}_{89}\text{Ac} \rightarrow ^{227}_{90}\text{Th} + ^{0}_{-1}\text{e}}$; $\boxed{^{227}_{90}\text{Th} \rightarrow ^{223}_{88}\text{Ra} + ^{4}_{2}\text{He}}$;

$\boxed{^{223}_{88}\text{Ra} \rightarrow ^{219}_{86}\text{Rn} + ^{4}_{2}\text{He}}$; $\boxed{^{219}_{86}\text{Rn} \rightarrow ^{215}_{84}\text{Po} + ^{4}_{2}\text{He}}$.

25. α to ^{233}Pa; β^{-} to ^{233}U; α to ^{229}Th; α to ^{225}Ra; β^{-} to ^{225}Ac; α to ^{221}Fr; α to ^{217}At; α to ^{213}Bi; α to ^{209}Tl; β^{-} to ^{209}Pb; β^{-} to ^{209}Bi.

Or

α to ^{233}Pa; β^{-} to ^{233}U; α to ^{229}Th; α to ^{225}Ra; β^{-} to ^{225}Ac; α to ^{221}Fr; α to ^{217}At; α to ^{213}Bi; β^{-} to ^{213}Po; α to ^{209}Pb; β^{-} to ^{209}Bi.

26. (d).

27. (c). $\dfrac{1}{2^2} = \dfrac{1}{4} = 25\%$. So it will have decreased by $100\% - 25\% = 75\%$.

28. $\boxed{\text{None}}$, it is totally independent of temperature, environment, and chemistry.

29. $\boxed{\text{No, the decay is exponential}}$, not linear.

30. (a) The half-life, $t_{1/2}$ would be $\boxed{\text{infinite}}$.

(b) $\lambda = \dfrac{0.693}{t_{1/2}} = \boxed{0}$.

31. (a) $(2.50 \times 10^6 \text{ decays/s}) \dfrac{1 \text{ Ci}}{3.70 \times 10^{10} \text{ decays/s}} = 6.76 \times 10^{-5} \text{ Ci} = \boxed{67.6 \ \mu\text{Ci}}$.

(b) 2.50×10^6 decays/s = $\boxed{2.50 \times 10^6 \text{ Bq}}$.

32. (a) 20 mCi = $(20 \times 10^{-3} \text{ Ci}) \dfrac{3.70 \times 10^{10} \text{ decays/s}}{1 \text{ Ci}} = \boxed{7.4 \times 10^8 \text{ decays/s}}$.

(b) 7.4×10^8 decays/s = $(7.4 \times 10^8 \text{ betas/s}) \dfrac{60 \text{ s}}{1 \text{ min}} = \boxed{4.4 \times 10^{10} \text{ betas/min}}$.

33. (a) Since 3 h is 3 half-lives, then $\left(\frac{1}{2}\right)^3$ or $\boxed{\frac{1}{8}}$ would be left.

(b) 1 d = 24 $t_{1/2}$, so $\boxed{\dfrac{1}{2^{24}} \text{ or approximately } 6 \times 10^{-6}\% \text{ of the original}}$.

34. $\lambda = \dfrac{0.693}{t_{1/2}} = \dfrac{0.693}{18 \times 60 \text{ s}} = 6.42 \times 10^{-4} \text{ s}^{-1}$;

$\lambda t = (5.92 \times 10^{-4} \text{ s}^{-1})(3600 \text{ s}) = 2.31$.

Thus, $\dfrac{\Delta N}{\Delta t} = \lambda N = \lambda N_0 \, e^{-\lambda t} = \dfrac{\Delta N_0}{\Delta t} \, e^{-\lambda t} = (10 \text{ mCi}) \, e^{-2.31} = \boxed{1 \text{ mCi}}$.

35. $\dfrac{\Delta N}{\Delta t} = \lambda N = \lambda N_0 \, e^{-\lambda t} = \dfrac{\Delta N_0}{\Delta t} e^{-\lambda t}$, ☞ $e^{-\lambda t} = 0.20$.

So $t = -\dfrac{\ln 0.20}{\lambda} = -\dfrac{t_{1/2} \ln 0.20}{0.693} = -\dfrac{(12.3 \text{ years}) \ln 0.20}{0.693} = \boxed{28.6 \text{ years}}$.

36. (a) $^{104}_{32}$Tc will have a $\boxed{\text{larger}}$ decay constant than $^{28}_{12}$Mg because the decay constant is inversely proportional

to half-life, $\lambda = \dfrac{0.693}{t_{1/2}}$.

(b) $\lambda = \dfrac{0.693}{t_{1/2}}$, ☞ $\dfrac{\lambda_{Tc}}{\lambda_{Mg}} = \dfrac{(t_{1/2})_{Mg}}{(t_{1/2})_{Tc}} = \dfrac{21 \text{ h}}{18/60 \text{ h}} = \boxed{70}$.

37. $\lambda = \dfrac{0.693}{t_{1/2}} = \dfrac{0.693}{8.04 \text{ d}} = 0.0862 \text{ d}^{-1}$, $\lambda t = (0.0862 \text{ d}^{-1})(1 \text{ d}) = 0.0862$.

So $N = N_0 \, e^{-\lambda t}$, ☞ $\dfrac{N}{N_0} = e^{-\lambda t} = e^{-0.0862} = 0.917 = \boxed{91.7\%}$.

38. (a) Bone A is $\boxed{\text{younger}}$. The activity decreases as time passes so a higher activity indicates a short time,

i.e., younger.

(b) From Example 29.5, the initial activity is $\dfrac{\Delta N_0}{\Delta t} = 16$ decays/g·min.

$\dfrac{4}{16} = \dfrac{1}{4} = \dfrac{1}{2^2}$, i.e., after 2 half-lives.

So $t = 2 \, t_{1/2} = 2(5730 \text{ years}) = \boxed{1.1 \times 10^4 \text{ years}}$.

39. After n half-lives, $\lambda t = \dfrac{0.693}{t_{1/2}} \, n t_{1/2} = 0.693n$.

So $N = N_0 \, e^{-\lambda t} = N_0 \, e^{-0.693n} = \dfrac{N_0}{(e^{0.693})^n} = \dfrac{N_0}{2^n} = \left(\dfrac{1}{2}\right)^n N_0$.

40. $t_{1/2} = 5730$ y. $\dfrac{28\,650\text{ y}}{5730\text{ y}} = 5$, i.e., after 5 half-lives.

So $\dfrac{N}{N_0} = \dfrac{1}{2^5} = 0.031 = \boxed{3.1\%}$.

41. $1 - 0.875 = 0.125 = \dfrac{1}{8} = \dfrac{1}{2^3}$, i.e., after 3 half-lives.

So $t_{1/2} = \dfrac{t}{3} = \dfrac{54\text{ min}}{3} = 18$ min. Therefore, it is $\boxed{^{104}\text{Tc}}$ from Table 29.1.

42. $\dfrac{\Delta N}{\Delta t} = \lambda N = \lambda N_0\, e^{-\lambda t} = \dfrac{\Delta N_0}{\Delta t}\, e^{-\lambda t}$,   ☞ $\dfrac{\Delta N/\Delta t}{\Delta N_0/\Delta t} = 0.20 = e^{-\lambda t}$.

Thus, $t = -\dfrac{\ln 0.20}{\lambda} = -\dfrac{t_{1/2}\ln 0.20}{0.693} = -\dfrac{(5.3\text{ years})\ln 0.20}{0.693} = \boxed{12\text{ years}}$.

43. $\lambda t = \dfrac{0.693}{t_{1/2}}\, t = \dfrac{0.693}{28\text{ years}} (150\text{ years}) = 3.7125$.

$N = N_0\, e^{-\lambda t}$,   ☞ $\dfrac{N}{N_0} = e^{-\lambda t} = e^{-3.7125} = 0.02442$.

Thus, the amount that will be in the sample is $(0.02442)(40\ \mu\text{g}) = \boxed{0.98\ \mu\text{g}}$.

44.   (a) $\lambda = \dfrac{0.693}{t_{1/2}} = \dfrac{0.693}{66.0\text{ s}} = \boxed{1.05 \times 10^{-2}\text{ s}^{-1}}$.

(b) $\dfrac{\Delta N}{\Delta t} = \lambda N = \lambda N_0\, e^{-\lambda t} = \dfrac{\Delta N_0}{\Delta t}\, e^{-\lambda t}$,   ☞ $\dfrac{\Delta N/\Delta t}{\Delta N_0/\Delta t} = 0.10 = e^{-\lambda t}$.

Thus, $t = -\dfrac{\ln 0.10}{\lambda} = -\dfrac{t_{1/2}\ln 0.10}{0.693} = -\dfrac{(66.0\text{ s})\ln 0.10}{0.693} = \boxed{219\text{ s}}$.

45.   (a) The mass of one nuclei is $(223\text{ u})(1.66 \times 10^{-27}\text{ kg/u})$.

So there were $\dfrac{25.0 \times 10^{-6}\text{ kg}}{(223\text{ u})(1.66 \times 10^{-27}\text{ kg/u})} = \boxed{6.75 \times 10^{19}\text{ nuclei}}$.

(b) $\lambda t = \dfrac{0.693}{t_{1/2}}\, t = \dfrac{0.693}{21.8\text{ min}} (60\text{ min} + 49\text{ min}) = 3.465$.

Thus, $N = N_0\, e^{-\lambda t}$,   ☞ $\dfrac{N}{N_0} = e^{-\lambda t} = e^{-3.465} = 0.0313$.

Therefore, there are $(0.0313)(6.75 \times 10^{19}\text{ nuclei}) = \boxed{2.11 \times 10^{18}\text{ nuclei}}$.

46.   (a) $\dfrac{7 \text{ d}}{3.82 \text{ d}} = 1.83$.   So $N \approx \dfrac{N_0}{2^{1.83}} = \dfrac{7.50 \times 10^{10} \text{ atoms}}{2^{1.83}} = \boxed{2.11 \times 10^{10} \text{ atoms}}$.

    (c) $\boxed{\text{No, the daughters themselves are radioactive}}$, giving rise to granddaughters, etc., down the chain to

    lead (Pb).

47. $\lambda t = \dfrac{0.693}{t_{1/2}} t = \dfrac{0.693}{1600 \text{ y}} (2100 \text{ y} - 1898 \text{ y}) = 0.0875$.

    $N = N_0 \, e^{-\lambda t}$,   ☞ $\dfrac{N}{N_0} = e^{-\lambda t} = e^{-0.0875} = 0.916$.

    Thus, the amount of radium that would remain is $(0.916)(10 \text{ mg}) = \boxed{9.2 \text{ mg}}$.

48. $\dfrac{\Delta N}{\Delta t} = \dfrac{475 \text{ decays/min}}{250 \text{ g}} = 1.9 \text{ decays/g·min}$.   From Example 29.5, $\dfrac{\Delta N_0}{\Delta t} = 16 \text{ decays/g·min}$.

    $\dfrac{\Delta N/\Delta t}{\Delta N_0/\Delta t} = \dfrac{1.9}{16} \approx \dfrac{1}{8} = \dfrac{1}{2^3}$, i.e., slightly longer than 3 half-lives.

    Thus, $t \approx 3 t_{1/2} = 3(5730 \text{ years}) = 17\,190 \text{ years}$.   Therefore, it is about $\boxed{17\,000 \text{ years}}$.

49.   The mass of U_3O_8 is $3(238 \text{ u}) + 8(16 \text{ u}) = 942 \text{ u}$.

    Thus, the fraction of U by mass is $\dfrac{3 \times 238}{942} = 0.758$.

    In 500 000 tons of U_3O_8, there are $(0.758)(500\,000 \text{ tons})(10 \text{ kg/ton}) = 3.8 \times 10^6 \text{ kg}$ of U today.

    4.6 billion years is about 1 half-life.

    Therefore there were $2(3.8 \times 10^6 \text{ kg}) = \boxed{7.6 \times 10^6 \text{ kg}}$ of U.

50.   (a) The end product is $\boxed{{}^{13}_{6}\text{C}}$ because the decay is ${}^{13}_{7}\text{N} \rightarrow {}^{13}_{6}\text{C} + {}^{0}_{+1}\text{e}$.

    (b) There were $N_0 = \dfrac{0.0015 \text{ kg}}{(13 \text{ u})(1.66 \times 10^{-27} \text{ kg/u})} = 6.95 \times 10^{22}$ nuclei.

    $\lambda = \dfrac{0.693}{t_{1/2}} = \dfrac{0.693}{10 \text{ min}} = 0.0693 \text{ min}^{-1}$. $\lambda t = (0.0693 \text{ min}^{-1})(35 \text{ min}) = 2.43$.

    $\dfrac{\Delta N_0}{\Delta t} = \lambda N_0 = (0.0693 \text{ min}^{-1})(6.95 \times 10^{22} \text{ nuclei}) = 4.82 \times 10^{21} \text{ decays/min}$.

    $\dfrac{\Delta N}{\Delta t} = \dfrac{\Delta N_0}{\Delta t} e^{-\lambda t} = (4.82 \times 10^{21} \text{ decays/min}) e^{-2.43} = \boxed{4.2 \times 10^{20} \text{ decays/min}}$.

    (c) $N = \dfrac{\Delta N/\Delta t}{\lambda} = \dfrac{4.23 \times 10^{20} \text{ decays/min}}{0.0693 \text{ min}^{-1}} = 6.10 \times 10^{21}$ nuclei,

    so the percentage of ${}^{13}\text{N}$ is $\dfrac{6.10 \times 10^{21}}{6.95 \times 10^{22}} = \boxed{8.8\%}$.

51.   (d).

52.   (a).

53. $\boxed{^1\text{H and }^2\text{H are stable and }^3\text{H is unstable}}$ because there are too many neutrons in ^{3}T.

54. $\boxed{^4_2\text{He, } ^{16}_8\text{O, } ^{40}_{20}\text{Ca, } ^{48}_{20}\text{Ca, } ^{208}_{82}\text{Pb}}$.

55.   (a) $\boxed{^{17}_8\text{O}}$, because of an unpaired neutron beyond a magic number.

        (b) $\boxed{^{42}_{20}\text{Ca}}$, because of a magic number difference making $^{40}_{20}$Ca more stable (both are paired).

        (c) $\boxed{^{10}_5\text{B}}$, because of lack of pairing.

        (d) $\boxed{\text{Approximately the same}}$ because both have 126 neutrons (paired and magic) and the different number of protons does not affect neutrons.

56. $\boxed{^{58}_{28}\text{Ni}}$.

57. $\boxed{\text{(b) and (d)}}$, others are odd–odd.

58. $\boxed{\text{(b) and (d)}}$ are unstable.

59. $E_b = \Delta mc^2 = (m_n + m_p - m_D)c^2$,

        so $\quad m_D = m_p + m_n - E_b/c^2 = 1.007276 \text{ u} + 1.008665 \text{ u} + \dfrac{2.224 \text{ MeV}}{931.5 \text{ MeV/u}} = \boxed{2.013553 \text{ u}}$.

60.   For carbon, 1 mole $(6.02 \times 10^{23}$ atoms) has a mass of 12 g.

        So $\quad (6.02 \times 10^{23})(12 \text{ u}) = 12 \times 10^{-3}$ kg, $\quad$ ☞ $\quad 1 \text{ u} = \dfrac{12 \times 10^{-3} \text{ kg}}{12(6.02 \times 10^{23})} = 1.66 \times 10^{-27}$ kg.

61.   (a) $E_b = \Delta mc^2 = (6m_H + 6m_n - m_C)c^2 = [6(1.007825 \text{ u}) + 6(1.008665 \text{ u}) - 12.000000 \text{ u}](931.5 \text{ MeV/u})$

            $= \boxed{92.2 \text{ MeV}}$.

        (b) $\dfrac{E_b}{A} = \dfrac{92.2 \text{ MeV}}{12 \text{ nucleon}} = \boxed{7.68 \text{ MeV/nucleon}}$.

62. $E_b = \Delta m c^2 = (8m_H + 8m_n - m_O)c^2 = [8(1.007825 \text{ u}) + 8(1.008665 \text{ u}) - 15.994915 \text{ u}](931.5 \text{ MeV/u})$

   $= 127.6 \text{ MeV}.$

   $\dfrac{E_b}{A} = \dfrac{127.6 \text{ MeV}}{16 \text{ nucleon}} = \boxed{7.98 \text{ MeV/nucleon}}.$

63. $\boxed{\text{Deuterium}}$ has the lower average binding energy per nucleon.

   For deuterium:

   $E_b = (m_H + m_n - m_D)c^2 = (1.007825 \text{ u} + 1.008665 \text{ u} - 2.014102 \text{ u})(931.5 \text{ MeV/u}) = 2.22 \text{ MeV}.$

   So $\dfrac{E_b}{A} = \dfrac{2.22 \text{ MeV}}{2 \text{ nucleon}} = 1.11 \text{ MeV/nucleon}.$

   For tritium:

   $E_b = (m_H + 2m_n - m_T)c^2 = [1.007825 \text{ u} + 2(1.008665 \text{ u}) - 3.016049 \text{ u}](931.5 \text{ MeV/u}) = 8.48 \text{ MeV}.$

   So $\dfrac{E_b}{A} = \dfrac{8.48 \text{ MeV}}{3 \text{ nucleon}} = 2.83 \text{ MeV/nucleon}.$

64. $E_b = (m_H + m_n - m_D)c^2 = (1.007825 \text{ u} + 1.008665 \text{ u} - 2.014102 \text{ u})(931.5 \text{ MeV/u}) = \boxed{2.22 \text{ MeV}}.$

65. The energy required is

   $E_b = (7m_H + 7m_n - m_N)c^2 = [7(1.007825 \text{ u}) + 7(1.008665 \text{ u}) - 14.003074 \text{ u}](931.5 \text{ MeV/u})$

   $= \boxed{104.7 \text{ MeV}}.$

66. $E_b = (m_n + m_{K\text{-}39} - m_{K\text{-}40})c^2 = (1.008665 \text{ u} + 38.963708 \text{ u} - 39.964000 \text{ u})(931.5 \text{ MeV/u}) = \boxed{7.80 \text{ MeV}}.$

67. The energy required is

   $E_b = (m_{He} + m_{Na} - m_{Al})c^2 = (4.002603 \text{ u} + 22.989770 \text{ u} - 26.981541 \text{ u})(931.5 \text{ MeV/u})$

   $= \boxed{10.1 \text{ MeV}}.$

68. For Al: $E_b = (13m_H + 14m_n - m_{Al})c^2 = [13(1.007825 \text{ u}) + 14(1.008665 \text{ u}) - 26.981541 \text{ u}](931.5 \text{ MeV/u})$

   $= 225.0 \text{ MeV}.$

   Thus, $\dfrac{E_b}{A} = \dfrac{225.0 \text{ MeV}}{27 \text{ nucleon}} = 8.33 \text{ MeV/nucleon}.$

   For Na: $E_b = (11m_H + 12m_n - m_{Na})c^2 = [11(1.007825 \text{ u}) + 12(1.008665 \text{ u}) - 22.989770 \text{ u}](931.5 \text{ MeV/u})$

   $= 186.6 \text{ MeV}.$

   Thus, $\dfrac{E_b}{A} = \dfrac{186.6 \text{ MeV}}{23 \text{ nucleon}} = 8.11 \text{ MeV/nucleon}.$

   Therefore, the nucleons are more tightly bound in $\boxed{\text{Al}}$ on average.

69. $E_b = (92m_H + 146m_n - m_U) c^2 = [92(1.007825\ u) + 143(1.008665\ u) - 235.043925\ u](931.5\ MeV/u)$

$\qquad = 1784\ MeV.$

So $\dfrac{E_b}{A} = \dfrac{1784\ MeV}{235\ nucleon} = \boxed{7.59\ MeV/nucleon}$.

70. (a) The mass of ^6_3Li is $\boxed{less}$. It takes energy (therefore mass, according to the special theory of relativity) to break up the Li atom to three protons and neutrons, and that energy is due to the mass difference between the Li atom and the three protons and three neutrons.

(b) $E_b = (3m_p + 3m_n - m_{Li})c^2$,

so $m_{Li} = 3m_p + 3m_n - \dfrac{E_b}{c^2} = 3(1.007276\ u) + 3(1.008665\ u) - \dfrac{32.0\ MeV}{931.5\ MeV/u} = \boxed{6.013470\ u}$.

71. (a) $2m_{He} = 2(4.002603\ u) = 8.005206\ u$. So the mass of $\boxed{two\ alpha}$ particles is less.

(b) For Be:

$E_b = (4m_H + 4m_n - m_{Be})c^2 = [4(1.007825\ u) + 4(1.008665\ u) - 8.005305\ u](931.5\ MeV/u) = 56.5\ MeV.$

For two He:

$E_b = 2(2m_H + 2m_n - m_{He})c^2 = 2[2(1.007825\ u) + 2(1.008665\ u) - 4.002603\ u](931.5\ MeV/u) = 56.6\ MeV.$

So the binding energy of $\boxed{two\ alphas}$ is greater.

(c) $\boxed{Yes}$, since two alphas are more stable.

72. (d).

73. (d).

74. Less ^{14}C would have been produced. A sample measured now would have its age overestimated.

75. $\boxed{No,\ the\ relative\ biological\ effectiveness\ (RBE)\ values\ are\ different}$. RBE for X ray is 1 and 20 for alpha from Table 29.4.

76. (a) $\boxed{Alpha\ particles}$, according to Table 19.4.

(b) For X rays: Dose (in rem) = Dose (in rad) × RBE = (1.0 rad) × (1) = $\boxed{1.0\ rem}$;

for α particles: Dose (in rem) = (1.0 rad) × (20) = $\boxed{20\ rem}$.

77. $\lambda t = \dfrac{0.693}{t_{1/2}} t = \dfrac{0.693}{2.7 \text{ d}} (30 \text{ d}) = 7.7$.

$\dfrac{\Delta N}{\Delta t} = \dfrac{\Delta N_0}{\Delta t} e^{-\lambda t} = (80 \text{ mCi}) e^{-7.7} = 3.6 \times 10^{-2} \text{ mCi} = \boxed{36 \ \mu\text{Ci}}$.

78. (a) $E = m \times \text{Dose} = (0.20 \text{ kg})(1.25 \text{ rad}) = \boxed{0.25 \text{ J}}$.

(b) Dose (in rem) = Dose (in rad) $\times$ RBE = (1.25 rad)(4) = 5.0 rem, which exceeds the maximum

permissible radiation dosage with background radiation included. So the answer is $\boxed{\text{yes}}$.

79. Dose (in rem) = Σ [Dose (in rad) $\times$ RBE] = (0.5 rad)(1) + (0.3 rad)(4) + (0.1 rad)(20) = 3.7 rem in two

months. So $\boxed{\text{yes}}$, the maximum permissible radiation dosage is exceeded.

80. The half-life of ^{60}Co is $t_{1/2}$ = 5.271 year, so within 1 h, the decay rate can be considered constant.

The decay rate is R = 1.00 mCi = $(1.00 \times 10^{-3} \text{ Ci})(3.7 \times 10^{10} \text{ nuclei/s/Ci}) = 3.70 \times 10^7$ nuclei/s.

The energy released by each nuclei is

(1.33 MeV + 1.17 MeV)$(10^6 \text{ eV/MeV})(1.6 \times 10^{-19} \text{ J/eV}) = 4.00 \times 10^{-13}$ J/nuclei.

With a 50.0% absorption, the total energy absorbed by the tumor in 1 h is

$E = (0.500)(3.70 \times 10^7 \text{ nuclei/s})(4.00 \times 10^{-13} \text{ J/nuclei})(3600 \text{ s}) = 2.66 \times 10^{-2}$ J.

The radiation dosage is then $\dfrac{E}{m} = \dfrac{2.66 \times 10^{-2} \text{ J}}{0.100 \text{ kg}} = 0.266 \text{ J/kg} = 0.266 \text{ Gy} = 26.6 \text{ rad}$.

Effective dose (in rems) = dose (in rad) $\times$ RBE = (26.6 rad)(1) = $\boxed{26.6 \text{ rem}}$.

Or effective dose (in Sv) = dose (in Gy) $\times$ RBE = (0.266 Gy)(1) = $\boxed{0.266 \text{ Sy}}$.

81. The isotope in the hair was $\boxed{^{75}_{33}\text{As}}$.

The decay is $^{76}_{33}\text{As} \rightarrow \boxed{^{76}_{34}\text{Se}} + ^{\ 0}_{-1}\text{e}$.

82. This can be determined by $\boxed{^{14}\text{C dating}}$. See Example 29.5 in the textbook.

83. (a) E_b = (7.075 MeV/nucleon)(4 nucleon) = $\boxed{28.3 \text{ MeV}}$.

(b) $E_b = (2m_p + 2m_n - m_{He})c^2$,

so $m_{He} = 2m_p + 2m_n - E_b/c^2 = 2(1.007276 \text{ u}) + 2(1.008665 \text{ u}) - \dfrac{28.3 \text{ MeV}}{931.5 \text{ MeV/u}} = \boxed{4.001501 \text{ u}}$.

84.   The first α decay to $^{230}_{90}$Th; the second α decay to $^{226}_{88}$Ra; the third α decay to $^{222}_{86}$Rn; the fourth α decay to $^{218}_{84}$Po; the first β decay to $^{222}_{85}$At; the second β decay to $\boxed{^{218}_{86}\text{Rn}}$.

85.   (a) $\lambda = \dfrac{0.693}{t_{1/2}} = 0.28875 \text{ min}^{-1}$, $\quad \lambda t = (0.28875 \text{ min}^{-1})(10 \text{ min}) = 2.8875$.

$N = N_0\, e^{-\lambda t} = (6.02 \times 10^{23} \text{ nuclei})\, e^{-2.8875} = \boxed{3.4 \times 10^{22} \text{ nuclei}}$.

(b) $\lambda t = (0.28875 \text{ min}^{-1})(60 \text{ min}) = 17.325$.

$N = (6.02 \times 10^{23} \text{ nuclei})\, e^{-17.325} = \boxed{1.8 \times 10^{16} \text{ nuclei}}$.

(c) After 10 min: $\dfrac{\Delta N}{\Delta t} = \lambda N = (0.28875 \text{ min}^{-1})(3.35 \times 10^{22} \text{ nuclei}) = \boxed{9.7 \times 10^{19} \text{ decays/min}}$;

after 1 h, $\dfrac{\Delta N}{\Delta t} = (0.28875 \text{ min}^{-1})(1.80 \times 10^{16} \text{ nuclei}) = \boxed{5.2 \times 10^{15} \text{ decays/min}}$.

86.   Refer to Example 29.4 in the textbook. $\dfrac{1}{16} = \dfrac{1}{2^4}$, i.e., after 4 half-lives,

so $\quad t = 4t_{1/2} = 4(5730 \text{ years}) = \boxed{2.29 \times 10^4 \text{ years}}$.

87.   (a) $\boxed{^{\ 0}_{-1}\text{e}}$.

(b) $\boxed{^{222}_{86}\text{Rn}}$.

(c) $\boxed{^{237}_{94}\text{Pu}}$.

(d) $\boxed{\gamma}$.

(e) $\boxed{^{\ 0}_{+1}\text{e}}$.

88.   (1) Alpha decay to $\boxed{^{235}_{92}\text{U}}$.

(2) Alpha decay to $\boxed{^{231}_{90}\text{Th}}$.

(3) Beta decay to $\boxed{^{231}_{91}\text{Pa}}$.

(4) Alpha decay to $\boxed{^{227}_{89}\text{Ac}}$.

89. (a) $E_b = (7.58 \text{ MeV/nucleon})(238 \text{ nucleon}) = \boxed{1.80 \times 10^3 \text{ MeV}}$.

(b) $E_b = (92m_p + 146m_n - m_U)c^2$,　so

$m_U = 92m_p + 146m_U - E_b/c^2 = 92(1.007276 \text{ u}) + 146(1.008665 \text{ u}) - \dfrac{1804 \text{ MeV}}{931.5 \text{ MeV/u}} = \boxed{237.997821 \text{ u}}$.

90. (a) $E = m\,c^2 = (12 \text{ u})(931.5 \text{ MeV/u}) = \boxed{1.118 \times 10^4 \text{ MeV}}$.

(b) $E = (4.002603 \text{ u})(931.5 \text{ MeV/u}) = \boxed{3.728 \times 10^3 \text{ MeV}}$.

91. (1) All nuclei with $Z > 83$ are unstable.

(2) All odd–odd nuclei are unstable except for ^{2}H, ^{6}Li, ^{10}B, and ^{14}N.

(3) Stable nuclei with $A < 40$ have about equal numbers of protons and neutrons.

(4) Stable nuclei with $A > 40$ have an excess number of neutrons, which becomes more obvious as A

increases.

So $\boxed{\text{(c) and (d)}}$ are stable.

92. (a) $^{229}_{90}\text{Th} \rightarrow \boxed{^{225}_{88}\text{Ra}} + {}^4_2\text{He}$.

(b) $^{225}_{88}\text{Ra} \rightarrow \boxed{^{225}_{89}\text{Ac}} + {}^0_{-1}\text{e}$.

93. $^6_3\text{Li} + {}^1_1\text{H} \rightarrow {}^4_2\text{He} + \boxed{^3_2\text{He}}$.

94. (a) $N_o = \dfrac{1.0 \times 10^{-3} \text{ kg}}{(198 \text{ u})(1.66 \times 10^{-27} \text{ kg/u})} = 3.04 \times 10^{21}$ nuclei.

$\lambda = \dfrac{0.693}{t_{1/2}} = \dfrac{0.693}{2.7 \times 24 \times 60 \text{ min}} = 1.78 \times 10^{-4} \text{ min}^{-1}$.

So $\dfrac{\Delta N_o}{\Delta t} = \lambda N_o = (1.78 \times 10^{-4} \text{ min}^{-1})(3.04 \times 10^{21} \text{ nuclei}) = \boxed{5.4 \times 10^{17} \text{ decays/min}}$.

(b) $\lambda t = (1.78 \times 10^{-4} \text{ min}^{-1})(30 \times 24 \times 60 \text{ min}) = 7.69$.

$\dfrac{\Delta N}{\Delta t} = \dfrac{\Delta N_o}{\Delta t}\, e^{-\lambda t} = (5.41 \times 10^{17} \text{ decays/min})\, e^{-7.69} = \boxed{2.5 \times 10^{14} \text{ decays/min}}$.

95. (a) $\dfrac{\text{nucleon}}{\text{volume}} = \dfrac{A}{4\pi R^3/3} = \dfrac{3A}{4\pi R^3} = \dfrac{3A}{4\pi R_o^3 A} = \dfrac{3}{4\pi R_o^3} = \dfrac{3}{4\pi(1.2 \times 10^{-15} \text{ m})^3}$

$\approx 1.4 \times 10^{44} \text{ nucleons/m}^3$.

(b) 1 nucleon has a mass of 1.66×10^{-27} kg,

so $\rho = (1.4 \times 10^{44} \text{ nucleon/m}^3)\dfrac{1.66 \times 10^{-27} \text{ kg}}{1 \text{ nucleon}} = \boxed{2.3 \times 10^{17} \text{ kg/m}^3}$.

96. $\lambda = \dfrac{0.693}{t_{1/2}} = \dfrac{0.693}{12.33 \text{ y}} = 0.0562 \text{ y}^{-1}, \quad \lambda t = (0.0562 \text{ y}^{-1})(6.00 \text{ y}) = 0.337.$

Thus, $N = N_0\, e^{-\lambda t}, \quad \mathbb{F} \quad \dfrac{N}{N_0} = e^{-\lambda t} = e^{-0.337} = 0.714 = \boxed{71.4\%}.$

97. (a) The nuclear density is $\boxed{\text{greater}}$ than the average density of the atom, since the nucleus occupies a much

smaller volume than the atom and both have about the same mass.

(b) For H atom: $\quad \rho = \dfrac{1.67 \times 10^{-27} \text{ kg}}{4\pi(0.053 \times 10^{-9} \text{ m})^3/3} = 2.7 \times 10^3 \text{ kg/m}^3.$

From Exercise 29.95(b), the nuclear density is $2.3 \times 10^{17} \text{ kg/m}^3.$

Thus, $\quad \dfrac{2.3 \times 10^{17} \text{ kg/m}^3}{2.7 \times 10^3 \text{ kg/m}^3} = 9 \times 10^{13} \approx 10^{14}$, i.e., the $\boxed{\text{nuclear density is greater by } 10^{14} \text{ times}}.$

(c) $\boxed{\text{No}}$. The average atomic density is much higher than hydrogen gas (most gases are typically

$\approx 2 \text{ kg/m}^3$) because the gas density includes mostly empty space between gas molecules.

98. $^{232}_{92}\text{U} \rightarrow {}^{228}_{90}\text{Th} + {}^{4}_{2}\text{He}.$

$E = \Delta mc^2 = (m_\text{U} - m_\text{Th} - m_\text{He})(931.5 \text{ MeV/u}) = (232.03714 \text{ u} - 228.02873 \text{ u} - 4.002603 \text{ u})(31.5 \text{ MeV/u})$

$= \boxed{5.41 \text{ MeV}}.$

CHAPTER 30

NUCLEAR REACTIONS AND ELEMENTARY PARTICLES

1.   (d).

2.   (d).

3.   In a chemical reaction, the nuclei are not changed, i.e., oxygen is still oxygen after the reaction. However, the nuclei are changed in a nuclear reaction .

4. $K_{min} = \left(1 + \dfrac{m_a}{M_A}\right)|Q|.$

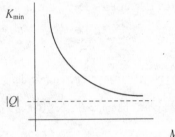

As the target mass M_A becomes very large, $K_{min} \rightarrow |Q|$.
If $Q = 0$, the incident particle would not need any kinetic energy to start the reaction.

5.   The reactants have more mass because energy is released in an exoergic reaction.

6.   (a) $^{41}_{19}K$.   (b) $^{135}_{52}Te$.   (c) $4(^1_0n)$.   (d) $^{14}_{7}N$.   (e) p or ^1_1H.

7.   (a) $^{14}_{7}N$.   (b) ^2_1H.   (c) $^{30}_{15}P$.   (d) $^{17}_{8}O$.   (e) $^{10}_{5}B$.

8.   (a) $^{41}_{18}Ar^*$.   (b) $^{236}_{92}U^*$.   (c) $^{236}_{92}U^*$.   (d) $^{18}_{9}F^*$.   (e) $^{138}_{56}Ba^*$.

9.   (a) $^{14}_{7}N^*$.   (b) $^{14}_{7}N^*$.   (c) $^{31}_{15}P^*$.   (d) $^{18}_{9}F^*$.   (e) $^{14}_{7}N^*$.

10.   (a) Initial mass $= m_C + m_H = 13.003\ 355\ u + 1.007\ 825\ u = 14.011\ 180\ u$.

Final mass $= m_{He} - m_B = 4.002\ 603 + 10.012\ 938\ u = 14.015\ 541\ u$.

Since the final mass is greater, the reaction is endoergic , i.e., it requires energy input.

(b) $Q = (m_C + m_H - m_{He} - m_B)c^2 = (13.003\ 355\ u + 1.007\ 825\ u - 4.002\ 603 - 10.012\ 938\ u)(931.5\ MeV/u)$

$= -4.06\ MeV$.

$K_{min} = \left(1 + \dfrac{m_a}{M_A}\right)|Q| = \left(1 + \dfrac{1.007\ 825}{13.003\ 355}\right)(4.06\ MeV) = \boxed{4.32\ MeV}$.

11.   For an reaction to occur spontaneously, the Q value must be greater than zero.

(a) $\boxed{^{22}_{11}\text{Na}}$. $Q = (21.991384 \text{ u} - 21.994435 \text{ u} - m_e) c^2 < 0.$ So $\boxed{\text{no}}$.

(b) $\boxed{^{222}_{86}\text{Rn}}$. $Q = (226.025406 \text{ u} - 222.017574 \text{ u} - 4.002603 \text{ u}) c^2 > 0.$ So $\boxed{\text{yes}}$.

(c) $\boxed{^{12}_{6}\text{C}}$. $Q = (15.994915 \text{ u} - 12.000000 - 4.002603 \text{ u}) c^2 < 0.$ So $\boxed{\text{no}}$.

12. $Q = (m_{\text{H-1}} + m_{\text{H-2}} - m_{\text{He}})c^2 = (1.007\ 825 \text{ u} + 2.014\ 102 \text{ u} - 3.016\ 029 \text{ u})(931.5 \text{ MeV/u}) = +5.49 \text{ MeV}.$

13.   (a) The Q value is expected to be $\boxed{\text{positive}}$, because this is a decay (spontaneous) process.

(b) $Q = (m_U - m_{\text{Th}} - m_{\text{He}})c^2 = (238.050\ 786 \text{ u} - 234.043\ 583 \text{ u} - 4.002\ 603 \text{ u})(931.5 \text{ MeV/u})$

   $= \boxed{+4.28 \text{ MeV}}$.

14. $Q = (m_O + m_n - m_C - m_{\text{He}})c^2 = (15.994\ 915 \text{ u} + 1.008\ 665 \text{ u} - 13.003\ 355 \text{ u} - 4.002\ 603 \text{ u})(931.5 \text{ MeV/u})$

   $= -2.215 \text{ MeV}.$

   $K_{\text{min}} = \left(1 + \dfrac{m_a}{M_A}\right) |Q| = \left(1 + \dfrac{1.008\ 665}{15.994\ 915}\right)(2.215 \text{ MeV}) = \boxed{2.35 \text{ MeV}}.$

15. $Q = (m_{\text{He}} + m_n - 2m_H)c^2 = (3.016\ 029 \text{ u} + 1.008\ 665 \text{ u} - 2.014\ 102 \text{ u} - 2.014\ 102 \text{ u})(931.5 \text{ MeV/u})$

   $= -3.270 \text{ MeV}.$

   $K_{\text{min}} = \left(1 + \dfrac{m_a}{M_A}\right) |Q| = \left(1 + \dfrac{1.008\ 665}{3.016\ 029}\right)(3.270 \text{ MeV}) = \boxed{4.36 \text{ MeV}}.$

16. $Q = (m_C + m_H - m_n - m_N)c^2 = (13.003\ 355 \text{ u} + 1.007\ 825 \text{ u} - 1.008\ 665 \text{ u} - 13.005\ 739 \text{ u})(931.5 \text{ MeV/u})$

   $= -3.003 \text{ MeV}.$

   $K_{\text{min}} = \left(1 + \dfrac{m_a}{M_A}\right) |Q| = \left(1 + \dfrac{1.007\ 825}{13.003\ 355}\right)(3.003 \text{ MeV}) = \boxed{3.24 \text{ MeV}}.$

17.   (a) The reaction is $\boxed{\text{endoergic}}$ by definition.

(b) $Q = (m_N + m_{\text{He}} - m_O - m_H)c^2$

   $= (14.003\ 074 \text{ u} + 4.002\ 603 \text{ u} - 16.99\ 9131 \text{ u} - 1.007\ 825 \text{ u})(931.5 \text{ MeV/u}) = -1.191 \text{ MeV}.$

   $K_{\text{min}} = \left(1 + \dfrac{m_a}{M_A}\right) |Q| = \left(1 + \dfrac{4.002\ 603}{14.003\ 074}\right)(1.191 \text{ MeV}) = \boxed{1.53 \text{ MeV}}.$

18. $Q = (m_{Li} + m_H - 2m_{He})c^2 = (7.016\ 005\ u + 1.007\ 825\ u - 4.002\ 603\ u - 4.002\ 603\ u)(931.5\ \text{MeV/u})$

$= +17.3\ \text{MeV}.$

Thus, it is $\boxed{\text{exoergic}}$.

19. $Q = (m_{Hg} + m_H - m_{Au} - m_{He})c^2 = (199.968\ 321\ u + 1.007\ 825\ u - 196.966\ 56\ u - 4.002\ 603\ u)(931.5\ \text{MeV})$

$= +6.50\ \text{MeV}.$

Thus, it is $\boxed{\text{exoergic}}$.

20. $Q = (m_{Be} + m_{He} - m_C - m_n)c^2$ $(9.012\ 183\ u + 4.002\ 603\ u - 12.000\ 000\ u - 1.008\ 665\ u)(931.5\ \text{MeV/u})$

$= \boxed{+5.70\ \text{MeV}}.$

21. $Q = (m_{H\text{-}3} + m_H - m_{H\text{-}2} - m_{H\text{-}2})c^2$

$= (3.016\ 049\ u + 1.007\ 825\ u - 2.014\ 102\ u - 2.014\ 102\ u)(931.5\ \text{MeV/u}) = -4.033\ \text{MeV}.$

$K_{min} = \left(1 + \dfrac{m_a}{M_A}\right)|Q| = \left(1 + \dfrac{1.007\ 825}{3.016\ 049}\right)(4.033\ \text{MeV}) = \boxed{5.38\ \text{MeV}}.$

22. $^{226}\text{Ra} \rightarrow\ ^{222}\text{Rn} +\ ^4\text{He}.$

$Q = (m_{Ra} - m_{Rn} - m_{He})c^2 = (226.025\ 406\ u - 222.017\ 574\ u - 4.002\ 603\ u)(931.5\ \text{MeV/u})$

$= 4.871\ \text{MeV}.$

From the conservation of energy, the kinetic energy of the recoiling daughter nucleus is

$K = 4.871\ \text{MeV} - 4.706\ \text{MeV} = \boxed{0.165\ \text{MeV}}.$

23.   (a) Since $K_{min} = \left(1 + \dfrac{m_a}{M_A}\right)|Q|$, the difference in Q value (3 times) is greater than the difference caused by

the target mass (15 and 20). The first reaction has $\boxed{\text{greater}}$ minimum threshold energy.

(b) For the first reaction: $(K_1)_{min} = \left(1 + \dfrac{1}{15}\right)|Q_1|,$

For the second reaction: $(K_2)_{min} = \left(1 + \dfrac{1}{20}\right)|Q_2|.$

Thus, $\dfrac{(K_1)_{min}}{(K_2)_{min}} = \dfrac{16/15}{21/20}\dfrac{|Q_1|}{|Q_2|} = \dfrac{16/15}{21/20}(3) = \boxed{3.05}.$

24. The total area of all the plates is $A = n\pi R^2$ and the area of the wall is $A_o = LW$.

So the probability is $\dfrac{A}{A_o} = \boxed{\dfrac{n\pi R^2}{LW}}$.

25. (a) $\pi R^2 = \pi R_o^2 (A)^{2/3} = \pi(1.2 \times 10^{-15}\text{ m})^2 (12)^{2/3} = 2.37 \times 10^{-29}\text{ m}^2 = (2.37 \times 10^{-29}\text{ m}^2)\dfrac{1\text{ b}}{10^{-28}\text{ m}^2}$

$= \boxed{0.24\text{ b}}$.

(b) $\pi R^2 = \pi(1.2 \times 10^{-15}\text{ m})^2 (56)^{2/3} = 6.62 \times 10^{-29}\text{ m}^2 = \boxed{0.66\text{ b}}$.

(c) $\pi R^2 = \pi(1.2 \times 10^{-15}\text{ m})^2 (208)^{2/3} = 1.59 \times 10^{-28}\text{ m}^2 = \boxed{1.6\text{ b}}$.

(d) $\pi R^2 = \pi(1.2 \times 10^{-15}\text{ m})^2 (238)^{2/3} = 1.74 \times 10^{-28}\text{ m}^2 = \boxed{1.7\text{ b}}$.

26. The electric potential energy is $U_e = \dfrac{kq_1 q_2}{r}$.

The total kinetic energy is $K_{\text{total}} = 2\left(\frac{3}{2}k_B T\right) = U_e$.

So $T = \dfrac{U_e}{3k_B} = \dfrac{kq_1 q_2}{3rk_B} = \dfrac{(9.0 \times 10^9\text{ N·m}^2/\text{C}^2)(1.6 \times 10^{-19}\text{ C})^2}{3(10^{-14}\text{ m})(1.38 \times 10^{-23}\text{ J/K})} = \boxed{5.6 \times 10^8\text{ K}}$.

27. (d).

28. (d).

29. (d).

30. (d).

31. $\boxed{\text{Fission: heavy nuclei splitting into lighter nuclei; fusion: light nuclei fuse into heavier nuclei}}$.

32. In a fission, the $\boxed{\text{original nuclei}}$ has more mass. Otherwise, there will be no energy released in the fission.

In a fusion, the $\boxed{\text{original nuclei}}$ also has more mass for the same reason.

33. The reaction products collide with the core materials and coolant and in the process heat the water that converts it to steam that powers a turbine.

34. The energy liberated is about 1 MeV per nucleon in fission products.

(a) $235 + 1 - 5 = 231$ nucleons are involved in the fission process,

so the energy released is (1 MeV/nucleon)(231 nucleon) = $\boxed{231 \text{ MeV}}$.

(b) $235 + 1 - 3 = 233$ nucleons are involved in the fission process,

so the energy released is (1 MeV/nucleon)(233 nucleon) = $\boxed{233 \text{ MeV}}$.

35. (a) $Q = (m_{\text{H-1}} + m_n - m_{\text{H-2}})c^2 = (1.007\ 825\ \text{u} + 1.008\ 665\ \text{u} - 2.014\ 102\ \text{u})(931.5\ \text{MeV/u})$

$= \boxed{2.22 \text{ MeV}}$.

(b) $Q = (2m_{\text{He-3}} - m_{\text{He-4}} - 2m_{\text{H}})c^2 = [2(3.016\ 029\ \text{u}) - 4.002\ 603\ \text{u} - 2(1.007\ 825\ \text{u})](931.5\ \text{MeV/u})$

$= \boxed{12.9 \text{ MeV}}$.

36. (a) $Q = (2m_{\text{H-2}} - m_{\text{H-3}} - m_n)c^2 = [2(2.014\ 102\ \text{u}) - 3.016\ 029\ \text{u} - 1.008\ 665\ \text{u}](931.5\ \text{MeV/u})$

$= \boxed{3.27 \text{ MeV}}$.

(b) $Q = (m_{\text{H-2}} + m_{\text{H-3}} - m_{\text{He}} - m_n)c^2$

$= (2.014\ 102\ \text{u} + 3.016\ 029\ \text{u} - 4.002\ 603\ \text{u} - 1.008\ 665\ \text{u})(931.5\ \text{MeV/u}) = \boxed{17.6 \text{ MeV}}$.

37. $0.02\ \text{eV} = 0.60^n (2.0 \times 10^6\ \text{eV})$, ☞ $n = -\dfrac{\log \dfrac{0.02}{2.0 \times 10^6}}{\log 0.60} = \boxed{36 \text{ collisions}}$.

38. (d).

39. (c).

40. $\boxed{\text{Neutrinos interact very, very weakly with matter}}$, so they can pass through huge quantities of matter

without being detected.

41. $\boxed{m = 0,\ v = c,\ \text{spin} = 1/2}$.

42. Neutrino has zero mass, so $E = pc = \dfrac{hc}{\lambda}$.

Therefore $\lambda = \dfrac{hc}{E} = \dfrac{(6.63 \times 10^{-34}\ \text{J} \cdot)(3.00 \times 10^8\ \text{m/s})}{(2.65 \times 10^6\ \text{eV})(1.6 \times 10^{-19}\ \text{J/eV})} = \boxed{4.69 \times 10^{-13}\ \text{m}}$.

---

43. $p = \dfrac{E}{c} = \dfrac{(2.65 \times 10^6 \text{ eV})(1.6 \times 10^{-19} \text{ J/eV})}{3.00 \times 10^8 \text{ m/s}} = \boxed{1.41 \times 10^{-21} \text{ kg·m/s}}$.

According to momentum conservation, the momentum of the beta particle plus the daughter nucleus is equal in magnitude and $\boxed{\text{opposite the neutrino direction}}$.

44. (a) According to the conservation of energy, $K_{max} = 3.51 \text{ MeV} - 2.65 \text{ MeV} = \boxed{0.86 \text{ MeV}}$.

(b) Since the daughter nucleus has zero kinetic energy in this case, the momentum of the beta particle is

$\boxed{1.41 \times 10^{-21} \text{ kg·m/s opposite that of the neutrino's}}$.

(c) When the kinetic energy of the beta particle is maximum, the kinetic energy and momentum of the daughter nucleus are $\boxed{\text{both zero}}$.

45. In a β^- decay: $^A_Z\text{P} \rightarrow\, ^A_{Z+1}\text{D} +\, ^{\ 0}_{-1}\text{e}$.

So $Q = (m_p - m_D - m_e)c^2 = \{(m_p + Zm_e) - [m_D + (Z+1)m_e]\}c^2 = (M_p - M_D)c^2$.

46. The daughter is ^{12}C. From Exercise 30.45, we have

$K_{max} = Q = (M_p - M_D)c^2 = (12.014\ 353 \text{ u} - 12.000\ 000 \text{ u})(931.5 \text{ MeV/u}) = \boxed{13.37 \text{ MeV}}$.

47. From Exercise 30.45, the maximum energy released in the decay is

$Q = (M_p - M_D)c^2 = (31.973\ 908 \text{ u} - 31.972\ 072 \text{ u})(931.5 \text{ MeV/u}) = 1.710 \text{ MeV}$.

So the energy of the neutrino is $1.710 \text{ MeV} - 1 \text{ MeV} = \boxed{0.71 \text{ MeV}}$.

48. In a β^+ decay: $^A_Z\text{P} \rightarrow\, ^{\ A}_{Z-1}\text{D} +\, ^0_{+1}\text{e}$.

So $Q = (m_p - m_D - m_e)c^2 = \{(m_p + Zm_e) - [m_D + (Z-1)m_e] - 2m_e\}c^2 = (M_p - M_D - 2m_e)c^2$.

49. From Exercise 30.48, the maximum energy released in the decay is

$Q = (M_p - M_D - 2m_e)c^2 = (13.005\ 739 \text{ u} - 13.003\ 355 \text{ u})(931.5 \text{ MeV/u}) - 2(0.511 \text{ MeV}) = 1.199 \text{ MeV}$.

So the energy of the neutrino is $1.199 \text{ MeV} - 1.190 \text{ MeV} = 0.009 \text{ MeV} = \boxed{9 \text{ keV}}$.

50. (a) Use the results from Exercises 30.45 and 30.48.

For a reaction to be energetically possible, the Q value has to be positive.

In a β^- decay, $Q = (M_p - M_D)c^2 > 0$,   so $M_p > M_D$.

In a β^+ decay, $Q = (M_p - M_D - 2m_e)c^2 > 0$,   so $M_p > M_D + 2m_e$.

Therefore, M_p for β^- decay must be $\boxed{\text{less}}$.

(b) $\boxed{\beta^-:\ M_p > M_D \text{ and for } \beta^+:\ M_p > M_D + 2m_e}$.

51.   (b).

52.   (a).

53.   The effects of the virtual exchange particles can be predicted and these predictions confirmed experimentally (scientific method).

54. $\boxed{\text{Protons: strong, electromagnetic, gravitational; electrons: electromagnetic, gravitational}}$.

55. $R = \dfrac{h}{2\pi mc}$,   ☞ $m = \dfrac{h}{2\pi Rc} = \dfrac{6.63 \times 10^{-34}\ \text{J·s}}{2\pi(10^{-15}\ \text{m})(3.00 \times 10^8\ \text{m/s})} = \boxed{3.5 \times 10^{-28}\ \text{kg}}$.

56.   It is $\boxed{\text{strong nuclear}}$ interaction.

$R = c\Delta t$,   ☞ $\Delta t = \dfrac{R}{c} = \dfrac{5.0 \times 10^{-16}\ \text{m}}{3.00 \times 10^8\ \text{m/s}} = \boxed{1.7 \times 10^{-24}\ \text{s}}$.

57.   (a) The range of interaction $\boxed{\text{decreases}}$ as energy of the exchange particle increases. If energy increases, the mass increases, and the range is inversely proportional to the mass, $R = \dfrac{h}{2\pi m_m c}$.

(b) $R < \dfrac{h}{2\pi m_m c} = \dfrac{hc}{2\pi m_m c^2} = \dfrac{hc}{2\pi E_o} = \dfrac{(6.63 \times 10^{-34}\ \text{J·s})(3.00 \times 10^8\ \text{m/s})}{2\pi(1.00 \times 10^9\ \text{eV})(1.6 \times 10^{-19}\ \text{J/eV})} = \boxed{1.98 \times 10^{-16}\ \text{m}}$.

58. $m_m = 264 m_e$,   so $\Delta E = m_m c^2 = 264(0.511\ \text{MeV}) = \boxed{135\ \text{MeV}}$.

59.   Since $(\Delta E)(\Delta t) \ge \dfrac{h}{2\pi}$,

$\Delta t \ge \dfrac{h}{2\pi\Delta E} = \dfrac{6.63 \times 10^{-34}\ \text{J·s}}{2\pi(140 \times 10^6\ \text{eV})(1.6 \times 10^{-19}\ \text{J/eV})} = \boxed{4.71 \times 10^{-24}\ \text{s}}$.

60.   (b).

61.   (a).

62. Quark flavor has one of six values. It can be changed by a weak interaction.

Quark color has one of three values. It can be changed by gluons.

63. All hadrons contain quarks and/or antiquarks. Quarks are not believed to exist freely outside the nucleus.

64. Baryons ("heavy ones") have half-integer intrinsic spin (1/2 or 3/2) and decay into products that eventually include a proton (except a proton). Mesons have integer spin values (0 or 1) and eventually decay into leptons and photons.

65. From Table 30.3:   (a) $\boxed{\pi^+}$.   (b) $\boxed{K^0}$.

(c) $\boxed{\Sigma^0}$.   (d) $\boxed{\Xi^-}$.

66. (a) The quark combination for a proton is $\boxed{uud}$.

(b) The proton has a charge of $+e$. $\frac{2}{3}e + \frac{2}{3}e - \frac{1}{3}e = +e$.

67. (a) The quark combination for a neutron is $\boxed{udd}$.

(b) The neutron has no charge. $\frac{2}{3}e - \frac{1}{3}e - \frac{1}{3}e = 0$.

68. (b).

69. (a).

70. (a) $\boxed{{}^4_2\text{He}}$.   (b) $\boxed{{}^1_1\text{H}}$.   (c) $\boxed{{}^{93}_{38}\text{Sr}}$.

(d) $\boxed{{}^{12}_6\text{C}}$.   (e) $\boxed{{}^{16}_7\text{N}}$.

71. (a) $\boxed{{}^7_4\text{Be}^*}$.   (b) $\boxed{{}^{60}_{29}\text{Cu}^*}$.   (c) $\boxed{{}^{236}_{92}\text{U}^*}$.

(d) $\boxed{{}^{13}_6\text{C}^*}$.   (e) $\boxed{{}^{17}_8\text{O}^*}$.

72. $Q = (2m_{\text{H-2}} - m_{\text{H-3}} - m_\text{H})c^2 = [2(2.014\ 102\ \text{u}) - 3.016\ 049\ \text{u} - 1.007\ 825\ \text{u}](931.5\ \text{MeV/u})$

$= \boxed{4.03\ \text{MeV}}$.

73. $^{14}_{6}C \rightarrow \, ^{14}_{7}N + \, ^{0}_{-1}e$.

$Q = (m_C - m_N)c^2 = (14.003242 \text{ u} - 14.003074 \text{ u})(931.5 \text{ MeV/u}) = \boxed{0.156 \text{ MeV}}$.

The mass of the electron in the products is not included in the calculation because it is already included in the mass of the N atom (see Exercise 30.45).

74. In an electron capture: $^{A}_{Z}P + \, ^{0}_{-1}e \rightarrow \, ^{A}_{Z-1}D$.

So $Q = (m_p + m_e - m_D)c^2 = \{(m_p + Zm_e) - [m_D + (Z-1)m_e]\}c^2 = (M_p - M_D)c^2$.

75. (a) From Exercise 30.74, the Q value in electron capture is

$Q = (m_{Be} - m_{Li})c^2 = (7.016930 \text{ u} - 7.016005 \text{ u})(931.5 \text{ MeV/u}) = 0.86 \text{ MeV}$.

From Exercise 30.48, the Q value in β^+ decay is

$Q = (M_p - M_d - 2m_e)c^2 = (7.016930 \text{ u} - 7.016005 \text{ u})(931.5 \text{ MeV/u}) - 2(0.511 \text{ MeV}) = -0.16 \text{ MeV}$.

So the answer is $\boxed{\text{electron capture}}$ since $\beta+$ decay is not energetically possible.

(b) If daughter recoil is ignored, the energy of the emitted neutrino is equal to the energy released in electron capture, i.e., $\boxed{0.86 \text{ MeV}}$.

76. (a) $\boxed{^{1}_{1}H}$.   (b) $\boxed{^{10}_{5}B}$.   (c) $\boxed{^{89}_{39}Y}$.   (d) $\boxed{^{2}_{1}H}$.

77. $Q = (m_O + m_n - m_C - m_{He})c^2 = (15.994\,915 \text{ u} + 1.008\,665 \text{ u} - 13.003\,355 \text{ u} - 4.002\,603 \text{ u})(931.5 \text{ MeV/u})$

$= -2.215 \text{ MeV}$.

$K_{min} = \left(1 + \dfrac{m_a}{M_A}\right)|Q| = \left(1 + \dfrac{1.008\,665}{15.994\,915}\right)(2.215 \text{ MeV}) = \boxed{2.35 \text{ MeV}}$.

College Physics

5/e — 4/e

Comparative Review

N = New
M = 4/e exercise number (modified for 5/e)
X = 4/e exercise number (unchanged)

Chapter 1

5/e	4/e	5/e	4/e	5/e	4/e
1.	1.	36. N		71.	67.
2.	2.	37. N		72. N	
3.	3.	38.	34. M	73. N	
4.	4.	39.	35.	74.	68.
5. N		40.	36.	75. N	
6. N		41.	37.	76. N	
7.	5.	42. N		77.	71.
8.	6.	43.	39.	78.	72. M
9.	7.	44.	40. M	79.	73.
10.	8.	45.	41. M	80.	74. M
11.	9.	46.	42.	81.	75.
12.	10	47.	43.	82.	76. M
13.	11.	48. N		83.	77.
14. N		49.	45.	84.	78.
15. N		50.	46.	85.	79.
16.	12.	51.	47.	86. N	
17.	13.	52.	48.	87.	81.
18.	14. M	53. N		88.	82.
19.	15.	54.	50.	89.	83. M
20.	16.	55.	51.	90.	84.
21.	17.	56.	52.	91.	85.
22.	18.	57.	53.	92.	86.
23.	19. M	58.	54.	93.	87. M
24. N		59.	55.	94.	88.
25.	21.	60.	56.	95.	89.
26.	22. M	61.	57.	96.	90. M
27.	23.	62.	58.	97.	91.
28.	24.	63.	59.	98.	92.
29.	25.	64. N		99. N	
30.	26.	65. N		100.	94.
31. N		66.	62.	101. N	
32.	28.	67.	63. M	102. N	
33.	29. M	68.	64. M		
34.	30.	69.	65.		
35.	31.	70.	66.		

N = New
M = 4/e exercise number (modified for 5/e)
X = 4/e exercise number (unchanged)

Chapter 2

5/e	4/e	5/e	4/e	5/e	4/e	5/e	4/e
1. N		36.	32.	71.	65.	106.	98.
2.	2.	37.	33.	72. N		107.	99.
3.	3.	38.	34.	73. N		108.	100.
4. N		39.	35.	74.	66.	109.	101.
5.	4.	40. N		75.	67. M	110.	102.
6.	5.	41. N		76. N		111.	103. M
7.	6.	42. N		77.	69.	112. N	
8.	7.	43.	39.	78.	72.	113.	105.
9. N		44.	40.	79.	73. M	114.	106.
10.	8. M	45.	41.	80.	70.	115. N	
11.	9.	46.	42.	81. N			
12. N		47. N		82.	74.		
13.	11.	48. N		83.	75.		
14.	12.	49.	43.	84.	76.		
15.	13.	50.	44.	85.	77.		
16.	14. M	51.	45.	86.	78. M		
17.	15. M	52.	46.	87.	79.		
18.	16. M	53.	47. M	88. N			
19.	17.	54.	48.	89.	81.		
20.	18.	55.	49.	90. N			
21.	19.	56.	50. M	91.	83. M		
22.	20.	57.	51. M	92.	84. M		
23.	21.	58.	52.	93.	85.		
24.	22.	59. N		94.	86.		
25.	23.	60.	54.	95.	87. M		
26. N		61.	55.	96.	88.		
27.	25.	62.	56.	97.	89.		
28.	26.	63.	57. M	98.	90. M		
29.	27.	64.	58.	99.	91.		
30.	28.	65.	59.	100.	92.		
31.	29.	66. N		101.	93.		
32.	30. M	67.	62	102.	94.		
33.	31.	68. N		103.	95. M		
34. N		69. N		104. N			
35. N		70.	64.	105.	97.		

N = New
M = 4/e exercise number (modified for 5/e)
X = 4/e exercise number (unchanged)

Chapter 3

5/e	4/e	5/e	4/e	5/e	4/e	5/e	4/e
1.	1.	36. N		71. N		106. N	
2. N		37.	33. M	72.	66.	107.	101.
3. N		38. N		73.	67.	108.	102.
4.	2.	39.	35.	74.	68.	109.	103.
5.	3.	40.	36.	75.	69. M	110.	104.
6.	4. M	41. N		76.	70.	111.	105
7.	5. M	42.	38.	77.	71.		
8.	6.	43.	39.	78.	72. M		
9.	7.	44.	40.	79.	73.		
10.	8. M	45.	41.	80.	74. M		
11.	9.	46.	42.	81.	75. M		
12.	10.	47.	43.	82.	76.		
13.	11.	48.	44. M	83.	77.		
14.	12.	49.	45. M	84.	78.		
15.	13.	50.	46.	85.	79.		
16.	14.	51.	47.	86. N			
17.	15. M	52.	48.	87.	81.		
18.	16.	53. N		88.	82. M		
19.	17. M	54. N		89.	83.		
20.	18.	55. N		90.	84.		
21.	19. M	56.	50.	91.	85.		
22.	20.	57.	51.	92.	86.		
23. N		58.	52.	93.	87.		
24. N		59.	53.	94. N			
25.	21.	60.	54. M	95.	89. M		
26.	22.	61.	55.	96.	90.		
27.	23. M	62. N		97.	91.		
28.	24.	63.	57.	98.	92.		
29. N		64.	58. M	99. N			
30.	26.	65.	59.	100	94.		
31.	27.	66.	62.	101.	95.		
32.	28.	67.	61. M	102.	96.		
33.	29.	68.	60.	103. N			
34.	30.	69. N		104.	98.		
35.	31.	70.	64.	105	99.		

N = New
M = 4/e exercise number (modified for 5/e)
X = 4/e exercise number (unchanged)

Chapter 4

5/e	4/e	5/e	4/e	5/e	4/e	5/e	4/e
1.	1.	36.	92. M	71.	63.	106.	98.
2.	2.	37.	33.	72.	64.	107.	99.
3. N		38.	34.	73.	65.	108.	100.
4. N		39.	35.	74.	66.	109.	101.
5.	3. M	40.	36.	75.	67.	110.	102.
6.	4. M	41.	37.	76.	68.	111.	103.M
7.	5.	42. N		77.	69.	112.	104.
8.	6.	43. N		78.	70 M		
9.	7.	44.	38.	79.	71. M		
10.	8.	45.	39.	80.	72.		
11.	9.	46.	40. M	81.	73. M		
12. N		47.	41.	82.	74.		
13.	11.	48.	42.	83.	75.		
14.	12. M	49.	43.	84. N			
15.	13.	50.	44.	85.	77.		
16.	14.	51. N		86.	78.		
17.	15.	52. N		87.	79.		
18.	16	53.	45. M	88.	80.		
19. N		54.	46.	89. N			
20. N		55.	47.	90.	82.		
21.	17.	56.	48.	91.	83.		
22.	18.	57.	49.	92.	84. M		
23.	19.	58.	50.	93.	85.		
24.	20.	59.	51.	94.	86.		
25. N		60.	52. M	95.	87.		
26.	22. M	61.	53.	96.	88.		
27.	23.	62.	54.	97.	89.		
28.	24.	63. N		98.	90.		
29.	25.	64.	56.	99.	91. M		
30.	26.	65.	57.	100. N			
31.	27. M	66.	58.	101.	93.		
32.	28. M	67.	59.	102.	94.		
33.	29.	68. N		103.	95. M		
34.	30.	69.	60.	104.	96.		
35.	31.	70.	62.	105.	97. M		

Wilson/Buffa, Physics 5/e − 4/e   COMPARISON GRID

N = New
M = 4/e exercise number (modified for 5/e)
X = 4/e exercise number (unchanged)

Chapter 5

5/e	4/e	5/e	4/e	5/e	4/e	5/e	4/e
1.	1.	36.	34.	71.	65.	106.	18.
2.	2.	37. N		72.	66. M		
3. N		38. N		73.	67.		
4. N		39. N		74.	68.		
5.	3.	40. N		75.	69.		
6.	4.	41.	35. M	76.	70.		
7.	5.	42.	38.	77.	88. M		
8.	6.	43.	39.	78.	97. M		
9.	7.	44.	40.	79.	71.		
10. N		45.	42.	80.	72. M		
11.	9.	46.	37. M	81.	73. M		
12.	10.	47.	43.	82.	74. M		
13.	11.	48.	45.	83.	75.		
14.	12.	49.	44. M	84.	76.		
15.	13. M	50.	46.	85.	77.		
16.	14.	51.	47.	86.	78.		
17.	15.	52.	48. M	87.	79.		
18.	16.	53.	49.	88.	80.		
19.	17.	54.	50. M	89.	81.		
20. N		55.	51.	90.	82. M		
21.	19. M	56.	52.	91. N			
22.	21	57.	53. M	92.	84.		
23.	20. M	58.	54.	93.	85.		
24.	22.	59.	55. M	94. N			
25.	23.	60.	56. M	95.	87.		
26.	24.	61.	57.	96.	89.		
27.	25.	62.	58.	97.	90. M		
28. N		63.	59.	98.	91.		
29.	27.	64. N		99.	92.		
30.	28.	65. N		100.	93.		
31.	29.	66.	60.	101.	94.		
32.	30.	67.	61.	102.	95.		
33.	31.	68.	62.	103.	96.		
34.	32. M	69.	63.	104.	98.		
35.	33.	70.	64. M	105.	99.		

N = New
M = 4/e exercise number (modified for 5/e)
X = 4/e exercise number (unchanged)

Chapter 6

5/e	4/e	5/e	4/e	5/e	4/e	5/e	4/e
1.	1.	36.	32.	71. N		106.	99.
2.	2.	37.	33.	72.	64.	107.	100. M
3.	3.	38.	34.	73.	65. M	108	101. M
4. N		39.	35.	74.	66.	109.	102. M
5. N		40.	36.	75.	67.	110.	103.
6.	4.	41.	37. M	76.	68.	111.	104.
7.	5.	42.	38.	77.	69.	112.	105.
8.	6.	43.	40.	78.	70.		
9.	7. M	44.	39.	79.	71.		
10.	8.	45.	41.	80.	72.		
11.	9.	46. N		81.	73.		
12.	10.	47. N		82.	74.		
13.	11.	48.	42.	83.	76.		
14.	12. M	49.	43.	84.	75.		
15.	13.	50.	44.	85. N			
16.	14.	51.	45.	86.	78.		
17.	15.	52.	46. M	87.	79.		
18.	16.	53.	47.	88.	80.		
19.	17.	54.	48.	89.	81. M		
20.	18.	55.	49.	90.	82.		
21.	19.	56.	50.	91. N			
22.	20. M	57.	51.	92.	84. M		
23.	21.	58.	52.	93.	85.		
24.	22.	59. N		94.	86.		
25. N		60.	53.	95.	87.		
26.	23.	61.	54.	96.	88.		
27.	24.	62.	55.	97.	89.		
28.	25. M	63.	57.	98.	90.		
29. N		64. N		99.	91.		
30.	26.	65. N		100.	92.		
31.	27.	66.	58.	101.	63		
32.	28.	67.	59.	102.	95.		
33.	29.	68.	60. M	103.	96.		
34. N		69.	61.	104.	97.		
35.	31. M	70.	62.	105.	98.		

N = New
M = 4/e exercise number (modified for 5/e)
X = 4/e exercise number (unchanged)

Chapter 7

5/e	4/e	5/e	4/e	5/e	4/e	5/e	4/e
1.	1.	36. N		71.	67. M	106.	102.
2.	2.	37.	35.	72.	68.	107.	103.
3. N		38.	36.	73. N		108	104.
4.	3.	39.	37.	74.	70.		
5. N		40.	38.	75.	71.		
6.	4.	41. N		76.	72.		
7.	5.	42.	39.	77.	73.		
8.	6.	43.	40.	78.	74.		
9. N		44.	41.	79. N			
10.	8.	45.	42.	80.	76.		
11.	9.	46. N		81.	77. M		
12.	10.	47.	43. M	82.	82.		
13.	11.	48.	44.	83.	79.		
14.	12.	49.	45.	84.	80.		
15.	13.	50.	46.	85.	81.		
16.	14.	51.	47.	86.	78. M		
17.	15.	52.	48. M	87.	83.		
18.	16. M	53.	49. M	88.	84.		
19.	17. M	54.	50. M	89.	85.		
20.	18.	55.	51.	90.	86.		
21.	19.	56.	52. M	91.	87.		
22.	20.	57.	53.	92.	88.		
23.	21.	58.	54.	93.	89.		
24.	22.	59.	55.	94. N			
25.	23. M	60.	56. M	95.	90.		
26. N		61.	57.	96.	92.		
27.	25.	62. N		97.	93.		
28.	26.	63.	59.	98.	94.		
29.	27.	64.	60.	99.	95.		
30.	28.	65.	61.	100.	96.		
31.	29.	66.	62.	101.	97.		
32.	30.	67.	63.	102. N			
33.	31.	68.	64.	103.	99.		
34.	32.	69.	65.	104.	100.		
35.	33. M	70.	66.	105.	101.		

N = New
M = 4/e exercise number (modified for 5/e)
X = 4/e exercise number (unchanged)

Chapter 8

5/e	4/e	5/e	4/e	5/e	4/e	5/e	4/e
1.	1.	36.	32. M	71.	65. M	106.	96.
2.	2. M	37.	33.	72. N		107.	97.
3.	3. M	38.	34.	73. N		108.	98.
4.	4.	39.	35.	74.	66.	109.	99.
5.	5. M	40.	36.	75.	67.	110.	100.
6. N		41.	37.	76.	68.	111.	101.
7. N		42.	38.	77.	69.	112.	102. M
8.	6.	43.	39.	78.	70. M	113.	103.
9.	7.	44.	40.	79.	71.	114.	104.
10.	8.	45.	41.	80.	72.	115.	105.
11.	9.	46.	42.	81.	73.	116.	106.
12.	10.	47.	43.	82.	74.	117.	107.
13.	11. M	48.	44.	83.	75.	118.	108.
14.	12.	49. N		84.	76.	119.	109.
15.	13.	50. N		85.	77.		
16.	14.	51.	45.	86.	78.		
17.	15.	52.	46.	87.	79.		
18. N		53.	47.	88.	80.		
19. N		54.	48.	89.	81.		
20.	16. M	55.	49. M	90.	82.		
21.	17.	56.	50.	91.	83.		
22.	18.	57.	51.	92.	84.		
23.	19.	58.	52.	93.	85.		
24.	20.	59.	53.	94. N			
25.	21.	60.	54.	95. N			
26.	22.	61.	55.	96.	86.		
27.	23. M	62.	56.	97.	87.		
28.	24.	63.	57.	98.	88.		
29.	25.	64.	58.	99.	89.		
30.	26. M	65.	59.	100.	90. M		
31.	27.	66.	60.	101.	91.		
32.	28.	67.	61.	102.	92.		
33.	29.	68.	62.	103.	93.		
34.	30.	69.	63. M	104.	94.		
35.	31.	70.	64.	105.	95. M		

N = New
M = 4/e exercise number (modified for 5/e)
X = 4/e exercise number (unchanged)

Chapter 9

5/e	4/e	5/e	4/e	5/e	4/e	5/e	4/e
1.	1.	36.	39.	71.	66.	106.	51.
2.	2.	37.	35. M	72.	67.	107.	100.
3. N		38.	36.	73.	68.		
4.	4.	39.	37.	74.	69.		
5.	5.	40.	38. M	75. N			
6. N		41. N		76.	70.		
7.	7.	42.	40. M	77.	71. M		
8.	8.	43.	41.	78.	72.		
9.	9.	44.	42.	79.	73.		
10.	10.	45. N		80.	74.		
11.	11. M	46. N		81.	75.		
12.	12. M	47.	45.	82.	76.		
13.	13.	48.	46.	83.	77.		
14.	14. M	49.	47.	84.	78.		
15.	15.	50.	48.	85.	79.		
16.	16. M	51.	49.	86.	80.		
17.	17.	52.	50.	87.	81.		
18.	18.	53. N		88.	82. M		
19.	19. M	54. N		89. N			
20.	20.	55. N		90.	84.		
21.	21.	56.	52. M	91.	85.		
22.	22.	57.	53.	92.	86.		
23.	23.	58.	54.	93.	87.		
24.	24.	59.	55.	94.	88.		
25.	25.	60.	56.	95.	89.		
26.	26.	61.	57.	96.	90.		
27.	27.	62.	58. M	97.	91.		
28.	28.	63.	59.	98.	92.		
29. N		64.	60.	99.	93.		
30. N		65.	61.	100.	94.		
31.	29. M	66.	62.	101.	95.		
32.	30.	67. N		102.	96.		
33.	31. M	68.	65.	103.	97.		
34.	32.	69.	64.	104.	98.		
35.	33.	70. N		105.	99.		

N = New
M = 4/e exercise number (modified for 5/e)
X = 4/e exercise number (unchanged)

Chapter 10

5/e	4/e	5/e	4/e	5/e	4/e
1.	1.	36. N		71.	65.
2.	2.	37.	33. M	72.	66. M
3.	3.	38.	34.	73.	67.
4.	4.	39.	35.	74.	68.
5. N		40.	36.	75. N	
6. N		41.	37. M	76.	69.
7.	5.	42.	38.	77.	70.
8.	6.	43.	39.	78.	71.
9. N		44.	40.	79.	72.
10.	8.	45.	41.	80.	73.
11.	9.	46.	42.	81. N	
12.	10.	47.	43.	82.	74.
13.	11.	48.	44.	83.	75.
14.	12. M	49.	45.	84.	76.
15.	13. M	50. N		85.	77.
16.	14. M	51. N		86.	78.
17.	15.	52.	46.	87.	79.
18.	16.	53.	47. M	88.	80.
19.	17.	54.	48.	89.	81.
20.	18.	55.	49.	90. N	
21.	19.	56.	50.	91.	83.
22.	20.	57.	51.	92.	84.
23.	21.	58.	52. M	93.	85.
24. N		59.	53. M	94.	86.
25. N		60.	54.	95.	87.
26.	22.	61.	55. M	96.	88.
27.	23.	62.	56.	97.	89.
28.	24.	63.	57.	98.	90.
29.	25.	64.	58.	99.	91.
30. N		65.	59.	100.	92.
31.	27.	66.	60.	101.	93.
32.	28. M	67.	61.	102.	94.
33.	29.	68.	62. M	103.	95.
34.	30.	69.	63.		
35.	31.	70.	64.		

N = New
M = 4/e exercise number (modified for 5/e)
X = 4/e exercise number (unchanged)

Chapter 11

5/e	4/e	5/e	4/e	5/e	4/e
1.	1.	36. N		71.	65.
2.	2.	37. N		72.	66.
3.	3.	38.	34.	73.	67.
4.	4.	39.	35. M	74.	68.
5.	5.	40.	36.	75.	69. M
6.	6.	41.	37.	76.	70.
7.	7.	42.	38. M	77.	71.
8.	8.	43.	39.	78.	72. M
9.	9.	44.	40.	79.	73.
10.	10.	45.	41.	80.	74.
11.	11. M	46.	42.	81.	75.
12.	12.	47.	43.	82.	76.
13.	13. M	48.	44.	83. N	
14.	14.	49.	45.	84.	78.
15. N		50.	46.	85.	79.
16. N		51. N		86.	80.
17. N		52.	48.	87.	81.
18.	16.	53.	49.	88.	82.
19.	17.	54.	50.	89.	83. M
20.	15. M	55.	51.	90.	21.
21.	20.	56.	52.	91.	85. M
22.	18.	57.	53.	92. N	
23.	19.	58.	54.	93.	56.
24.	84. M	59.	55.		
25.	23.	60. N			
26.	24.	61.	57.		
27.	25. M	62.	58.		
28.	26.	63. N			
29.	27.	64. N			
30.	28.	65.	59. M		
31.	29.	66. N			
32.	30.	67.	61.		
33.	31.	68.	62. M		
34.	32.	69.	63.		
35.	33.	70.	64. M		

N = New
M = 4/e exercise number (modified for 5/e)
X = 4/e exercise number (unchanged)

Chapter 12

5/e	4/e	5/e	4/e	5/e	4/e	5/e	4/e
1.	1.	36. N		71.	63.	106.	96. M
2.	2.	37.	31.	72.	64. M	107. N	
3.	3.	38.	32. M	73.	65. M	108	98.
4.	4. M	39.	33.	74.	66.	109.	99.
5.	5.	40.	34.	75.	67.	110.	100.
6.	6.	41.	35.	76. N		111.	101.
7.	7.	42.	36. M	77.	68.	112. N	
8.	8.	43.	37.	78.	69.	113.	21.
9.	9.	44.	38.	79.	70.	114.	103.
10.	10.	45.	39.	80. N			
11.	11.	46. N		81.	71.		
12. N		47.	41.	82.	72. M		
13. N		48.	42.	83.	73.		
14. N		49.	43.	84.	74.		
15. N		50.	44. M	85.	75.		
16.	12. M	51.	45.	86.	76.		
17.	13. M	52. N		87.	77.		
18. N		53. N		88.	78.		
19.	15. M	54.	46.	89.	79.		
20.	16. M	55.	47.	90.	80.		
21.	17. M	56.	48.	91.	81. M		
22.	18.	57.	49.	92.	82.		
23.	19. M	58.	50.	93.	83. M		
24.	20.	59.	51.	94.	84.		
25. N		60.	52. M	95.	85.		
26.	22.	61.	53.	96.	86. M		
27.	23.	62.	54.	97.	87.		
28.	24. M	63. N		98.	88.		
29.	25.	64.	56. M	99.	89.		
30.	26.	65.	57.	100.	90.		
31.	27.	66.	58.	101.	91.		
32.	28.	67.	59.	102.	92.		
33.	29.	68.	60.	103.	93.		
34.	30.	69.	61.	104.	94.		
35. N		70.	62.	105.	95.		

N = New
M = 4/e exercise number (modified for 5/e)
X = 4/e exercise number (unchanged)

Chapter 13

5/e	4/e	5/e	4/e	5/e	4/e	5/e	4/e
1.	1.	36.	35.	71.	63.	106.	94.
2.	2.	37.	36.	72.	64.	107.	95.
3.	5.	38.	37.	73.	65.	108. N	
4.	6.	39.	38.	74.	66.	109.	97.
5.	3.	40.	21. M	75.	67. M	110.	98.
6.	4.	41.	39.	76.	68.	111.	99.
7. N		42.	18. M	77.	69. M		
8. N		43.	19. M	78. N			
9.	7.	44.	40.	79.	70. M		
10.	8.	45.	16.	80.	71.		
11.	9.	46. N		81.	72.		
12.	10.	47.	41.	82.	73.		
13.	11.	48.	42.	83.	74.		
14.	12.	49.	43. M	84.	75.		
15.	13.	50.	44. M	85.	76.		
16.	14. M	51.	45. M	86. N			
17.	15. M	52.	46.	87. N			
18.	17. M	53.	47.	88. N			
19. N		54.	48.	89.	79.		
20.	22	55.	49.	90.	77.		
21.	23.	56.	50.	91.	78.		
22. N		57.	51.	92.	80.		
23.	24.	58.	52.	93.	81.		
24.	25.	59. N		94.	82. M		
25.	26.	60.	53. M	95.	83.		
26.	27.	61.	54.	96.	84.		
27.	28.	62. N		97.	85. M		
28.	29.	63.	55.	98.	86.		
29.	30.	64.	56.	99.	87.		
30. N		65.	57.	100.	88.		
31. N		66.	58.	101.	89.		
32.	32.	67.	59.	102.	90.		
33.	33.	68.	60.	103.	91.		
34.	31. M	69.	61. M	104.	92.		
35.	34.	70.	62.	105.	93.		

N = New
M = 4/e exercise number (modified for 5/e)
X = 4/e exercise number (unchanged)

Chapter 14

5/e	4/e	5/e	4/e	5/e	4/e
1.	1.	36.	33.	71.	65.
2.	2.	37.	34. M	72.	66.
3.	3.	38.	35.	73.	67.
4.	4.	39.	36.	74. N	
5.	5.	40.	29. M	75.	68.
6.	6.	41.	37.	76.	69.
7.	7.	42.	38.	77.	70.
8.	8.	43.	39.	78.	71.
9. N		44.	40. M	79.	72.
10.	10.	45.	41.	80.	73.
11.	11.	46.	42.	81. N	
12.	12.	47.	43.	82.	74.
13.	13.	48.	44.	83.	75.
14.	9.	49.	45.	84.	76. M
15.	15. M	50.	46.	85.	77. M
16.	14.	51.	47.	86.	78.
17. N		52.	48.	87. N	
18.	16. M	53.	49.	88.	81.
19.	17.	54.	50.	89.	82.
20.	18.	55.	51.	90.	83.
21.	19.	56.	52.	91.	85.
22.	20.	57.	53.	92.	86.
23. N		58. N		93.	87.
24. N		59. N		94.	88.
25. N		60.	54.	95.	89. M
26.	23.	61.	55.	96.	90.
27.	24.	62.	56.	97.	91.
28.	25.	63.	57. M	98.	92.
29.	26.	64.	59.	99.	93.
30.	27.	65.	58. M	100.	94.
31. N		66.	60.	101.	95.
32.	28.	67.	61.	102.	79.
33.	30. M	68.	62.	103.	80.
34.	31.	69.	63.		
35.	32.	70.	64. M		

N = New
M = 4/e exercise number (modified for 5/e)
X = 4/e exercise number (unchanged)

Chapter 15

5/e	4/e	5/e	4/e	5/e	4/e
1.	1.	36.	30.	71.	61.
2.	2. M	37.	31. M	72. N	
3.	3.	38.	32.	73.	63. M
4.	4.	39.	33.	74.	64.
5.	5.	40.	34.	75.	65.
6. N		41.	35.	76.	66.
7. N		42.	36.	77.	67.
8.	6.	43.	37.	78.	69.
9.	7.	44.	38.	79.	68.
10.	8. M	45.	39.	80.	70.
11.	9. M	46.	40.	81.	71.
12.	10.	47.	41.	82.	72. M
13.	11.	48. N		83.	73.
14. N		49. N		84.	74.
15.	13.	50.	42. M	85.	75. M
16. N		51.	43.	86.	76.
17. N		52.	44.	87. N	
18.	14.	53.	45.	88.	78.
19.	15.	54.	46. M	89.	79.
20.	16.	55.	47.	90.	80.
21.	17.	56.	48. M	91.	81.
22.	18.	57.	49.	92.	82.
23.	19.	58.	50.	93.	83.
24. N		59.	51.	94.	84.
25. N		60.	52.	95.	86.
26.	20. M	61.	53.	96.	87.
27.	21. M	62.	54.	97.	85. M
28.	22.	63.	55. M	98.	88.
29.	23.	64.	56.	99.	89.
30.	24. M	65.	57.		
31.	25.	66.	58. M		
32. N		67.	59.		
33.	27.	68.	62.		
34.	28.	69. N			
35.	29.	70.	60.		

N = New
M = 4/e exercise number (modified for 5/e)
X = 4/e exercise number (unchanged)

Chapter 16

5/e	4/e	5/e	4/e	5/e	4/e
1.	1.	36.	36.	71.	69.
2.	3.	37.	37.	72.	70.
3.	2.	38.	38.	73.	71.
4.	4. M	39. N		74.	72.
5.	5.	40.	40.	75.	73.
6.	6. M	41.	41.	76.	74.
7. N		42.	42.	77. N	
8.	8.	43.	43.	78.	76.
9. N		44.	44.	79.	77.
10.	10.	45.	45.	80.	78.
11.	11.	46.	46.	81.	79.
12.	12.	47.	51.	82. N	
13.	13.	48.	47.	83.	81.
14.	14.	49.	48.	84.	82.
15.	15.	50.	49.	85.	83.
16.	16. M	51.	50.	86. N	
17.	17. M	52.	52.	87. N	
18.	18. M	53. N		88.	84. M
19.	19.	54.	54. M	89.	85. M
20.	20.	55.	55.	90.	86.
21.	21.	56.	56.	91.	87. M
22.	22.	57.	57.	92.	88. M
23.	23.	58.	58.	93.	89.
24.	24.	59.	59.	94.	90.
25.	25.	60.	60.	95.	91.
26.	26.	61.	61.	96.	92.
27.	27.	62.	62.	97.	93.
28.	28.	63. N		98.	94.
29.	29.	64.	64. M	99.	95.
30.	30.	65. N		100.	96.
31.	31. M	66. N		101.	97. M
32.	32.	67.	65.	102.	98.
33.	33.	68.	66.	103.	99.
34.	34.	69.	67.	104. N	
35.	35.	70.	68. M		

N = New
M = 4/e exercise number (modified for 5/e)
X = 4/e exercise number (unchanged)

Chapter 17

5/e	4/e	5/e	4/e	5/e	4/e
1.	1.	36. N		71.	63.
2.	2.	37.	31.	72.	64.
3.	3.	38.	32.	73.	65.
4.	4.	39.	33.	74.	66.
5.	6.	40.	34. M	75.	67.
6. N		41.	35.	76.	68. M
7.	7.	42.	36. M	77.	69.
8.	8.	43.	37.	78.	70.
9.	9.	44.	38.	79.	71.
10.	10. M	45.	39.	80.	72.
11. N		46.	40.	81.	73.
12.	11.	47.	41.	82.	74.
13. N		48.	42.	83.	75.
14. N		49.	43. M	84.	76. M
15.	12.	50.	44.	85.	77.
16.	13.	51.	45.	86.	78.
17.	14.	52.	46.	87.	79.
18.	15.	53.	47.	88.	80.
19.	16. M	54.	48. M	89.	81.
20.	17.	55.	49.	90.	82.
21.	18. M	56.	50.	91.	83.
22.	19.	57.	51.	92.	84. M
23.	20.	58.	52.	93.	85.
24.	21.	59.	53.	94.	86.
25.	22.	60. N		95.	87.
26. N		61.	56.	96.	88.
27. N		62.	54.	97.	89.
28.	25.	63.	55.	98.	90.
29.	26.	64.	57.	99. N	
30.	5. M	65.	58.	100.	92.
31.	23.	66.	59.	101.	93.
32.	24.	67. N		102.	94.
33.	27. M	68. N		103.	95.
34.	28.	69.	61.		
35.	29.	70.	62.		

Wilson/Buffa, Physics 5/e – 4/e   COMPARISON GRID

N = New
M = 4/e exercise number (modified for 5/e)
X = 4/e exercise number (unchanged)

Chapter 18

5/e	4/e	5/e	4/e	5/e	4/e	5/e	4/e
1.	1.	36. N		71.	65.	106.	98. M
2.	2.	37.	34.	72.	66.	107.	99.
3.	3.	38.	35.	73.	67.		
4.	4.	39.	36.	74. N			
5. N		40.	38.	75. N			
6. N		41.	39.	76.	68. M		
7.	5.	42.	40.	77.	69. M		
8.	6.	43.	41.	78.	70.		
9.	7. M	44. N		79.	71.		
10.	8.	45. N		80.	72.		
11.	9.	46.	42.	81.	73.		
12.	10. M	47.	43.	82.	74. M		
13.	11.	48.	44.	83.	75. M		
14.	12.	49.	45.	84.	76.		
15.	13.	50.	46. M	85.	77.		
16.	14. M	51.	47.	86.	78.		
17.	15. M	52.	48.	87.	79.		
18.	16. M	53.	49.	88.	80.		
19.	17.	54.	50.	89.	81.		
20.	18.	55.	51.	90.	82.		
21.	19.	56.	52.	91.	83.		
22.	20.	57.	53.	92.	84.		
23.	21.	58. N		93.	85.		
24.	22.	59. N		94.	86.		
25.	23.	60. N		95.	87.		
26.	24.	61.	55.	96.	88.		
27.	25.	62.	56.	97.	89.		
28.	26.	63.	57. M	98.	90.		
29.	27.	64.	58.	99.	91.		
30.	28.	65.	59. M	100.	92.		
31.	29.	66.	60.	101.	93.		
32.	30.	67.	61.	102.	94.		
33.	31.	68.	62.	103.	95.		
34.	32.	69.	63.	104.	96.		
35.	33.	70.	64.	105.	97.		

N = New
M = 4/e exercise number (modified for 5/e)
X = 4/e exercise number (unchanged)

Chapter 19

5/e	4/e	5/e	4/e	5/e	4/e
1.	1.	36.	72.	71.	32. M
2.	2.	37.	73.	72.	34.
3.	3.	38.	52. M	73.	35.
4.	4.	39.	53.	74.	33. M
5.	5.	40.	54.	75.	36.
6.	7.	41.	55.	76.	37.
7.	6.	42.	56.	77.	38.
8.	8.	43.	57.	78.	39.
9.	9.	44.	58.	79.	40.
10. N		45.	59.	80.	41.
11. N		46.	60.	81.	42.
12.	10.	47.	61. M	82.	43.
13.	11.	48.	62. M	83.	45.
14.	12. M	49.	63.	84. N	
15.	13.	50.	64.	85. N	
16.	14.	51.	65.	86.	46.
17.	15.	52.	66. M	87.	47.
18.	16. M	53.	67.	88.	82. M
19.	17.	54.	68. M	89.	83.
20.	18.	55.	69.	90.	84.
21.	19.	56.	70.	91.	85.
22.	71.	57.	20.	92.	86.
23.	74.	58.	21. M	93.	87.
24.	75.	59.	22.	94.	88. M
25.	76.	60.	23. M	95.	89.
26.	77.	61. N		96.	90.
27	80.	62. N		97.	91.
28.	78.	63.	26.	98.	92. M
29.	79.	64.	24.	99.	93. M
30.	81.	65.	25.	100.	94.
31.	48.	66.	27.	101.	95.
32.	49.	67.	30.		
33.	50.	68	28.		
34.	51.	69	29.		
35. N		70.	31.		

N = New
M = 4/e exercise number (modified for 5/e)
X = 4/e exercise number (unchanged)

Chapter 20

5/e	4/e	5/e	4/e	5/e	4/e
1.	1.	36.	32.	71.	66.
2.	2.	37.	33.	72.	64. M
3.	4.	38.	34.	73.	67.
4.	3.	39.	35. M	74. N	
5.	5.	40.	36.	75. N	
6. N		41.	37.	76.	68.
7. N		42.	38.	77.	69.
8.	6.	43.	39.	78.	70.
9.	7.	44.	40. M	79.	71.
10.	8.	45.	41. M	80.	72.
11.	9.	46.	42.	81.	73.
12.	10.	47.	43.	82.	74. M
13.	11.	48.	44.	83.	75.
14.	12.	49.	45.	84.	76.
15.	13.	50.	46. M	85.	77.
16.	14.	51. N		86.	78.
17.	15.	52. N		87.	79.
18.	16.	53.	47.	88.	80.
19.	17.	54.	48. M	89.	81. M
20.	18.	55.	49.	90.	82.
21.	19. M	56.	50.	91.	83.
22.	20.	57.	51.	92.	84.
23.	21. M	58.	52.	93.	85.
24.	22.	59.	53.	94.	86.
25.	23.	60.	54.	95.	87.
26.	24.	61.	55. M	96.	88.
27.	25.	62.	56.	97.	89.
28. N		63.	57.		
29.	26.	64.	58.		
30.	28.	65.	59.		
31.	29.	66.	60.		
32.	30.	67.	61.		
33.	31.	68.	62.		
34. N		69.	63.		
35. N		70.	65.		

N = New
M = 4/e exercise number (modified for 5/e)
X = 4/e exercise number (unchanged)

Chapter 21

5/e	4/e	5/e	4/e	5/e	4/e
1.	1. M	36.	34.	71.	65. M
2.	2.	37.	35.	72.	66.
3.	3.	38. N		73.	67.
4. N		39.	36.	74.	68.
5. N		40.	37.	75.	69.
6.	4.	41.	38.	76.	70.
7.	5.	42. N		77.	71.
8.	6. M	43.	39.	78.	72. M
9.	7.	44.	40.		
10.	8.	45.	41.		
11.	9.	46.	42.		
12. N		47. N			
13.	11.	48. N			
14. N		49.	43.		
15.	13.	50.	44.		
16.	14.	51.	45.		
17.	15.	52.	46.		
18.	16.	53.	47. M		
19.	17.	54.	48. M		
20.	18.	55.	49. M		
21.	19.	56.	50. M		
22.	21.	57.	51.		
23.	22.	58.	52.		
24.	24.	59.	53. M		
25.	23.	60.	54. M		
26.	25.	61.	55.		
27.	26.	62.	56. M		
28. N		63.	57.		
29. N		64.	58.		
30.	28.	65.	59.		
31.	29.	66.	60.		
32.	27.	67.	61. M		
33.	30.	68.	62.		
34.	31.	69.	63.		
35.	33.	70.	64.		

N = New
M = 4/e exercise number (modified for 5/e)
X = 4/e exercise number (unchanged)

Chapter 22

5/e	4/e	5/e	4/e	5/e	4/e
1.	1.	36.	30.	71.	63.
2.	2.	37.	31. M	72.	64.
3.	3.	38.	32.	73.	65.
4.	4.	39.	33.	74.	66.
5. N		40.	34.	75.	67.
6. N		41.	35.	76.	68.
7. N		42.	36.	77.	69.
8. N		43.	37.	78.	70.
9.	14.	44. N		79.	71.
10.	7.	45.	39. M	80. N	
11.	8.	46.	40.	81. N	
12.	9. M	47.	41. M		
13.	10. M	48.	42.		
14.	12. M	49.	43. M		
15.	13. M	50.	44.		
16.	11.	51.	45.		
17.	15. M	52.	46.		
18.	16.	53.	47.		
19.	17.	54.	48. M		
20.	18.	55.	49.		
21.	19.	56.	50.		
22. N		57.	51.		
23.	20.	58.	52.		
24. N		59.	53.		
25.	21.	60.	54.		
26.	22.	61.	55.		
27.	23.	62. N			
28.	24. M	63. N			
29.	25.	64.	58.		
30. N		65. N			
31. N		66.	59.		
32. N		67. N			
33.	27.	68.	60.		
34.	28. M	69.	61.		
35.	29.	70.	62. M		

N = New
M = 4/e exercise number (modified for 5/e)
X = 4/e exercise number (unchanged)

Chapter 23

5/e	4/e	5/e	4/e	5/e	4/e
1.	1.	36.	32. M	71.	65.
2.	2.	37.	33.	72.	66.
3.	3.	38.	34.	73.	67.
4.	4.	39.	35.	74.	68.
5.	5.	40.	36. M	75.	69.
6.	6. M	41.	37. M	76.	70.
7.	7.	42.	38. M	77.	71.
8. N		43.	39.	78.	72.
9. N		44.	40.	79.	75.
10.	8.	45.	41.	80.	73. M
11.	9.	46.	42.	81.	74.
12.	10.	47.	43.	82. N	
13.	11.	48.	44.	83. N	
14.	12.	49.	45.	84.	76.
15.	13. M	50.	46.	85.	77.
16.	14.	51.	47.	86.	78. M
17.	15.	52.	48.	87.	79.
18.	16.	53.	49.	88.	80. M
19.	17.	54.	50. M	89.	81.
20.	18.	55. N		90. N	
21.	19.	56. N		91.	83.
22.	20. M	57.	51.	92.	84.
23.	21.	58.	52.	93.	85.
24.	22.	59.	53.	94.	87.
25. N		60.	54. M	95.	86.
26. N		61.	55.	96.	88.
27.	23.	62.	56.	97. N	
28.	24.	63.	57.	98.	89.
29.	25.	64.	58.	99.	91.
30.	26. M	65.	59.	100.	92.
31.	27.	66.	60.	101.	93.
32.	28. M	67.	61.		
33. N		68.	62.		
34.	30.	69.	63. M		
35.	31.	70.	64.		

N = New
M = 4/e exercise number (modified for 5/e)
X = 4/e exercise number (unchanged)

Chapter 24

5/e	4/e	5/e	4/e	5/e	4/e
1.	1.	36.	32. M	71. N	
2.	2.	37.	33.	72.	61.
3.	3.	38.	34.	73.	62.
4.	4.	39.	35. M	74.	63. M
5.	5.	40. N		75.	64.
6.	6.	41.	37.	76.	66.
7. N		42. N		77.	67.
8. N		43. N		78.	68.
9.	7.	44.	38.	79.	69.
10.	8. M	45.	39.	80.	70.
11.	9.	46.	40.	81.	71.
12.	10.	47.	41.	82.	72.
13.	11. M	48.	42. M	83.	73.
14.	12. M	49.	43.	84.	74. M
15.	13.	50.	44.	85.	75.
16.	14.	51.	45. M	86.	76.
17.	15. M	52.	46. M	87.	77. M
18.	16. M	53.	47.	88.	78.
19.	17.	54.	48.	89.	79.
20.	18. M	55.	49. M	90.	80.
21.	19.	56.	50.	91.	81.
22.	20.	57.	51.	92	82.
23.	21.	58.	52. M		
24.	22.	59.	53.		
25.	23.	60.	54.		
26.	24.	61.	55.		
27. N		62.	56.		
28. N		63.	57.		
29.	25.	64.	58.		
30.	26.	65. N			
31.	27.	66. N			
32.	28. M	67. N			
33.	29.	68.	59.		
34.	30.	69.	60.		
35.	31.	70. N			

N = New
M = 4/e exercise number (modified for 5/e)
X = 4/e exercise number (unchanged)

Chapter 25

5/e	4/e	5/e	4/e	5/e	4/e
1.	1.	36.	34.	71.	51. M
2. N		37.	35. M	72.	66.
3.	3.	38.	36.	73.	67.
4.	4. M	39.	37.	74.	68.
5.	5.	40.	38.	75.	69.
6.	6.	41.	39.	76.	70.
7. N		42.	40.	77.	71.
8. N		43.	41.	78.	72.
9.	7.	44.	42. M	79.	73.
10.	8. M	45.	43.	80.	74.
11.	9. M	46.	44.	81.	75.
12.	10.	47.	45.	82.	76.
13.	11.	48. N		83.	77.
14.	12.	49. N		84.	78.
15.	13. M	50.	46.	85.	79.
16.	14.	51.	47.	86.	80.
17.	15.	52.	48.	87.	81.
18.	16.	53.	49.	88.	82.
19.	17.	54.	50. M	89.	83.
20.	18.	55. N		90.	84.
21.	19.	56.	52.	91.	85.
22.	20.	57.	53.	92.	86.
23.	21.	58.	54.	93.	87.
24.	22.	59.	55.		
25.	23.	60.	56.		
26.	24.	61.	57.		
27.	25.	62. N			
28.	26.	63.	58.		
29.	27.	64.	59.		
30.	28.	65. N			
31.	29.	66.	61. M		
32.	30.	67.	62. M		
33.	31.	68.	63.		
34.	32. M	69.	64.		
35.	33.	70.	65.		

COMPARISON GRID

N = New
M = 4/e exercise number (modified for 5/e)
X = 4/e exercise number (unchanged)

Chapter 26

5/e	4/e	5/e	4/e	5/e	4/e
1.	1.	36.	39. M	71.	72.
2.	2.	37.	40.	72.	73.
3.	3.	38.	41. M	73.	74.
4.	4. M	39.	42.	74. N	
5.	6.	40.	43. M	75.	75.
6.	8.	41.	44. M	76.	76.
7.	9.	42. N		77.	77.
8.	10.	43.	45. M	78.	78.
9.	11.	44.	46.	79.	79.
10. N		45.	47.	80.	80.
11.	14.	46.	48.	81.	81.
12.	16.	47.	49.	82.	82.
13.	17.	48.	50.	83.	83.
14.	18.	49.	51.	84.	85.
15. N		50.	52.		
16.	21.	51.	53.		
17.	22.	52.	54.		
18.	23.	53.	55.		
19.	24.	54.	56.		
20.	25. M	55.	57.		
21. N		56. N			
22. N		57.	61.		
23. N		58.	60. M		
24.	27. M	59.	59.		
25.	28.	60. N			
26.	29. M	61.	62.		
27.	30.	62.	63.		
28.	31.	63.	64.		
29.	32. M	64.	65.		
30.	33.	65.	66.		
31.	37.	66.	67.		
32.	34.	67.	68. M		
33.	35.	68.	69.		
34.	36.	69.	70.		
35.	38.	70.	71.		

N = New
M = 4/e exercise number (modified for 5/e)
X = 4/e exercise number (unchanged)

Chapter 27

5/e	4/e	5/e	4/e	5/e	4/e
1.	1.	36.	34.	71.	67.
2.	2.	37.	35.	72.	68.
3.	3.	38.	36.	73.	69.
4.	4.	39.	37.	74.	70.
5.	5.	40.	38.	75.	71.
6.	6.	41.	39.	76.	72.
7.	7.	42.	40.	77.	73.
8.	8. M	43.	41.	78.	74.
9.	9.	44.	42.	79. N	
10.	10. M	45.	43.	80.	75.
11.	11.	46.	44.	81.	76.
12.	12.	47. N		82.	78.
13.	13.	48.	46.	83.	79.
14.	14.	49.	47.	84.	80.
15.	15.	50.	48. M	85.	84.
16.	16.	51.	49.	86.	85. M
17.	17.	52.	50.		
18. N		53.	51.		
19. N		54.	52.		
20.	18.	55.	53.		
21.	19.	56. N			
22. N		57. N			
23.	21.	58.	54.		
24. N		59.	55.		
25.	23.	60.	56.		
26.	24.	61.	57.		
27.	25.	62.	58.		
28.	26.	63.	59.		
29.	27.	64.	60.		
30.	28.	65.	61.		
31.	29.	66.	62.		
32.	30.	67.	63. M		
33.	31. M	68.	64.		
34.	32.	69.	65. M		
35.	33.	70.	66.		

N = New
M = 4/e exercise number (modified for 5/e)
X = 4/e exercise number (unchanged)

Chapter 28

5/e	4/e	5/e	4/e
1.	1.	36.	34. M
2.	2.	37.	35.
3.	3.	38.	36.
4. N		39.	37.
5. N		40.	38.
6.	4.	41. N	
7.	5. M	42. N	
8.	6.	43.	39. M
9.	7.	44.	40.
10.	8. M	45.	41.
11.	9.	46.	42.
12.	10.	47.	43.
13.	11. M	48.	44.
14.	12.	49.	45. M
15.	13.	50.	46.
16.	14.	51.	47.
17.	15.	52.	48.
18.	16.	53.	49. M
19.	17.	54.	50.
20.	18.	55.	51.
21.	19. M	56.	52. M
22.	20.	57.	53.
23.	21.	58.	54.
24.	23.	59.	55.
25.	22.	60.	56.
26.	24.	61.	57.
27.	25.	62.	58.
28.	26.	63.	59.
29.	27.	64.	60.
30.	28. M		
31.	29.		
32.	30.		
33.	32.		
34.	31.		
35.	33.		

N = New
M = 4/e exercise number (modified for 5/e)
X = 4/e exercise number (unchanged)

Chapter 29

5/e	4/e	5/e	4/e	5/e	4/e
1.	1.	36.	34. M	71.	69.
2.	2.	37.	35.	72.	70. M
3.	3.	38.	36. M	73.	71.
4.	4.	39.	37.	74.	72.
5.	5.	40.	38.	75. N	
6. N		41.	39.	76.	73.
7.	7.	42.	40.	77.	76.
8.	8.	43.	41.	78.	74.
9.	9.	44.	42.	79.	75.
10.	6.	45.	43.	80. N	
11.	10.	46.	44.	81.	77.
12. N		47.	45.	82.	78.
13.	11.	48.	46.	83.	79.
14.	12.	49.	47.	84.	80.
15.	13.	50.	48. M	85.	81.
16.	18.	51.	49.	86.	82.
17.	16. M	52.	50.	87.	83.
18.	14.	53.	51.	88.	84. M
19.	15.	54.	52.	89.	85.
20.	17. M	55.	53.	90.	86.
21.	19.	56.	54.	91.	87.
22.	20.	57.	55.	92.	88.
23.	21.	58.	56.	93.	89.
24.	22.	59.	57.	94.	90.
25.	23. M	60.	58.	95.	91.
26.	24.	61.	59.	96.	92.
27.	25.	62.	60.	97.	93. M
28.	26.	63.	61. M	98.	94.
29.	27.	64.	62.		
30.	28.	65.	63.		
31.	29.	66.	64.		
32.	30.	67.	65.		
33.	31. M	68.	66.		
34.	32.	69.	67.		
35.	33.	70.	68. M		

N = New
M = 4/e exercise number (modified for 5/e)
X = 4/e exercise number (unchanged)

Chapter 30

5/e	4/e	5/e	4/e	5/e	4/e
1.	1.	36.	32.	71.	65.
2.	2.	37.	33.	72.	66. M
3. N		38.	34.	73.	67.
4.	3.	39.	35.	74.	68.
5. N		40.	36.	75.	69. M
6.	4.	41. N		76.	70.
7.	5.	42.	37.	77. N	
8.	6.	43.	38.		
9.	7.	44.	39. M		
10.	8. M	45.	40.		
11.	9.	46.	41.		
12.	10.	47.	42.		
13.	11. M	48.	43.		
14.	12.	49.	44.		
15.	13.	50.	45. M		
16.	14.	51.	46.		
17.	15. M	52.	47. M		
18.	16.	53.	48.		
19.	17.	54. N			
20.	18.	55.	49.		
21.	19.	56.	50.		
22.	20.	57.	53. M		
23.	21. M	58.	51.		
24.	22.	59.	52.		
25.	23.	60.	54.		
26.	24.	61.	55.		
27.	25.	62.	56.		
28.	26.	63.	57.		
29.	27.	64.	58.		
30.	28.	65.	59.		
31. N		66.	60. M		
32. N		67.	61. M		
33.	29.	68.	62.		
34.	30.	69.	63.		
35.	31.	70.	64.		